THE HISTORY OF
The American
Sailing Navy

BOOKS BY HOWARD I. CHAPELLE

The History of American Sailing Ships
American Sailing Craft
The Baltimore Clipper
Yacht Designing and Planning
Boatbuilding
The History of the American Sailing Navy

PRESIDENT *and* ENDYMION
January 15, 1815

From a painting by George C. Wales. Reproduced through the
courtesy of the Marine Historical Association, Mystic, Connecticut.

★ ★ ★ ★ ★ ★ ★ ★ ★ ★ ★

THE HISTORY OF
The American Sailing Navy

THE SHIPS
AND THEIR DEVELOPMENT

By HOWARD I. CHAPELLE

BONANZA BOOKS • NEW YORK

DEDICATED

TO THE MEMORY OF

GEORGE C. WALES

Marine Artist

Contents

Illustrations

Plans

Text Figures

Introduction

AMERICAN naval history is far more than a running account of naval battles or a panegyric of naval officers. The qualities and characteristics of the ships engaged in noted actions are obviously an important consideration in any naval history. Where steam men-of-war are concerned there is a wealth of material available. In modern times there have been many books giving detailed information on the men-of-war of all the leading powers, which enable the historian and student to estimate the advantages, or disadvantages, under which an action was fought. Modern historians not only take into consideration the power and quality of naval ships, but they also examine the administrative problems of a naval power and its political, economic, and material well-being, to determine the exact national condition of the contending forces. This approach to the subject has widened the field of investigation, in all phases of history, far beyond the bare narrative of naval actions that was once considered to be acceptable naval history.

The period in which sailing men-of-war were employed in the American Navy was an important era, for it saw not only the founding of the United States but also its rise as a naval and maritime power. The traditions of the Navy were established and the foundations of a national maritime policy were laid. However, historians attempting to evaluate important naval actions and the state of national naval power in sailing-ship days find it most difficult to judge the effectiveness of American naval vessels: there are often questions as to the true size of certain ships, the effectiveness of their armament, and their relative speed. An examination of the standard naval histories will show that there has been much confusion in this particular matter; ships are either over-estimated or underestimated in size, power, speed, and effectiveness.

An attempt to establish exact information on various naval ships in the early years of American naval history was found to be difficult; the material was distributed in institutional and private hands or had been buried in government warehouses or storage files. As a result the naval historians were usually forced to fall back on published sources and to attempt with these a new and better analysis. The official records were particularly scanty with regard to the characteristics of naval vessels, and the official lists were commonly contradictory. Even a casual examination of the official records indicated that a great deal of such material had disappeared. It is not surprising, therefore, to find that American naval historians could not give a satisfactory account of naval actions in sailing-ship days, or that they were unable, in many cases, to analyze or evaluate properly the factors that won or lost a naval battle—as indicated by the contradictions in the accounts of actions contained in standard American naval histories.

An account of the development of American naval ships will also open a new approach to the history of ship design and construction. It is often accepted that progress is merely the discovery of new ideas, but experience has shown again and again that until the new ideas are generally accepted there can be no widespread improvement. In the field of shipbuilding, and particularly in governmental shipbuilding, there has usually been some resistance to the introduction of all new ideas. This has invariably been caused by the existence of a vested interest in the status quo, which assumes that the proposed improvements would in some way harm or annoy it. The peculiar position of government with relation to competition often aggravates the resistance to improvement by securing the position of the interests in power. It will be seen that, as a result, the appearance of new ideas, and even widespread acceptance of them, did not insure immediate benefits to the national navy. This makes possible some examination, at least, of the official reasons for neglecting what now appear to have been obvious advantages. Since this involves appraisals of the ability and character of men in authority, it can readily be seen that the history of naval shipbuilding is a matter reaching beyond a mere narrative of technical advance and retrogression if an accurate estimate is to be expected.

There are others besides naval historians and students in this field who have an interest in detailed information on American sailing men-of-war. Perhaps marine artists are the most exacting of these. Here there is a desire for

the extremely detailed information on the shape and appearance of noted
men-of-war that is required to draw accurate pictures of famous battles. Every
artist soon learns that contemporary pictures of naval actions are usually un-
trustworthy in the delineation of both the ships in the battle and their relative
positions. In fact, contemporary pictures of some of the naval actions in the
War of 1812 have been found to be wholly imaginary and completely misleading. The knowledge of this has led some marine artists to become extensively interested in that portion of the field of marine research dealing with the
design, construction, and rigging of ships of the past. The composition of a
picture of a naval action becomes, for such artists, a study of the course of the
action in minute detail, with the relative position of the ships plotted in dia-
grams, together with a careful study of the plans of the ships involved, if these
are available. By this method accuracy is insured and often an unusual composition is made possible as well. The work of the late George C. Wales, consisting of water colors of the naval actions of the War of 1812, is a notable
example of this search for accuracy in delineation and fact.

Another group having particular interest in shipbuilding history is that
composed of ship-model builders, professional and amateur. This group requires the same accurate and well-detailed information on individual ships that
is desired by marine artists. However, the ship-model builder often has a
much wider interest in types of vessels than is found in marine artists; the
modelists often choose some unusual and forgotten type of unimportant small
war vessel as a subject, whereas the artist is commonly concerned only with
noted ships.

The general reader's interest is more difficult to estimate; yet it is possible that
the craftsmanship of the naval constructors in the design of some ships may win
appreciation. There are also the curious and often astounding viewpoints of
governmental administration in so technical a field as shipbuilding that will
warrant attention. In a period when great governmental power is deemed an
admirable thing, it would be valuable to give time to an examination of some
details of the functioning of a bureaucracy in so vital a matter as progressive
shipbuilding, which might readily be assumed to represent any scientific development in governmental hands.

It seems apparent that there is a place for a study of the development of
American sailing men-of-war. This should not only include an account of the
historical development of the art of designing ships, but should also show, as
far as possible, the trends in technical thought and administrative control that

in some way affected the American naval ships. The study of purely combat craft would be insufficient, for the supporting service craft (which made the operation of fighting ships effective) need attention if the general efficiency of the national navy at any given period is to be estimated. Such an examination is of course limited in scope. It is apart from the history of naval operations: the stories of gallant naval fights, wily strategy, victory, and defeat. Rather it is an account of the long years of effort, on the part of a few statesmen, naval officers, and constructors, to build a navy capable of upholding the national honor and security should the occasion arise. Perhaps it can be said that naval shipbuilding can be considered a monument to national forethought. Too often, in American history at least, it has been a monument to the neglect of that quality on the part of both the public and its political leaders.

The study to be presented here was outlined, to some extent at least, by an examination of the published naval histories of the wars in which American sailing ships engaged. This enabled some estimate to be made of the questions that particularly troubled naval writers in the past. The limitation of the period of sailing ships in the American Navy could be readily established by accepting the dates of the building of the first and last naval sailing vessels for combat purposes. It seemed particularly desirable to attempt some explanation of the background of American naval ship design and building that began with the Revolution, and this led to research into the naval vessels built in America, in the colonial period, for the British Navy.

It was intended to illustrate the account with reproductions of the contemporary designs of American sailing men-of-war, but these were found to be in such a state that redrawing was necessary. Not only was the physical condition of many plans so poor that they could not be reproduced, but also, final examination of the plans showed that alterations, additions, and revisions were made which were not shown on the original design but which required representation. Redrawing, and in a few cases tracing alone, has been attempted with the greatest care to show the individual ship as faithfully as the writer's knowledge would permit. Many errors existed in the old plans; in correcting these there was always the possibility of erroneous interpretation, but it is hoped that these are not numerous, or serious in nature.

It is apparent that the naval constructors in early days were not required to furnish plans in great detail. Lines and offset tables, a few deck arrangement plans and spar dimensions, or a rough sail plan, were usually considered adequate for building even a large sailing man-of-war. This condition prevents the presentation of completely detailed plans without a good deal of reconstruction in most cases. There are enough sources of information on such matters as rigging and masting available in technical books contemporary with sailing men-of-war to make such reconstructions almost wholly unnecessary here. There are also many books on shipbuilding in the sailing-ship period which describe the basic methods of ship construction in practice during various eras. This makes it unnecessary to enter into a long description of ship construction except where it is desirable to indicate the exact state of American naval construction at some important period. The deck arrangements, fittings, and rigging details of naval ships were almost standardized, with relatively few changes taking place in, say, twenty years. However, it should be observed that early shipbuilding and rigging books are misleading in one respect: they do not describe conditions exactly as they were at their dates of publication but rather are valid for the period ten to twenty years earlier in the majority of cases. Thus, Chapman's noted book, *Architectura Navalis Mercatoria*, does not represent the height of shipbuilding progress in the plans it contains, at its date of publication, 1768. Rather these plans show the height of development at a period of ten to twenty years earlier.

An attempt has been made to show the interrelation of naval shipbuilding, authorization, construction funds, design, building, and general naval shipbuilding policy, with national affairs and leadership. It seems necessary to place much importance on the administrative control of naval construction, for the official records make it plain that this was often an important factor. Controversial matters of credit for the design of certain ships, the influence of individuals and groups, the soundness of policy, and similar subjects are necessarily examined in detail. Such matters as these are, of necessity, discussed as matters of personal opinion, but the conclusions are based on an examination of official records and correspondence, or, where available, upon the private papers of individuals involved.

It is impractical to list the sources on which this study is based; most of them are fragmentary, and so the individual reference would become involved and lengthy. Basically, the account is founded on surviving plans in the National Archives, which include all those taken from the files of the Navy Department. A few plans which formerly existed in the storage files of the Navy have disappeared, but copies of some of these had been made before the originals were lost. Other important sources include the Lenthall Collection in the Franklin Institute, Philadelphia, Pa.; the Fox Papers in the Peabody Museum,

Salem, Mass.; the Humphreys Papers in the Pennsylvania Historical Society, Philadelphia, Pa.; and the remarkable "Admiralty Collection of Draughts" now in the National Maritime Museum, Greenwich, London, England. The official naval correspondence in the National Archives and in the Office of Naval Records and Library, and scattered papers of naval officers in various histori-cal societies and in the Library of Congress have also been used extensively. Offsets and specifications of naval ships in the National Archives are scanty for the sailing-ship period but have been utilized wherever possible. Plans used in the study have been referenced in detail on the plates; the numbers are for the index of the Navy plan files in the National Archives.

Acknowledgment

THE author is under obligation to acknowledge the assistance of many who have had interest in American naval history or in marine research. These kind friends have given information or helped in the location of plans and papers that have been of inestimable value in this study of American sailing men-of-war. Particular thanks are due to

The late George C. Wales
The late George H. Stegmann
The late Admiralty Curator C. Knight

and to

Commodore Dudley W. Knox, U.S.N. (Ret.)
Captain Stephen C. Rowan, U.S.N. (Ret.)
Lt. Comdr. Marion V. Brewington, U.S.N.R. (Ret.)
Admiralty Curator H. S. Richardson
Mr. David Foster Taylor
Mr. Alfred S. Brownell
Walter Muir Whitehill
Vernon D. Tate
Mr. Bryant K. Rogers
Mr. Kenneth Roberts
Mr. R. C. Anderson
Professor Charles M. Gay
Mr. Clarkson Cranmer
Mr. Wayne B. Yarnall

and to the staffs of the National Archives, Office of Naval Records and Library, Library of Congress, Franklin Institute, Pennsylvania Historical Society, Maine Historical Society, Library of the City of New York, Peabody Museum, Salem, Mass.; Newburyport Historical Society; the Naval Museum at Annapolis; the Mariner's Museum, Newport News, Va.; the New York Historical Society; the Boston Public Library; and the National Archives, Ottawa, Ont.

HOWARD I. CHAPELLE

Cambridge, Maryland

Nomenclature Used in Ship Plans

LENGTH between perpendiculars was not consistent in the original draughts of United States Navy ships and seems to have been established at the fancy of the designer. In many cases the after perpendicular was placed at the intersection of the "cross seam," or lower edge of the transom, with the inner rabbet of the sternpost, but in some cases it was at the underside of the lower deck, where it intersected the inner rabbet on the post. In a few cases it was at the "height of breadth" line, where this met the transom. The position of the fore perpendicular also varied; sometimes it was at the intersection of the "height of breadth" line and the inner rabbet of the stem, or at the intersection of the underside of the main deck and the inner rabbet of the stem. In rare cases the perpendicular appears to have been placed without regard to either the deck or "height of breadth." This lack of system made the comparison of length on the basis of "length between perpendiculars" meaningless; so in this book the plans have been drawn with the dimensions and location of perpendiculars brought to a standard system. Except in rare cases the "length between perpendiculars" is the dimension from an after perpendicular placed at the intersection of the cross seam and the inner rabbet of the sternpost to the intersection of the underside of the main deck with the inner rabbet of the stem. In 74's the fore perpendicular would be located at the intersection of the underside of the lower deck with the inner rabbet of the stem and the after perpendicular at the intersection of the same deck line with the inner rabbet of the sternpost.

"Room" and "space" in these plans is the equivalent of the distance between frames, center line to center line. Literally it means space between each pair of frames, in the clear, plus the room required for one complete frame. The sequence of frame numbers or letters in the plans serves to indicate the number of frames between each pair of stations.

Rabbet of the sternpost, stem, and keel is shown by double lines, the inner being the inner rabbet and the outer the outer rabbet. Except in a few cases, the lines of ships shown here are to the inside of the planking. Hence sheer lines are to the underside of rail cap or other mouldings, and deck lines are to the underside of the deck plank at the inside of the ship's side planking.

"Port sill," or "port cill," is a line at the height of the underside of a line of gun ports and shows only, in a ship, when it also represents the top of a belt of thick planking.

Wales are the belt of thick plank on a ship's sides. The wales are shown by horizontal lines in the profile of the ship, more or less paralleling the sheer. In some ships, there was another and slightly thinner belt above the thick wale, the top of which was usually at port-sill height, as in the schooner *Grampus* of 1820–21. The lower edge of the thick wale was dubbed off fair with the bottom plank in United States Navy ships built after 1812, and hence the bottom of the wale did not show on the completed vessel, though often indicated in the plans. The retention of this line was intended to give the builders an idea of the depth of the thick planking forming the wales. After 1824 the top of the wales was also dubbed off and the vessel's sides then became smooth, without step-ups or step-downs being visible in the side planking.

★ ★ ★ ★ ★ ★ ★ ★ ★ ★

CHAPTER ONE

The Colonial Period

THE PROBLEMS of creating a navy in the American colonies at the outbreak of the Revolution were not far different fundamentally from what they would be today in a colonial possession that had revolted against its national government. Then, as would be the case in the present, money had to be raised, a naval organization set up, ships designed and built, arms bought or manufactured, supplies and munitions collected, and the vessels manned. It is obvious that success depended upon all of this being accomplished with the least possible delay. To do this, experienced men were very necessary in all stages.

The importance of trained and experienced men during the Revolution can be illustrated by the general lack of success of the Continental Navy as compared to the Army. The former lacked experienced naval officers and, with few exceptions, had to operate with merchant marine masters and mates whose inexperience in warfare led to many disasters. The Army, however, found some colonial officers who had either seen service in the British Army or were veterans of the colonial wars against the French and Indians. When these officers were in command, operations were usually successful or, at the worst, great disasters were avoided. There were exceptions to this, of course; some of the colonial naval officers who were ex-privateersmen proved highly competent, just as did some of the militia officers in the Army. However, it took time for both to become accustomed to the needs of regular warfare, and this in itself made them less valuable in the early and important phases of the war.

It will be shown that the ships of the Continental Navy were, on the whole, excellent men-of-war. Just as success at sea or in the land campaigns of the Revolution indicated the existence of trained officers and enlisted personnel, the qualities of these ships, combined with their early appearance in the war, indicate the existence of shipwrights trained in naval construction. The trained officers of the armed services could not have come from purely civilian experience; the shipwrights who designed and built the ships of the Continental Navy could not have been developed by the sole experience of merchant-ship construction. There is little in the way of satisfactory record of the men who were responsible for the design of the Continental ships, but examination of the history of colonial shipbuilding in the century prior to the outbreak of the Revolution will show logical reasons for the excellence of the design of American-built men-of-war that made up the bulk of the Continental Navy.

To appreciate fully the state of colonial shipbuilding at the outbreak of the Revolution, it is necessary to know, in general terms at least, the position that had been reached in the art of ship design at the time and the causes of the distinctions between men-of-war and merchant craft. The opinion that ships of the colonial period were designed and built by eye, without plans or model, is apparently a common one. The impression that the ships and small craft of this period were clumsy, slow, ill-formed, and poorly rigged is equally general. Many of these opinions and impressions can be traced to the poor contemporary paintings and illustrations that have survived to recent times. These are very misleading, for the marine art of the period was stylized and highly conventional in detail. As a result, the hulls are shown excessively full and round, with the freeboard made to appear excessive, and the proportion of length to beam and freeboard inadequate for good sailing qualities. The sails are shown as though they were cut to bag excessively, so much so that weatherliness would be impossible to obtain. These contemporary pictures, added to uninformed conclusions reached by some modern historians, have naturally led to the idea that the ships were poorly designed and probably built without the aid of plans. This whole concept of shipbuilding in colonial times is incorrect, as can be readily proved by the building plans that have survived; these are, of course, the most accurate evidence that can be presented.

Shipbuilding began in the American colonies as soon as settlements were firmly established. In most cases shipwrights and boatbuilders were brought over from the homeland so that vessels necessary for colonial transportation could be constructed; these included craft necessary for protection against enemies. At an early date the Spaniards built men-of-war in Mexico, Central America, and Cuba to protect their treasure fleets in American waters. The Dutch and English also built small war vessels at various times. These combat ships were usually constructed in temporary government dockyards by shipwrights brought into the colony for this particular purpose; when their work was done they were usually sent home. This practice prevented the colonies from developing a large shipbuilding industry or naval construction and confined the bulk of their building to small craft to be used in the colonial coasting trade.

American naval shipbuilding, in what is now the United States, may be said to have begun with the building of the fourth-rate *Falkland* for the British Navy at Portsmouth, New Hampshire, in 1690. Not only was she a regular man-of-war and a fairly large ship, but she was contract-built by a privately owned shipyard, employing colonial shipwrights who remained in the colony when their work on this ship was finished. The *Falkland* was followed by the building of a few other vessels before the time of the Revolution, which resulted in the creation of a group of colonial shipwrights experienced in naval construction who could pass on their knowledge through apprentices. It would be easy to overemphasize the importance of this; nevertheless, the matter undoubtedly played some part in the development of American naval construction in the Revolution, and so requires careful investigation and consideration.

The building of these men-of-war in private shipyards in the American colonies is a good indication of the ability and knowledge of their shipwrights. It is difficult to imagine that contracts for large men-of-war would be placed in the American shipyards if their men were incapable of reading plans and ignorant of naval practice. Long before the colonial shipyards began to build warships, naval construction had become a specialized field in ship design and construction and the monopoly of national governments. As a result, all training in this field had likewise become a government monopoly. There were no technical schools then, as there are today, to give a general training in all branches of marine architecture. Therefore knowledge of warship design in colonial times indicated either training in a government dockyard or an apprenticeship to a shipwright or builder who had been a dockyard apprentice. There is little doubt that there were dockyard-trained ship-

builders in the colonies, men who had served an apprenticeship in a government yard and who had emigrated to the colonies; in fact, the existence of
the contract-built men-of-war of colonial construction is in itself sufficient
evidence of this. These men would take apprentices, who would receive the
equivalent of a dockyard training. This insured them of what was then an
education in the latest and most scientific shipbuilding practices, including the
making and use of plans.

The use of plans to design ships was not a new thing in 1690. The practice
had existed in England for about a century or more and had become a standard
requirement in naval work by all the great maritime powers. The British Admiralty had ordered the retention of plans as early as 1650, and plans from
1675 still survive. The methods of projection required to make plans of the
hull form of a ship had developed slowly from the crude drawings of the
late sixteenth century, so that by 1675 reasonable accuracy could be expected.
The advantages of plans were recognized, not only in government dockyards,
but also in many of the merchant shipyards.

The close of the sixteenth century had seen some improvement in the model
of British Navy ships, brought about by the efforts to combat the Spanish
during Elizabeth's reign. In these years the ships had become larger and more
weatherly, though shipbuilders were still generally uneducated and many
ships were dangerous and ill-formed.

The histories of maritime nations show periods when all the factors necessary for improvement in shipbuilding and design come into being and a
nation's naval power and maritime interest reaches a zenith. The seventeenth
century was such a period in English history. Rulers and ministers came to
power whose ambition made naval power necessary; the cultural and economic levels of the nation were raised by foreign adventures and explorations;
interest in science became marked; wars created national danger that turned
public interest to the Navy, and ship designers and builders of genius appeared.
As a result, not only did the English become the leading naval power, but also,
for a short period at least, their warships were superior to those of the rest
of the world.

The opening of the century had found the British Navy insufficient for
national ambitions and requirements. An inquiry was instituted and steps
were taken to improve the naval establishment. Administrative reforms were
made and a particular effort was directed to obtaining better men-of-war. To
improve the design of naval ships, the "Shipwrights' Company," or shipbuild-

ing guild, was given increased responsibilities in the design of new naval vessels. A master of the guild was created, who was made an important member of the civil staff of the naval establishment. This office was filled, by an election in 1606, by Phineas Pett, "gentleman and sometime master of arts at Emmanuel college, Cambridge." Pett was far more than an educated gentleman; he was an experienced shipbuilder and a designer with very advanced ideas for the period. In 1610 he designed the *Prince Royal*, which at the time of her launch was considered to be a model man-of-war in all important respects, including sailing qualities, fighting power, and impressive appearance. In 1612 the Shipwrights' Company was given a new charter and increased prestige. Pett was elected the first master under the new charter. As Commissioner of the Royal Dockyard at Chatham he was also the responsible ship designer of the Royal Navy.

Pett pressed his ideas for improvement vigorously and made plans for a number of large men-of-war. His masterpiece was the *Royal Sovereign*, launched in 1637. This ship was on a greatly improved model and was of great size and power for her time. Because of her good qualities as a man-of-war, the model of this ship influenced the design of Royal Navy vessels for well over a century after her launch. The *Royal Sovereign* had a long career and saw much hard service. She was altered in 1651, when her topworks were reduced, and rebuilt in 1659–60. While awaiting a second rebuilding in 1696 she was accidentally destroyed by fire.

Phineas Pett died in 1647, when in his seventies, and was succeeded by his son Peter Pett. All told, four members of this great English shipbuilding family served as master or assistant master shipwrights in the Royal Navy, between 1612 and 1678. The last master shipwright of the family, also named Phineas, whom Pepys considered a "very knave" and a thorough scoundrel, designed and built the galley-frigate *Charles Galley* in 1675. This vessel and her sisters had a great reputation and will be referred to again. In the design of the *Charles Galley*, Phineas Pett is said to have had the assistance of that noted yachtsman, patron of shipbuilders, and amateur naval architect, Charles II. Charles had a keen personal interest in the technical problems of ship design and construction. He employed, in addition to members of the Pett family, Sir Anthony Deane, who rose to prominence as a designer of naval ships during Charles's reign. Deane designed one of the new galley-frigates, in competition with Phineas Pett, a number of yachts, and a large number of men-of-war. The sailing qualities of all of these were generally better than had previously been known. Deane also seems to have been responsible for the first "establishment" (standardized dimensions of naval ships), drawn up in 1675. He acted as instructor to Peter the Great of Russia in 1698, during the latter's visit to England to study shipbuilding. Deane also devised a method of calculating displacement and prepared a thesis on ship design.

The period between 1670 and 1695 may be said to have marked the high water of scientific study in all the fields relating to the improvement in English warship design in the seventeenth century. By 1690 the models of English men-of-war had reached a high degree of excellence, and the competition of France in ship design and construction had only recently been felt. The construction of the *Falkland* in America at this time gave the colonial shipwrights who worked on her an opportunity to see what were then, perhaps, the most advanced ideas in naval ship design and construction, at least in a moderate-sized ship.

The eighteenth century opened with Great Britain in possession of about one-third of the whole of Europe's naval power. The French had begun to improve their ships markedly by the time of Charles II and had adopted the old Spanish policy of building ships very large for the number of guns they were intended to carry. In addition they began a study of hull form and searched for improved construction methods. While well aware of this, the British tried to find means to economize in the maintenance of their huge naval organization. The carving and painting that had been so profusely used on men-of-war were reduced or eliminated, and interior joinerwork in cabins or on deck was omitted or simplified.

In the sixteenth century some efforts had been made to set up standard dimensions for each class of war vessel in the Royal Navy. This was to guide designers in planning new ships to make sure that the vessels of a given rate had some similarity and approximately the same qualities. Probably it was hoped that this would lead to the use of spars, sails, and rigging that were interchangeable in a given rate or class of ship. Obviously such an idea has a great attraction to a government agency under pressure to economize. Just as "standardization" has become attractive to modern armed services, so the "establishment" became popular with the British Admiralty. The idea of one of the smaller British ships capturing a larger ship of the enemy appealed to national pride, and this, plus the economy that was supposed to be possible, led to the fixing of the dimensions of each rate at a minimum that was then thought practical in peacetime, to be modified as required with the passage of time. With the effort to obtain a cheaper fleet in the early eighteenth century, the "establishment" received much attention and an attempt was made to make all ships conform to the approximate dimensions of their class in the Royal Navy. The results of the peacetime standardization represented in the "establishment" were the same as much of the military and naval standardization of more recent times. Designs for new ships and equipment became obsolete but remained in use until war losses brought home the necessity of change. The stagnation of peacetime standardization was replaced at great cost by the free development forced by wartime competition with an active and enterprising enemy.

The history of the "establishments" between 1706 and 1745 illustrates the effects of peace and war upon the idea of standardization. During this period there were five "establishments": 1706, 1719, 1733, 1741, and 1745. Through these revisions the 60-gun ships, for example, were increased in length of the gun deck but six feet, in beam about four and a half feet, and in depth about three feet. Economy and shortsightedness prevented the English from setting up "establishments" that assured, at the time each new one was instituted, vessels larger than those of any continental power, even though war experience had shown the need time and again.

Actually, the advantages hoped for in the "establishments" were never fully realized. Changes required by war and by the efforts of designers and builders to obtain good qualities in all new ships led to the evasion of the restrictions of the "establishment" as much as could be dared. It was not uncommon for a ship, built in the year a new "establishment" became official, to exceed the standard dimensions by a number of feet. However, the general effects of the "establishment" were still apparent. Ships were small for the number of guns they carried and so were slower and less powerful than the larger vessels used in the continental navies. The sense of power that sprang from the possession of the biggest navy in the world and the satisfaction of victories achieved by a well-manned naval service, combined with the effects of the "establishment," led to a slowing down in the British efforts to improve their naval ship designs, and from 1700 to 1770 there were relatively few improvements. Ships grew in size and the sails and rigging were improved somewhat, but after the bomb ketch had been introduced into the Royal Navy, late in the seventeenth century, no new type of man-of-war appeared until the cutter and schooner were adopted, about 1760. The only changes that took place in this period in the ships of the Royal Navy were the creation of new rates by means of new class designations. From late in the seventeenth century to the American Revolution, the French gradually took the lead in quality of ship design, and their dominance in this field was marked throughout the greater part of the eighteenth century.

The "rating" of ships in the Royal Navy has been referred to so often that some explanation of this system of designation is necessary. The rates, in 1700, were first to sixth: first was 100 guns, second 90 guns, third 70 guns, fourth 54–60 guns, fifth 30–40 guns, and sixth 18–24 guns. The exact number of guns in each rate was never constant; gradually the first rate included all ships from 100 guns upward, the second 90 to 98, the third 64 to 80, the fourth 50 to 60, the fifth 30 to 44, and the sixth 20 to 28. Below the sixth were sloops, bombs, fireships, and other small craft. By 1750 the term "rate" was rarely used, except in some official lists, and was replaced by the gun-number, as "100-gun ship," "44-gun ship" and "20-gun ship," because of the vagueness of the rating designation.

The first half of the eighteenth century, marked by stagnation in British naval ship design, was in the colonies an active period of naval shipbuilding. Not only were a number of naval ships built in the colonies, but also the naval wars brought captured vessels into the colonial ports where shipbuilders and designers might see them. Men whose livelihood depends upon ship design and construction are usually observant and critical. There can be no doubt that such colonials noted any improvements in the design of foreign craft or of the men-of-war built in the colonies.

In judging ship design, the colonial American shipwright had an advantage that relatively few European builders possessed. This was the American's interest in and knowledge of fast-sailing ships and the elements of design necessary to obtain this quality. A combination of international unrest, geographical location, and the oppression of colonial maritime trade by the mother country had forced the American colonials to build fast vessels for practically all trades, even for fishing. The settlements were commonly too small and weak to man heavily armed vessels, even if large armaments were otherwise possible. Fast craft were readily obtained and were both cheaper to build and less expensive to operate. The danger of loss of the colonial craft had a tendency to place a premium on low-cost construction and developed Americans who were unusually competent, or expert, in this matter. All sections of the colonies where the shipbuilding industry existed produced fast, cheap vessels for at least fifty years prior to the Revolution.

The distinction between a man-of-war and a merchant ship in colonial times was less obvious than it is today, but it was just as real. From the time guns had been introduced on shipboard, the design of fighting ships had become more complex. By 1700 the merchant vessel was no longer a successful substitute for a man-of-war, no matter how well armed and manned she might be. Only in small craft, in fact, could a merchant vessel be utilized in warfare, and even here, only the special, small, fast ships built for adventure or illegal trade were of any use in war. Merchantmen were employed, of course, when emergency made their use necessary for convoy duty in colonial warfare, but the vessels were rarely successful as fighting ships. They were to some extent counterparts of the heavily armed merchant "cruisers" used in the last war for the same purpose.

Owing to the need of convoy guards, a number of merchant ships were purchased and armed by the Royal Navy during the years of the American Revolution. Since most of these ships were built before 1770, and since some plans survive, it is readily possible to make comparisons between merchant ships and men-of-war of the mid-portion of the eighteenth century. There is no reason to suppose that there were great differences between these purchased merchant ships and the colonial vessels, for, in fact, a few of these convoy guards appear to have been American-built.

The technical problems raised by the conflicting requirements of the service of naval vessels in the days of sail and wooden hulls were serious, and they were much more difficult to solve than in the case of the contemporary merchantman. Usually merchantmen were either small, fast-sailing craft of small capacity or slow ships having large holds. The rarest type was one in which ability to carry large cargoes was combined with fast sailing. In fact, it was not until well into the end of the sailing-ship period that such merchant vessels were required and developed. Achieving strength in small wooden ships was not a serious problem, but in long vessels it presented an almost insurmountable difficulty to shipbuilders until well after the Revolution.

The armament and its inherent requirements created the most troublesome problems in the design of sailing men-of-war. Muzzle-loading guns, smooth-bored, often poorly cast of inferior metal and employing shot that did not fit the bore correctly, made rapid fire and accuracy impossible of attainment in colonial times and for long afterward. The only practical way to make the fire of such guns effective, even at very short ranges, was to concentrate them as much as possible in the broadside of a ship. This could be accomplished by placing the guns close together in a row along the side of the ship, leaving space enough between them to permit the gun crews to work. When there were two or more decks, the obvious step was to arm these in a similar manner also, if they were of sufficient height in the ship to be of any use in rough water. However, as the height of guns above water was increased, their weight increasingly affected the ship's stability. It was soon discovered that the arming of a number of decks was limited not only by the size of the ship, but by her stability, and that the most practical approach was to place the larger and heavier guns low in the ship and to arm any available upper deck with lighter and less effective guns. The ends of the ship had to be armed not only to defend the vessel against attacks at the bow or stern but also to permit fire when chasing or being chased. The limitations of space and the interference of rigging would prevent such guns from being very numerous; therefore, effectiveness could be obtained only by employing the guns having the longest range and the greatest accuracy at the ends of the ship. But excesses in this direction were prohibited by the great weight and length of guns of this description.

As the number of guns increased, a greater number of men was necessary to work them. Not only was it necessary to fight the guns; it was also necessary to have enough men in addition to handle the sails and rigging in action, and to do the other work required to maneuver the vessel. By 1700 the number of crew required to work the guns had become so great that it was impractical to place enough men aboard to man both sides of the ship completely in large men-of-war. Huge crews required much space for provisions and water, particularly as men-of-war, to be really effective, had to be capable of remaining at sea for extended periods of time without being supplied from shore or from other ships. The stores had to be located in the hold, for the gun, or upper, decks must be unobstructed enough to fight the guns and to work the gear required to handle the vessel.

The guns, being muzzle-loaders, were run inboard by tackles, or by recoil, to load. Inboard of these guns, when run in, there had to be room to permit movements of large numbers of men and space to pass ammunition. Deck openings were necessary to allow men and ammunition to pass from deck to deck, but these must not interfere with the guns in any way. Thus the armament not only determined the deck arrangements, but also had some control over the amount of beam, or width, of the ships.

Speed was a very desirable feature in men-of-war; a fast vessel could overtake a fleeing enemy ship, or, if necessary, escape from a pursuing one. Speed and weatherliness, or the ability to sail close to the direction of the wind, combined with the ability to turn quickly, gave great advantages in battle maneuvers, permitting choice of position and the use of the broadside batteries to the best advantage. However, speed required sharp, or fine, ends to the hull, which reduced stowage space and weight-carrying ability. It also required a large sail area, with resulting long spars, lofty masts, and a great deal of rigging. The weight of sails and rigging added to that of the guns increased the burden carried in men-of-war.

Strength in hull and spars was essential. The man-of-war had to be strong enough to carry the great weight of guns and stores placed arbitrarily in the hull for fighting efficiency rather than with any regard to the structural requirements. It also had to withstand the tremendous shocks of collision in action, when boarding tactics were employed, and the effects of hits from gunfire upon the ship. The structure and decks had to be strong enough to take the recoil of the guns. The spars had to be stout to carry the large sails even when injured by a hit. Stout bulwarks were very desirable, even on small craft, in order to protect the crew from small-arms fire, to take the shock of recoil of the guns, and to avoid excessive damage in collision.

The necessity of designing ships with the guns well above the water line became obvious in very early times. This position permitted the guns to be fired in heavy weather, or when the ship was pressed with sail. In the days of short-range weapons, the advantage of a high firing position was obvious. But lofty weights soon raised the problem of stability, and the lofty rig required for speed aggravated the difficulty. Throughout the sailing-ship period the problems of stability in men-of-war were a matter of grave concern to all naval designers. Ballast seemed to be the answer to some extent, but this took up space and led to deep draft. The ability of men-of-war to operate in shoal water was an obvious advantage; however, the requirements of weatherliness and stability made this an ideal rarely accomplished.

The seaworthiness of all men-of-war was another important factor, for even the smallest was expected to be able to stay at sea in any weather and to make long voyages. Stability was important in this, as was strength and weatherliness. Hull form played a part in obtaining seaworthiness, but the distribution of weights in relation to that of displacement was also important. The latter determined to a great extent whether a ship would ship water in heavy weather, as well as the length and severity of the roll of the hull in heavy seas and the strains placed upon her structure, affecting her strength. The quickness and length of the roll played a great part in the accuracy of the gunfire, in a day when loading was slow and the mechanics of firing were both slow and uncertain. The ideal man-of-war should therefore roll slowly and easily, without jerk, and without an excessive length of roll that might submerge the gun muzzles, or flood the ports and decks. This too was an ideal rarely accomplished in any sailing man-of-war design.

The effects of these requirements in warship design were conflicting and difficult of satisfactory solution. The greatest problems arose in the effort to obtain speed and gun power. The weights involved in the latter made for heavy displacement hulls, full in shape and wholly unsuited for fast sailing, or even weatherliness. Except in scout and messenger craft of small size, where armament was of minor importance, the naval designer could not aim for speed alone; on the other hand, he could not design solely for fighting power without regard to weatherliness and maneuvering ability, which in themselves were usually elements of speed. After many attempts to combine speed and gun power, naval designers gradually turned to establishing ships of special classification, in which each class or type was designed for a particular purpose. In these classes the most powerful ships were the largest in dimensions, which in colonial times carried 100 guns. Scaling down from this to smaller ships the number of guns was reduced by 10 in each class. Ships of the line, or in modern parlance, battleships, were the 70-, 80-, 90-, and 100-gun ships. The modern heavy cruiser or small battleship was represented in colonial times by the 40-, 50-, and 60-gun ships, while light cruisers were represented by 20- and 30-gun classes. Below the 20-gun ships were brigantines, snows, ketches, and other small craft, with from 4 to 18 guns, as well as special craft such as bomb vessels, galleys, gunboats, and the service craft used for supply ships, transports, and exploration, or for the duties of dockyard service. The rates that were fashionable in European navies changed from time to time, and the 24-, 36-, 44-, 64-, 74-, and 98-gun ships became common in the middle of the eighteenth century. Later the 28-, 32-, and 110-gun ships came into use. The element of speed was expected less in large ships, but as the minimum rates were approached fast sailing became increasingly desirable. The number of guns that classified a ship was the total of those she mounted on carriages;

some small cannon were mounted on upright timbers called "stocks" and were known as "swivels" or "howitzers," or by other names, but were never included among the "guns."

Rowing vessels still played an important part in colonial times, and nearly all small sailing men-of-war were fitted to row. Oar ports located between the gun ports, or on a lower deck if practical, permitted the large crews to move the vessel in a calm by means of long sweeps or oars, each worked by a number of men. Some vessels were particularly designed to be rowed efficiently, such as some of the sailing "galleys" of the late seventeenth and early eighteenth centuries; these ships were usually sharp and light, though otherwise like the regular sailing man-of-war. The true galley type, in which sails were either dispensed with entirely, or made a mere auxiliary to the oar, had gradually been confined to gunboats and to vessels intended to operate in certain geographical areas exclusively—the Mediterranean, for example. Oars were employed in vessels up to 40 guns in many navies as late as 1820, and in all small men-of-war brigs, schooners, and cutters until the end of the sailing-ship period.

The solutions to the problems involved in designing a satisfactory man-of-war differed with each of the great maritime powers. Obviously, the solutions to many of the problems were to build men-of-war as large as possible in all dimensions, or to exaggerate some one dimension. Length gave the greatest advantage in both speed and gun power, but here the designer was blocked by the elastic wooden hull made up of many members that could not be secured tightly enough not to move when the vessel was under strain. Long hulls not only strained and leaked, but they lasted only a short time without repair and were therefore very expensive. Though many attempts were made before the American Revolution to design and build very large or long men-of-war, progress in overcoming the difficulty in their construction was extremely slow. Gradually, however, improved structural design permitted an increase in length.

Another way to obtain the great displacement necessary in men-of-war, and also to obtain strength, was to increase the beam or width of the ship, its depth in the water, or its height out of the water in proportion to its length. These solutions, however, produced slow ships, lacking in weatherliness and maneuverability. Deep draft, if carried to an extreme, was an obvious disadvantage.

By the mid-eighteenth century, England, France, Holland, and Spain had each chosen a particular compromise in dimensions and proportions, which soon became national characteristics of their men-of-war. England generally chose small ships, with rather deep draft, full ends, and slow-sailing qualities. France decided on long, rather narrow ships, fine at the ends and fast-sailing, though usually rather weakly built. Holland selected wide shoal models in which sailing was sacrificed for ability to operate in the shoal waters of her coasts. Spain preferred ships of rather great size, but marked generally by relatively high freeboard. In colonial times, the French and Spanish men-of-war gradually improved, so that by 1740 it was commonly recognized that they were designed on better principles than the British ships. In addition to these elements of size and proportion, each nation gradually developed particular hull forms, so that the hull profile and the shape of the ends and of the mid-section also became national characteristics in their naval vessels.

The physical characteristics required in men-of-war were not the only things that made them different from their merchant-ship sisters and made their development entirely independent. The commercial vessels were designed, built, and owned by private individuals. The man-of-war, on the other hand, was the property of the national government in all respects—design, construction, arming, fitting, manning, and operation. The training of men for each of these matters was also conducted by the government. The monopoly in naval construction was under the direct control of a bureaucracy of long standing in colonial times, just as it is today. This monopoly was encroached upon only when private individuals built and owned privateers in time of war, or when a national emergency arose that forced the government to build men-of-war in private shipyards because its own facilities were inadequate to enlarge the navy fast enough. The relation of naval ship design and construction to those of merchant ships in colonial times was not very different from that existing very recently. Designers and builders of commercial vessels rarely knew much about naval vessels unless their early training had been in government work, or they had had experience in wartime naval construction let in some private yard or had worked in a dockyard when war had forced the employment of additional personnel. Then, as in recent years, the government agency responsible for the naval establishment acted independently in developing the design of men-of-war, improving their construction, arming, and fitting without using the nation's civilian facilities to any marked extent.

As a result of this monopoly of the man-of-war, improvement is not constant and, as a general rule, occurs at times quite different from the periods of rapid evolution in merchant craft. The private owner's only concern is to have a ship that is fitted for her trade and that can meet competition, either from her own compatriots or from foreigners. If a ship's design does not permit this, or if she is otherwise unfitted for her trade, she is not repeated in new construction. If her designer, builder, or owner is so conservative or so wedded to an unsuccessful model that he will not keep abreast of the improvements made by competitors, he soon goes bankrupt. As a result, improvements in merchant ships are constantly being made, except in wartime, when merchant shipping and shipbuilding are disrupted. In naval shipbuilding the situation is just the opposite. The reasons for this are easily found in the history of all maritime nations. Peace and economy in government lead to standardization and to neglect in naval construction, and if there is no fear of war the public becomes indifferent to naval matters, particularly to the need for improvement. The bureaucracy that is responsible for naval shipbuilding is left to routine matters, and pressure is brought to bear by political factions to economize, either by complete standardization or at least by elimination of change and improvement. Inefficient or obsolete ships, guns, and equipment remain in use. Designers and technicians lose interest, and the money granted the naval establishment is usually diverted to the maintenance of worn-out ships, repairs to buildings and shore establishments, and unnecessary expenditures in administration. It is not uncommon to find a naval power, after a long period of peaceful stagnation, entering a war with poor ships and equipment, but with huge and largely useless shore establishments and administrative organizations. In a period of prolonged peace the development of the merchant ship has usually been rapid, and so, on the outbreak of war, the naval vessels are in all important respects generally far inferior to their commercial sisters.

When war occurs, however, the picture is commonly reversed. The naval establishment is reorganized and made efficient; poor designers and technicians are removed from responsible offices, standardization or conservatism becomes outmoded, and the design of naval craft rapidly improves in all possible respects and at tremendous cost. If the national danger is great and public interest is, as a result, very high, the naval craft soon outstrip the ships of commerce. If the war is long, it is not uncommon to find that the naval vessels at its end are years ahead of their times, while the design and development of merchant ships are still where they were at the beginning of the war. There are, of course, some craft developed for trade in wartime, such as blockade runners or other vessels suited only to a special requirement. But however great the part played by civilian ship designers, builders, and owners in the wartime development of such types, it is soon found that this class of ship is wholly unsuited for peaceful trade and so must be discarded, though some of the features of design may be adapted to improve the postwar merchantman. The emphasis on emergency requirements in merchant ships built during a war almost invariably makes them expensive to operate in postwar trade. This was almost as true in colonial times as in the more recent years, though of course there have been impressive differences in the scope of modern war.

That the naval ship designers have shown extreme conservatism at times has invariably been due to the causes, just outlined, that are created by a long period of peace. Like the designers of merchant craft, the naval constructor is influenced by education and training. In the long history of naval architecture there have been many periods, both in the past and in recent times, when curious ideas were fashionable and pseudo science ruled much of the education of ship designers. If the colonial ship designer cluttered up his ship with masses of carving that served no useful purpose, he differed but little from his modern counterpart, who decorates his ship with materials shaped in fantastic and useless forms to "streamline" a vessel too slow to require such treatment. If the early ship designer had undue respect for mechanically drawn hull sections, he resembled the modern designer who has too much regard for mathematical formulae and not enough for the practical problems of hull form and actual design.

The chief cause of naval conservatism, however, is the stagnation in the development of combat technique that occurs at times when war is rare, or victory easily achieved. Then the naval ship designer has no new problems to meet and has to consider only the lessons of the past. New ships may be designed in such a time, but they are suited for the "last" war instead of for a future one. Such craft have not only proved to be useless, but have even menaced national security by creating public overconfidence in a "powerful" navy. The young men, officers and naval constructors alike, who rise to prominence by means of ability in time of war, grow old in peace, satisfied with the existing state of things and living in the past glory of the "last" war. Having no competition to cause them alarm, they soon cease to have new ideas; finally they come to resent and fear any innovation that might rouse them to mental activity. The stupidity and pompousness of such men in recent times was as common in the colonial period, and just as dangerous.

Stagnation in a peacetime naval service is usually first apparent in the administrative functions of the bureaucratic establishment. The reason for this is that senior officers are commonly appointed to such posts and are then in a position to make their opinions felt in shipbuilding policies. The administrative function is a powerful one in any naval service, since it not only controls the financial arrangements of the naval shipbuilding establishment but also may affect selection or assignment of technical personnel. Naval shipbuilding has rarely been controlled by trained technicians at the "policy-making level"; rather the higher levels of administrative control have been in the hands of either senior naval officers or political appointees. Under such a system as this it is not surprising to find there has rarely been a steady effort to maintain a really progressive naval shipbuilding program over a long period of peace. In truth, the administrative control of a navy wholly decides the effectiveness of the arm in the long run. This is particularly true with regard to naval ship design. Naval history of the great maritime powers shows time and again that the presence of progressive and capable naval architects in a naval establishment will not alone assure an effective fleet; the administrative control must be equally progressive and competent, and the political interest must be favorable.

Let us now consider the details of colonial naval shipbuilding history and by more specific evidence see the state of ship design and design methods. Unfortunately the lack of definite records leaves many matters to speculation. However, on the face of the existing evidence, it will be apparent that the colonial shipbuilders, who had naval experience, were in all probability as well trained and as competent as the majority of European ship designers and builders of the period. The inferences that may be drawn from the existing evidence might well explain the excellence of the men-of-war of the Continental Navy.

The names of all the ships that were built for the Royal Navy in the colonies are not recorded, or have not yet been discovered. There are conflicting lists and confusion in ship names; however, it is known that the *Bedford* was built in New England not long after the *Falkland*, and also another ship whose name is not recorded with certainty. It is probable that both of these ships were built before 1730. In 1745–49 two vessels were built by contract—the 24-gun

Boston at Boston, Massachusetts, and the 44-gun ship *America* at Portsmouth, New Hampshire. The *Boston* was launched in 1747 or 1748; the *America* in 1749. From 1755 to the outbreak of the Revolution, the Admiralty built a great many small men-of-war on the Great Lakes and on Lake Champlain. The sloops *Oswego* and *Ontario* and the schooners *Vigilant, Lively,* and *George* were built in 1755. In 1756 the brig *London,* the snow *Halifax,* and the sloop *Mohawk* were constructed. In 1759 and 1760 three more snows were built—the *Mohawk, Onandaga,* and *Missisaga.* Between 1763 and 1771 the schooners *Huron, Brunswick, Michigan, Charlotte,* and *Victory,* and the snows *Haldemand* and *Seneca* were built. The largest of these was only 84 feet long. On the seacoast, between 1760 and 1771, at least three schooners were built— the *Sir Edward Hawke, Marble Head,* and *Earl of Egmont*—and about a dozen others purchased, some of them on the stocks.

Except for the large vessels built prior to 1749, the naval vessels built in the colonies were of trifling force and were of no great importance in giving an opportunity for study of the problems of naval construction. The schooners were an American type and were built from American plans or models. The sloops were mere patrol craft and were also built on colonial plans or models. The snows and the brigs were of slightly more importance than the rest; they ranged from 60 to 84 feet length on deck and were of man-of-war design. However, their models appear to have been very shoal, making them suitable for use on the uncharted lakes; in this they differed somewhat from their ocean-going sisters. It will be seen that, however unimportant were the ships built in the colonies after 1749, there was some opportunity for observant colonial shipwrights who were enterprising enough to search for work away from home to obtain experience in construction of naval vessels and, perhaps, a slight knowledge of some of their inherent problems of design. The large men-of-war, however, might logically be assumed to have played a far more important part in the education of the Revolutionary War naval ship designers.

The design of the Royal Navy ships built in colonial America is an interesting field for speculation, for there is little in the way of satisfactory evidence of design responsibility. It is probably safe to assume that these large vessels were built from plans supplied by the Admiralty, but there is difficulty in proving that the ships were actually built in strict conformity with these designs. Since the Admiralty was responsible for preparing the contract, it is apparent that the design and specifications would be prepared by its designers. It would be particularly desirable to illustrate the contract and specifications with plans or a model, in view of the distance between the Admiralty designers and the colonial contractors, in order to obtain satisfactory results. However, the Admiralty practice appears to have been one that has not been entirely unknown in modern American naval construction—the use of a "contract design," which was for guidance only. In recent times the builder has often prepared a detailed and sometimes much-altered design which, though based on the "contract design," was actually an entirely new one when finally approved and completed. The Admiralty seems to have used this system very often in colonial times, furnishing a builder with a plan, or model, based on the "establishment," or plans of an earlier ship. This was not a binding design, however, and the builder was permitted to change the hull form, the appearance, and even the dimensions of the vessel, providing he built a ship equal or superior to the "establishment," as set forth in the contract. The only important difference between the Admiralty practice and that of our modern contracts was that the colonial builder does not appear to have been required to have his revised design approved before construction and so did not make a model or plan for this purpose. The Admiralty agent, or superintendent, was given authority to decide the suitability of the builder's proposed changes or improvements without having to submit them to the Admiralty. This was, of course, the only practical method in a time of very slow communications. Thus, the Admiralty often had no accurate plan of a new ship during construction unless for some reason, such as a controversy between builder and Admiralty superintendent about size, arrangement, or hull form, it was decided that an exact plan should be prepared. However, it was obvious that a plan of all important ships was highly desirable. As a result, when a new ship was completed, the Admiralty often had the ship docked and measured and a correct and well-detailed plan made. This was particularly common when the introduction of copper sheathing, after 1761 in the Royal Navy, made estimates of the cost of this rather expensive metal important. Accurate hull form was required to make such estimates, and drawings were made of nearly all new ships of any importance when built or captured. These plans also show, in many instances, the later alterations in fitting, mast positions, or other details, made after the ship came into the hands of the British Navy.

Usually the "design plan" showed very little detail, and even the stern, or transom, elevation was omitted. The plan made from a ship, however, was usually well detailed, showing much of the carving and outboard detail and, sometimes, very complete deck arrangements superimposed on the outboard elevation. It is usually possible, therefore, to distinguish the contract design from the plan of the ship as built, when both are found. As has been said, the two plans did not exist in all cases. The colonial-built ships are most unsatisfactory in this respect, for with one exception either no plans exist at all or they have not yet been found and identified. It will be seen that the "establishment" cannot be a very satisfactory guide as to shape or appearance of these vessels. The Admiralty practice of the time also made the "establishment" quite ineffective in producing ships sufficiently alike for standardization of fittings while, on the other hand, it prevented a builder from having so free a hand that he would dare to attempt any great innovation in model or proportions, or even in increased dimensions, beyond minor degree, as has been stated earlier.

The question of whether plans or models were used in colonial contracts can be answered only so far as existing records indicate. Plans or "draughts" are occasionally mentioned in the few surviving ship contracts; models are almost never referred to. However, the existence of half-models of Admiralty ships built as early as 1714–19 show that such models were sometimes used. These early half-models were usually made by the use of "moulds"—pieces cut like half a frame, or a cross section, of a hull, mounted at intervals of every three or four frame spaces on a board cut to the profile of the ship and then ribbanded with wooden strips to fair the moulds. Usually in those that have survived to the present time the models were wholly or partly planked in lieu of the ribbands. These early models are, in fact, the same in principle as the American "hawk-nest" half-model, used to design small craft as late as the first part of the present century. In respect to the Admiralty half-models of this description, however, the available evidence suggests that they were not used to design ships, but rather were made from plans to illustrate the effects of changes from the original design. It is possible that some of these models represent "return draughts" from builders, showing the ship they proposed to build and indicating the differences from the hull form and dimensions, or proportions, in the original "establishment." Contrary to a popular conception, half-models were not invented by any American and were not used in America before plans were employed in ship design. Models were often employed in conjunction with plans or "draughts," to show officials who could not read a plan just what the intended ship looked like. At times when plans were in general use, the poorly trained commercial ship designer, who was unable to make a drawing, undoubtedly made a hawk-nest half-model, working by "art and eye" in the same manner as a man making a new design of a ship on paper. This, however, was not considered "scientific" at a time when the hull sections were thought best formed by employing tangent arcs formed to a rule; so it was rarely, if ever, employed in the design of naval vessels. It must also be noted that it was considered easier to transfer the scale dimensions from a plan to the full-size drawing of the ship's frames on the mould-loft floor than it was to do this from a model, even at a far later date than the colonial period.

The use of plans or a model implies the use of a mould loft. The latter is either a platform or the floor of a building smooth enough to draw upon. The shapes of timbers in the ship's structure are drawn full size by transferring scaled dimensions at chosen ordinates in the plan or model to their full-sized counterparts on the mould loft so as to reproduce accurately to full size for the ship the miniature curves of hull shape shown in plan or model. The mould loft in American colonial shipyards will be discussed later. No shipbuilder could use either a half-model or a plan if he was not capable of using a mould loft. If he could work from a model, he could work from a plan. So in either case the existence of a plan or a model indicates that the builder of the ship was competent to understand either. Like many later sailing-ship designers, some early builders found it difficult to make good and attractive plans but could make a model and paint and decorate it like the proposed ship, and so they used these to sell their ideas to owners. Hence the possibility that some of the very old Admiralty half-models were used in lieu of "return draughts" to show a ship as proposed by the builder.

Another type of model much used by the Admiralty was a complete hull model, framed and partly planked, with carvings, deck layout, and exterior details. This type of model was often rigged, all work being done to accurate scale. Today these are known as "Admiralty models" as a class, and they are now, as when they were built, primarily decorative. Originally these models were used to show the statesmen and politicians what fine ships the Navy intended to build and were pictorial in exactly the same way and for the same purpose as the modern ship models which are today seen in many government and naval buildings in this country. They served little or no purpose in either design or construction of new ships beyond insuring, perhaps, that the government officials would be sufficiently impressed by the models to grant the money necessary for the new ships. Solid half-models were also made in early times, though they were less popular than the frame or "hawk-nest" model. The Admiralty block models, dating from about 1732, were made of a solid block of wood. The use of narrow plank the thickness of the spacing of the water lines in the block to permit an easy transfer of the hull shape to the mould loft does not appear until after the Revolution. This may be an American invention, but such a claim will require more support than existing American traditions and the known half-models now offer.

The colonial shipyard differed in no important respect from a contemporary yard in Europe. In the period before the Revolution the shipyards were without machinery; all work was done with hand tools. Even water-power sawmills appear to have been very rarely employed. Sawn timber and plank were got out by "saw gangs" of three or four men. Two of these worked a long ripsaw fitted with handles at each end which were set at right angles to the sides of the saw blade instead of vertically, as in the modern two-man crosscut saw used to fell trees. The logs were rolled over a pit, or onto a crude platform and, with one man below the log and one on it, the saw was worked by hand to get out plank, or curved timbers such as frames. The remaining members of the saw gang moved the timber to the pit or platform, or shifted timber and steadied it as the progress of sawing required. There was much waste of timber; four planks to a log was the rule. Much of the shaping of timbers, both plank and heavy structural members, was done with the broadax, a heavy hewing tool, and with the lipped adz—the latter cutting across the grain and the former in line with it. With these two hand tools a skilled man could do accurate and rapid work; in fact, these two tools are still used today in wooden shipbuilding. Other small hand tools were employed—common handsaws, axes, hatchets, hammers, mauls, mallets, augers, chisels, and gouges which were crude fore-runners of the same tools today. Timber was moved about the yard and ship-ways by gangs of men, teams of oxen, and horses. Wheeled timber carriages were also used in which a large timber could be slung between two high wheels working on an arched axle. The latter was used to aid in lifting a log prior to slinging it by raising and lowering the tongue, which acted as a lever, with the axle at wheel-hubs as the fulcrum. Ships and boats were rarely built under cover, and often there was no building on the shipyard site itself, mould loft and tool shed or stable being on near-by property. The vessels were erected on timber ways, supported by sleepers laid on the ground or by piles. In a few yards the ways were supported by rough stone piers. Some yards had wharves in the yard area for use in finishing a ship after her launch, though until after the Revolution such refinements appear to have been rare in American yards, at least outside the larger towns.

In America the location of shipyards was governed more by the availability

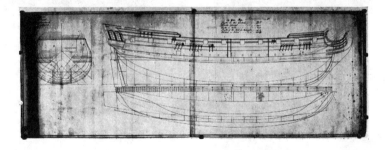

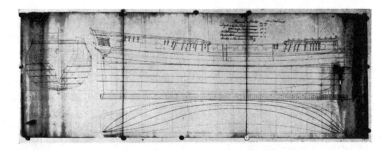

PLATE I. (Top) Model of a British 24-gun ship, 9-pdrs., of 1730–45. She measured 113′ on the gun deck, 93′ on the keel, 32′ beam, 11′ depth of hold, and 511 tons. (Center and bottom) Sheer draughts of two British 24-gun ships of 1741–45, GARLAND and MERMAID.

PLATE II. *Model of the 44-gun ship* AMERICA, *1749, in the Athenaeum, Portsmouth, New Hampshire.*
Courtesy Peabody Museum, Salem, Mass.

of timber than by depth of water or by other favorable building conditions. The shipbuilding towns were usually those near a good supply of timber or timber-exporting ports. A good supply of skilled labor was required because transportation was slow, and it was not wholly uncommon for a shipyard to have facilities to house labor, or at least the more skilled portion of it. Large settlements, like Boston, Portsmouth, and New York, depended largely on water transport of timber to supply their shipyards. All of the colonies on the seaboard had shipyards; those yards in the larger settlements usually had the most skillful workers, just as in more recent times, but the country yards were the least expensive.

The art of lofting ships—drawing their shape and structural members in full size, to get out the frames and bent timber to agree with a plan or model—must have developed as soon as plans or models were employed. Little has been written about this part of shipbuilding, even in comparatively recent times. Like the drawing of plans, it has been a "mystery" of the art of shipbuilding, not only in colonial times but long after. The exact date of the introduction of lofting into America is unknown, though probably the mould loft was used by some of the shipwrights brought to America in the early seventeenth century. Lofting practice in America before the Revolution—in fact, before 1800—was rather crude, and some parts of the ship—the stern, for example—were not laid out full size prior to setting up. The stern was usually built "by eye" except that the rake was taken from plan or model. As a result, the appearance of ships built to the same plan varied a good deal and ships did not always conform closely to the design in shape or dimensions. Accuracy was a matter of training and skill; the government-trained shipwrights were usually far more competent loftsmen than those trained in commercial yards, because the difficulties inherent in naval construction required greater care and accuracy in the preliminary steps of building. By 1700 the methods of lofting the frames, stem, and sternposts and laying off the decorative parts of the ship had been pretty well established. The method now employed of obtaining bevels does not appear to have been known, as the use of the ax and adz and the lack of power saws made it impractical to bevel frames before they were set up in place on the keel. Lofting of the stern and other difficult parts of the hull was developed in England about 1760 and in America about thirty-six years later.

The colonial shipbuilding industry suffered from many troubles. The lack of money in most colonies naturally limited shipbuilding orders and made employment rather uncertain. Metal for fastenings, sailcloth, rope, caulking material, and paint were commonly scarce and expensive. The cost of preparing the timber for ship construction was relatively great, and this usually prevented a builder from keeping on hand a stock of timber that would be seasoned when required. In addition to this, it took a great many years for the colonists to become acquainted with the shipbuilding properties of American timbers, most of which had not been known or used in Europe. In fact, the question of the properties of ship timber remained a matter of violent controversy in America until comparatively recent times, and even now there is not universal agreement. As a result, much timber went into colonial-built ships that rotted very fast, either because it was too green, or because an unsuitable species had been used. However, in spite of the difficulties, the colonial yards were capable of turning out cheap and strong vessels.

Very little metalwork was used in colonial-built vessels; this was also true of most European vessels of the period. All hull fastenings, so far as possible, were wooden pegs, or treenails, driven into holes bored for the purpose and with the ends wedged. Light construction was secured by handmade wrought-iron nails and spikes. Bolts were commonly set up by "upsetting" or riveting, rather than by threaded stock and nuts, and there was very little ironwork used in spars and rigging; chain was rarely seen. The armament of a ship and her anchors employed more metal than her whole structure. Because of the cost of large metal tools, there were few clamps, or jacks, used in building a vessel; her plank was shored, wedged, and pulled into place by tackles and ingenuity.

In spite of having to saw out plank, hew timber to shape, and bore for all fastenings by hand, and also to plank without proper clamps, the colonial shipwrights could turn out sizable vessels in a remarkably short time. This was accomplished not because the vessels were very simple or easy to build, but because a lifetime of use made the colonial adept in the handling of all hand tools and ingenious in overcoming apparent difficulties. Ships were actually built in the woods when necessity arose and drawn to water over the snow by oxen. Improvisation was always a necessity in colonial shipbuilding.

The colonial shipwright was usually a carpenter, caulker, joiner, and painter —in fact, a jack of all the trades necessary to build the hull of a ship. Sailors could rig a ship and make sails, but the shipwright had to make the masts and bowsprit, build spars and tops, and even make blocks. Crude manually operated wooden lathes were used to turn out stanchions and other turned work, and there was usually a wood carver in the community who could fashion figureheads and outside joinerwork or carvings. Many of the men employed in these early American yards could build a boat, a ship, a house, or a barn, make furniture, and repair a wagon. Many of these men were very skillful, and they worked long hours, for a day's work was from sunrise to sunset, six days a week, with few holidays. There were no steady jobs to give security in the colonies. So valuable were shipwrights in colonial times that they were exempt from militia duty or naval impress.

The competence of the colonial American shipbuilder in the construction of fast vessels has been mentioned. This grew out of his need for such craft when his traders were harassed by the national enemies created by numerous wars, by pirates, and, not least, by the laws, regulations, and customs duties at home. Smuggling was common, and there were opportunities for other illegal activities in commerce for which a fast vessel was much better than insurance, or even armament. Hence the American rapidly developed the functions of design that produced both speed and weatherliness in most sizes of vessels. It is probable that many of his ideas were based on the fast ships of the seventeenth century. He apparently took over bodily the model of the early "Jamaica sloop," later called the "Bermuda sloop," as a basis for the fast American schooner. The search for speed in some sailing vessels was almost as acute in pre-Revolutionary years as it was in the early nineteenth century; in both periods the emphasis in America was on small, fast vessels.

Though there were many different rigs used in European sailing vessels in the colonial period, Americans seem to have employed the ship, brigantine, schooner, snow, and sloop rigs almost exclusively after 1700. A few ketches were built, and there were some odd rigs used in small craft—lateen, sprit, and leg-of-mutton. One-masted square-rigged small craft were in use on lakes and rivers. Except for the schooner, however, there is no evidence that these rigs differed in any important respect from their European counterparts. While there has been a traditional claim that an American invented the schooner in 1713, in the light of existing evidence this is no longer worthy of serious consideration. The Americans, however, may justly claim to have developed the rig from that of small boats to that of large vessels in the eighteenth century; by the mid-century they had become almost the sole exponents of this rig in seagoing craft.

Since no plans have been found that represent a colonial-built vessel of earlier than about 1745, a plan of an English man-of-war of 1732 is presented to show the quality of ship design of the time and to illustrate the methods of drawing then in vogue in the Royal Navy. This plan is for a brigantine or snow, classed as a "sloop" and ordered to be built at Deptford, England, May 5, 1732. The drawing shows a long, low vessel well fitted to carry armament such as was then in use, and capable of good speed under sail and oars. It is evident that some sacrifice in weatherliness has been made in her design to obtain shoal draft and ability to row. Two oar ports between each pair of gun ports gave her sixteen sweeps on a side; with two or three men to each sweep she could be swept along at about three knots in a calm. There can be little doubt that this vessel would sail quite well, for her lines, though perhaps full by modern standards of yacht design, are as good as those of many sailing commercial vessels of a century or more later. The name of this sloop of war is believed to be *Cruizer*, for this vessel was built at Deptford in the year shown on the plan, and she was of the dimensions given (Figure 1).

The naval "sloops" had appeared in the Royal Navy as armed small craft in the last half of the seventeenth century. They were probably sloop-rigged with one mast. However, by 1725 "sloops" in the Navy were vessels with the guns on one deck without regard to rig. The vessels thus rated, however, were either one- or two-masted, and carried from 8 to 18 guns. Like the other rates of the period, the sloop classification changed from time to time; by the last quarter of the century a "sloop of war" came to mean a vessel commanded by an officer one grade below a captain in the Navy. Ship-rigged sloops of war did not become common until about the end of the American Revolution.

It will be seen that the *Cruizer* was rather well decorated with carving, though on a much reduced scale as compared with earlier vessels. She appears more modern than one would expect because of her unbroken sheer and low freeboard. The bow, though decorated with an ornate carving, is simple and light in structure. In the completed vessel there would be a light wooden or iron brace from figurehead to the bracket below the cathead on each side, at about the level of the moulding at the underside of the carvings along the bulwarks. The stern is that known as "lute" or "pink," something like that later used in the New England "pinky" fishing schooners. The lute stern, though having the appearance of a pink stern, was different in construction, and its underside was planked in, rather than left open as in the pinky. This type of stern was strong and rather simple in construction and, between 1714 and 1745, was rather popular in the smaller men-of-war of the Royal Navy. The deck arrangement in general was very practical. The deck was flush in the way of the eight gun ports a side, but at bow and stern the deck was raised to make a stern cabin and short forecastle. In neither case does the raised deck reach the rail

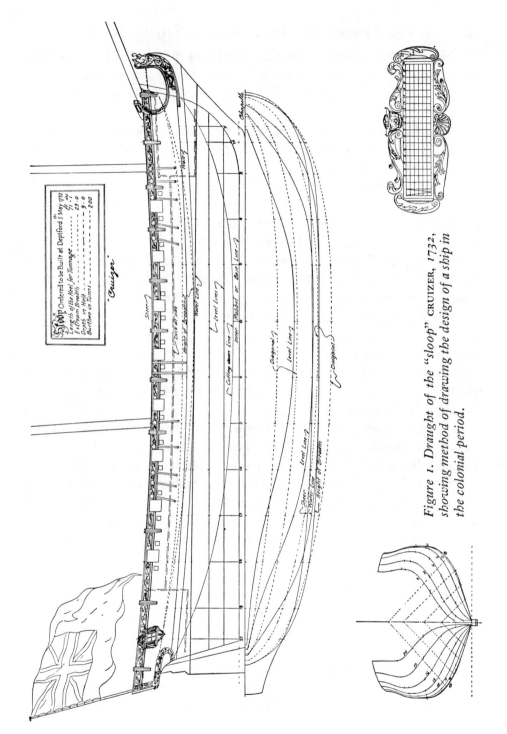

Figure 1. Draught of the "sloop" CRUIZER, 1732, showing method of drawing the design of a ship in the colonial period.

top. Not only did these decks give the space below them somewhat more head-room, but they also gave a commanding position from which to steer the vessel and made the deep bulwarks less of a handicap forward in handling the anchor and its gear.

In model and arrangement the *Cruizer* represents nothing very unusual in her time. Some of these "sloops" had raised quarterdecks and low breaks fore and aft in the sheer, as seen in the other examples, but the day of the towering fore and after "castles" was long past. There were hulls that were sharper than *Cruizer*'s, as well as many that were much fuller. The proportion of depth and beam to length shown in the plan was not rigidly adhered to in all "sloops" built in the same period, as will be seen. It is to be noted, too, that the "estab-lishment" appears to have been quite ineffective in standardizing designs in the "sloop" class. Men-of-war in this category in the Royal Navy after 1732 were usually brigantine, snow, or ketch rigged, the snow being apparently the most common rig in this class. By this time the one-masted vessel had become rare among the combat vessels of the Royal Navy, and it did not reappear until the cutter was introduced about 1760.

The method used to project the hull shape of the *Cruizer* shows the progress that had been made in fairing the lines of a ship in a plan by 1732. The prin-ciples involved are not entirely dissimilar to the "diagonal" method, which some small-craft designers still use. This is exactly the same principle that was used in the "hawk-nest" half-model. The sections of the hull having been sketched, they were faired, to make certain that plank could be bent over them, by "diagonal" lines in the plan and by battens or ribbands of wood in a model, the latter being very narrow and thin so as to avoid breaking in the rather sharp curves caused by the full ends of the hull. The "diagonals," being so much like battens or ribbands in principle, were discovered to be a simple way of fairing the lines of a ship in the drawing or in the mould loft, and also gave points of measurement for lofting.

In order to understand the process of drawing the hull form, it is necessary to know a little about the principles involved in both the half-model and the drawing of the "lines." The latter term has long been the common shipbuilding term for the drawing that shows the shape of a hull. A half-model and a draw-ing of the "lines" have much in common. Both represent but one-half of the ship; since both sides of the hull athwartships are alike, there is no need to make more than one-half in a model or a plan. The half-model gets its name from this feature.

The plan and model, then, show one side of the ship; in the model the profile, plan, and cross sections are combined in one block or structure, but this is not practical in a drawing, because of the confusion of lines that would result. Early attempts to delineate a ship's form on paper having shown this to be true, the designers tried to separate the three elevations of the plan. The result was three distinct views of the hull that together represented everything obtained in a half-model—the profile, plan view, and cross sections. On the profile, or side elevation, the outboard appearance could be designed, the carving could be shown, and all the data necessary to locate the masts, gunports, and structural members, and the shape of bow and stern, rudder, and sheer (top of rail) could be included. The plan or elevation below the profile, in the *Cruizer*'s plan, is the "half-breadth" plan, and shows a view from above the half-model as though the latter were so transparent that marks on the bottom of the model could be seen. This elevation shows the shape of the rail and deck as viewed from above, as well as other curved lines necessary to prove that the cross sections are in such relation to one another that planking can be bent around them. The plan that shows the cross sections, placed to one side of the profile elevation as a rule, is known as the "body plan." It shows, first, the shape of the cross sections of the hull located at certain chosen frames; next, the location of the lines used to "fair" the hull (the equivalent of the strips of wood or ribbands on the hawk-nest half-model); and finally the location of measurements (necessary to project most curved lines to be shown in either profile or half-breadth plans) that are plotted on the cross sections in the body plan, even though they may not be represented by lines there as in the example. It may be said here that the location of such measuring lines is usually shown in the body plan and such lines became increasingly numerous in the eighteenth century.

The various curved lines in the plan of a ship's hull form may be best understood by imagining a half-model made of some easily cut material—wax, for instance. This model is a solid block of wax that is shaped exactly like half the ship on either side of the center line and cut vertically along the longitudinal center line so that the back of the model is the exact shape of the hull profile. Perhaps it will be more easily understood if it is assumed that there are to be three identical half-models. One of these half-models, then, is laid on the paper to correspond to the profile or side elevation of the ship as in the plan of the *Cruizer*. This part of the drawing is often called the "sheer plan." By custom, the three elevations in the drawing of a ship's form are known as plans, rather than as elevations, in other types of drawing the "plan" being only that view taken from above the object drawn. On the model that now represents the "sheer plan," the locations of various lines are marked on the model, at the designer's pleasure or best judgment. First he must have the location of the cross sections so that they may be reproduced at exactly the same place in the full-size ship. Since no two sections will be exactly alike, this is important. To save time he will decide to locate the cross sections on various selected frames so that these can be reproduced in the mould loft and act as control sections that will govern the shapes of all the others required. Depending upon the size of the ship, he may take from two to four, or even more, frame spaces as the interval between his control sections.

In the *Cruizer* the designer has chosen to use every third frame, measured from the one that is the largest, or the "midsection." The location of this, in the model, is readily determined, but when the designer is drawing a plan without reference to an existing model he locates this section according to his judgment, experience, and theory of design, just as the man who made a model had to do. Now, from this section, marked ✖ on the plan, he lays off every third frame, and numbers them accordingly, using numbers for the stations abaft the midsection. Because of the confusion that would otherwise arise, the designer used letters to designate the stations selected in the forebody, the hull forward of the midsection. In later times the stations were numbered, beginning at either end of the hull, but the method shown in the plan of the *Cruizer* was common throughout most of the sailing-ship era. The location of the stations having been laid off, the model is marked with lines vertical to the keel to show these frames. If the stations are widely spaced it will be desirable to have additional control frames at bow and stern, where the curves change shape rapidly, to insure that the mould loft will accurately reproduce the shape of hull intended by the designer. Therefore, at bow and stern, additional frames are shown—in the example, *N* in the forebody and *21* in the afterbody. It will be seen that *N* is one frame space from *M* and *21* is two frame spaces from *19*. This is entirely a matter of judgment, and there was no rule that governed the location of these extra stations or control frames, other than that they fall on a frame and be spaced to insure accuracy in the mould loft.

The model may now be marked with the position of the water line, which theoretically should be determined by the weight of the ship and her displacement. These matters being impossible to determine accurately before the ship was designed, the draftsman located the water line at a draft that was specified in the order for the ship, or according to his judgment. This seems a great difficulty at first glance, but practically this was easy, for in a sailing man-of-war there would have to be ballast, and the amount of this might be adjusted somewhat to give the desired draft. However, unlike the modern racing yacht, the exact draft was of little importance in a sailing man-of-war, for it could vary as much as a number of feet between light draft, when the vessel was not loaded, and the load draft, when the vessel was ready for sea. Obviously the latter would actually change constantly as her stores, water, provisions, and ammunition were consumed. It was only necessary, then, for the designer to conform in general to a draft requirement, if the latter was to be limited. The chosen water line might be parallel to the bottom of the keel or not, as the designer thought best. Usually the sailing water line was located on the completed ship so that the depth from the water line to the bottom of the keel was slightly greater aft than at the bow; this is called "drag." In the *Cruizer* the designer has attempted to approximate the sailing water line and has shown the "drag." This line having been marked on the model, other water lines (or perhaps a more easily understood term would be "level lines") are marked on the model. In the example these are parallel to the keel and arbitrarily spaced at, say, two feet. This is wholly arbitrary, and the spacing is decided on the basis of accuracy in the mould loft, just as the spacing of control frames was. Sometimes the level lines were made parallel to the sailing water line instead of to the keel; here again it was merely a matter of individual preference on the part of the designer.

If the model were now inspected it would be seen that the location of two types of cross sections now exist. The vertical marks will indicate where the vertical and transverse sections may be taken, while the water line and the additional level lines indicate the logical position of some horizontal and longitudinal sections. In order to lay these off a base line has to be located.

In order to simplify his work both the model maker and the draftsman represented the hull form as though the outside planking on the finished ship were not in place. The reason for this is obvious, for they were seeking, primarily, to establish the shape of the frames, which in turn fixed the form of the hull of the completed ship. Now, since the depth of the keel was usually rather great, both for strength and to protect the bottom of the hull in case of running on shore or hitting a rock, and since it was not always straight in profile, greater accuracy by the shipwrights would be insured if the chosen base line were close to the actual frame structure. As a result, the custom was established of placing the base line at the inner "rabbet" along the keel; this was the line of the joint between the inside of the planking and the side of the keel. To make the vessel watertight here, it was thought necessary to groove the sides of the keel in a shallow V to take the edge of the lowest plank of the bottom. This was known as the "rabbet," the innermost edge of the triangular groove being called the "inner rabbet." Actually in most vessels of the period this was usually the top of one of the timbers making up the keel. This line, then, was the base line. The level lines were often spaced from it by measurement, and the stations of the control frames stood perpendicular to it. In a few vessels the bottom of the keel was not parallel to the base line but had greater depth at one end, though this is not the case in the example.

Any other information that would determine the height of any part of the ship's structure could be marked on the "sheer plan" or, as in this case, the model representing it. The varying heights of the deck, for example, could be represented by a line and the position of mouldings to decorate the hull; the gun ports and oar port locations, channels, and any other detail thought desirable could be shown.

Leaving this model for the moment, a duplicate is taken and marked with the vertical cross sections shown in the one used to represent the "sheer plan." The model is now cut along each of these vertical lines. The cut faces of each section can be traced on the paper to represent the "body plan" by using common base and center lines when drawing each face of the sections of the model. The sections forward of the midsection are grouped on one side of the center line; those abaft the midsection are on the opposite side. The midsection is drawn twice, once on each side of the center line.

The model may now be glued together and recut on new lines. These are diagonal to the center line as represented by similar lines on the body plan of the *Cruizer*. These diagonal lines intersect on the center line of the body plan and join the midsection at points that correspond on each side, thus making every diagonal line correspond in angle to the center line on each side. If the glued model is cut along these lines, we would have longitudinal sections whose curved edges each represent the shape of these lines as they pass around the hull.

The third model may now be marked with the water line and the level lines established on the model representing the profile, or sheer, plan. The deck profile may also be established. In colonial days another line was used in addition—the "height of breadth" line used to determine section shape in the mould loft. To obtain this, refer to the body plan and mark on each section the point that appears to have the greatest beam—or, to put it differently, the point that is farthest from the section's center line. These points were transferred to the corresponding frames or stations on the sheer-plan model and a curve struck through them. If there is no one point of greatest beam in a section, the upper and lower limits of the greatest beam in every section are established and transferred. This is the case in the *Cruizer*, and it will be noted that there are two dotted lines on the profile, one a little below the deck line, and one meeting the water line amidships. These represent the "height of breadth." In some drawings the half breadth of the deck is drawn on the "half-breadth plan," but in colonial times this was rare in small craft and the "height of breadth" line was used instead, as in *Cruizer*.

Next, the top of the third model is laid off, from a center line below and parallel to the base line of the sheer-plan model. The new view is the "half-breadth plan" of the top of the rail or sheer. Owing to the profile curve this cannot be traced but must be drawn from measurements at each station or control frame. The model is now cut along the water line and the level lines; each may be traced in outline on the "half-breadth plan" as in the sections—except the water line, which must be laid off by measurements, as in the rail, because it is not parallel to the base and must be foreshortened. The stations must be the lines in the sheer, projected downward. The new lines are represented in the *Cruizer* by solid lines in the "half-breadth plan."

The second model may again be used. It will be recalled that it was cut into diagonal sections longitudinally. The outline of each of these sections may be traced on the "half-breadth plan" so that the plane used is the true or cut face of each and the straight edges correspond with the center line, as in the *Cruizer*'s plan. Next, one of the models may be cut along either of the "height of breadth" lines (both are the same when projected, since their half breadths are identical, and both must be foreshortened in drawing) and lay this off as in the rail or sheer half breadth. The deck might be projected in the same manner, if it were to be shown.

There is one more line in the sheer plan of the *Cruizer* to be explained. This line starts well up at the bow and curves downward under the midsection almost to the base, then passes upward to the stern above the water line. This was called the "cutting down" line and is used in framing the vessel. It represents the tops of the frame timbers, where they cross the keel. This is really an arbitrary line, since it is located by sketching typical frame elevations to scale and laying off the line from these. This line serves no purpose in hull form and is for construction purposes only. Drawings used later on will show other lines, but these will be explained in the references to these plates.

It will be seen from this description that the plan reduces a model to a series of intersecting planes, or cross and longitudinal sections, so that measurements can be more readily taken to reproduce the sections and profile full size on the mould-loft floor. Of course, the skill to determine what would be the best shapes for the profile, sections, water line, level lines, and diagonals, and how to bring them into a predetermined relationship, requires education, experience, and imagination. The methods by which this skill is obtained are described in detail in books on marine design and are outside the scope of this discussion; we are concerned here only with the explanation of the meanings of the various parts of a ship's plan.

The colonial builder was expected to build a ship from this one plan together with instructions or specifications. A deck plan might be furnished to show how the vessel was to be arranged and also the size and position of hatches or any other deck furniture. Sometimes there were plans or sketches of lower decks (or platforms) on which cabins and other below-deck spaces were shown. It was by no means unusual, however, for the builder to have the "draught," like the plan of the *Cruizer*, and nothing else except written or verbal directions as to deck arrangements. No spar or rigging plan was furnished, but merely a set of spar and mast dimensions based on the "establishment," or on a similar vessel, to serve merely as a guide to the sparmaker and builder. Few other plans were made for construction, though there are in existence a number of contemporary drawings that show comparisons between ships, or the parts of certain ships, that were drawn up for discussion by technicians but which were not sent to a builder.

Calculations of the factors in ship design were employed in colonial times. In the late seventeenth century a number of great mathematicians tried to express the elements of ship design in formulae. It was soon learned that it was possible to calculate the weight of a ship from her plan, supposing that she was brought to any water line that could be marked on a correct drawing of the hull form. Estimates of the weight of the structure of a ship, with the weights of everything that was placed aboard, were also made and were used extensively in naval ship design. Efforts were made to explore stability, rolling, resistance, weatherliness, and steering qualities of ships, with particular emphasis on the mathematical approach to these subjects. In addition, a great deal of effort was directed to the mechanical methods of forming the curves

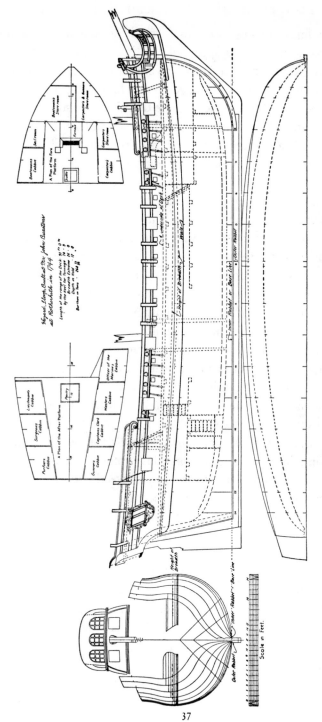

Figure 2. Draught of the HAZARD, *sloop of war, 1744, brigantine- or snow-rigged, showing lines used in fairing the hull re-ferred to in the text.*

that make up the lines of ships. Sections formed by tangent arcs and straight lines were proposed and widely accepted. Mathematically constructed diagonals were investigated, and the great Swedish naval architect, Chapman, proposed the use of a predetermined diagonal to which a ship's hull should conform in order to be fast. While none of these theories have survived in modern practice, they initiated the trend toward the use of mathematical expressions of the functions in naval architecture that has existed since. The use of mathematics in design gradually assumed such importance that it was considered essential in the education of naval architects, even to the exclusion of the "art" of making plans and forming hulls. Not only did the use of mathematical terms serve to impress the student and layman with the "science" of naval architecture, the equivalent of the "mysteries of the art" of the seventeenth and eighteenth centuries; these terms also gave a satisfactory feeling of accurate measurement of factors that could otherwise be only vaguely defined. However, by the end of the nineteenth century it was apparent that mathematics would not serve to insure good design without a thorough knowledge of hull-form characteristics. Hence the modern emphasis on model testing. The use of the test model to discover the probable performance of a design prior to building was first attempted in a crude experiment by an Englishman, Beaufoy, in the last decade of the eighteenth century. It might be said with some truth that neither mathematics nor the test model has yet insured good design, for the failure of modern ships to operate satisfactorily is by no means unknown.

The colonial shipbuilder just previous to the Revolution does not appear to have engaged in mathematical investigations extensive enough to have been recorded; he was concerned with what were perhaps the more practical trends of the period. During the seventy years preceding the Revolution, the practical developments of ship design were in a general increase in the dimensions of ships, sharper models, lower freeboard, and fewer encumbrances of unnecessary decoration and topworks than had previously been fashionable. Rigging became less cumbersome and much lighter in these years. The rise in importance of such types of fast seagoing small craft as the English cutter, the French lugger, and the American schooner in this period were perhaps the outstanding accomplishments of ship designers, developed by trial-and-error methods without the aid, apparently, of mathematical investigations.

Except for the fast schooner, the Americans cannot be credited with any original or unusual improvement in ship design prior to the Revolution. Their large privateers in the colonial period were undoubtedly sharp and fast but

were very little different in model from their British sisters. Some of these vessels are referred to as "frigates." Lest this lead to an assumption that such
privateers were the same as men-of-war of this class, it must be explained that
"frigate" was used to distinguish a type of merchant ship in this period, as
well as a special type of man-of-war. The "frigate-built" merchantman had
one flush deck and a raised quarterdeck and forecastle; in this respect the merchant "frigate" had exactly the same deck arrangement that marked her man-
of-war sister. This build, however, did not imply that the merchant "frigate"
or the privateer with this deck arrangement was designed to meet the man-of-
war requirements described earlier. The merchant frigate was still primarily
a carrier; the privateer was a fast ship first and a combat ship second. In colonial
times merchant-ship models were described by many names—"frigate," "hag-
boat," "pink," "bark," "cat," "flyboat," and "galley"—that referred to build
or to the shape of the stern rather than to rig or even to the model of hull. Regardless of the original meaning of these names, they had by 1760 assumed
technical meanings that were employed by shipbuilders to distinguish rather
trifling variations in construction, arrangement, stern design, and general model.
A "bark," "cat," or "frigate" might be small or large and rigged as a ship, snow,
sloop, brigantine, or schooner. This is well shown in *Architecturia Navalis
Mercatoria*, a book of ship plans by the great Swedish naval architect, Frederick
Hennik Af Chapman. This book was published in 1768 but represented vessels
of from twenty to forty years earlier and showed the numerous types of
merchant-ship builds, including "frigates," and also privateers and men-of-war.

To supplement the drawing of the *Cruizer*, the plans of two more sloops of
war of the middle portion of the eighteenth century are shown, the brigantine
or snow *Hazard* (Figure 2), built in 1744, and the ketch *Speedwell* (Figure 3),
built eight years later. The plan of the *Hazard* has been used to identify some
of the lines mentioned when describing the projections in the plan of the
Cruizer. These plans, traced from the original drawings, repeat many of the
projections employed in the drawing of the *Cruizer*, but show important details of the arrangement of the decks. The plan of the *Speedwell* indicates
that the fairing of her lines was done by some method employing tangent arcs
in the sections; the line of radii is shown in her half breadth and indicated on
the sections. Compared to the *Cruizer*, these vessels are fuller and somewhat
more burdensome. Plans similar to these were without doubt prepared by
American shipbuilders for many colonial vessels prior to the Revolution.

The purpose of the plan or model was to permit the design of a hull on a small convenient scale so that the form could be readily seen and judged. However, in order to make the hull design of use, some regard had to be given to the means by which the small-scale hull form was to be reproduced in the full-size ship. For obvious reasons the plan was more convenient in the transfer of measurements from small scale to full size; also the drawing could be readily copied with accuracy equal to that of the original; this was not the case with models. These practical factors, in addition to those of supposedly "scientific" nature, such as mechanical design of sections, gradually brought about the ascendancy of the plan over the half-model in naval design throughout the sailing-ship period. With this emphasis on the art, it is not surprising to find the naval draftsmen of the eighteenth century capable of producing plans of great accuracy and beauty of workmanship. In fact, the marine draftsman of the eighteenth century was capable of producing drawings of greater beauty than have since been seen in this field.

It is fortunate that the state of colonial shipbuilding before the Revolution can be judged by evidence more concrete than mere opinion and a comparison of the known facts of British naval construction with the probabilities of early American naval shipbuilding. The existence of plans of the 24-gun ship *Boston,* built by Ben Hallowell at Boston, Massachusetts, between 1747 and 1748, gives an opportunity to support many of the statements that have been made concerning the quality of colonial shipbuilding. If the plans of the earlier ships were available, more complete evidence would be possible, but no plans of the *Falkland* or the *Bedford* have yet been discovered.

The 24-gun ships were the only men-of-war in the Royal Navy of "frigate build" in the first half of the eighteenth century, there being no class between the two-decked 40- or 44-gun ships and the 24's. The 30-gun ships proposed in the "establishments" were not built in this rate but were completed as small 40-gun ships, armed on two decks, and for this reason they were not in the "frigate" class as armed and built. The "frigate" has already been referred to in regard to merchant ships. By 1745 the term had come to describe not only a build of vessel, but, in the naval service, a ship with one deck fully armed, an armed quarterdeck, and an unarmed forecastle deck. The latter was gradually armed in the last quarter of the century. The early development of the "frigate" is a matter of European shipbuilding history, rather than American. Beginning as a name of a small galley type, the term "frigate" appears to have come to mean a fast ship, and finally a ship of a specified build and armament in naval services. The earlier colonial-built naval ships were two-decked and

PLATE III. Humphreys' model for the projected 74-gun ship of the Revolution, in Independence Hall, Philadelphia.

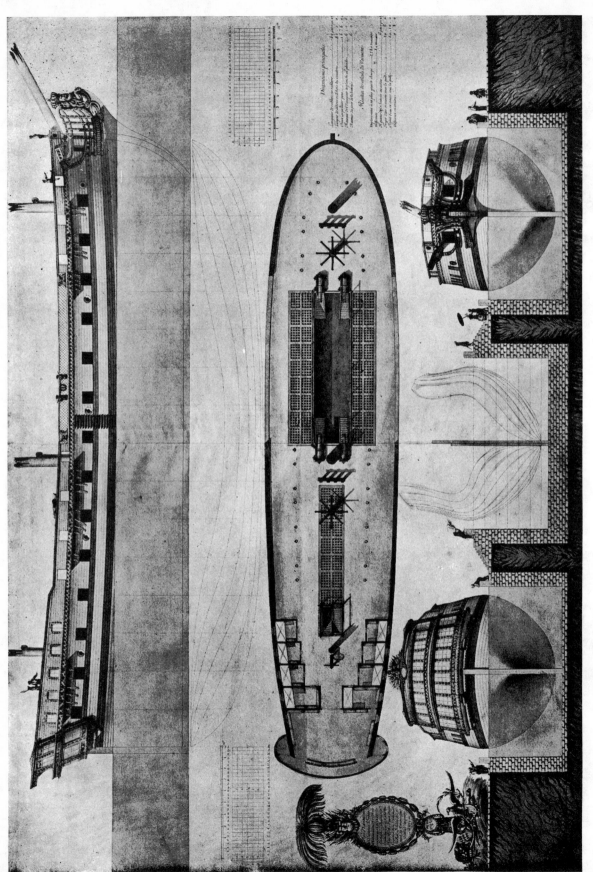

PLATE IV. Drawing of the SOUTH CAROLINA, *ex* L'INDIEN, *from* Souvenirs de Marine, *Vol. V.*

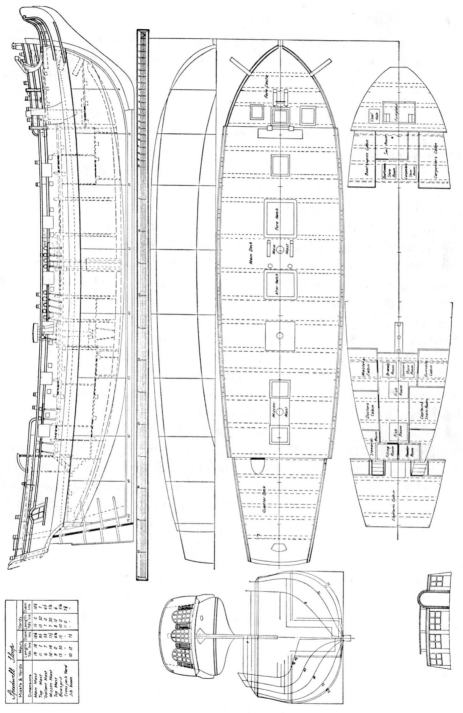

Figure 3. Draught of the SPEEDWELL, *sloop, 1752, ketch-rigged. Plan shows the use of radii in fairing the lines.*

carried 40 or more guns, so the *Boston* appears to have been the first "frigate" built in America for naval service. Whether or not she preceded merchant "frigates" cannot be stated, so the importance of her being the "first" of the type is open to some question.

The plan of the *Boston*, shown in Figure 4, requires little technical explanation. It has been redrawn in the modern manner employing sections, water line, and level lines, as explained in the case of the *Cruizer*. The diagonals are the same in projection, but the deck has been used instead of the "height of breadth" lines. The only other addition is the use of "buttock lines." These are longitudinal sections representing vertical planes through the hull parallel to the longitudinal center line; they were introduced into American plans in the last decade of the eighteenth century. Except for the buttocks and more numerous water or level lines, there has been no important change in the methods of drawing the form of a ship since the middle of the eighteenth century. The plan of the *Boston* shows the lines of the hull and the outboard appearance and also an inboard elevation which shows, in profile, the upper deck arrangements. No deck plan is shown, for none has yet been found.

The plan shows a well-formed hull, of large displacement, which should have sailed quite fast. It will be noted that she has sharp, rather V-shaped sections rather than the round, almost barrel-shaped sections of the *Hazard*. She has twelve ports on each side on the main deck and ports for three guns on each side on the quarterdeck, which would permit her carrying 30 guns if all her ports were filled. She probably actually carried 28 guns, for the *Boston* was almost the same length as a 28-gun frigate built in 1758. There was one port on the lower deck which was probably used as an entry or loading port rather than to mount a gun, though such ports appear to have had guns temporarily mounted in them in some of the 24's when in action. It will be seen here that the guns which a ship actually carried could easily exceed her "rate," a characteristic that marked sailing men-of-war from this time. On the quarterdeck, upright timbers are seen along the rail; these were the "stocks" of the swivel guns, which were small-bore cannon mounted on an oarlock-shaped pivot set in the head of each stock. The top of the stock was banded to prevent the timber from splitting with the force of the recoil. The swivels were never counted as "guns," and often the small carriage guns on the quarterdeck were also excluded. This allowed a satisfactory difference in the statement of the force of a ship when she won or lost a battle—each side quoting the actual number of guns in the enemy ship and the "rate" of their own.

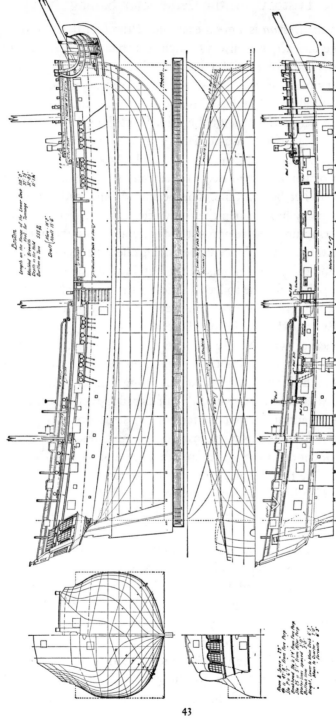

43

Figure 4. Draught of the 24-gun ship BOSTON, 1748. The earliest plan yet found of an American-built ship.

The plan of the *Boston* is a good example of the fact that the sweep of the deck lines, fore and aft, was always much less than in the sheer and outside mouldings. This had existed as far back as Elizabethan times in sailing ships, as contemporary plans of drawings show, but is contrary to many artists' conceptions. The "beakhead bulkhead" is also to be seen in this ship. This was a heavy bulkhead across the bow of the ship, from the gun deck upward. The beakhead deck, or platform, was usually a little above the gun deck in small ships, and in many this part of the vessel's hull looked as if a small piece of the upper portion of her bow had been sawed out of her model, leaving a rectangular notch in her bow profile. The beakhead bulkhead had been an outgrowth of the galley hull. When the forecastle was added to the galley it was a rectangular structure, square across the fore end to allow a number of guns to be mounted there to fire directly ahead. This became a conventional design in later ships, and the platform outside the bulkhead in the bow was then used to handle sail and also for the toilet facilities of the crew. The space was made greater by extending the platform into the cutwater by gratings, placed inside the headrails. By 1740 the beakhead bulkheads were slowly going out of fashion in the small men-of-war. Nearly all sloops, like *Cruizer*, had been given a "round" bow—that is, one without the beakhead bulkhead. In the larger ships the beakhead bulkhead was often masked by being built in a shape like a cupid's bow in plan view, as seen in the *Boston*'s half-breadth plan, where it is shown in dotted lines representing the outside face of this structure. Also, the beakhead bulkheads became increasingly shallow and less prominent.

The arrangement of this ship was probably more or less standard in her class for the period. The hawse holes were on the lower deck, and a deep manger was made by a high bulkhead across the bows directly under the foremost gun port to prevent the lower deck from flooding when she plunged into a head sea (without her hawses being stopped with wooden plugs, as was done at sea in these vessels). Her fireplace, for cooking, was under the forecastle deck, abaft the foremast, and apparently this space was enclosed by a light bulkhead, part of which extended abaft the end of the forecastle deck. Probably the after part of this was permanently fixed, while the rest could be taken down in action. Abaft the mizzenmast, on the gun deck, there appear to have been light bulkheads across the ship to make cabins for the captain and perhaps one for the first lieutenant. The rest of the officers berthed aft on the lower deck, the crew berthing forward. Except for the guns abaft the mizzen and the wheel just forward of it, the quarterdeck was clear of obstructions and was used for handling the ship. The forecastle was also a working deck with two hatches, one for the fireplace chimney and one just forward of the mast.

There are two plans of the *Boston* in the Admiralty files. Both were obviously made after the ship was built. One plan shows a short quarterdeck, the other a long one with an alteration added that apparently carried her gangways forward at the same level as the quarterdeck. The latter plan is used to represent the ship here, for it can safely be assumed that this plan represented her in service.

That the plans of the *Boston* were made after she was built can be established by comparing them with the design plans of ships of her class and period—for example, those of the *Garland*, built in 1748, and the *Mermaid*, built in 1749. The latter design has a long quarterdeck and apparently belongs to the latest establishment, 1745, then in force. It seems reasonable to suppose that the *Boston* was built on the 1741 establishment and altered to fit the 1745 establishment. These design plans show very little detail compared to the *Boston* plans.

The *Boston* was about 5 feet longer than the *Garland*, but looked much like her in profile. She was much sharper in model and had far more deadrise. Compared to the *Mermaid*, the *Boston* is also longer by 3 feet and has an entirely different hull model. From this it would appear that her American builder had redesigned her, while adhering reasonably closely to the contract design. He could not have been more restricted in this matter than were the English contractors in naval ships constructed in private yards. As far as can be judged from the plans, the American builder turned out a vessel equal in appearance and finish to those of the English builders. This is some proof of the competence of a colonial yard in this class of construction and probably in design as well.

The 24-gun ships of the various "establishments" since 1719 had changed little. The earlier ships had their oar ports on the lower deck at the level of the sill of the single port on that deck and carried no carriage guns on the quarterdeck. These ships, in fact, anticipated the "quarterdecked sloops" of the end of the eighteenth century, except that the majority of the latter did not have a raised forecastle deck. The 24-gun ships were armed with long guns, nine- or twelve-pounders, with threes or sixes on the quarterdeck. All of these ships had much the same rig. The photograph (Plate 1) of a model of a 24 in the Science Museum, Kensington, England, illustrates the appearance of a ship of an earlier "establishment" than the *Boston*, but with the same rig.

The ship rig used in the *Boston* was little different from that used at the beginning of the century. She had long lower masts and fairly long topmasts on all three masts. Short topgallant masts were fidded on the fore and main masts only, the mizzen topmast having a long pole instead. The yards on all three masts were shorter than was later the fashion. The mizzen carried a lateen spanker yard; in earlier ships this carried the triangular lateen sail, but about 1748 the four-sided spanker sail came into use in the Royal Navy in the smaller classes. This new sail was set abaft the mizzenmast, the fore part of the lateen yard being barren. Gaff spankers had been introduced much earlier in the sloops and small vessels, but were not common on vessels of more than 20 guns until about the time of the American Revolution. The lateen yard survived, in some large men-of-war, until almost to the end of the century. Above the lateen yard were the mizzen square topsail and the topgallant sail.

In addition to the working sails set on the three yards on fore and main, and on the two above the spanker on the mizzen, naval ships carried a large number of light-weather sails when the occasion demanded. Two square sails could be set, one under the bowsprit and another under the jibboom. Royals could be hoisted above the fore, main, and mizzen topgallant sails; and in addition to four staysails set between the bowsprit and foremast, five could be set between main and fore, and four more between mizzen and main. In addition to all these, a topsail could be set above the spanker yard and studding sails could be rigged out on the spanker. All told, a ship could carry as many as thirty sails in very light winds. Studding sails came into general use in naval vessels shortly before the American Revolution, being employed on the yards of the fore and main masts. The four-sided spanker, when used on a lateen yard, was not secured to the masts with hoops; a hemp "horse" was used, fastened to the mizzen trestletrees and set up on deck, and to this the sail was secured with hanks, as in a staysail. This "horse" was also used in naval snows until about the middle of the eighteenth century. It was finally replaced with the trysail mast, which was stepped abaft and close to the lower mast, with its head secured in the lower trestletrees. This was an innovation apparently taken from merchant ships of this rig. It was desirable, in men-of-war, to have all yards rigged so that they could be quickly brought down on deck. For this reason the foreyard in schooners and the mainyard in cutters also employed a rope "horse," but in these rigs the "horse" was set up from the trestletrees to deck on the foreside of the masts.

The cut of sails in 1750 differed somewhat from that used in both British and American men-of-war after the Revolution. The sails had great hoist in proportion to spread, in the lower courses and topsails particularly, and were not as "square," and did not have such spread, as they had about 1800. Flax sailcloth was used in the Royal Navy; the weave seems to have been rather loose. Because of the material used, the fore-and-aft sails did not stand very well.

The *Boston* had a rather short life, being broken up in February, 1752. It may be that this was because of the use of green timber in her construction, for the American-built men-of-war are said to have been unsatisfactory for this reason until after the Revolution.

The other ship built about the time of the *Boston* was a 44-gun ship armed on two decks and with a few light guns on the quarterdeck. She was built at Portsmouth, New Hampshire, by a builder whose name cannot be read in the Admiralty records with certainty; it appears to be N. Messervé.[1] Launched in 1749, this ship is listed by Charnock in his *History of Marine Architecture,* published in 1800, as the *Boston.* However, it appears from other lists that this is an error and that the name of the ship was *America,* which bears out the local traditions at Portsmouth. The *America* was 139′ 1″ on the lower deck and was about six feet longer than called for in the 1745 establishment for 44-gun ships, under which she was built; this again indicates that her American builder was allowed to take liberties with the contract design. No plan has been found of this ship, and it is probable that no "as-built" drawing was made. A model, now in the Portsmouth Athenaeum, is supposed to be of this ship and shows a vessel of this class, as can be seen in the photographs (Plate II). However, the question of how accurate the model is has never been settled.

The *America,* like the *Boston,* had a rather short life. In fact, the only American-built man-of-war in colonial times that appears to have lasted well was the *Falkland,* which was rebuilt in 1719–20. The American-built ships did not stand alone in respect to having short lives; the average life of ships in the Royal Navy during the colonial period was only about ten years. Only a few ships served more than this time without extensive repairs or rebuilding. It appears that insufficient attention was given to seasoning timber and to the ventilation of the ships. This matter became so serious in the Royal Navy

---

[1] Messervé was a prominent shipbuilder in New Hampshire, Lieutenant Colonel of Colonel Moore's regiment in the first siege of Louisbourg, 1744, and Colonel of a New Hampshire regiment the next year. Went to Crown Point under Abercrombie. Went with Amherst to the second siege of Louisbourg, as Colonel, in charge of 200 ship carpenters. Messervé died there, as did his son, in 1758, of smallpox. Many of the colonial shipbuilders were senior officers in the militia and some held commissions in regular regiments.

that both the causes of rot and the methods of ventilation received extensive study late in the eighteenth century.

No study of colonial shipbuilding in America is complete without reference to the schooners. In this type, the Americans had developed a small seagoing cruiser which was of great usefulness to the naval services, for it was usually weatherly and fast. Unlike the cutter, the schooner when built to large dimensions did not become difficult to handle. In the years immediately preceding the Revolution, schooners had become numerous in American waters, being employed in fishing, in coasting, and particularly in the illegal trades. British naval officers had observed the qualities of these vessels, and a number were built and purchased for naval service just before the Revolution. Most of these schooners were small, carrying four to ten guns, and were intended to be used in the suppression of smuggling on the American coast. The sharp-model schooner had developed in America and was built extensively on the shores of Chesapeake Bay and at New York. In Massachusetts many of the fishermen were on the sharp model. Contemporary newspaper accounts show that during the French and Indian War of 1754–63 a number of fishing schooners captured by the French were operating on the New England coast as cruisers. These schooners were noted as being good sailers, and some were said to be exceptionally fast.

As an example of a schooner of the period built for naval service, the *Marble Head*, built at New York in July, 1767, will serve. This vessel was designed by an American and represents many of the elements of design that later distinguished the noted American "clipper" schooners. This particular schooner was much like the sharp fishing schooners owned in Marblehead, Massachusetts, at the time, if one may judge by the rare descriptions of the latter vessels. The choice of name strengthens such an inference. The drawing of the *Marble Head*, shown in Figure 5, represents a hull capable of sailing well, yet burdensome enough to carry a rather heavy armament for her size. Her model was very closely related to that of the contemporary and noted Bermuda sloop, as may be seen by comparing the *Marble Head*'s drawing with that of the Bermuda sloop from Chapman's book, shown in Figure 6. These sloops are known to have been widely copied in America before the Revolution, and in contemporary advertisements schooners were stated to have been built on their model.

The end of the war with France, in 1763, and the unrest in the years that preceded the beginning of the Revolution, put a stop to the construction of British men-of-war in any of the colonies except for the building of small vessels on the lakes and the schooners for suppression of American smuggling. We are left without definite knowledge of the connection between naval shipbuilding in the colonies in the thirty years preceding the Revolution and that for the

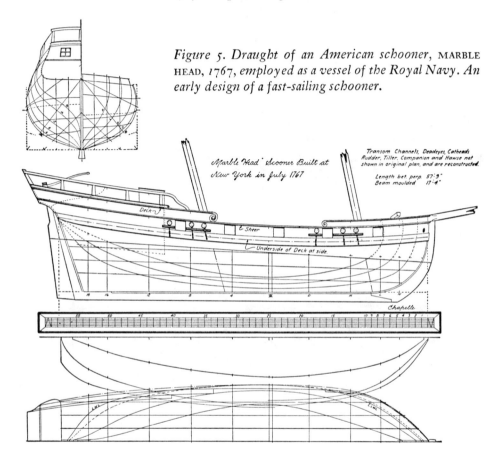

Figure 5. Draught of an American schooner, MARBLE HEAD, *1767, employed as a vessel of the Royal Navy. An early design of a fast-sailing schooner.*

Continental Navy, owing to the lack of records of the names and history of most of the designers of the American ships of the Revolution. However, the inferences that can be drawn, as will be shown later, indicate that the colonial period furnished the experience which developed the ships of the Continental Navy. The Americans had built regular men-of-war, and perhaps had designed some of them; they had developed and built the schooner, both as a fast class of vessel and as modified for a small man-of-war; they had armed and fitted ships for naval service within the colonies; they were abreast of the develop-

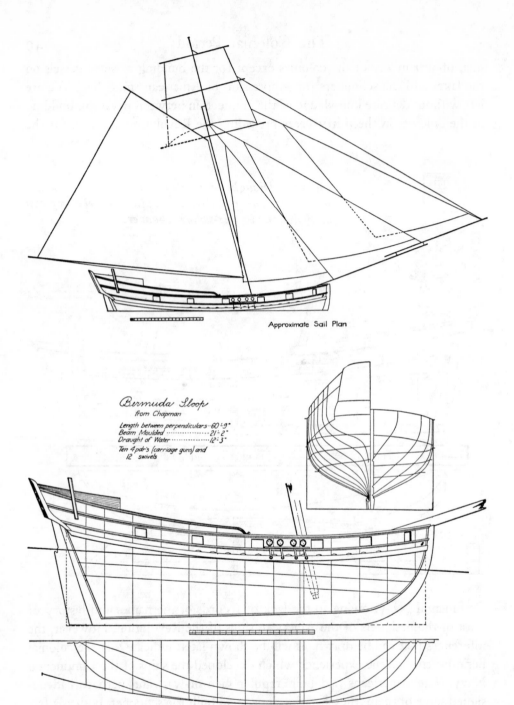

Approximate Sail Plan

Bermuda Sloop
from Chapman

Length between perpendiculars · 60'-9"
Beam Moulded · · · · · · · · · · · 21'-2"
Draught of Water · · · · · · · · · 12'-3"

Ten 4 pdr's (carriage guns) and
12 swivels

Figure 6. Draught of a Bermuda sloop after Chapman, showing the form of vessel believed to be the parent-type of early American craft built for fast sailing.

ments in contemporary ship design in Europe; the colonies where the agitation for rebellion was greatest in the pre-Revolutionary years were those where the last large men-of-war were built. These added up to a background that might explain the American ability to design and build, in certain classes, some of the finest men-of-war in the world immediately after the Revolution began.

★ ★ ★ ★ ★ ★ ★ ★ ★

CHAPTER TWO

The Continental Navy
1775-1785

THE AMERICAN Revolution did not begin with dramatic suddenness; its coming was foretold by some twelve years of political unrest and rioting. This had been sufficient to permit the intelligent to decide that war was a possibility, if not a certainty, long before actual hostilities began. On the American side, however, little could be done to prepare for such an eventuality. There were garrisons in many colonial towns and cities, British men-of-war on the coasts, numerous revenue vessels and customs officers in the ports, as well as many loyalists among the population. Hence any very obvious preparations for rebellion could be readily prevented. Among the Americans there was at first no plan for organized rebellion against the Crown, and public support for this came into being slowly. In spite of warnings and the efforts of some colonial leaders, nothing was done, therefore, to prepare for war beyond arming the militia and collecting some munitions. Except for reinforcing some of the more important garrisons and adding to the revenue vessels, the British government also neglected to prepare for the approaching storm. Had the British ministers shown more competence and less indolence, they could have prevented the colonists from making any effective preparations whatever in the creation of equipment and accumulation of munitions.

Throughout the early part of 1775 open warfare rapidly developed, so that by early fall a colonial army was in the field and American privateers were at sea. Some civil organization had also taken place in the colonies; the delegates to the Continental Congress had been elected and the Congress was in session. Early in October the delegates had appointed a naval committee to buy and fit out vessels for service against the Crown. This committee at once became active and acquired with the funds at hand such vessels as were available and reasonably suited for the purpose. It is plain, however, that the Continental Congress was well aware that merchant vessels could serve for no more than an emergency fleet. While the committee was searching for suitable craft, procuring them, and getting down to work fitting out purchased merchantmen, the Rhode Island delegates began to draft an act to build regular men-of-war. The committee succeeded in obtaining two ships, six brigs or brigantines, three schooners, and five sloops. In addition, the colonial army under Washington obtained four schooners in Massachusetts which were sent to sea to seize munitions needed by the army besieging Boston. Arnold and other Army officers had captured a sloop and two schooners on Lake Champlain. The vessels fitted out by Washington were returned to their owners when their mission was completed, and the Lake Champlain craft could be employed only on the lake. In addition to the vessels procured by the congressional committee for naval services, there were also a number of sloops, schooners, and brigantines of small size bought for packets.

The two ships purchased were quite serviceable craft and were armed with 20 or 24 guns. They were the Philadelphia merchant ship *Black Prince* of about 450 tons, which was renamed the *Alfred*, and the *Sally* (probably also a Philadelphia ship) of about the same size as the *Alfred* and renamed *Columbus*. At first these ships were fitted out with 24 9-pdrs., but the *Alfred*, at least, was soon reduced to 20 guns. Both ships appear to have been rather slow sailers and to have had all the weaknesses of converted merchantmen in naval service.

The brigs, brigantines, and schooners were somewhat more effective craft, for many of them were fast and of fair size, considering their rig and type. The *Andrea Doria* appears to have been a 14-gun brig carrying 4-pdrs., but little is known about her. The *Cabot* was another 14-gun brig and was such a good vessel that she was taken into the Royal Navy after her capture, so her dimensions have survived. She was 74′ 9½″ long on deck, 53′ 7″ on the keel, 24′ 8″ beam, 11′ 4″ depth of hold, and about 189 tons measurement. While in the Royal Navy she took part in the action on Dogger Bank in 1781; she was condemned and sold out of service June 25, 1783. Another brig of the same type was the *Lexington,* 14 guns, 86′ long on deck and 24′ 6″ beam. Her original name was *Wild Duck* and she crossed royal yards. There were also the brigantines *Hampden* and *Washington*, the latter obtained at Plymouth, Massachusetts, and also the brig *Reprisal*, 16 guns, about which very little is known. The schooners were almost entirely sharp-built vessels, some on the model becoming popular on the Chesapeake, others on the sharp Marblehead fisherman model used in New England. The *Fly*, sometimes known as the *Cruizer*, was purchased at Baltimore and carried 6 9-pdrs. The *Wasp*, ex *Scorpion*, was also a Baltimore schooner, while the *Warren* was a fast Marblehead vessel. These schooners were usually employed as packet and dispatch vessels and did little or no cruising.

The vessels fitted out by General Washington were probably Marblehead fishermen and were named *Franklin, Harrison, Hancock,* and *Lynch;* their original names do not appear. Probably one of these was the *Hannah*, for which some New Englanders claim the honor of being the first American Navy ship. This claim is apparently based on mere oral tradition in Marblehead and cannot be well supported. Probably it is on a par with the Gloucester tradition of the "invention" of the first schooner and is not to be taken more seriously. The *Harrison* was obtained at Plymouth.

The sloops, except the one on Lake Champlain, were seagoing traders, some of them on the sharp "Bermudas mould" and fast sailers. *Hornet* ex *Falcon* was of this type, purchased at Baltimore and fitted with 10 guns. The other sloops were the *Providence* ex *Katy*, bought at Providence and armed with from 6 to 12 guns, the *Sachem* of 10 guns, the *Independence* of 10 guns (lost at Cracoke Inlet, North Carolina, in 1778), and the 4-gun *Mosquito*, destroyed in the Delaware in 1778.

The packets are difficult to identify; one was the schooner *Georgia Packet* and another was the *Baltimore*, brigantine. The *Hornsnake* is also mentioned in this year. Some of these packets may have been chartered vessels.

The Lake Champlain prizes were a schooner, the *Royal Savage*, and a ketch or schooner, the *Liberty*. There was also a sloop, the *Enterprise*, of 12 4-pdrs. These vessels were the nucleus of the American squadron on Lake Champlain in 1776–77. All were shoal-draft hulls of relatively small size.

The purchased Continental vessels, though poorly armed and manned, were of some service in commerce raiding, for munitions and supplies were much needed. The greater number of these small craft never saw naval action, but were utilized to carry dispatches and diplomatic agents, or were engaged in commerce raiding, or used to carry freight, as circumstances or their size dictated. Nearly all Continental Navy vessels were employed as packets at one time or another.

The *Alfred* was captured by H.B.M. ships *Ariadne*, 20 guns, and *Ceres*, 14 guns, on March 9, 1778, and the *Columbus* was chased ashore and then burned by her crew at Point Judith, Rhode Island, April 1 of the same year. The brig *Andrea Doria* was burned in the Delaware in 1777 to prevent capture. The *Cabot* was driven ashore and captured by H.B.M. frigate *Milford* in March, 1777, and was taken into the Royal Navy as before mentioned. The brig *Lexington* was taken by the British cutter *Alert*, 10 guns, September 20, 1777; *Hampden* was condemned in 1776 at Providence, Rhode Island, after having run ashore; the *Washington* was captured by H.B.M. ship *Fowey* off Cape Ann, Massachusetts, in December, 1775. The *Reprisal* foundered on the Newfoundland Banks in 1778, all hands but the cook being lost. Of the schooners, the *Fly* was burned in the Delaware in 1778, and the *Wasp* was blown up to prevent capture. The *Warren* was captured by the frigate *Milford* in 1776. The sloop *Hornet* was blown up at about the same time as the *Fly* and *Wasp* were destroyed in the Delaware; the sloop *Providence* was blown up by her crew in the Penobscot in 1779, and the *Sachem* is supposed to have been destroyed in the Delaware with the *Hornet*, though this is not certain. The Lake Champlain prizes were either lost in the naval action in the fall of 1776 or were destroyed by their crews to prevent capture in 1777.

While the new Continental Navy was being established by the purchase of ships, the Continental Congress had gone about obtaining some first-class men-of-war of the frigate class. On December 13, 1775, they had passed an act, on the motion of the Rhode Islanders, by which a total of thirteen frigates were to be built: five of 32, five of 28, and three of 24 guns. These were to be ready for sea about the last of March, 1776, or in three months. When it came time to decide which of the colonies were to be selected to build new ships, and how many each was to build, there was a great deal of political interest involved, and perhaps some wishful thinking as well. Working in haste, the Continental Congress delegates assigned the ships to the colonies having the greatest political influence, without regard to their actual ability to produce. At any rate, it was decided that two ships were to be built in Massachusetts, two in Rhode Island, two in New York, four in Pennsylvania, and one each in New Hampshire, Connecticut, and Maryland. Thus Pennsylvania, in spite of having all of her shipbuilding eggs in one basket, Philadelphia, got twice as many ships as any other colony—the justification being an allegation that she had more shipwrights than the other colonies chosen—an absurd claim in the light of both colonial shipbuilding records and actual accomplishment of the program.

To make the act effective, the Congress utilized the previously established "Marine Committee," which was composed of one member from each of the insurgent colonies. Each member had the responsibility of supervising the accumulation of supplies and materials for the naval vessels. The member from each of the colonies fortunate enough to get a ship or two to build began to look about for a builder. In nearly every case the builder selected was of a political complexion satisfactory to the congressional delegate. The results of this shortsighted policy, based on political factors rather than the probabilities of warfare, were soon apparent. While this practice resulted in some cases in the selection of very competent builders and supervisors, nevertheless it led to the unfortunate concentration of a number of building contracts in one town or city, and often in a single shipyard. It may now seem obvious that the selection of large ports, or situations controlled by such ports, was extremely risky, but concentration of war contracts in "target areas" has long been an American practice that, unless corrected, may again bring us to grief. There were, of course, seemingly logical justifications for this concentration. In the large ports there were supposedly ample supplies of labor and the maximum availability of materials. These places were supposedly safe from attack, at least in the early months of the war. But as has often been the case in war, the unexpected happened: in many building locations it was found that both labor and materials were scarce, and the British blockaded or captured the large ports or the entrances to the important waterways. As a result, the program rapidly lost effectiveness.

The credit for the design of the new ships has long been a matter of controversy and cannot be settled beyond any reasonable doubt at this time. The most recent attempt to establish the designer's name was made by Lieutenant Commander M. V. Brewington in an article in *The American Neptune*, Vol. VIII, No. 1 (January, 1948). Brewington has established the correct names of some of the builders and supervisors not previously stated and has given the first comprehensive account of the difficulties that led to the use of more than one design for each of the three classes of frigates. In this article Brewington submitted a strong claim on behalf of Joshua Humphreys. This claim is almost entirely based on the correspondence of William Whipple, delegate to the Continental Congress for New Hampshire. Whipple stated that thirty-one days after the passage of the Act of December 13, 1775, Joshua Humphreys "laid the plans of several men-of-war" before the Marine Committee and that these were approved and copies ordered sent to each of the builders.

The difficulty in fully accepting this claim without more evidence is in the fact that the one official plan that has survived is the one that was used by Humphreys himself to build the frigate allotted to the Humphreys yard, and *this was not drawn by Humphreys*. The argument supporting this assertion is as follows:

The two plans from the Revolutionary War period preserved by the Humphreys family were one of the *Randolph* and one of a 74-gun ship, both of which are now in the National Archives. The plan of the 74 will be taken up later; for the moment it is only of importance to say that it was obviously drawn by the same man that drew the plan of the *Randolph*—the "Wharton and Humphreys Draught," so called. The draftsmanship of a ship designer is as readily recognized as a man's handwriting. The methods used to shape the hull, or to "fair" it, the shape of bow, stern, and cross sections, the neatness of workmanship in the joining of curved lines, and many idiosyncrasies of drawing are invariably sufficient to permit identification of the draftsman, even though his name is not signed to a plan—providing, of course, that there is enough information to permit identification of his workmanship. Now, there is sufficient in the case of Joshua Humphreys, for he was actively employed as a United States Navy constructor during the period 1794–1801; there are two plans in existence that can be definitely identified as his personal handiwork. These are still in the file of Navy plans. They are a draught of a 74-gun ship of 1799 (40–15–6 I) signed by Humphreys and drawn by him, not only by his own statement but also on those of two of his contemporary naval constructors; and an unsigned plan of one of the *Constitution* class of 1794, obviously in the same hand as the 1799 74-gun ship, and named the *Terrible* on the draught (one of the names selected by Humphreys for the frigates) (40–15–6 A). Allowing for the period of from eighteen to twenty-four years that had intervened since the Revolutionary War vessels had been designed, the draftsmanship shown in the plans known to have been made by Humphreys is so different from that of the Revolutionary War frigate and the 74 that it can be said with certainty that the Wharton and Humphreys draught and the Revolutionary War 74-gun ship plan *were not drawn by Joshua Humphreys*. It might also be said, with justice, that Joshua Humphreys was a very poor draftsman; the Revolutionary War

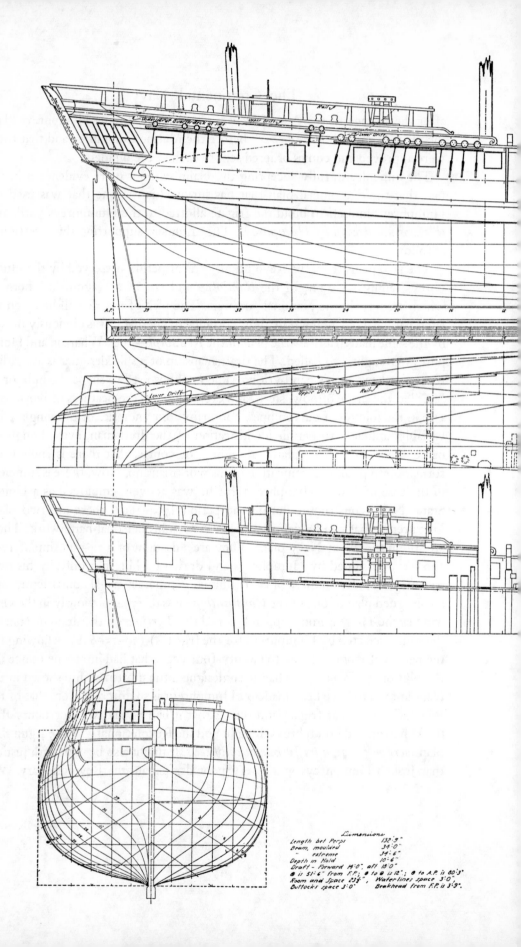

Dimensions

Length bet Perps   132'-9"
Beam, moulded   34'-0"
    extreme   34'-6"
Depth in Hold   10'-6"
Draft - Forward 14'-0"; aft 15'-0"
Ⓑ is 51'-6" from F.P.; Ⓑ to Ⓐ is 12"; Ⓑ to A.P. is 60'-3"
Room and Space 23⅞", Waterlines space 3'-0"
Buttocks space 3'-0"   Breakhead from F.P. is 3'-9".

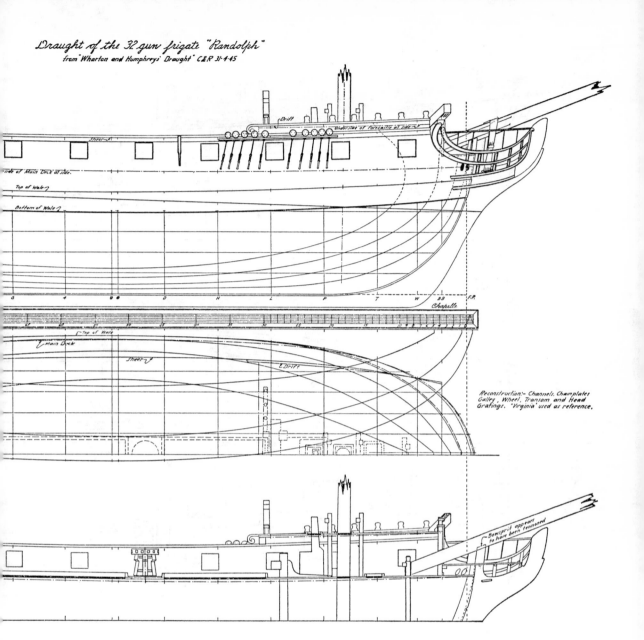

Plan 1. Draught of RANDOLPH after "Wharton and Humphreys Draught," showing the official designs for the 32-gun frigates.

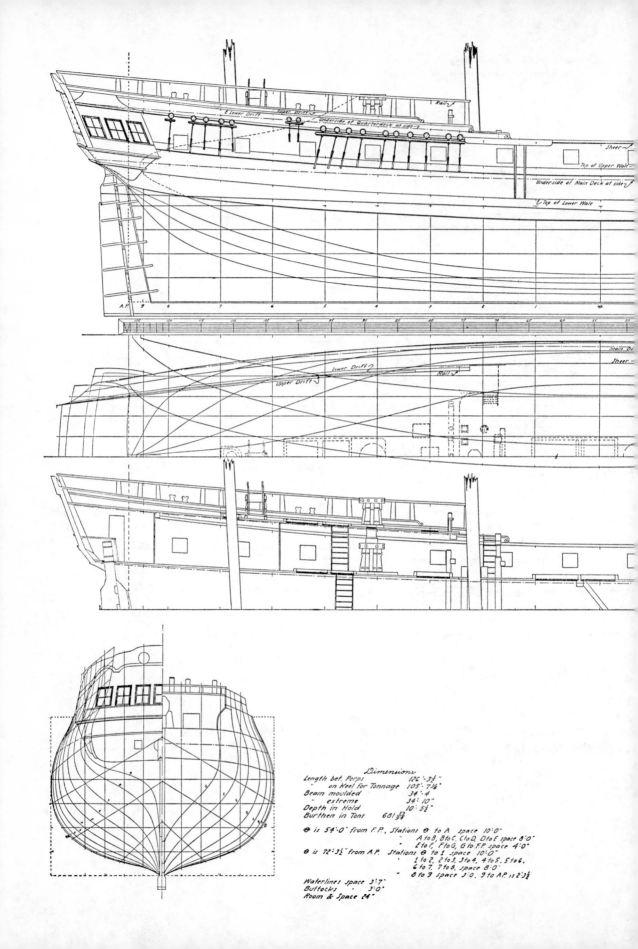

Dimensions

Length bet. Perps   126'-3½"
     "   on Keel for Tonnage   105'-7¼"
Beam moulded   34'-4"
     "   extreme   34'-10"
Depth in Hold   10'-5½"
Burthen in Tons   681 ³⁷⁄₉₄

Θ is 54'-0" from F.P., Stations Θ to A space 10'-0"
                        " A to B, B to C, C to D, D to E space 8'-0"
                        " E to F, F to G, G to F.P. space 4'-0"
Θ is 72'-3½" from A.P. Stations Θ to 1 space 10'-0"
                        " 1 to 2, 2 to 3, 3 to 4, 4 to 5, 5 to 6,
                        " 6 to 7, 7 to 8, space 8'-0"
                        " 8 to 9 space 5'-0", 9 to A.P. 12'-3½"

Waterlines space 3'-7"
Buttocks   3'-0"
Room & Space   24"

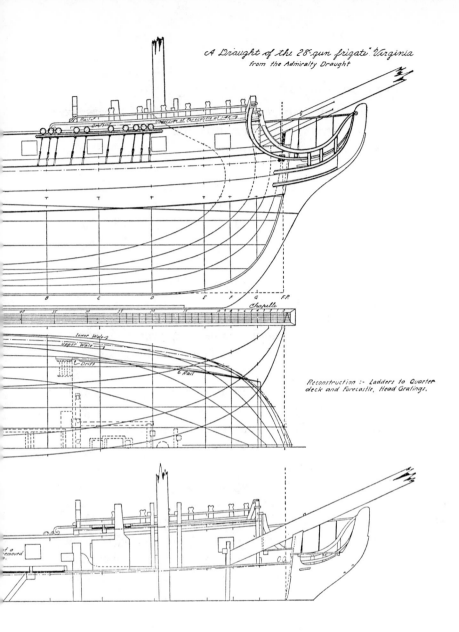

A Draught of the 28-gun frigate Virginia
from the Admiralty Draught

Reconstruction :- Ladders to Quarter
deck and Forecastle. Head Gratings.

Plan 2. Draught of VIRGINIA, 28 guns, after the Admiralty draught made after her
capture.

plans are the work of a good draftsman, revealing a great deal of experience in making plans. It is obvious that, less than a year after going into partnership with Wharton, Humphreys could not have had an apprentice more skilled in drawing than his master.

Joshua Humphreys was a Quaker, born in Haverford, Delaware County, Pennsylvania, on July 17, 1751. About 1765 he was apprenticed to a well-known Philadelphia shipwright and builder, James Penrose, who died in 1771, a short time before Humphreys could complete his apprenticeship. Penrose's widow not only gave him his time, but employed him as master shipwright to complete a ship that had been building at the time of her husband's death. Humphreys was about twenty-one years old at this time.

In 1774, when Humphreys was twenty-three, he went into partnership with his cousin, John Wharton, who was probably a trained shipwright and somewhat older than Humphreys. Wharton was also a politician; he was a close friend of Robert Morris of the Marine Committee and soon became a member of the Pennsylvania Committee of Safety and of the Navy Board, Middle District. He resigned from the latter in January, 1781. Wharton's connections gave the firm an inside track to both Continental and provincial shipbuilding contracts.

There is nothing in the career of this firm that indicates any reason why Humphreys could be considered a "leading" ship designer or builder in Philadelphia as early as 1775. Certainly he was not well known in the colonies at any time during the Revolution. It cannot be denied, however, that the record shows he presented plans to the Marine Committee early in 1776, either in behalf of his firm or of someone employed by Wharton and Humphreys. It is unlikely that he would represent any other builder. Then, if he did not draw the designs, which seems to be a proved fact based on the evidence of the existing plans, who did? Perhaps it was Wharton, or someone not yet identified. It is worthy of mention that, when a question arose about the ships building in Rhode Island, it was not Humphreys who was sent to investigate, but a Nathaniel Falconer of Philadelphia. It is also to be remarked that Humphreys seems to have been omitted from any supervisory capacity in the construction of the Pennsylvania frigates; this would seem to have been a logical duty, were he the designer.

Humphreys' long connection with naval shipbuilding and ship design requires extensive examination to establish the credit actually due him. It is a notable fact that there is little acceptable evidence to fix the names of the designers of many of the early American ships of war.

Designs were prepared, probably in Philadelphia, and approved by the Marine Committee. Copies were ordered which were to be sent to each of the builders or to the sponsors and supervisors. However, the plans were large, being on a scale of three-eighths of an inch to the foot (the surviving plan was originally about five feet long and two feet wide) and there were no suitable means of transmitting these drawings to the distant colonies, since such large plans could not be enclosed in letters. The copies of the ships' plans were completed and ready to be sent out by the second of February, 1776, but it was not until the twelfth that a messenger could be found, a John Bull, who was going from Philadelphia to Cambridge, Massachusetts, with the payroll of the Continental Army at Boston. Bull apparently carried plans for the ships to be built in Massachusetts and New Hampshire. No account seems to exist of how plans were sent to Rhode Island and Connecticut, but one clear-cut fact stands out: plans were not delivered in New England in time to permit any of the frigates to be finished by March, 1776, as required by the authorization. As a result, some of the New England builders seem to have either made their own plans or obtained plans locally. Whoever was responsible for the plans presented at Philadelphia, only the ships built in Pennsylvania and Maryland can be said with certainty to have been built according to the official plans, though there are logical reasons for assuming that those built in New York and Connecticut were also in accordance with the approved drawings. At best, the information on whether or not the official plans were followed exactly is circumstantial, for there is no positive evidence. At least five of the frigates obviously were not built to the official draughts, on the evidence of the archives or of plans made from the ships in question after their capture by the British.

The political considerations that decided which of the colonies were to build the frigates naturally extended to the selection of all individuals concerned in their actual construction, at least in most of the provinces. In New Hampshire, the Marine Committeeman turned the contract over to John Langdon, a Portsmouth merchant-politician and former delegate, who in turn let the work out to three Portsmouth, or Kittery, shipwrights: James K. Hackett, James Hill, and Stephen Paul. Thomas Thompson, master mariner, was made inspector, and a clerk of the yard was appointed. The important function of purchasing was, of course, retained by Langdon.

In Massachusetts, Thomas Cushing handled the matter for the committeeman. Though there were, of course, many yards available, he selected one firm in Newburyport for the construction of both the frigates assigned to the colony.

The builders chosen were Jonathan Greenleaf and Stephen and Ralph Cross; the inspectors were John Avery and John Odin, while Cushing naturally saw to all purchasing matters.

Rhode Island set up a political clambake to handle the business. A board, or committee, of eleven men, with the provincial governor as chairman, was first established. Each member of this board appointed a representative to carry out his assignment. This spread out the gravy very handsomely, but somehow failed to satisfy the citizens. Eventually the whole project was turned over to Daniel Tillinghast. Two builders were selected, Benjamin Talman and Sylvester Bowers, both in Providence. Each was to build a ship.

Connecticut had only one vessel to let out, and the Marine Committeeman took care of the matter neatly by having his brother, Barnabas Deane, handle the contract, which he let to John Cotton of Chatham, Connecticut, where the vessel was laid down.

New York had a board, or commission, in charge of building the two frigates assigned the colony, which was appointed by the committeeman, the latter taking care, of course, to handle some of the very profitable procurement himself. No change in this procedure seems to have taken place. Here again one builder was selected for the two frigates, with an inspector for each ship. The builder was Lancaster Burling of Poughkeepsie; the inspectors were Augustus Lawrence and Samuel Tudor. The vessels, however, were destroyed before they could be completed and prepared for sea.

Pennsylvania's Marine Committeeman set up a board, with himself as chairman. This board, or commission, set up subcommittees, each with certain responsibilities. The matter was well handled in this case, for each subcommittee was made up of local tradesmen, such as master shipwrights, merchant-accountants, ship chandlers, and the like. The contracts were spread out as much as possible by giving one ship to each of four shipyards: one to Wharton and Humphreys, one to Grice and Company, one to Manuel, Jehu, and Benjamin Eyre, and one to Warwick Coats. Brewington states that the builder of one of the frigates was given as "Bruce & Co.," but that no such firm has been found in contemporary tax lists or records; so he logically assumes that the name was misspelled and that Grice was intended. This is also supported by a statement of a member of the Grice family later engaged in naval construction. Only two of the Pennsylvania-built ships were completed, and only one got to sea under the American flag.

Maryland's Marine Committeeman also set up a board or commission to handle the single contract, which was let to George Wells at Fell's Point, with Jesse Hollingsworth as inspector. Wells had to obtain additional shipwrights to speed up construction, and he seems to have employed a good part of those available in the colony. In addition he had the help of groups of Baltimore citizens, and even militia companies were employed on occasion.

The relative importance of the builders and the supervisors, so far as the individual ships were concerned, is not clear. Some of the supervisors were undoubtedly shipwrights (as in Pennsylvania); others were ship captains, or possibly political henchmen of the local committeeman. It is probable that some of the builders merely furnished the yard, tools, and labor while the supervisors actually controlled the construction of the ships. For this reason, perhaps, the Marine Committee correspondence might lead one to believe that the supervisors were actually the shipbuilders. Even at a much later date than the Revolution, it was the custom to write to the superintendents as though they were the builders rather than as though they were mere inspectors.

Many of the places where the congressional delegates had assumed there would be a sufficient supply of labor soon complained of a shortage of skilled shipwrights. These shortages were due to a variety of causes, particularly the increase in privateer construction and the dispersion of skilled men to other localities for economic reasons. It was also the practice in some colonies to turn out the shipwrights for militia duty. The lack of preliminary planning in the allotment of materials, armament, and supplies was another difficulty which caused extensive delays in construction. An attempt to centralize the control of the new ship construction by the Continental Congress was certainly another important factor in causing delays.

Though some of the Continental delegates and Marine Committee members were merchant-shipowners, who must have known that it was practically impossible to complete the new frigates in the time required by the Act of 1775, this did not prevent them from passing the bill without modification of the completion date. It is highly probable that they established the size and the rates of the ships to be built; in any event the Marine Committee appears to have arranged for the designs and to have approved "several" of them when complete. They also attempted to make numerous decisions regarding the specifications and to let the contracts for the armament. There was undoubtedly a natural anxiety to make contracts on some sound basis, and a design and specification for each class of ship was a logical move. So, in spite of the expressed intention to complete the program in about 108 days, it should be noted that 31 days were spent in preparing the designs, prior to approval, and then 20 days more were required to make the necessary copies. Ten days more were needed to find a messenger to transmit the plans of at least five of the ships, with the additional delay of the messenger's time in reaching his destination. As has been remarked upon earlier, this situation not only accounted for much of the delay met with in building the ships, but also was the practical reason for the variations in design of each of the three classes of frigates built under the Act of 1775.

This congressional authorization was intended to produce three distinct classes of ships, graduated in dimensions and armament, so as to obtain 24-, 28-, and 32-gun frigates. Hence it is reasonable to assume that there were to be three official designs or "draughts." This is supported to some extent by existing plans. One of the official draughts of the 32-gun class has survived, and one plan of the 28-gun class was made from the ship after her capture by the British. These seem to indicate that another basic design was used for the latter ships. No plan of the 24-gun class has yet come to light, but the British captured ships of all three classes and made measurements of them. These dimensions can be produced to support the assumption that there were three designs. The 24-gun class measured about 117′ 9½″ on the berth deck, 32′ 10½″ beam, and 9′ 8½″ depth in the hold. The 28-gun class measured approximately 126′ 3½″ on the berth deck, 34′ 10″ beam, and 10′ 5½″ depth in the hold. The 32-gun ships were to measure about 132′ 9″ on the berth deck, 34′ 6″ beam, and 10′ 6″ in the hold. Four plans of ships built under the authorization of December 13, 1775, have survived, three made from measurements taken off the ships captured by the British, showing the vessels as built, and one showing a design that may safely be assumed to be one of the official draughts prepared for the Marine Committee. In addition there are dimensions of three other ships taken into the Royal Navy, of which no draughts have yet been found.

The surviving plans have been carefully redrawn from the original sources to permit clear reproductions. While some "restorations" have been made, these are indicated on the plans so that, in the event additional information comes to light, the material extracted from the original sources can be identified without having to obtain and consult the originals. The reconstructed portions could then be corrected, if it should be possible. In general, all restoration is based on ships similar to the one shown.

Perhaps the most satisfactory way to explore the designs and qualities of these ships will be to begin with the ships' plans that can reasonably be assumed to represent the original designs prepared for the Marine Committee, and then to discuss the ships whose designs appear to have been quite different. In this manner the degree of variation in the designs can be shown and the problems involved in identifying the designers can be more readily presented.

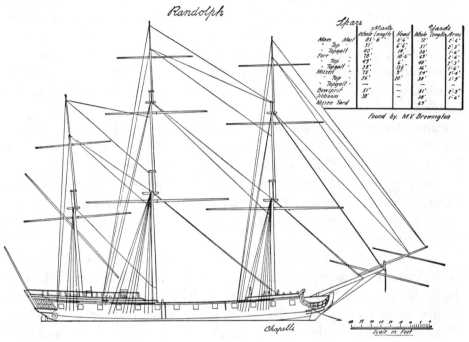

Spar plan of RANDOLPH *from Humphreys' dimensions. (See Plan 1.)*

Obviously, in view of what has already been said about the delays in the distribution of the plans of the ships, the ships built at Philadelphia, or near by, would with reasonable certainty have followed the official designs. Of the four ships built at Philadelphia, the official building plans of one have been preserved —the *Randolph*, 32 guns, built by Wharton and Humphreys. This plan was in the possession of Joshua Humphreys and later in the hands of his son Samuel, who was also a naval constructor. When Samuel Humphreys died, many of the plans in his possession were left in the office files and so became part of the plan-archive files of the United States Navy. Only two plans belonging to Joshua Humphreys (of the period of the Revolution) have survived; both are of naval ships. In addition there is in existence a half-model, supposed to have been built from one of these drawings, of a 74-gun ship. The Humphreys plans are now in the National Archives with other sailing-ship plans of the Bureau of Construction and Repair, United States Navy Department. The index numbers of all plans hereafter referred to are those of the National Archives index.

The frigates that were intended to be built on the same lines as those of the *Randolph* were as follows: *Raleigh* at Portsmouth, New Hampshire; *Hancock* at Newburyport, Massachusetts; *Warren* at Providence, Rhode Island; and the *Washington*, along with the *Randolph*, at Philadelphia. Actually, none of the ships building under the new program were given names until June 6, 1776, at which time the Continental Congress selected the name for each ship then building.

Plan 1 shows the redrawn plan of the *Randolph*, based upon the original draught (31–4–45) and refaired. Corrections have been made in redrawing to carry out the alterations noted in ink script on the original plan; these alterations also appear in the Humphreys papers. The most important of these were changes in steeve or angle of the bowsprit, location of the masts, and lengths of forecastle and quarterdecks. The original plan shows the general deck arrangement as shown in Plan 1.

The design is of a sharp frigate of the period, following in a general way the British frigates of the period in arrangement of decks and armament. In 1756 the Royal Navy had built four sister 32-gun frigates which proved very satisfactory cruisers. They were the *Southampton*, *Vestal*, *Minerva*, and *Diana*. These were 124′ 4″ on the berth deck, 34′ 0″ beam, and 12′ 0″ depth of hold. Though beakhead bulkheads had by this date almost disappeared in ships below the rate of frigate, the *Southampton* class retained this feature to about the same extent as seen in the *Randolph*'s plan. The next year the British built four more similar 32's, *Alarm*, *Niger*, *Eolas*, and *Stag*. These new ships were slightly sharper-ended than the previous four and measured 125′ 0″ on the berth deck, 35′ 2″ beam, and 12′ 0″ in the hold. In the new ships, the beakhead bulkhead disappeared entirely, the bows being carried up to the forecastle. The British 36-gun frigates were of similar dimensions, so far as beam and depth were concerned, but were about four feet longer than the *Alarm* class. Thus it will be seen that the *Randolph* was a larger ship than the standard frigate of her rate in the British Navy; in fact, she was even longer than the next higher rate, the 36-gun frigate.

The American model used in the *Randolph* differed a good deal from the hull forms found in the majority of contemporary British or French frigates: the American had much more deadrise, or angle of rise, in the bottom, rounder and more regular curves in cross section, far more rake (or slope forward) to the bow, and somewhat less depth and freeboard. Judging by the frame spacing and other evidence, the American ship must have been somewhat more lightly built than her English sisters. There is no evidence of any attempt to copy a foreign model of naval vessel in the American plan—a matter which has been the subject of much careless assumption on the part of some American writers. There is now ample opportunity to explore this matter fully. There are large numbers of plans of naval ships of all maritime nations in the Admiralty Collection of Draughts, National Maritime Museum, Greenwich, England; hence any reasonable comparison can be made. The frigate models used by each of the great maritime powers—England, Spain, Holland, and France— had become well established long before the American frigates were authorized, and, judging by a comparison of plans, it is apparent that the American hull model was not a copy, but was rather the natural development of a previous search for speed under sail in craft smaller than frigates. The lessons taught in these small vessels were applied to the *Boston* of 1748 and to the Revolutionary War frigate designs; certainly by 1775 the Americans must have had very strong opinions on how to design a fast-sailing ship. The Americans took one page out of the French book, for they made each of the new frigate classes larger than the same rates in the British Navy. However, there is no evidence to show whether this was a deliberate copying of French naval policy or whether it was the result of independent observation and theory, as expressed in the earlier *Boston*.

The *Randolph* was one of the two Pennsylvania-built frigates to be completed and the only one to make a cruise under the Continental flag. She was blown up in action with H.B.M. 64-gun ship *Yarmouth* off Barbados, British West Indies, March 17, 1778, all hands but four seamen being lost. Little is known about her sailing qualities beyond what might be concluded from her drawings, which indicate a very fast ship for the time.

The only other plan that can logically be assumed to represent one of the three basic designs approved by the Marine Committee in 1776 is the draught of the *Virginia*, one of the 28-gun class, built at Baltimore, Maryland (Plan 2). In this case the plan is not the original design, but one drawn from measurements made from the ship after her capture by the British. The difficulties that prevented the official plans from getting to New England did not apply to the Maryland frigate; this, with the appearance of the ship as shown in the Admiralty draught, makes it safe to assume the *Virginia* to be representative of the official design of her class. The ships intended to be built as 28's were, in addition to *Virginia*, the *Providence* in Rhode Island, the *Trumbull* in Connecticut, the *Montgomery* in New York, and the *Effingham* in Pennsylvania.

The *Virginia* so resembled the *Randolph* that the writer assumed the ships to have been built on the same lines when he received the draught of the former ship, in 1929, from C. Knight, formerly the Admiralty Curator. On casual inspection it appeared that the *Virginia* had been built by altering the spacings of the water lines and frames from those of the *Randolph*, but when both plans had been redrawn it became plain that this was not probable. It must now be assumed that there was an independent design for the *Virginia*'s class. On the basis of the appearance of the *Virginia* it is also fully apparent that the design of this ship was made by the same man who prepared the draught of the *Randolph*. The dimensions and appearance of the *Virginia* may be safely assumed to represent the official design for the 28-gun class.

A number of comparisons between the plans of the *Virginia* and *Randolph* might be made. The *Virginia* has more deadrise and is deeper, and her bow rake is much less than that of the *Randolph*. Though fully six feet shorter, she is beamier and is actually a more burdensome vessel; for this reason she was rated as a 32-gun frigate by the British after her capture. It is also to be noted that the corrections mentioned as being written on the original draught of the *Randolph* were apparently carried out in the *Virginia*. It is possible that these corrections or alterations were the comments of the Marine Committee, or of their advisers, when the draughts of the three classes of ships were being reviewed prior to approval. The low knightheads shown in both the *Randolph* and *Virginia* are worthy of notice; knightheads were usually very prominent in ships having beakhead bulkheads. The low knightheads shown gave little support to the bowsprit, which depended upon the gammoning and, apparently, a tenon at the stemhead to resist lateral strain. The lack of knightheads of sufficient height to support the bowsprit must have put a heavy strain on the beakhead bulkhead. It seems probable that the low knightheads were an idiosyncracy of the designer. The original plan of the 74-gun ship preserved by Humphreys showed a similar knighthead structure; however, the model built by Humphreys of a ship of this class showed the usual prominent knightheads of the period. Possibly the designer had little experience in large ships and was unaware of the tremendous strains incurred in the head rig of such ships as these frigates and the 74-gun ship.

While the *Virginia* strongly resembles the *Randolph*, it is possible that the official design if available would have shown an even greater likeness, especially since some allowance has to be made for the builder's privilege of making changes. The *Randolph* was certainly the handsomer of the two, but of course this is largely due to the greater length and lower freeboard of the 32-gun ship.

It will be noted that neither of these ships carried guns on their forecastles, which was also true of contemporary British frigates of 28 and 32 guns. About 1780 the British 36-gun frigates were built to carry forecastle guns, but it is not known whether this practice was characteristic of their earlier ships of this class. It will be seen that the Revolutionary War frigate was armed in almost the same manner as the colonial-built *Boston* of 1748 and was, in a general way at least, a very similar ship in all important respects. It should be remarked that none of the surviving plans of the American frigates authorized in 1775 show sweep ports; this is an omission difficult to understand. However, these ships could be swept by using the gun ports, after shifting the guns out of the way, as was sometimes done in European navies. It is possible, of course, that the lack of sweep ports on the Admiralty plans was due to a draftsman's slackness, though this is a doubtful explanation.

George Wells had difficulty in completing the *Virginia*, and the frigate did not get out of the Chesapeake under American colors. In trying to get to sea in 1778, after being blockaded for more than a year, she ran aground in the Bay and was taken by the British ships *Emerald* and *Conqueror*. The *Virginia* was bought for the Royal Navy and remained in that service for about six years before being condemned.

The *Randolph* is the only 32-gun frigate for which we have what was apparently the official draught. The two surviving plans of the other three—the *Raleigh*, the *Hancock*, and the *Warren*—were made from the completed ships after their capture by the British. The *Raleigh* was built by James K. Hackett, James Hill, and Stephen Paul at Portsmouth, New Hampshire. Though the Continental Congress had intended to have the frigates afloat by the end of March, 1776, the delay in getting the designs to the New England builders would surely have prevented the accomplishment of this even if there had been no other causes. The *Raleigh* is a representative case; her plan did not reach Cushing, in Massachusetts, until February 26, and it was then forwarded to Portsmouth through the builders at Newburyport. This would have prevented the *Raleigh* from being started until more than a month after the plan reached her builders, for she would have to be lofted and the moulds or templates made before she could be set up.

The New Hampshire group had apparently been aware of the situation and had taken the initiative to go ahead while the Continental Congress and its Marine Committee were having designs made, approving them, getting copies, and then trying to find a way to get the plans to the builders. It is apparent that soon after the contract was in their hands the Portsmouth builders started their own design and completed it, lofted the lines, and made the moulds, and that they had begun to get the timber out by the time the official plans reached them from Philadelphia. There is no known statement as to who was responsible for the design of the *Raleigh*, although the most likely person was William Hackett.

William Hackett was born at Salisbury, Massachusetts, May 1, 1739. He became an apprentice to his father and uncle about 1751, and eventually took over the yard at Salisbury Point. Sometime prior to 1774 he and his cousin James operated the yard together, and they continued to do so on and off for about thirty years, except for some work done in Portsmouth, New Hampshire. They are said to have used the site of the present Portsmouth Navy Yard there, and it is possible that the *Raleigh* was constructed on this location. James K. Hackett, usually called "Colonel" or "Major" Hackett, seems to have been the senior partner and business head of the firm and William the designer and master builder. As a boy William Hackett saw the British 44-gun ship *America* built at Portsmouth, and it is possible that his elders worked on this ship. By the end of the Revolution William Hackett acquired a great reputation as a ship designer in New England; his cousin James remained the businessman and had many interests besides shipbuilding. The latter had a mental breakdown late in life, caused by financial reverses. There is no doubt that William Hackett was the leading ship designer in the vicinity when the *Raleigh* was building.

There were, of course, others in this part of New England who were able to design ships. None, however, seem to have become as prominent as Hackett, who seems to have been unusually competent both as a builder and as a designer. We know that he was able to draw; one of his plans is in existence. The other designers who were prominent in this part of New England were John Peck of Boston and one member of the Coffin family of Newburyport. The Coffins operated a yard at Newburyport, Massachusetts, and for this reason might have had some connection with the *Hancock* or *Boston* rather than with the *Raleigh*. Peck is known to have been busy with vessels building around Boston at this time.

The plan of the *Raleigh* is shown in Plan 3, redrawn from the Admiralty draught of the vessel, made soon after her capture. Her dimensions follow those of the *Randolph* rather closely, but her hull form is quite different. The similarity of the *Raleigh*'s dimensions to those of the official design, in spite of the fact that the design was well along before the official draught reached the builders, can be readily explained.

The Continental Congress, or its Marine Committee, had obviously specified the dimensions of the ships they wanted prior to the preparation of the official designs. The merchant-shipowners would have felt themselves fully competent to pass on this matter, and it was one that had to be decided before getting out contract drawings and agreements, to obtain uniformity in the latter. Obviously Langdon, who had formerly been a delegate to the Congress and active in the naval debates, must have had complete information on the proposed ships and must have known the approved dimensions. It is also very probable that Hackett, or whoever the designer may have been, made a final comparison when the official draught finally came to hand. It would have been far too late to make a change in hull model or dimensions, but minor alterations and adjustments of arrangement could have been made to comply reasonably well with what the official draught indicated. The *Raleigh*, as built, measured 131′ 5″ long on the berth deck, 34′ 5″ beam, and 11′ 0″ depth in the hold. She was of an entirely different model from that of the *Randolph* and the 28-gun *Virginia*, approaching very closely the hull form of the English 32's of 1758, the *Alarm* class. Like that British class she had a round bow, without any sign of a beakhead bulkhead. The quarterdeck and forecastle were lower and less prominent than in the ships built in Philadelphia and Baltimore. The *Raleigh*'s midsection was marked by a sharp and deep tumble home, in the manner popular in English frigates, and the deadrise of the bottom was similar, somewhat less than in the *Randolph* and much less than in *Virginia*. The model of the hull of the *Raleigh* was, in fact, very similar to that of a contemporary British frigate; the Admiralty drawing shows a well-modeled English-type frigate and nothing more. The round bow exhibited in the *Raleigh* was by no means new, for the British frigates had adopted this construction before the Revolution began. The beakhead bulkhead did not go out of fashion entirely during the period when the American frigates were building; this feature was retained in some foreign frigates and ship sloops as late as the early 1790's, and in ships of the line until after the beginning of the nineteenth century.

The *Raleigh* was launched May 21, 1776, and a contemporary newspaper stated that she was "built" in sixty working days. It should not be necessary to accept this as more than an indication that she was built very rapidly; this was the time from the setting up of her keel to the date of launch, and probably does not imply calendar days. At any rate, the work of lofting the lines, getting out the moulds, and obtaining the timber to start the ship is not included, nor is the time required to finish and rig the ship after her launch. It is evident from correspondence that her building time from lofting to sailing covered the period from late February to midsummer.

The career of this ship in the Continental Navy was rather inglorious and shows that good ships alone are not enough to bring success in naval warfare. On September 4, 1776, the *Raleigh* under Thomas Thompson (her inspector while building) and the *Alfred*, Captain Elisha Hinman, sighted the British West Indian convoy homeward bound, guarded by the 22-gun ship *Camel*, the 14-gun sloop *Druid*, and the 16-gun sloop *Weazel*—the two sloops being ship-rigged. The *Camel* was a converted merchantman like the *Alfred*, but smaller. The convoy was well spread out. The *Raleigh* appeared to windward of the convoy, while the *Alfred* was a few miles to leeward. The British *Druid* engaged the *Raleigh* and, though a much smaller and weaker ship, actually drove her off. The *Raleigh* and *Alfred* then apparently made sail and were followed by the *Camel* and *Weazel* until the Americans had reached a distance where they were no longer a threat to the convoy. The American accounts claimed that a squall broke off the action and that the American ships then waited for the British to engage them. In view of the fact that the two American ships were much larger, faster, and more powerful than the three small English convoy guards, this explanation will hardly stand inspection. It is not surprising that Thompson did not long remain in command of the *Raleigh* after this abortive attack on the West Indian convoy. The *Raleigh* was finally taken by the British on the 25th of September, being driven on shore by the *Experiment*, 50 guns, and the 28-gun frigate *Unicorn*, while trying to escape. John Barry, then her captain, and some of the crew were able to get ashore in the *Raleigh*'s boats. The ship was pulled off undamaged and was taken into the Royal Navy as a 32-gun 12-pdr. frigate. She was condemned and sold out in July, 1783.

It will be seen that the Continental Navy had some very poor officers. Many were political appointees without the qualifications needed for command; others were temperamental and resentful of discipline. Nearly all were without combat experience. The failure of the Continental Navy to accomplish much with the fine frigates built during the Revolution was due almost entirely to a lack of skilled officers, trained and well-disciplined crews, and competent over-all command and planning.

One of the two ships built in Massachusetts was the 32-gun frigate *Hancock*, shown in Plan 4 as redrawn from the Admiralty draught made after her capture and purchase by the Royal Navy. This ship was built at Newburyport, with the 24-gun *Boston*, by Greenleaf and Cross. Greenleaf seems to have been in charge of the construction of the *Hancock*, and the Cross brothers were responsible for the *Boston*. Here again there is confusion about the design. The *Hancock* when completed was somewhat different from any of the other ships. For one thing, she was larger, measuring 136′ 7″ long on the lower deck, about 35′ 6″ beam, and 11′ ½″ depth in the hold. Her model was somewhat like the *Raleigh*'s in profile, but her midsection was very much like the *Randolph*'s, though she was both wider and deeper than the Philadelphia ship. She had neither a regular beakhead bulkhead nor a round bow of the usual type. She was round-bowed to the main sheer, but from here up to the forecastle rail line she was suddenly flared out just forward of the catheads, as though she had first been built with a beakhead which later had been finished off round. This is a rather unusual feature, though it is to be seen occasionally in a few other ship plans of the period in the Admiralty Collection of Draughts. There is no apparent advantage of this form of bow except to give some additional room on the forecastle at the catheads; and even this is obtained at the expense of strength. It is evident from the plan of the ship that the builders had departed entirely from the official Marine Committee plan, producing an original design in both model and dimensions. It is highly probable that the same thing had taken place in Massachusetts that had occurred in New Hampshire: the official design not coming to hand, the builders went ahead with a design of their own without waiting for the Philadelphia plans. Like the New Hampshire people, the Massachusetts men knew what the desired dimensions were to be and in the process of working up a new design made each of the ships still larger. Perhaps some local pride went into these matters, and it would not be difficult to imagine that the Massachusetts builders would try to outdo the Philadelphia ships in all possible particulars. In this case they might truthfully be said to have succeeded, for the *Hancock* was described by the British as the "finest and fastest frigate in the world."

Little is known about Jonathan Greenleaf, except that he was a successful shipbuilder who entered a partnership with the Cross brothers of Newburyport sometime prior to the Revolution. The Cross yard had been established by the father of the Cross brothers about 1728–30. Stephen and Ralph Cross, Jr., took over the yard with Greenleaf just before the Revolution; the elder Cross was then alive, and in fact lived until 1788. Ralph Cross, Jr., was born in 1738, his older brother Stephen in 1731. The latter died in 1809, after holding a number of civic offices. Ralph Cross was interested in military affairs and rose through the grades from captain to brigadier in the Massachusetts militia. The designer of the *Hancock* may have been one of the Cross brothers, or he may perhaps have been William Hackett, for the latter is known to have had business relations with the Cross brothers and to have designed at least one ship for their yard at a much later date.

It is quite obvious, at any rate, that the builders produced in the *Hancock* a ship that was different from the official design in all important respects except rate, and by far the handsomest ship of those whose plans have been found. The Massachusetts men, though handicapped by the delay in receiving plans, had made no complaint to Philadelphia, but had gone ahead with designs of their own, regardless of the Marine Committee. It is well, perhaps, to state that the variations from the official plan of the 32-gun frigates could not possibly be charged to improper lofting, for in nearly all cases the ships' lines have no similarity to the approved draught and depart so markedly in dimensions or proportions that the designs are obviously distinct from the Philadelphia drawing. Were there merely slight variations in dimensions or in model, the rather crude and incomplete lofting methods of the period might be held accountable. But where there are such marked differences, as in the case of both the *Raleigh* and the *Hancock*, this seems to be an impossible explanation. The *Virginia* might be said to indicate how the characteristics of the design were retained in a finished ship by the methods of lofting employed at the time, even though she may have departed from the original design in many respects. Since it is reasonable to assume that the designer of each of the frigates built in New England probably revised his plans once the official draught was at hand, the curious combination of similarities and wide departures seen in each ship, as compared with the official draught, is readily understandable.

The *Hancock* and the 24-gun ship *Boston* got to sea early in 1777—the *Hancock* commanded by Captain Joseph Manly, the *Boston* by Captain Hector McNiell. On June 27 they chased the small British 28-gun frigate *Fox*, which the fast *Hancock* soon overtook and captured. On July 6 the three ships were sighted and chased by H.B.M. 44-gun ship *Rainbow* and the brig *Victor*. By daybreak of the 7th the Americans had been joined by a sloop, which was soon burned. At about 6 o'clock in the morning another sail was sighted, which proved to be the British 32-gun frigate *Flora*. The Americans then broke their formation and endeavored to escape. The American ships were foul and out of trim, particularly the *Hancock*. The *Rainbow* chased the *Hancock* and, being clean and well sailed, overtook the American on the morning of July 8, after a long chase in light winds. The *Fox* was retaken by the *Flora*, but the *Boston* escaped. McNiell was cashiered for not having remained in formation and for not supporting Manly. The *Hancock* was taken into the Royal Navy as the *Iris* and became a favorite cruiser by making fortunes for her officers through the capture of prizes. In 1780 she fought an indecisive action against the French frigate *Hermione* and would have taken her had not another French frigate appeared. In 1781 the *Iris* chased and took the American 24-gun ship *Trumbull*. Late in the year the *Iris* was captured by a French squadron in the West Indies and became a cruiser in their naval service. When old, she was dismantled and became a powder hulk at Toulon, where she was found by the British when that port was taken in 1793. When the British evacuated Toulon the old *Iris*, ex *Hancock*, was blown up—the last survivor of the Continental Navy then afloat.

The 32-gun frigate *Warren* was built at Providence, Rhode Island, from a design by Sylvester Bowers. The same thing had happened in Rhode Island that had taken place in New Hampshire and Massachusetts. The official plans did not arrive promptly, so the committee, or board, in charge had the design of the *Warren* prepared by a local master shipwright, Sylvester Bowers, who also was the master shipwright on the 28-gun *Providence*. Benjamin Talman was the master shipwright on the *Warren*. The *Providence* and *Warren* were both completed. The *Warren* was burned to prevent capture August 14, 1779, while part of the Penobscot expedition. No plans of the ship exist, but the following dimensions may be correct: length on the lower deck 132′ 1″, beam 34′ 5½″, and depth of hold 11′ 0″. It is known that Bowers was instructed by the local committee to adjust his design as much as possible to agree with the Marine Committee plan once the latter came to hand. Apparently this change

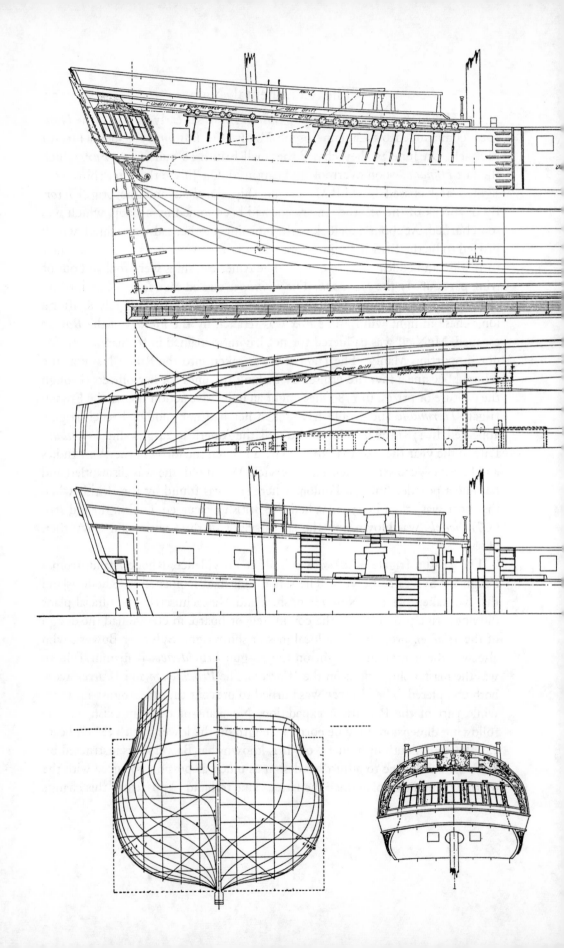

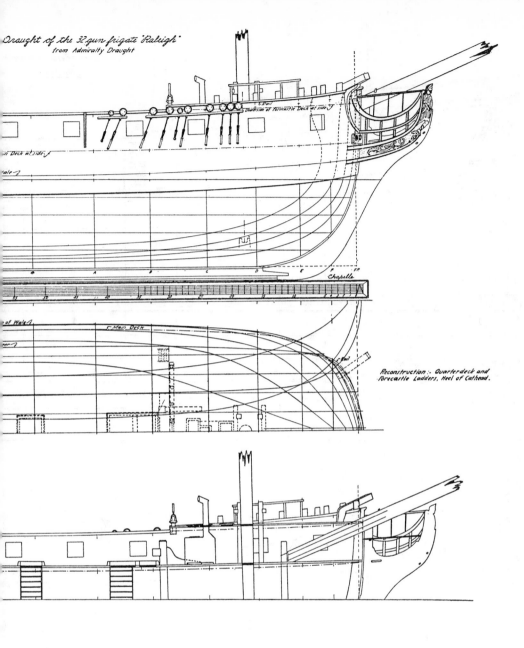

Draught of the 32 gun frigate 'Raleigh'
from Admiralty Draught

Underside of Forecastle Deck at side J

n Deck at side J

ale J

Chapelle

of Wals J

er J

F. Main Deck

Rail

Reconstruction :- Quarterdeck and
Forecastle Ladders, Heel of Cathead.

Plan 3. Draught of RALEIGH, 32 guns, after the
Admiralty draught made after her capture.

Dimensions
Length bet. Perps   131' 5"
   " on keel for Tonnage 110' 7¼"
Beam Extreme   34' 5"
   " Moulded   34' 0"
Depth in Hold   11' 0"
Burthen in Tons   696 ⁶⁴⁄₉₄

Ø is 52'0" from F.P.   from Ø to A is 10'0",
                         " A to B and B to C is 9'0",
                         " C to D is 8'0"
                         " D to E is 7'0"
                         " E to F is 5'0", F to F.P. is 4'0"
Ø is 79'5" from A.P.   from Ø to 1, 1 to 2 and 2 to 3 is 10'0"
                         " 3 to 4, 4 to 5 and 5 to 6 is 9'0"
                         " 6 to 7 is 9'0", 7 to 8 is 7'0"
                         " 8 to 9 is 5'0", 9 to A.P. is 1'5"
The Load line crosses the Rabbet, at the Bow 13'6", at the stern 14'7"
above the Base, from which waterlines space at 2'9" intervals,
Buttocks space 3'0".   Room & Space probably 2'4".

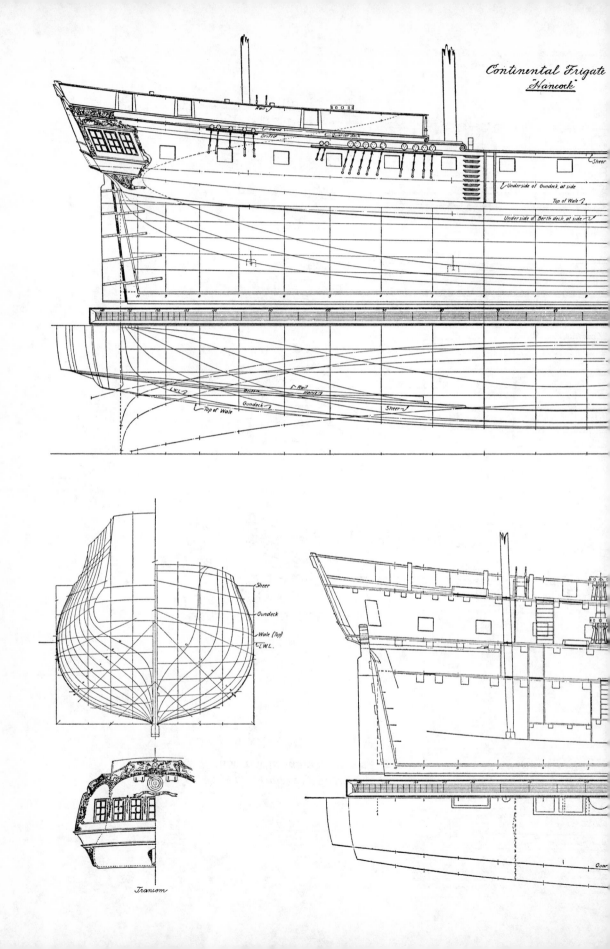

Continental Frigate
"Hancock"

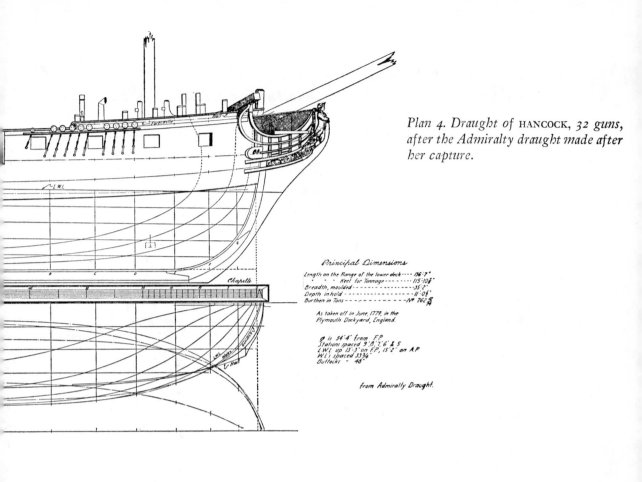

Plan 4. Draught of HANCOCK, 32 guns, after the Admiralty draught made after her capture.

Principal Dimensions

Length on the Range of the lower deck ---- 136·7"
"   "   Keel for Tonnage ----- 115·10⅝"
Breadth, moulded ----------------- 35·2"
Depth in hold ------------------ 11·0½"
Burthen in Tons --------------- № 762 ⁵⁄₉₄

As taken off in June, 1779, in the
Plymouth Dockyard, England.

∅ is 54'4" from F.P.
Stations spaced 9'6", 7'6" & 5"
LWL up 13'·3" on F.P. 15'·2" on A.P.
WL's spaced 33¾"
Buttocks " 48"

from Admiralty Draught.

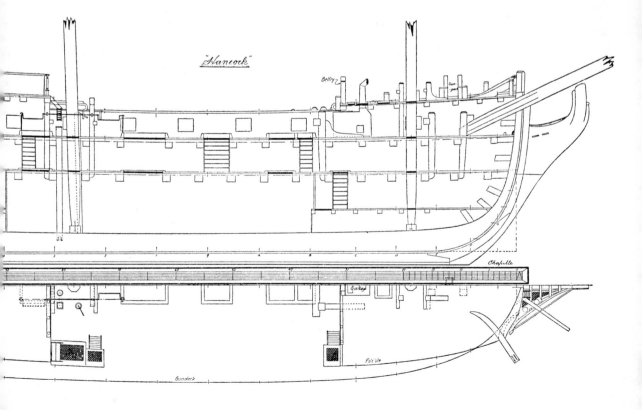

"Hancock"

was limited to topside appearance, if, indeed, the instructions were ever carried out.

The remaining 32-gun frigate was the *Washington*, built in Philadelphia by Manuel, Jehu, and Benjamin Eyre, and launched August 7, 1776. She was not finished, being scuttled on November 2 of the next year to prevent capture. The hull remaining above water was burned in May, 1778; the bottom was salvaged and sold at Philadelphia. It is reasonable to suppose this ship was a sister of *Randolph*.

The 28-gun frigates, intended to be like *Virginia*, were built on two plans, apparently, for the *Providence* measured 126′ 6½″ on the berth deck, 33′ 8″ beam, and 10′ 5″ depth of hold. Though her dimensions were quite close to the *Virginia*'s, the difference in beam indicates that her builder, Sylvester Bowers, had prepared a new design for her as he had for the 32-gun *Warren*. The *Providence* was launched at Providence, Rhode Island, in May, 1776. Four years later, on May 12, 1780, she was captured by the British when they took Charleston, South Carolina. The *Providence* was taken into the Royal Navy as a 32-gun frigate and sold out in March, 1783, when the Royal Navy was reduced in size by the disposal of old vessels and those needing much repair.

The *Trumbull* was built at Chatham, Connecticut, by John Cotton. Work was started on the lofting of the ship about the end of February, 1776. From what little is known of the vessel it is highly probable that she was built to the official design. This frigate got to sea but was taken by H.B.M. *Iris* off the Capes of the Delaware, as previously mentioned. She was not taken into the Royal Navy, which indicates that the survey found her to be either rotten or a poorly built ship. This vessel has been confused with a large American privateer ship, the *Governor Trumbull*, 20 guns, which was taken by H.B.M. *Venus* in the West Indies. The *Governor Trumbull* was bought into the Royal Navy as the *Tobago*, 20 guns.

The *Montgomery* was one of the two New York frigates never completed; they were built by Lancaster Burling at Poughkeepsie and burned on October 6, 1777, in the Hudson, to prevent capture. The two ships had been launched about the end of October, 1776, but had been slow in completing owing to various causes—the British capture of New York City and the diversion of men and some materials to the squadron on Lake Champlain being perhaps the most important. The closing of the Hudson had made their completion useless in any case by late September, 1776.

The *Effingham* is supposed to have been built by the Grice yard at Philadelphia. She was launched on the 7th of November, 1776, and was scuttled the next year, with the 32-gun *Washington*. The British capture of Philadelphia and then the seizure of the Delaware by their fleet had effectively ended the building program in Pennsylvania by the last of November, 1777.

The 24-gun frigates accomplished little, yet they appear to have been good ships of their class. Only two of the three ordered were completed. The *Boston*, built by the Crosses of Newburyport, got to sea with the *Hancock*, but was not captured until the fall of Charleston, South Carolina, on May 12, 1780. She was taken into the Royal Navy as the *Charleston*, 20 guns, and was sold out and broken up in 1783. No plans have been found, but her measurements as taken off were 114′ 3″ on the berth deck, 32′ 0″ beam, and 10′ 3″ depth of hold. The *Delaware* of the same class, built at Philadelphia by Warwick Coates, was captured in the Delaware River when the British began operations there in the fall of 1777. This vessel was taken into the Royal Navy under the same name as a 28-gun frigate and her measurements were taken off as 117′ 9½″ on the berth deck, 32′ 10½″ beam, and 9′ 8½″ depth of hold. The *Delaware* was sold out of the Royal Navy in March, 1783. The third 24-gun frigate was the New York-built *Congress*, built by Burling at Poughkeepsie. She was not only launched about the same time as the *Montgomery* but was also destroyed at the same time and place, near Esopus. The *Delaware* and the *Congress* were probably built to the Marine Committee designs, so the dimensions of the *Delaware* may be assumed to be those authorized by the Continental Congress.

It is possible to give a few details of the ships completed under the Act of December 13, 1775, in addition to those shown in the plans. It will be noted that two of the plans, those of the *Hancock* and the *Raleigh*, show extensive ornamentation at bow and stern, while the Admiralty plan of the *Virginia* (which was also made from a completed ship) shows none. It is probable that few of the ships actually were without much carving; the inventory of the *Virginia* shows she had a "warrior" figurehead, but whether this implied an Indian or some specific individual like John Smith is by no means certain. It was the general practice, apparently, to give these ships a figurehead, an effigy of the person for whom she was named. Hence it is logical to assume that this was the case in the *Randolph*. The ships named for towns or colonies probably had figureheads having some traditional reference to their namesakes. Since the carvings for the Continental ships could be made while they were under construction, from the draught or by reference to the mould-loft work, there would be no delay in finishing the ship by the use of carving, for only minor alterations were required to fit them properly.

The rig of the Continental frigates varied a good deal because of the variety of dimensions and models. From the little information available it appears that they all carried a spritsail and sprit-topsail under the bowsprit. Most of them do not appear to have crossed royal yards, though all certainly had pole royal

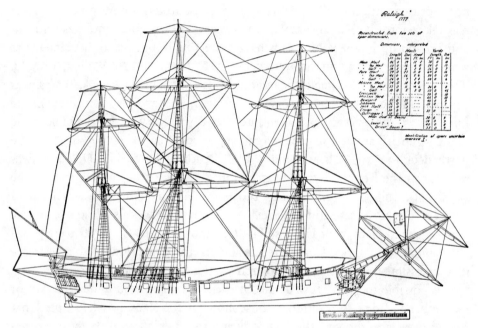

Figure 7. Spar and sail plan of RALEIGH, *1777, from spar dimensions. (See Plan 3.)*

masts. The *Hancock* had royals across on her main and fore masts, set on poles rather than on fidded royal masts, according to a British agent. She also had a lateen yard on her spanker, though its sail did not extend forward of the mizzenmast. On this was set a square-yard ringtail, apparently. The *Boston*, built in the same yard, had a gaff spanker. Both ships used a light mast, in lieu of a flagpole on the taffrail, on which was hoisted a lateen yard and sail, the sheet of which was set up on an outrigger over the stern. The *Raleigh* apparently had about the same rig except that she carried no royal yards. Her spar dimensions are somewhat difficult to interpret, but she carried both a mizzen yard and a crossjack, as well as a driver yard and boom, and a long flagpole. The reconstructed sail plan attempts to show the rig (Figure 7). It will be noted that this ship carried studding sails on fore and main. During the Revolution the lateen yard on the mizzen was slowly going out of fashion, so it is found that ships were rigged either way in this period. The rake of the masts in American ships often showed a peculiarity at this time: the foremast was either vertical or had a slight rake forward, while the main and mizzen often raked aft, the mizzenmast more sharply than the main. The bowsprit steeve was being gradually reduced. In the drawing of the *Randolph* the original showed that the heel was to be stepped below the gun deck, but the instructions written on the draught called for the bowsprit to be stepped above the gun deck, which would not only reduce the steeve, or angle, of the bowsprit, but would also give this spar a more secure step.

The painting of the Continental frigates seems to have been done by the builders or the captains to suit their fancy. The materials for painting some of the ships were white lead, yellow ocher, black oil paint, and Spanish brown. Red paint, made from iron oxide, was also used. The carved work was picked off in the colors considered suitable to the subject—white, blue, yellow, brown, and red being used. The sides of the vessels were usually yellow with black mouldings or narrow stripes, or were black with red, white, and yellow stripes in very narrow bands. Some vessels were painted red, but it is believed these were only small craft such as the vessels built on Lake Champlain. The decks were usually oiled, with the bulwarks red or brown. All nettings and weather cloths were black; in a few cases the weather cloths in the head rails at the bow were painted to represent panels or even carving. Netting and weather cloths were used in the waist of the ship, from quarterdeck to forecastle, to mask the heads of the gun crews that would be exposed by the low bulwarks. The quarterdeck rails were often closed in, or raised, in the same manner.

The following descriptions were written by a British agent in Boston:

Hancock, A man's head with yellow breeches, white stockings, blue coat, and yellow buttonholes, small cocked hat with yellow lace, has a mast in lieu of an ensign staff with a lateen sail on it, has a fore-and-aft driver boom with another across, two topgallant royal masts, pole mizzen topmast, whole mizzen yard and mounts 32 guns. Has rattlesnake carved on the stern, netting all around the ship; stern black and yellow quartergalleries, all yellow.

Boston, An Indian head with bow and arrow in the hand, painted white, red and yellow, two topgallant royal masts, pole mizzen on which she hoists a topgallant sail; painted nearly like the *Hancock* with nettings all around, has a gaff, a mast in lieu of an ensign staff with lateen sail on it and mounts 30 guns.

Brig *Lexington*, two topgallant yards and royals, square tuck, painted yellow and a low round(ed) stern painted lead color, black sides and yellow mouldings.

Ship privateer *Reprisal;* Stern painted black and yellow, mouldings on quarters white, black side, no quartergalleries, a figurehead, three topgallant yards and three long mastheads for royals.

The plan of the Continental Congress for the use of the new ships was based on the same optimism that established their estimate of the time required to build the vessels. There were, in fact, no allowances for the tremendous difficulties in completing the ships, getting them to sea, and assembling them to form squadrons. The individual ships that were completed were too weak to break the blockade at any of the ports where they had been building, and so escaped to sea only by stealth. On the other hand, the new ships were far more powerful and expensive than was necessary for commerce raiding or for the packet service. Once any of the ships got to sea, there were no supplies available, except by capture from the enemy, for there were no colonial bases or supply vessels.

The British had effectively cut the Continental Congress's shipbuilding program and canceled the greater part of their naval plans for the future by their capture of New York and the resultant closing of the Hudson, followed by their investing of the lower Delaware and seizure of Philadelphia, and, finally, by the blockade and invasion of the Chesapeake itself. These operations led to the capture of the *Delaware* and the *Virginia*, and to the destruction of the unfinished *Washington, Effingham, Montgomery*, and *Congress*—to say nothing of the loss of a number of the small craft obtained through the Act of October, 1775.

As things turned out, the ships built in the smaller and less important ports were, with the one exception of the *Randolph*, the only vessels that cruised under the Continental flag. Had the British shown any initiative even these ships could have been prevented from escaping to sea, for the British intelligence is known to have been well informed, and it certainly possessed complete and correct information as to the number and location of the ships building for the Continental Navy. However, the Continental Congress made it easy for the British by ordering many American naval ships into the Delaware and to Charleston, South Carolina, so that the capture of the ships was made certain when these localities were attacked. The tactical plans for the Continental Navy seem to have been as vague and ineffective as those of the Continental Congress for military operations. The politicians and demagogues insisted on directing both military and naval operations and movements in spite of continuous disasters.

During the year 1776 the Marine Committee and its agents procured a number of small craft: the cutter *Dolphin* of 10 guns, a schooner named *Enterprise*, the sloops *General Mifflin* and *General Schuyler*, and the galleys *Washington* and *Lady Washington*, the packet *Spy*, and a vessel named *General Arnold*, apparently a small schooner. In addition they bought or built a number of row barges, sloops, gundalows, and radeaux to aid the various state navies in defending the coast, particularly in the vicinity of New York and Philadelphia. One prize was taken into service, the small 10-gun sloop, or schooner, *Racehorse*. She was one of the vessels destroyed in the Delaware in 1777. The records are so incomplete that it is impossible to list the names of all of the small craft owned or manned by the Continental Navy; a great many vessels were private craft chartered to the Continental Congress, and these cannot usually be distinguished from national vessels.

While the ships ordered under the Act of December 13, 1775, were still under construction or fitting out, a new act was passed by the Continental Congress on November 20, 1776, authorizing additional new construction. This directed the building of three 74-gun ships, five 36-gun frigates, an 18-gun brig, and a packet. Three ship sloops appear to have been authorized soon afterward, though the act for building them has not been discovered. Since all the vessels ordered in the Act of 1776, except two 74's and the 18-gun brig, can be accounted for with certainty, it is rather unlikely that the three ship sloops were substitutes for uncompleted vessels previously authorized, though this could possibly be the case.

The three 74's were to be fast, powerful ships. It was intended that one was to be built at Philadelphia, one at Boston, and one at Portsmouth, New Hampshire; probably all were to be built to the same design, as had been the case with the earlier frigate classes. One plan of these American Revolutionary War 74's has happily been preserved by Humphreys and is now in the National Archives (40–15–6, G; 40–15–6, H). This plan of the 74 is in the same hand as that of the *Randolph*, and there can be no question that both were drawn by the same designer. The draftsmanship, the method of presenting the bow and of showing the wales, and also the methods of fairing, are notably alike in the originals. The hull form used in the 74 is very similar to that of the

Randolph in all respects. In addition to this draught of a 74, Joshua Humphreys built a half-model of a 74 for the Navy Board, or Board of Admiralty, and this too has been preserved. The model, a planked decorative half-model in a fairly good state of preservation, is now on exhibit at Independence Hall, Philadelphia.

An assumption that all this is sufficient to indicate that Humphreys was the designer of the 74's faces the same difficulty that raises doubt that he designed the *Randolph*. In addition, close examination of the half-model shows that it is not like the plan in many important respects. Plan 5 shows the design of the 74 redrawn with the restorations noted. The half-model has different quarter galleries, the forecastle rails are not as shown in the plan, and it appears that the model does not have quite the same lines forward as the draught indicates. The writer is of the opinion that the model was made by Humphreys from the draught, to show how he intended to build the 74 to be constructed at Philadelphia, and that he "improved" on the design as a sales argument. Why would he have departed in any detail in making the model if he had made the draught? Further, his papers in regard to the Revolutionary War 74 refer to the "model" and not to the draught. The fact that Humphreys appears to have retained the model indicates that it was not one ordered by the local Navy Board, or by the Continental Admiralty Board, but one he made in an effort to obtain the contract for building the Philadelphia 74. Humphreys prepared a set of spar dimensions for his model which would fit the draught. The sail plan is reconstructed on this basis in Figure 8. There can be no acceptable claim that Humphreys designed either the *Randolph* or the 74 until it can be explained how this was accomplished in drafting work not done in his hand.

Owing to the trend of war which put Philadelphia in the hands of the enemy, no 74 was built there. One 74 had some work done on her at Boston, but this does not indicate that she was ever actually laid down. Only one, in fact, was ever built—the *America*, at Portsmouth, New Hampshire. Colonel James K. Hackett was the builder, with his cousin William the master shipwright or foreman. The ship was laid down in May, 1777, but work proceeded very slowly; only about twenty-four carpenters were employed on her because of a lack of materials and funds. Various orders concerning the ship indicate that instructions were given at one time to depart from the original plan by cutting down the vessel to 56 or 60 guns, but these orders were apparently countermanded. In early June, 1779, the Congress instructed Robert Morris to complete the ship as soon as possible. Later in the month it appointed John Paul

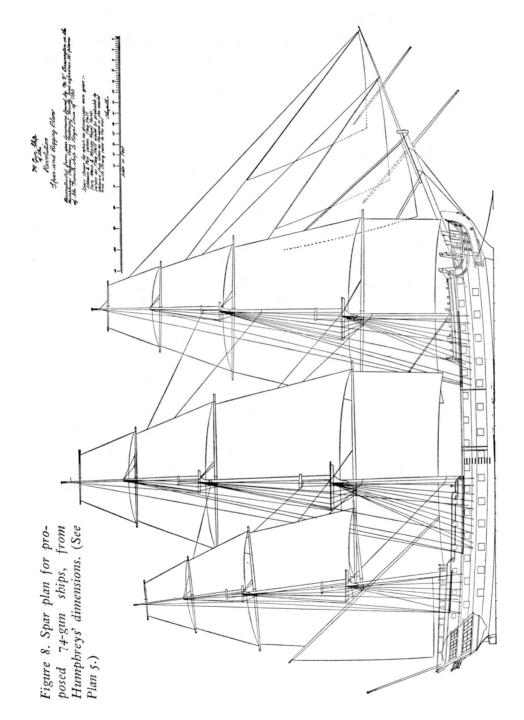

Figure 8. Spar plan for pro-posed 74-gun ships, from Humphreys' dimensions. (See Plan 5.)

Jones her commander, which also made him the resident inspector or supervisor. In spite of the efforts of Morris, the construction of the ship was very
slow.

Robert W. Neeser, in an article entitled "The True Story of the *America*"
(No. 126 of *The Proceedings of the United States Naval Institute*), quoting
an unknown source, gives the following leading dimensions of the Portsmouth-
built ship: 182' 6" length on upper deck, 50' 6" extreme beam, 23' 0" depth
of hold, 150' 0" length on the keel. Thus if the vessel was built on the same
plan that Humphreys had, then the Hacketts made the ship 3' 0" longer on
the keel and 3' 0" wider in beam, but without much change in over-all length.
The measurement on the upper deck is assumed to be from bow rabbet to
rudderpost; if any other assumption is made, then the *America* would be shorter
than the draught preserved by Humphreys, and would not then agree with
the keel measurement given by Neeser. According to the account given in
the reference, Jones found the ship much less complete than he had been led
to expect. He also made extensive changes in the ship's design, so far as upper
works were concerned. He shifted the mainmast three frames aft, lengthened
quarterdeck and forecastle, and raised the waist so that the upper sheer line
was flush, which permitted gangways to be used the full length of the waist.
He reduced the quarter galleries and lengthened the light poop deck somewhat,
on which, Jones reported, the bulwark rail was fitted to fold down. The figurehead was the Goddess of Liberty, with the right arm raised and pointing upward and ahead. On the left arm there was a shield with thirteen stars of silver
on a blue background.

It is difficult to fit the dimensions and the changes noted to the Humphreys
plan, but it must be emphasized that the reference quoted by Neeser was obviously written some time after the Revolution and even if authentic is not
trustworthy, since it was undoubtedly written from memory.

Jones states that Colonel or Major Hackett was not able to judge the proper
scantlings, but that he found the leading shipwright, William Hauscom (Hanscom?) able to work these out. The context of the reference is that the ship's
model was on the original draught, while Jones and "Hauscom" made changes
in the topsides and were responsible for the scantlings. Contemporary accounts
at Portsmouth give the credit for the design of the *America* to William Hackett.
The account given by Neeser is subject to suspicion, for it appears obvious
that Jones found the ship in frame, yet he seems to claim Hackett could not
calculate the scantlings. Either Jones claims too much, or the authority used

for the Neeser article is not authentic. At any rate, it is quite impossible to establish at this time the real part that William Hackett had in the design of this ship.

The *America* was launched November 5, 1782. In the meantime, however, on September 3 the Continental Congress had presented her to France to replace the French 74, *Magnifique*, lost in Boston Harbor, in order to show their gratitude to the French king for his help against England. The ship was turned over to her French commander immediately after her launch. Her career in the French navy was short, however, as in 1786 she was found to be rotten and was broken up. The French report indicates that the *America* did not combine all the qualities which a vessel of her class should have, but does not specify what the faults were. In view of the rather sharp lines shown in the draught preserved by Humphreys, it seems probable that the *America* (if built on these lines) lacked the displacement to carry her lower deck guns high enough above the water. The *America* is reported to have been armed with 30 long 18-pdrs., 32 long 12-pdrs., and 14 long 9-pdrs., the latter upon her forecastle and quarterdeck. If this is true, then the *America* had one more port to a side on her lower deck than was called for in the draught in the Humphreys papers; also the ship in the latter was not intended to carry guns on the forecastle. Humphreys' half-model shows the same port arrangement as in the draught. The plan of the Revolutionary War 74 shows a solid rail on the forecastle deck without gun ports or stanchions indicated; the Humphreys half-model shows an open rail, or "drift," also without gun ports or stanchions. Plate III shows the Humphreys half-model: the model and the plan should be compared and both studied with relation to Neeser's statements.

Of the remaining vessels authorized by the Act of November 20, 1776, only the plan of the 36-gun frigate *Confederacy* has been found. It is the Admiralty plan made from measurements of the ship after she was captured and bought into the Royal Navy. The *Confederacy*, launched 1778, was built at Norwich, Connecticut, on the Thames River, by Jedidiah Willets, who may have been either the builder or the supervisor.

There is a possibility that she represents the official design of her class, and there is a plausible argument for such an assumption, based on her lines and those of the ships of the Revolution preserved by Humphreys. A comparison of her lines, shown in Plan 6, with those of the *Randolph* and the Revolutionary War 74-gun ship shows a slight resemblance in hull form and in the appearance of the bow and the beakhead bulkhead, as well as a faint likeness in the ends of the quarter and forecastle rails. The resemblance is sufficiently strong, in the opinion of the writer, to indicate that the *Confederacy* was designed by the same man who designed the *Randolph* and the 74-gun ship.

The *Confederacy* was a remarkable vessel. She was very long for a ship of her rate, almost 160' on deck. Her dimensions were 154' 9" on the berth deck, 37' 0" beam, 12' 3" depth in the hold. Comparing these with the dimensions of a contemporary British 36-gun frigate of about 1780, the *Flora*, we find the latter only measured 137' 0" on her berth deck, 38' beam, and 13' 3" depth of hold. Thus the American was almost 23 feet longer, with a foot less in beam and depth. This was not the only peculiarity of the *Confederacy:* she was almost a "galley-frigate" and had much in common with the British galley-frigate *Charles-Galley* (built at Woolwich in 1676 by Phineas Pett), which measured 131' 1" on her lower deck, 29' 0" beam, and 8' 1½" depth of hold. The *Confederacy* was very like the older *Charles-Galley* in her proportion of depth to length and in the relatively narrow beam. Both vessels were fitted to row on the lower deck, the *Charles-Galley* having more sweeps. Rowing on the lower deck in frigates was not uncommon, however, for both the *Southampton* and *Alarm* classes of 32's built for the Royal Navy in 1756 and 1757 show this feature. This location of the sweep ports was going out of fashion by 1775. What makes the *Confederacy* so much like the older galley-frigates is not merely where she carried her sweep ports, but rather the combination of this with narrow beam and shoal depth. The *Confederacy* was on a fairly sharp model, like the early galley-frigates, and was designed for speed. The ship was armed frigate-fashion, like her earlier compatriots, and had royal poles but no royal yards. Just abaft her wheel, on the quarterdeck, she had a speaking tube leading to the berth deck, which was intended to be used to direct the men who steered the ship there by means of the heavy tiller and its ropes in the event the wheel on the quarterdeck was shot away.

The *Confederacy* was an ornate ship, profusely carved. She was very handsome and comparable to *Hancock* in all respects. She had one oddity in a large vessel of this period: her keel was slightly rockered forward. The *Confederacy* was described at the time of her capture as being a very fast ship and well built.

This ship saw very little service under the Continental flag, for she was captured off the Virginia Capes in 1781 by H.B.M. ships *Orpheus* and *Roebuck*. She was a rather unfortunate vessel. In 1779 she was to carry a French diplomat to Europe, and after many delays she finally got away—only to be heavily

damaged in a gale off the Bahamas at the end of the year. She had to put into
Martinique to be rerigged. On finally returning to the Delaware it was found
she required extensive refitting. After her capture the Royal Navy bought her
in and rated her as a 36-gun frigate under the name *Confederate*. She was sold
out and broken up about 1783.

The second frigate laid down under the new authorization was the *Alliance*,
built at Salisbury Point on the Merrimack River, Massachusetts, in 1777. Wil-

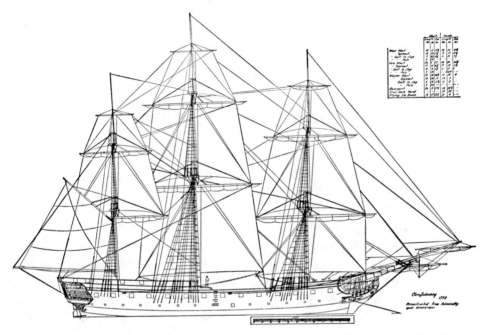

Figure 9. Spar and sail plan of CONFEDERACY *after Admiralty dimensions. (See Plan 6.)*

liam and James Hackett were the builders, and the first is traditionally the designer of the ship. Little is known about the design of this vessel. A contemporary report states that she was 151′ 0″ on the lower deck, 36′ 0″ beam, and
12′ 6″ depth of hold. She would thus be about the same type as the *Confederacy*, if these dimensions are correct, but slightly smaller in size. She was rated
variously as a 32- and a 36-gun frigate, the latter being the correct rating. This
vessel was given a great reputation for speed and survived the war in the American service; she was sold at Philadelphia June 3, 1785. The ship usually carried
40 guns—28 18-pdrs. and 12 9-pdrs.

The third frigate was the *Bourbon*. Laid down at Middletown, Connecticut, early in 1780, she was launched in July, 1783, after much delay because of lack of funds. In September of 1783 she was recommended to be sold, and nothing further is known about her.

The remaining two frigates authorized were to be built at Gosport, Virginia. These vessels were not completed. The work was first ordered stopped in 1778; then it was decided to complete one of them. But this ship too had her construction discontinued when the British invaded Virginia, and both the unfinished hulls were finally burned during the ensuing campaign. Thus the five frigates authorized by the Act of 1776 had been started, but only two were ever completed and placed in naval service.

The *Ranger* may have been intended for the 18-gun brig authorized under the Act of 1776, but this is very doubtful. It is more probable that she was one of the three ship sloops supposed to have been authorized shortly after the Act of November 20, 1776, came into force. Certainly she was not a frigate cut down during construction. The three ship sloops were the *Ranger*, *Saratoga*, and *General Gates*. The *Ranger* was captured and taken into the Royal Navy, so her dimensions have survived: 116' 0" on the main deck, 34' 0" beam, and 13' 6" depth of hold. She carried 18 6-pdrs., a small armament for so large a vessel. She was about as large as the 24-gun ships authorized in '75 and was a quarterdecked ship. A contemporary account says that she was oversparred. *Ranger* became a noted name in the American Navy because of this ship sloop. She was a successful cruiser but finally fell into the hands of the British at the fall of Charleston, and was taken into the Royal Navy as the *Halifax*.

The second sloop was probably the *General Gates*, about which little is known. A vessel of this name was apparently building somewhere in New England, as correspondence relating to her was directed to the Boston Navy Board. The vessel seems to have been completed in 1778 and was ordered sold immediately. This causes a doubt as to the identification; the vessel was sold in 1779, long before the war ended. There were also a number of privateers of the same name, though none of them were ships.

The third sloop was the *Saratoga*, built at Philadelphia by Humphreys. Her dimensions have not been found. There are references to her in the Humphreys papers as being a brigantine, but it has been well established that she came out ship-rigged. Perhaps she was the "brig" authorized in the Act of 1776, altered. The *Saratoga* was lost on her maiden cruise in 1780.

Humphreys also built a packet, the *Mercury*, which was probably the one authorized in the Act of 1776. A packet service, to be maintained with three vessels between America and France, was established by the Continental Congress in 1780. This service was under the control of the Board of Admiralty that succeeded the Marine Committee. A number of packets were built during the Revolution, including another *Mercury*, one of three packets ordered in Massachusetts, built from a design by John Peck at Plymouth, Massachusetts, in 1780. She is believed to have been a schooner, while the Philadelphia-built ship may have been a ketch. The British captured a ketch-rigged packet of this name and gave her dimensions as 72' 5" long on the main deck, 20' 5" beam, and 8' 8" depth of hold. This ketch, taken by H.B.M. ships *Fairy* and *Vestal* off the Banks of Newfoundland, September 10, 1780, was reported by her captors to be a new vessel.

Of the vessels authorized by the Act of 1776, two 74's, three frigates, and perhaps the 18-gun brig were never completed. The lack of funds had delayed some, danger of capture had led to the destruction of two of the frigates, and the capture of the chosen site for building one of the 74's had prevented her ever being laid down. The delays were the main factor that prevented the ships from being completed; the colonies had become exhausted, and shipbuilding materials, munitions, and sound money were now lacking. The limits of financing new ships by the Continental Congress had actually been reached by the Act of 1775, and very little money was left for the program established in 1776. It is difficult to trace the new ships because of the very incomplete records on some of them, owing to a loss of the official papers, the chaotic administrative control of the Continental Navy, and the informal methods resulting from the stress and haste of war.

The administrative problems of building new ships and controlling the activities of the Continental ships led to a slow development in organization. The original Marine Committee lasted until the end of 1779. By this time it was fully apparent that the large and cumbersome Marine Committee was not functioning: the members could not assemble often enough, and there were usually too many conflicting ideas when they did meet. Therefore Congress set up a Board of Admiralty of five members, October 28, 1779. This board took over the Navy Boards established by the Marine Committee in 1777. These had been located at three important ports with the apparent aim of decentralizing control and permitting administrative functions to be exercised without the delays caused by the need of communicating with the congressional board. There were three such Navy Boards in existence, one at Boston, the Eastern Department, one at Philadelphia (or elsewhere in Pennsylvania and in New Jersey when Philadelphia was in the hands of the British), and the third at Baltimore, the Southern Department. The Pennsylvania Navy Board was usually referred to as being in the "Middle District." This board was so close to the Continental Congress that the latter's naval committees usually usurped its functions. The Board of Admiralty was not much of an improvement over the old Marine Committee, for the same difficulty existed in getting the five members to meet, and the old habit continued of dealing directly with local contractors and agents, by-passing the local Navy Boards. The Navy Boards were likewise ineffective; the members would rarely be able to assemble, and as a result only one or two of the board members would be active. Gradually the Navy Boards were replaced, in fact if not in theory, by one member who really acted as the Navy Agent for a district.

The next step was to propose a "Marine Department" headed by a Secretary, but this idea finally degenerated into the mere establishment of an "Agent of Marine," without a headquarters staff. Finally, when the appointment of the agent was under consideration, Congress hedged and gave the position to Robert Morris, the Financial Agent, on a temporary basis (September 6, 1781). On November 2 of the same year they made the assignment permanent; thus the duties of the Agent of Marine became part of the function of the Financial Agent. Morris had been perhaps the most active person in naval affairs, so the choice is easily excused. Under Morris, the local Navy Boards gradually declined in activity and the single agent as a substitute seems to have been accepted. It should be remembered that the difficulties of these committees and boards were due to the slow means of travel and communication, rather than to derelictions of the members themselves. The propensity of governments to attempt control of functions by committees, boards, or councils explains the insistence with which the idea of group control of the Continental Navy was retained, in the face of the obvious weaknesses of the system in the colonies.

The armament of all of the new Continental frigates was a grave problem. Prior to the Revolution the manufacture of cannon was unknown in America. Under all the circumstances then existing it was natural, perhaps, that the British government did not allow such activities. While there were numerous colonial foundries and iron mines in New England, New York, Pennsylvania, and the South, there was no one available who was experienced in the business of cannon manufacture. In spite of this, the Continental Congress planned to fit all the new ships with American-made guns. To make this really difficult, they

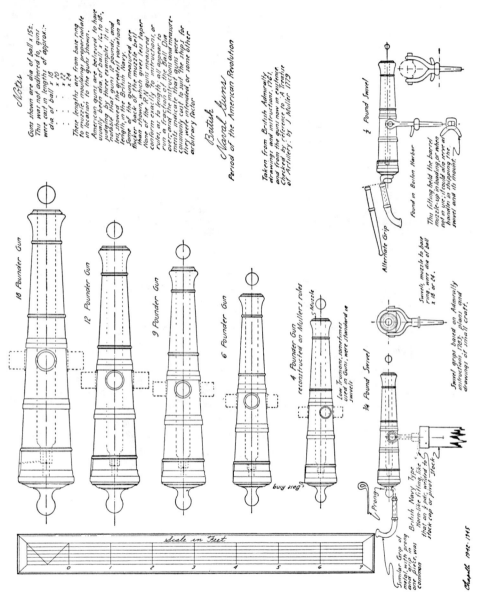

Figure 10. British naval guns and swivels of the American revolutionary period.

89

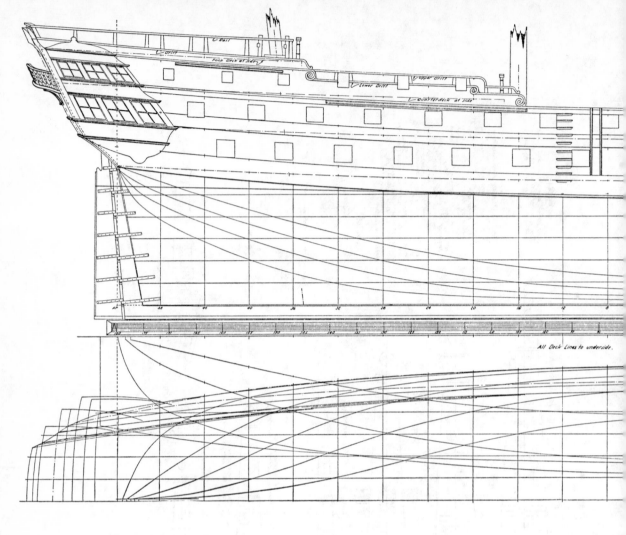

All Deck Lines to underside.

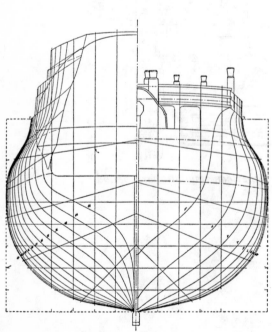

Dimensions

Length bet. Perps.   180'·0"
    on Keel   147'·0"
Moulded Beam   49'·0"
Extreme   49'·8"
Depth in Hold   19'·0"

Room & Space 25" ; ⊕ is 71'·10" from F.P.
W.L.'s & Buttocks spaced 4'·0".

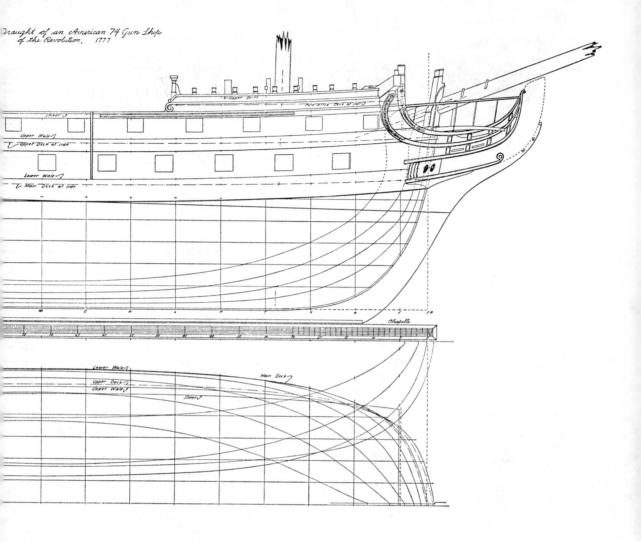

Plan 5. Draught of the 74-gun ship, 1777, probably the official design for the American 74's projected by the Continental Congress.

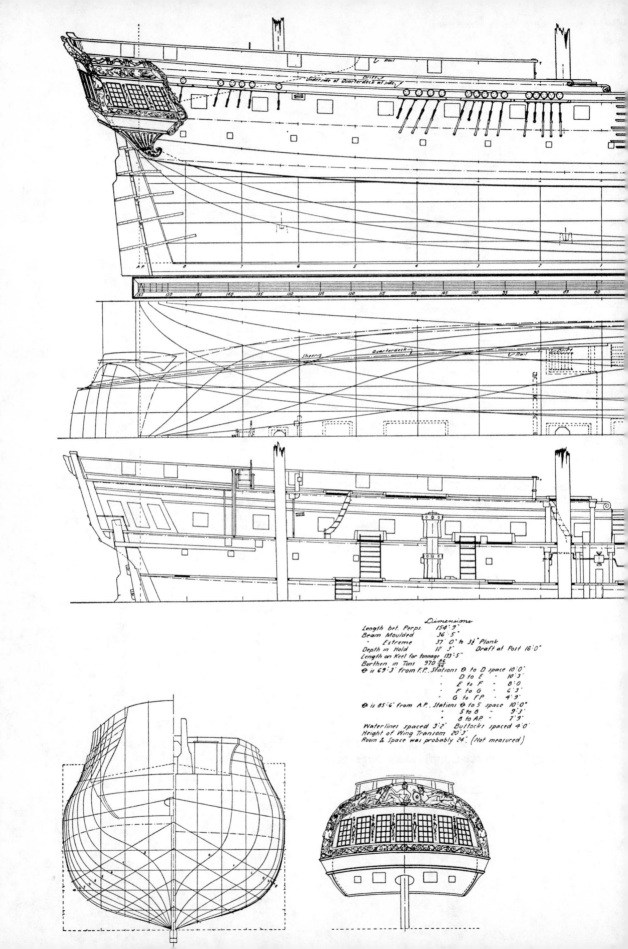

Dimensions

Length bet. Perps.   154' 3"
Beam Moulded   36' 5"
  "   Extreme   37' 0" to 3½" Plank
Depth in Hold   12' 3"   Draft at Post 16' 0"
Length on Keel for tonnage 133' 5"
Burthen in Tons   970 65/94
Ⓐ is 69' 3" from F.P. Stations Ⓐ to D space 10' 0"
  "   D to E   "   10' 3"
  "   E to F   "   8' 0"
  "   F to G   "   6' 3"
  "   G to FP   "   4' 9"
Ⓐ is 65' 6" from A.P. Stations Ⓐ to S space 10' 0"
  "   S to 8   "   9' 3"
  "   8 to AP   "   7' 9"
Waterlines spaced 3' 2" Buttocks spaced 4' 0"
Height of Wing Transom 20' 3"
Room & Space was probably 24". (Not measured)

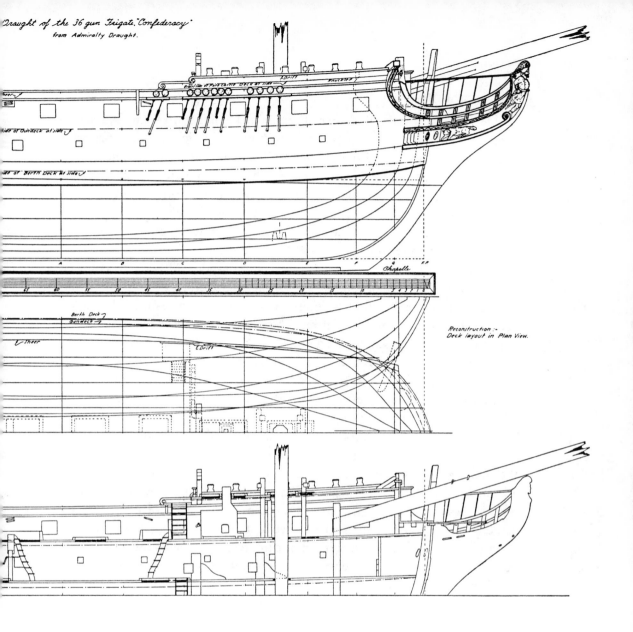

Plan 6. Draught of CONFEDERACY, after the Admiralty draught made after her capture.

decided, at first, to have all the naval cannon made in Pennsylvania and hauled overland to the shipyards where the frigates were building. It is not surprising to find that this plan failed almost completely and that at the last moment other arrangements had to be made, with the results usual in such cases during war-time. The record of the Continental Congress in the management of naval affairs was extraordinarily inept throughout the Revolution.

It was intended, of course, to arm the new ships with standard guns: the 24-gun frigates were to have 24 9-pdrs., the 28-gun frigates, 26 12-pdrs. and 2 6-pdrs.; the 32-gun frigates, 26 12-pdrs. and 6 6-pdrs. All were to have co-horns or swivels in proportion. Because of the failure of the foundries in Penn-sylvania to produce the necessary guns, the ships finally came out with a rather mixed and unsatisfactory armament. These armaments changed a good deal in the ships that got to sea, so that there was never any standardization through-out the Revolution. The *Randolph* was fitted out with 26 12-pdrs., 10 6-pdrs., and 12 cohorns. The *Raleigh* had to complete her armament in France and finally had the same number of guns as the *Randolph*, but only two cohorns. The *Virginia* was fitted with 24 12-pdrs., 6 4-pdrs., and 6 swivels. The *Warren* had a very mixed armament—12 18-pdrs., 14 12-pdrs., 8 9-pdrs., and a few swivels. The *Boston* had 5 12-pdrs., 19 9-pdrs., 2 6-pdrs., and 4 4-pdrs., with the addition of 16 swivels. The *Delaware* had 22 12-pdrs. and 6 6-pdrs., with an unrecorded number of swivels. The *Hancock* had 24 12-pdrs. and 10 6-pdrs., besides swivels. All but a few ships had a mixture of American-made guns, cast in foundries in Connecticut, Rhode Island, Massachusetts, Pennsylvania, and Maryland, with guns captured from the British and French guns purchased abroad. There were some few cannon in the colonies when the war began, old fieldpieces and captured French guns of the war of 1756–63; it is probable that some of these also found their way aboard Continental vessels.

When the new program of 1776 came up, the Navy Board of the Eastern District was to arm the *Alliance* and *Confederacy*, frigates, as well as the *Ranger*, sloop of war. It was also to furnish guns for the *Bourbon*, but did not do so, since the frigate was never completed. It must also have been the re-sponsibility of this board to find guns for the 74 *America*. At any rate, they ordered all the guns for the *Alliance* and *Confederacy* from one foundry in Connecticut; when this failed to deliver, they transferred the contract to a Massachusetts foundry, which also failed to deliver in full. The two ships were intended to be armed with 28 12-pdrs. and 8 6-pdrs. each. The *Alliance* carried

28 12-pdrs. and 8 9-pdrs. in service, while *Confederacy* apparently had 28 12-pdrs. and 8 6-pdrs. The *America*'s armament has been described earlier.

The American-made guns were usually copies of the English naval guns in nearly all respects. They were generally of cast iron. Some brass guns were also manufactured, but these were apparently intended for fieldpieces and not for shipboard. The proportions of all parts of a naval gun of the period were based on the diameter of the shot used in it, but each foundry seems to have used its own factors, so that the guns were not standard in length or weight, though maintaining the bore within narrow tolerances. The location of the trunnions often varied; some foundries placed them in line with the bore, while others placed them below the center line of the bore. Naval guns above 9-pdrs. rarely had low trunnions, apparently. The variation in the guns resulted in trouble when gun carriages had to be made before the guns were cast; often the carriages had to be altered when the guns were in hand. Figure 10 shows some of the common British naval guns of the Revolution according to the official designs, but these were not closely followed in casting. Many guns built according to these plans were thicker-walled at the muzzle and so had less taper than shown. Many were longer as well. The guns shown were what were usually termed "short guns," as can be seen by the notes on the variations in length contained in the drawing. Lieutenant Commander Brewington has given an excellent account of the casting of the guns for the Continental Navy in *The American Neptune*, January and April, 1943 (Vol. III, Nos. 1 and 2).

The swivels were far less standardized than cannon. They ranged from what might be termed heavy muskets to small cannon. This class of weapon was supported by an oar-lock type of mount set in the rail of the vessel or on vertical timbers outside the rail called "stocks." Since the mounting of these guns could not be very secure, the size of swivels was limited to the relatively low power that would result in light recoil. The maximum bore of the swivel type of gun was about 2" and the weight of shot was usually less than one pound. Loose shot could be fired, and this made the swivel a very effective gun against personnel in close-range fighting. For this reason many ships carried a few swivels in their tops, as well as in vantage points along the rails, particularly raised above the main rails on the quarterdeck or poop. The gun was extensively used in the early colonial merchantmen for defense purposes and was also popular in small vessels on the American lakes, as it was all that was needed to fight off any Indian (or outlaw) attack on these wilderness seas.

The most common swivels in American hands during the Revolution were guns of the cannon type, from 34″ to 36″ extreme length and from 1½″ to 1¾″ bore, throwing shot of from one-half to three-quarters of a pound. Most of the guns were miniature cannon in appearance. A few had wooden grips secured to their breeches; these were often merely straight sticks, but sometimes they were curved much like a huge pistol grip. There were some smaller swivels of this type (with barrels about 28″ long) that had flintlocks attached, but most of the swivels were fired with a slow match—rope yarn impregnated with gunpowder, pitch, or other material to allow slow combustion. These small swivels fired shot from 1″ up to 1½″ in diameter. There were other swivel-mounted guns of even lighter nature. There were heavy musketlike weapons, with a flintlock firing lead shot somewhat less than 1″ in diameter. These guns were from 60″ to 72″ long and were commonly known as "buccaneering pieces," after the earlier freebooters who had made them popular. Another light weapon of this class was the "blunderbuss," a short, heavy bell-muzzle gun for firing loose shot. Both the buccaneering piece and the blunderbuss had shoulder stocks like muskets. They were never classed as "guns" in rating a ship's armament, nor in fact were swivels as a class so rated.

Some ships carried large swivel cannon of about 2″ bore mounted on heavy wooden brackets inboard the rail; these guns were also used as boat cannon. They were often called "howitzers" but were generally considered to be swivels. "Cohorn," or "coehorn," was a generic name for short light cannon and included light mortars, howitzers, and the smaller swivels—in fact, any cannon-type weapon that could be unshipped and carried by one or two men. Americans seem to have applied the name principally to swivels, with hand-grips at the breech.

In addition to making naval guns longer than standard, the foundries often made them thicker-walled, or "double-fortified." This greatly increased their weight, but also made them capable of handling heavier charges of powder, which increased range. Such cannon were considered equal to the standard gun next above them in weight of shot. Double-fortified guns were usually longer than standard and were used as bow guns, particularly on heavy gunboats. Such guns were apparently rarely above 18-pounders.

With the crude methods employed in manufacturing both guns and shot, it is not surprising to find that the variation between bore and shot diameters was often great. The clearance around the shot in the bore of a gun, termed "windage," was often excessive in both American and British guns. The French guns were more accurately made, and when used with the shot intended for them were much favored for chase guns at bow or stern. The quality of powder also left much to be desired. The American-made powder was particularly poor because of low-quality ingredients and unevenness in their proportions. The cannon sights were usually no more than notches filed in the base ring and muzzle bell; a few guns are said to have had some type of rear sight attached to them, but the design is unknown. It is not surprising to find that the shooting in naval actions of the Revolution was very inaccurate.

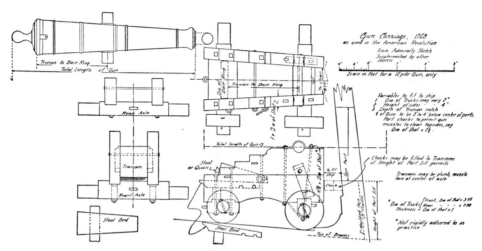

Figure 11a. Gun carriage, 1768, as used during the American Revolution.

The "short gun" was the standard British Navy cannon, as opposed to the "long guns," having more length. The American-made guns seem to have been longer than the British standard, though the lack of identified guns makes any general statement regarding American cannon of this period of doubtful value. It appears that some American foundries made guns on the French models, which were somewhat longer than similar British cannon, but it is not known whether many such guns were placed aboard any of the frigates. The "short guns" of the Revolution were not, however, the carronades. These were invented in England in 1779, and by 1781 they were extensively used in the British Navy. They appeared too late in the war, however, to have reached American hands.

The gun carriages were of the type common on shipboard in the eighteenth century, consisting of two heavy side pieces, or frames, mounted on two axles and four wheels; the wheels as well as the axles and side frames were all of timber. The mounts were made to fit the guns, whose measurements were used to determine the size of each part of the gun carriage. The height of the gun ports above the deck was the only factor outside the gun that was used in

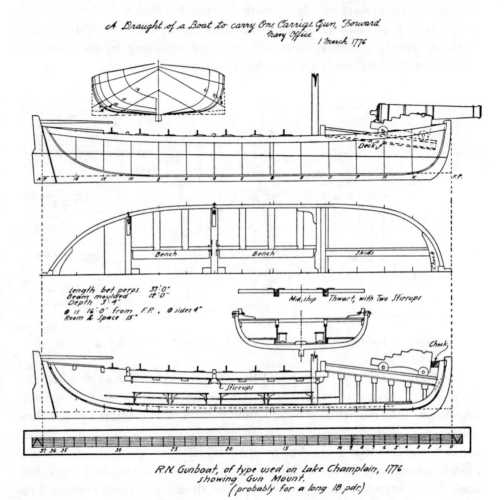

Figure 11b. Draught of a gunboat, to carry one gun, of the type employed by the British on Lake Champlain, 1776.

designing a gun carriage. Figure 11 shows the standard British Navy gun carriage of the period. In gunboats having cramped decks, the gun was often mounted on a carriage without wheels, or "trucks": the side frames slid on two heavy timber skids. Some had timber tracks with the carriage trucks retained. British Navy gun carriages were painted red or brown, the guns were black, and the tompions or muzzle plugs were red or yellow, made with a button like the breech of the gun.

In addition to the ships built for the Continental Navy there were a number of vessels of all types purchased or borrowed for naval service from 1777 to the end of the war. In 1777, when the British moved against Philadelphia, the Continental Navy seems to have borrowed or at least manned a number of the Pennsylvania State Navy gunboats. The xebecs or galleys, *Champion* and *Repulse*, carrying 2 long 24-pdrs., 2 18-pdrs., and 4 9-pdrs., were the most important. Both vessels were destroyed to prevent capture. A packet named the *Fame* is mentioned this year, and a 10-gun brigantine, the *Resistance*, was fitted out at New London, Connecticut, for the Continental service. She was captured by Howe's fleet in 1778. A sloop named *Surprise* was also employed in the Continental Navy.

By far the most numerous additions to the American fleet in the year 1777 were the vessels obtained abroad, particularly in France. Benjamin Franklin and Silas Deane had been attempting to get ships from the French for over a year. Deane's instructions from Congress in 1776 were to try to buy or borrow eight ships of the line, an extremely optimistic idea on the part of a particularly hopeful group of politicians. Some small vessels were obtained by devious means early in 1777. Two fast cutters were purchased to act as dispatch vessels, and the *Surprise* of 10 guns was bought by agents at Dover, England, and fitted out at Dunkirk, France. However, the French government seized her and surrendered her to the English. She was said to be a large vessel of her class, and a vessel of this type and name was in the Royal Navy in 1779 which measured 67′ 3″ on deck, 28′ 11″ beam, and 9′ 0″ deep in the hold. Another dispatch cutter was bought at Dunkirk, the *Revenge*, of 14 6-pdrs. and 22 swivels. This vessel reached America and was sold at Philadelphia in 1780 as unserviceable. The *Dolphin*, of 10 guns, another cutter, was also purchased as a dispatch boat in France. These cutters were involved in a number of intrigues by American and British agents, the latter attempting to get possession of the American secret dispatches and the American agents trying to prevent it, and also if possible to involve the French government in the war.

The American agents in France finally did obtain two frigates. The 28-gun *Queen of France* was purchased and sent to America. She was an old ship and was sunk at Charleston, South Carolina, May 11, 1780, to prevent capture by the British on the surrender of that city. By far the most important ship they obtained, however, was *L'Indien*, which passed through their hands in a curious manner. This was a new and very powerful ship built to a French design at Amsterdam, Holland, early in 1777. Soon after the American agents got her they were apparently forced to give her up to the French, who in turn sold her to the Duke of Luxemburg, by whom she was finally loaned to South Carolina. She was renamed *South Carolina*, and after reaching America, she was taken off the Delaware Capes on December 19, 1782, by the *Astrea*, 32, *Diomede*, 44, and *Quebec*, 32, after an eighteeen-hour chase. The importance of the *South Carolina*, ex *L'Indien*, was not in her career, but in the effect her great size and power is said to have had on later American men-of-war. The *South Carolina* was about 154′ 0″ on the main deck, about 40′ 0″ beam, and 16′ 6″ deep in the hold; she carried 24 36-pdrs. and 12 12-pdrs., all French-type guns. The combination of her heavy armament and great length caused her to hog, and she was considered to be a weakly built ship. Because of this she was not purchased for the Royal Navy after her capture. A plan of the ship was published in Vice-Admiral Paris' monumental *Souvenirs de Marine*, Vol. 5; this is reproduced in Plate IV. The drawing shown is not the building plan, of course, but an ornamental draught made after the ship was completed.

The Americans were less successful in 1778, when they acquired only five vessels, most of which were small craft. They obtained the packets *Phoenix* and *Independence*, the latter a brig or brigantine; a prize British transport brig which had been cut down into a galley or block ship of 8 guns—the *Pigot*; a small packet named the *Despatch*; and a merchant ship that was purchased at New Orleans, the *Rebecca*, which was renamed *Morris* and armed with 24 guns. The *Morris* had a very short career, however, as she was lost in a Gulf hurricane, August 18, 1779.

The year 1779 was much more productive; not only did the Continental service obtain ships by purchase and capture in home waters, but they also obtained a number of vessels in France. At home, the ship *Morris* was replaced by a schooner of the same name, presented by some citizens residing in the Spanish colony of Louisiana. The *Providence* frigate had captured a British naval brig, the *Diligent* (or *Diligence*) of 14 guns. This was a regular British Navy brig of war, 88′ 5¾″ long on deck, 24′ 8″ beam, and 10′ 10″ deep in the hold. She was built in 1776 and originally carried 10 guns and 12 swivels. She was burned in the disastrous Penobscot Expedition. A sloop named the

Argo, carrying 12 12-pdrs., was also obtained. Another sloop, the *West Florida*, was captured in the Gulf and taken into service, but was sold at Philadelphia in 1780 as unserviceable. The vessels acquired in France, however, were of far greater importance than any of these. The European squadron commanded by John Paul Jones, which was formed at this time, was made up of such ships as an old French East Indiaman, the *Duc de Duras*, renamed the *Bon Homme Richard*, 42 guns. Little is known about this ship, but the approximate dimensions of her class of Indiamen were as follows: length on the main deck 152' 0", beam 40' 0", depth of hold 19' 0". She seems to have had two decks and a long quarterdeck; there were, however, very few guns on the lower deck. She was sunk in action with H.B.M. ship *Serapis*, 44, on September 23, 1779. The *Pallas*, another old merchantman in Jones' squadron, armed with 30 guns, was finally returned to the French, from whom she had been obtained. A 12-gun brig, the *Vengeance*, a large cutter named *Cerf* (ex *Stag*), of 18 guns, and the 20-gun ship *Ariel* were also borrowed from the French and returned. These ships formed the European squadron and were never brought to America.

The frigate *Deane*, a small 32-gun ship, was obtained on a more permanent basis. She was built at Nantes, France, in 1779, to the order of Franklin and Deane, apparently on a plan obtained from one of the French naval constructors. The draught of this ship seems to have been sent to America, but it has not been found. The dimensions of the *Deane* were given as 96' 0" on the straight of keel, 32' 0" beam; if these are correct then she was as small as the American 24-gun ships authorized in 1775. She was renamed *Hague* in 1782 and was decommissioned at Boston in 1783. Her armament was given at one time as 24 12-pdrs., 2 6-pdrs., and 8 4-pdrs., with a few swivels.

In the year 1780 only one vessel appears to have been obtained, the *Active*, which was employed as a packet. In 1781 no vessel was added to the Continental Navy, but in the next year two ships were obtained: the ex-Indiaman *Duc de Lauzun*, purchased in France and sold there the next year, and the *General Washington*, a 32-gun ship, formerly a British vessel named *General Monk* which had been taken off Cape May, New Jersey, April 2, 1782, by the Pennsylvania state cruiser *Hyder Alley*. The *General Washington* was sold out of the Continental service in 1784. She carried a battery of 24 9-pdrs. and 8 6-pdrs.; she was 130' 9" long and 32' 8" beam and had the reputation of being a fast sailer and a good ship.

The very high standard of design exhibited in the American frigates, as evidenced in the plans that have survived, indicates that there was more knowledge of the specialized field of naval ship design in America than has usually been assumed. It seems apparent that this knowledge was not confined to a single locality, but was spread out along the coast. Every large shipbuilding town evidently had men who were acquainted with the technicalities of warship design and construction. It is unfortunate that so little has been found about the education and experience of the men who may have designed the American frigates of the Revolution, even though their connection with the vessels is mere speculation. The most reasonable assumption, for the present at least, is that the designers were men who had served apprenticeships under Admiralty-trained shipwrights. The quality of the design and drafting shown in the plans of the *Randolph* and the Revolutionary War 74-gun ship might support the assumption. Without assuming such training it is difficult to explain their ability to turn out such plans and men-of-war equal or superior to those of Britain and France.

In attempting to establish the methods and theories actually employed in American ship design during the colonial and Revolutionary War periods, we come face to face with an almost insurmountable difficulty, the lack of records. There are no books or manuscripts, apparently, that were written by early American ship designers, and the various collections of papers of naval constructors do not include any before 1792, except Humphreys', and his are far from complete in technical matters. As a result all statements concerning the basic principles of design in this period must be founded on analysis of the relatively few plans that have survived. This is insufficient to permit any real exploration of the probable aims of the designers. Their ideas on the hull-form theories then prevalent in Europe, and the use of calculations and similar technical aids to design, are not available to us. All of the evidence that may be extracted from ship plans of the early periods of American naval development, and the few technical references at the end of the eighteenth century that pertain to Revolutionary War vessels, show that the American designers leaned toward sharp-bottomed ships, of relatively great length in proportion to other dimensions, and with very fine ends for the time. The American designs almost invariably show long, easy runs and moderately full entrances. The excesses in hull form that marked some French experiments in design during the last half of the eighteenth century are not found in contemporary American designs.

It is probable that the variations in the final designs of the Revolutionary frigates were not only due to the various reasons that have already been discussed, but might also have been the result of the old Admiralty practice of allowing deviations from the "contract plans." If the theory of Admiralty-trained shipwrights existing in America prior to the Revolution is correct, it would be quite reasonable to expect that the men they trained would have the same attitude toward the official draughts of the Marine Committee that had existed toward the Admiralty plans of the earlier period—the attitude that they were interesting and informative but by no means a Holy Writ to be followed without "improvements" or other likely interpretations.

The Revolution left many ideas on naval construction that were to affect warship design and building in later years. The desirability of "big" frigates was firmly established in American minds; speed under sail and heavy gun power were deemed the basic specifications of a man-of-war. The failure of small vessels to accomplish much at sea during the Revolution caused such craft to be looked upon as relatively unimportant. The cost and time required to build ships of the line and the expense of maintaining such ships caused the Americans to consider them excessively costly. Their observation of such unusual ships as the *South Carolina*, ex *L'Indien*, and the *Confederacy* had shown them that special consideration would have to be given to longitudinal strength, in long ships, to carry a heavy armament. They had discovered that great length not only permitted a more powerful battery but created a fast-sailing man-of-war, compared to the short ships popular in the British Navy.

There had been little opportunity to show what a squadron of men-of-war could accomplish. Hopkins' squadron attacked Nassau, in the Bahamas, in 1776, but without spectacular results. Arnold's squadron was finally defeated, and the importance of its action against the British was not apparent at all. John Paul Jones' European squadron had failed because of jealousy among the officers, and only the capture of the *Serapis* had attracted attention; but this was looked upon, with some reason, as a single-ship action. The disastrous American expedition to the Penobscot River, in Maine, in the summer of 1779 had cost the colonies many ships and men and had most certainly added nothing to the reputation of squadron actions, so far as Americans were concerned.

Without extensive or particularly successful operations by Continental squadrons, there had been no need for an organized supply-ship system. Since there were no regular dockyards, no service craft were needed. Only the packet ships (not the later passenger vessels but rather small fast-sailing dis-

patch craft) had been required, in addition to the frigates. The colonial privateers, combined with the few Continental frigates that got to sea, had been very
effective and had won fame as commerce raiders. When two frigates or
privateers worked together, on the other hand, there were often failures that
resulted in recriminations and scandal. All of these factors caused great emphasis to be placed upon the employment of single vessels of great power and
speed rather than a fleet or squadrons. Because of this tactical concept the
United States was to develop some of the finest and largest frigate designs
the world had seen. The frigates of the Revolution, built upon superior models
and having both speed and gun power above their rates in other navies, were
the beginning of a trend in naval construction which was to make the United
States a "frigate nation," replacing France as the leading exponent of this
class of naval ship. The American emphasis on large ships of superior design
intended to be capable of extensive operations alone, rather than upon a well-
integrated fleet or squadron, controlled naval shipbuilding in the United States
throughout the remaining years of the sailing man-of-war period and continued, with few exceptions, well into the steamship era. This American idea
was soon to be adopted by many of the great maritime powers when the great
ships of the American Navy had once been seen.

No account of the American Revolution would be complete without reference to the naval activities on Lake Champlain. So far as the Americans were
concerned, the fleet was Army-controlled; it had been built and manned
by Army personnel, and it fought under a brigadier general. Its officers were
either Army officers with sea experience, or privateersmen and merchant officers brought in from the coast. In spite of this, the Lake Champlain squadron
must be considered a part of the Continental Navy, for the Army's part in its
creation and operation was the result of the lack of a formal line of demarca-
tion between the duties and responsibilities of the Continental Navy and Army.
Early in the war, Washington had commissioned four schooners and the Army
had a great many seafaring men in uniform: there was one regiment almost
entirely composed of sailors which served as a marine-transport service as well
as for combat. Army officers served at sea, and at least one commanded a vessel.
Naval officers commanded soldiers. Expediency rather than set responsibilities established the duties of the two services.

The responsibility for furnishing materials, equipment, and supplies was
shared by the Continental Congress, New York, Pennsylvania, Connecticut,
Rhode Island, and Massachusetts. Men were obtained from the maritime colo-

nies and from the regiments in the vicinity of Lake Champlain. It will be seen that the Lake Champlain squadron was neither Continental nor state in character; it was the product of an emergency and the energy and leadership of such men as Arnold, Schuyler, and others of the Army, and of Governor Trumbull of Connecticut.

The Americans had attempted to hold the St. Lawrence after their attack on Quebec in the winter of 1775–76 by the use of a small squadron of armed vessels and the remains of their "Northern Army." The squadron was largely made up of "gundalows" (or praams) which had been built on the St. Lawrence and on the Richelieu River, below the rapids at Chambly. These small craft ranged from about 50 to 64 feet in length and from 16 to 20 feet beam and had been hastily built and fitted. Some were open boats with a forecastle deck on which a heavy gun was mounted, with two to four smaller guns on the broadside. The larger gundalows were decked and had bulwarks (some had a raised quarterdeck) and carried from 6 to 10 guns. All gundalows could be rowed with sweeps when necessary. Some had an outside keel to help them go to windward, but most appear to have been without this appendage. Those having a raised quarterdeck employed the space under it for quarters; the smaller craft had no quarters, and the crews either slept in the open or under a sail rigged as a tent or awning.

The American "gundalow," or, as it is sometimes spelled in contemporary reports, "gundalo" (properly, "gondola"), was double-ended—that is, sharp at bow and stern. Usually she was perfectly flat-bottomed, without either deadrise or fore-and-aft rocker like her European sister the "prame" or "praam." The latter was a Dutch type of hull that had been adopted by many European navies for shoal-water service, carrying rigs most suited for their size and service. Many naval prames were large and were square-rigged, either ship or brig. The American gundalow was occasionally built with from three to five inches of deadrise, giving her a "V-bottom." When deadrise was employed, the gundalow was built with an equal amount of fore-and-aft rocker in her bottom; the chines (the lines formed by the intersection of the sides and bottom on each side of the hull) met the rabbet (line of intersection of the bottom with the outside keel) at the heels of the stem and sternpost. Unlike the bottom, the sides of a gundalow or of a prame usually had curved timbers. The side frames were all on the same curve or mould, except at the extreme bow and stern, where it was necessary to change the shapes of the frames slightly to permit the planking to run fair to the stem and sternposts. The side timbers all flared out heavily from the bottom, except at the ends of the hull; at the bow the flare was great, but at the stern it was commonly less than amidships. The large Dutch prames carried leeboards, but there is no record of these being employed in the American vessels. The gundalow as a rule had a single mast, on which was set a square course and topsail. Some of the gundalows also carried a single jib set flying from the stem, or from a hemp span over it to allow the bow gun to clear the headstay and still fire straight ahead. The jib was probably used to help steering and to aid in swinging the vessel around in action. The larger gundalows had a bowsprit and one or two headsails; the bowsprit was usually fitted to reef in, cutter fashion. The gundalows were heavily sparred and canvased, as they were very stiff. Some vessels of this type were fore-and-aft-rigged, but there is no record of such rigs having been used on either the St. Lawrence or Champlain gundalows.

The American squadron on the St. Lawrence was trapped when the British advanced down the river, and all the vessels were either captured or destroyed when the Americans retreated southward in June, 1776. Among the vessels captured by the British was a large gundalow, which they carefully took apart and moved to St. Johns, on the Richelieu above the rapids. There they reassembled her and employed the vessel against the Americans, in the campaign of the fall of 1776 on Champlain. In the British service she was known as the *Loyal Convert;* her original name was said to have been *Convert.* A rather sketchy plan was made of her when she was reassembled, and this has been found among the Admiralty draughts. A reconstruction of her lines is shown in Figure 12, based on the profile, midsection, and outline of the rail shown in the Admiralty drawing. The body plan is restored on the basis of the hull form of the European prames and other evidence. The vessel had one mast and a bowsprit when she came into British hands, but late in the summer of 1776 a gaff mizzen was added. A rough portrait of this gundalow is included in a sketch of the British squadron made by an officer, C. Randle, just before the naval action of the 11th of October, 1776, and this portrait shows the mizzen; she then carried 7 9-pdrs., though designed to carry 10 guns. There is no evidence that the British changed the vessel, though it is possible that they raised her and added a quarterdeck. In model, below the wales she was very like the later gundalows built on Lake Champlain. Arnold seems to have had a great deal of interest in the St. Lawrence vessels and may have been responsible for their general design, as he was later for the gundalows and galleys on Lake Champlain.

The Americans abandoned St. Johns on June 18, 1776, taking away with them the frame timbers of a small vessel they had found building there when Montgomery captured the place in the fall of 1775. They then had three vessels afloat on Champlain: the large sloop *Enterprise*, armed with 12 4-pdrs.; the

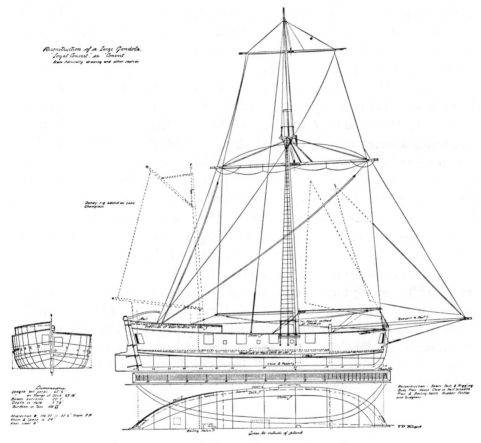

Figure 12. Draught of hull and sail plan of LOYAL CONVERT, *ex American* CONVERT, *a large gundalow on Lake Champlain, 1776.*

schooner *Royal Savage*, armed with 4 6-pdrs., 8 4-pdrs., and some swivels; and the schooner or ketch *Liberty*, of 4 4-pdrs. and 4 2-pdrs. All these vessels had been captured by Montgomery or Arnold in the fall of 1775.

A new schooner was started at Ticonderoga, the *Revenge*, to carry 4 4-pdrs. and 4 2-pdrs., besides some swivels. The Americans hastily set up another shipyard at Skenesboro (Whitehall, New York), and laid down additional craft:

a cutter with the frame timber brought from St. Johns, four large galleys, and eight or nine gundalows. The object of this building was to create a squadron that would defeat or delay the British when they came southward on Champlain. There were neither tools, men, nor supplies immediately available, so desperate efforts had to be made to procure everything necessary from neighboring colonies. Some of the materials intended for the frigates building in New York and Pennsylvania, which could not be completed because their escape was cut off by British captures, were diverted to Champlain.

The British established their base at St. Johns and began to erect several vessels that had been sent in frame from England. A ship sloop (the *Inflexible*) is said to have been put together in twenty-eight days. Two schooners were erected, the *Maria* and the *Carleton*, also the *Loyal Convert*, described earlier, and finally a large "radeau" or block ship, the *Thunderer*. The latter's lines are shown in Figure 13, redrawn from an Admiralty sketch plan in the same manner as was done in the case of the *Loyal Convert*. The *Thunderer*, the most powerful vessel on the lake, was rigged as a bomb ketch, carrying two large howitzers, 6 24-pdrs., and 6 12-pdrs. The British also brought over from the St. Lawrence twenty gunboats each having one gun, four long boats with a field gun each, and twenty-four provision boats or "bateaux."

Both British and Americans employed craft called "bateaux," which were undoubtedly rowing boats much like the gundalows but smaller. They may have been similar to the more recent "lumberman's bateau" or "drive boat," a flat-bottomed double-ended skiff 28' to 32' long, having widely flaring sides something like a dory's. The Americans also used many scows, or flatboats, which also seem to have been called "bateaux." Flat-bottomed scows, skiffs, and punts were in common use in colonial times; they were sometimes called "moses boats" or "pirogues," though the latter name was usually applied to dugout canoes.

"Radeaux" were also employed by the Americans as harbor defense craft, and these were, like gundalows, popular with the state navies set up by some of the colonies. A radeau was nothing more than a rather large sailing scow; the model was probably based on the Thames River barges of the period so far as the English and Americans were concerned. The radeau usually had rounded sides and curved side frames like the gundalows, but had square or scow-shaped bow and stern. Some were flat-bottomed, and some were entirely flat-sided as well; but others, like the *Thunderer*, were quite pretentious in model, having deadrise which also led to some fore-and-aft rocker in the

Figure 13. Draught of the British radeau THUNDERER on Lake Champlain, 1776.

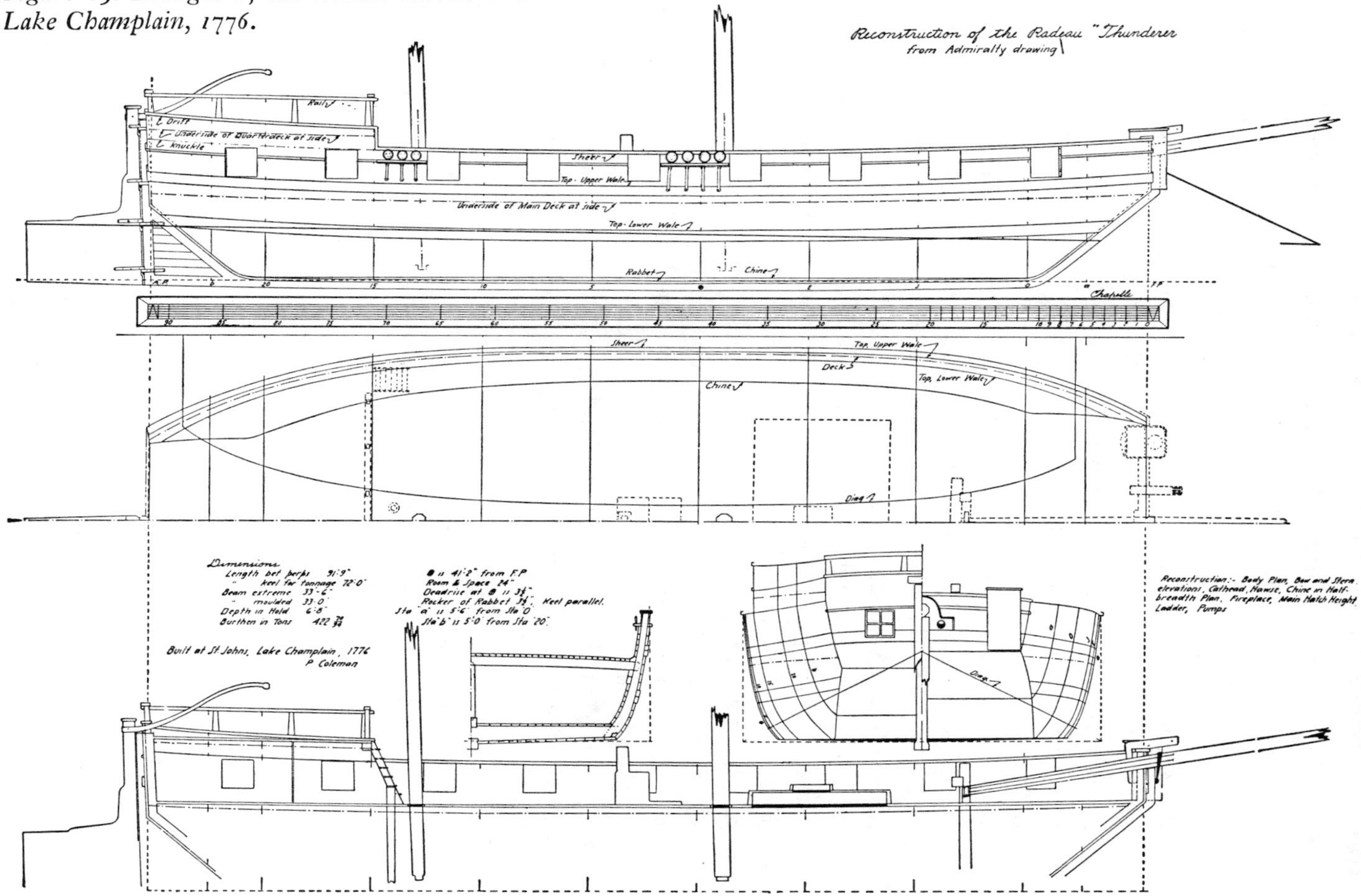

bottom. The radeaux usually had an outside keel, and they were rigged as schooners, sloops, brigs, and ketches, or even as ships. It is said that some of the American radeaux sailed very well in smooth water, but most of them could not get to windward except under sweeps. The name "radeau" gradually went out of usage in America, but "gundalow" remained in use as late as the early part of the present century as a name for shoal, flat-bottomed sailing river and harbor craft, though "scow" was more commonly used as a type name.

The Americans had the greatest difficulty in preparing their squadron for action. In fact, it appears that a few of the vessels were not completed in time and that others went into action before they were ready. The cutter was completed and named *Lee*. She was a small shoal vessel and was taken into the British service after her capture, so a plan is in existence. Figure 14 shows a redrawing of the Admiralty draught, with a sail plan reconstructed from various contemporary sketches of the vessel. She was a small cutter, not much larger than a small gundalow, but was finished like a large vessel with a raised quarterdeck, deep bulwarks, and gun ports. She carried 1 12-pdr., 1 9-pdr., 4 4-pdrs., and 2 swivels. Her dimensions were 43′ 9″ long on deck, 16′ 3½″ beam, and 4′ 8″ depth of hold. Though the frames taken from St. Johns were helpful in completing her, she took a good deal more time to build than a large gundalow, and was probably no better a vessel. The *Loyal Convert* measured 62′ 6″ on deck, 20′ 3″ beam, and 3′ 7½″ depth in the hold; it can be seen that she was a far more efficient fighting craft than the cutter-rigged *Lee*.

The four galleys were the *Washington*, *Congress*, *Trumbull*, and *Gates*. Only the first three were completed in time to see service in the fall of 1776. The appearance of the galleys can be seen by the plan of one in the Admiralty collection made from the vessel after her capture. Only this galley, the *Washington*, was captured and, like the cutter *Lee*, was employed by the British. Her plan, redrawn from the Admiralty draught, is shown in Figure 15. These galleys were round-bilged, and their model was generally much like that of the *Lee*, but with greater length in proportion to beam and depth. The galleys were rigged with two lateen sails and sparred with masts of about equal length. The *Washington* was rerigged as a brig in the British service, and it is doubtful that the vessel originally had the channels shown in the Admiralty plan of her. A bowsprit was also added when her rig became that of a brig. The *Washington* was 72′ 4″ on deck, 20′ 0″ beam, and 6′ 2″ in the hold; it is probable that the other galleys were similar in all respects. The *Gates* was not completed in time to take part in the action against the British squadron; she was destroyed by her crew in 1777 to prevent capture.

The gundalows were probably nearly alike, allowing for the lack of time

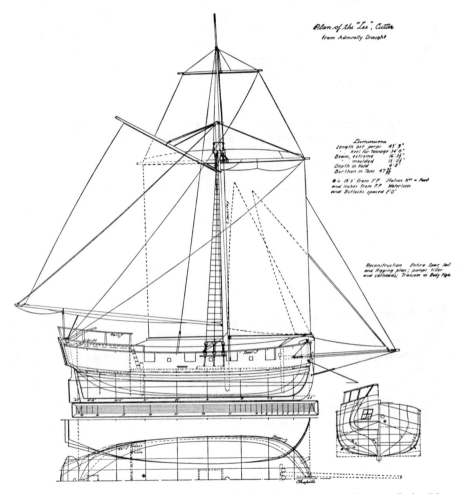

Figure 14. Draught of the cutter LEE, *in the American squadron on Lake Champlain, 1776, from an Admiralty draught made after her capture.*

to prepare plans complete in all details, if indeed any plans were made. One of the gundalows that were sunk in the action with the British has been found and raised by T. F. Hagglund, who has made arrangements for the preservation of this interesting marine relic. The gundalow, which was the *Philadelphia*, was in a remarkable state of preservation. Her drawing, shown in Figure 16,

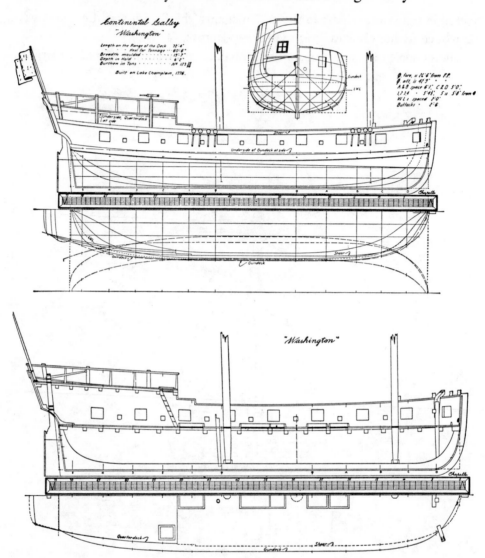

Figure 15. Plans of the galley WASHINGTON *in the American squadron on Lake Champlain, 1776, after an Admiralty draught.*

was made from measurements assembled by Mr. Hagglund, Colonel E. P. Hamilton, and the writer, and is reasonably correct, allowing for the distortion caused by age, long submersion, and perhaps hasty building. The workmanship exhibited in the relic is very good, being obviously that of expert shipwrights. The *Philadelphia* was an open boat measuring 53′ 4″ over the posts,

15' 6" beam, and 3' 10" depth amidships. Arnold's specification for gundalows is shown in the same drawing for comparison; his design was 48' 0" on the keel, 16' 0" beam, and 3' 6" depth. A drawing was made in his specification

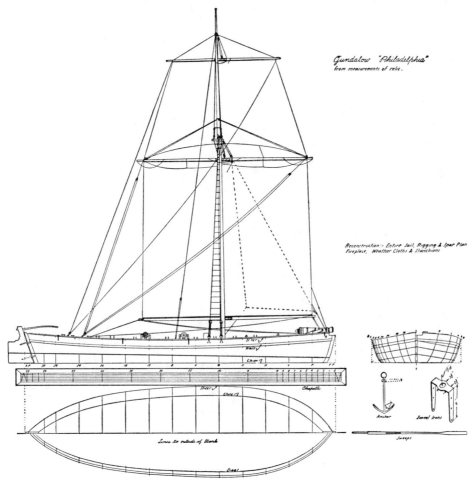

Figure 16a. Plan of the gundalow PHILADELPHIA *as taken off the relic raised from Lake Champlain in 1935, showing her probable appearance in Arnold's action.*

that roughly indicated the general form he proposed, and this is the basis of the reconstruction of his design.

In the *Philadelphia* the bottom was planked fore-and-aft on closely spaced floor timbers, apparently twice as numerous as the side timbers, which seem to be spaced 18" to 20" on centers. Arnold called for the floor timbers to be spaced 18″ on centers. The *Philadelphia* had a heavy keelson, 6″ x 8½″ on the flat, and was entirely flat-bottomed, but Arnold intended the gundalows to have 4″ deadrise and rocker. The *Philadelphia* seems to be spiked throughout, while Arnold expected to "half trunnel and half spike." The decks in the *Philadelphia* seem to have had no crown, though Arnold required 4″; the crown obviously would serve no useful purpose, as no scuppers were cut in the sides of the hull, since the decks or platforms were too close to the load

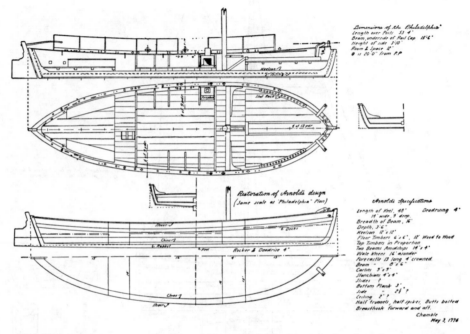

Figure 16b. A restoration of Arnold's original design for the American gundalows on the St. Lawrence and Lake Champlain.

water line. The bow of the *Philadelphia* has been cut down to clear the muzzle of her 12-pdr. bow gun, whose mount must have been lower than intended to require the rail to be lowered in this manner.

The arrangement of the *Philadelphia* shows evidence of hurried building; it is well designed for the purpose intended, however. The hull just abaft the forecastle, and in the way of the mast, has no flooring or deck, the ceiling is exposed, and there is space to store things in the well thus formed and under the forecastle. Abaft the well there is a low deck or platform about 14′ long supported by six 12″ x 12″ beams laid on the ceiling and notched over the keelson. There are five knees on each side, resting on the deck and the beams, and reaching to the rail to stiffen the sides. They also rest on the side timbers and side ceiling. On this deck are two 9-pdrs., one on each side firing over the rail. They are not opposite one another, to give more room around the guns. There was a roughly built fireplace of brick on the port side against the rail and just abaft the mast position. Abaft the gun platform there was another well about 3′ 6″ long in which there was a hatch through the ceiling on each side of the keelson for bailing. Abaft this was the quarterdeck platform for helmsman and officers. Two arms chests were located on this platform.

The rail caps were fitted to take tholes for the sweeps and were capped for swivel pivots. The tholes and pivots were not located alike on port and starboard. As a result, the location of cleats and rail bitts was not the same on both sides of the boat. There were sockets in the rail cap for stanchions to support weather cloths which masked the gun crews from enemy sharpshooters. There were not enough weather cloths available, so in the action of October 11 most of the vessels used boughs of evergreens as a substitute. The probable arrangement of weather cloths is shown in the plan.

The rig shown in Figure 16 is wholly a restoration based on very incomplete sketches made by the British officer, C. Randle, who drew the British squadron. The gundalows carried topsails as shown, but it is not certain whether the topmast was a pole or a separate spar fidded as in a large vessel. There are other sketches of the American squadron besides that of the British officer; one found by Mr. S. H. P. Pell is shown in Plate V. This indicates that the gundalows had the weather cloths always rigged around the stern, perhaps to make them look more impressive than they really were.

The gundalows were ballasted with stones, which were stowed under the quarterdeck platform on the *Philadelphia*. These were to trim the boat by the stern and to counteract the weight of the relatively large gun placed in the eyes of the boat. Trim by the stern undoubtedly helped steering under sail, but a boat like a gundalow could not sail on the wind. The American gundalows of the *Philadelphia*'s type must be considered as being of the galley class—rowing rather than sailing boats. Nevertheless, the addition of an outside keel would have made them capable of sailing on the wind, and it is curious that this appendage was omitted in the *Philadelphia*, for it is to be seen in the *Loyal Convert* and was called for in Arnold's specifications for a gundalow.

The gundalows built for the Champlain squadron were *Philadelphia*, *New York*, *Connecticut*, *Providence*, *Jersey*, *New Haven*, *Spitfire*, and *Boston*.

There was apparently another gundalow, the *Success,* but she was not in the action of October 11 and there is no record of what became of her. Either she was one of the vessels not completed in time to join Arnold, or she was renamed and was one of the vessels of the American squadron.

The schooners of the squadron were rather flat-floored craft with cutwaters and, perhaps, figureheads or other carvings. They carried square topsails on fore and main masts. All had short, high quarterdecks. The *Liberty* seems to have been rigged as a fore-and-aft ketch, almost as though she were a sloop with a mizzen added. In one sketch of her she had a single square yard on the foremast and no square topsails. The *Enterprise* was a sloop having square main course and topsail, and she apparently also had a cutwater. The hull models of these craft undoubtedly were somewhat similar to that of the *Lee* or the galley *Washington.* This assumption is supported by the fact that the British schooners had hull models somewhat like these vessels.

The naval action between the American and British squadrons began on October 11 and continued in a running fight until the 15th, during which period the *Royal Savage, Congress, Philadelphia, Connecticut, Jersey, Providence, Spitfire, New Haven,* and *Boston* were either burned or sunk, and the *Washington* and *Lee* were captured. This action ended the campaign, and it was not until 1777 that the British were able to destroy, capture, or force the Americans to burn the last of the Champlain squadron. The *Gates, Trumbull, Revenge, Liberty, New York,* and, perhaps, the questionable *Success* were thus accounted for, with the British in possession of the whole lake.

The Lake Champlain squadrons are particularly interesting in that the various vessels that composed them were built to suit the requirements of use on the lake. They were designed for shoal water and for rapid construction with very limited facilities. Shoal-draft sailing craft were not well known to either the Americans or the British in this period, so when such vessels were required they were usually small and of the rowing or galley class. The disinclination to employ leeboards in naval craft is not readily explained, for the British at least used them extensively in their river barges. If an outside keel were employed it would increase the draft to an undesirable degree, and the centerboard was as yet unknown. However, one of the British officers on Champlain in 1776, Lieutenant Schank, had begun experiments with the forerunner of the centerboard, the "drop keel," in 1774 at Boston. His experience in the leewardly lake vessels intensified his interest in the problem, and he is said to have proposed some kind of drop keel in the radeau *Thunderer*, but his ideas were not adopted. It was not until he was a captain and about twenty years had passed since his service on Champlain that he was able to get the British Admiralty to adopt his scheme in shoal-draft naval vessels.

The armament of the American squadron on Lake Champlain was composed of guns obtained from Fort Ticonderoga and other captured posts, along with some that were brought from the coasts. It appears from what has been found that British field guns, as well as naval cannon, were used. There were also some old French guns that were serviceable. The *Washington* had four different calibers of cannon: 2 18-pdrs., 2 12-pdrs., 2 9-pdrs., and 4 4-pdrs. in her broadside, with the addition of 1 2-pdr. gun and 8 swivels on her quarterdeck. Some of the galleys had 1 18-pdr., 1 12-pdr., 2 9-pdrs., and 6 6-pdrs. in addition to from 6 to 8 swivels. Only the gundalows had what might be termed a standard armament: 1 12-pdr. in the bows and 2 9's amidships. Small arms consisted of muskets and a few Pennsylvania-type rifles.

The American vessels appear to have been painted red, or barn color, if the existing sketches are trustworthy. Some of the gundalows were unpainted, however, as paint did not arrive in time and the boats were required at once. It is probable that the bottoms of some, at least, were tarred. Owing to the haste with which the boats were built and the variety of sources from which materials were obtained, it can be assumed that the vessels were not standardized in any respect. For example, on the evidence of the *Philadelphia* and the Admiralty sketches of captured craft some of the vessels had chain plates and deadeyes, some had metal chain plates but no deadeyes, and some had deadeyes without any metal chain plates.

Little is known about the qualities of the American vessels on Champlain, as practically nothing is said in any of the reports, British or American. With their relatively powerful rig, the gundalows were very fast off the wind but could not work to windward. The galleys and the *Lee* were more weatherly than some of the schooners; the *Royal Savage* in particular is said to have been a very poor sailer. The vessels in both squadrons were primarily gun carriers, with ability to row and to work in the comparatively confined areas of the lake, with very little attention given to weatherliness. The prevailing winds and the shape of the lake were deemed to make sailing to windward impractical in the shallow hulls permitted there. The *Thunderer* could not work to windward any better than the American gundalows, and the British ship

Inflexible does not appear to have been much better. The British schooners and the large gundalow *Loyal Convert* were the most useful of the British ships.

The gradual tapering off of hostilities after the fall of Yorktown made it unnecessary to attempt to obtain more vessels. When the war ended, the Continental Navy was disbanded and the few remaining ships were sold to private owners. In spite of the numerous weaknesses that developed from excessive political interference in building, fitting, and manning the ships, as well as the dictation of tactics by congressional delegates, the Continental Navy was able to produce excellent ships and a few very competent fighting officers. While successes against the ships of the Royal Navy had not been numerous, the Americans had done great damage to the British merchant marine by means of their Continental naval force, aided by numerous privateers. The control of naval affairs by committees and boards had shown inherent weakness, and it had become apparent that a single individual supported by a bureau or staff would be required to administer a national fleet. The Continental Congress did not develop the latter organization, but toward the end of the war it did establish a single authority in the "Agent of Marine."

As we have seen, the designing of American ships had not been confined to a government agency during the Revolution, in spite of the efforts of the Marine Committee. Excellent though the designs approved by the Marine Committee had been, circumstances had permitted the builders of many of the naval ships to produce designs of their own; and some of the ships—the *Hancock*, for example—had been superior vessels. Perhaps this was one of the reasons that led to the pre-eminence of the Americans as frigate designers in the years that followed the Revolution.

★ ★ ★ ★ ★ ★ ★ ★ ★ ★

CHAPTER THREE

The Federal Navy
1785-1801

WHEN THE Revolution ended, the Continental Congress could no longer maintain the Navy. Its personnel was dismissed and the few ships remaining were sold. The Army was also disbanded; the veteran regiments of the Continental Line were mustered out. These acts of the Congress were forced upon it by a variety of causes: lack of funds, the war-weariness of the public, and a fear that the troops and the naval personnel might attempt to seize control of the infant nation. The chief cause, however, was that the Congress lacked the power to raise funds and did not have the confidence of the individual state governments. The year 1786 found the country without a national force of any kind and defended only by local militia companies. There was no national currency, and violent internal jealousies were disturbing the trade relations among the states. The new nation was not respected abroad and was subject to outrages and acts of aggression by even the most backward and weak of foreign powers.

In spite of the handicap of internal troubles and a lack of currency and banking facilities, the Americans built up a large merchant marine as soon as the Revolution was over. Their ships appeared in the Mediterranean, the North Sea, the Baltic, and even the Pacific, seeking trade. Laden with raw materials and such goods of American manufacture as were available, the American vessels carried on a barter trade to obtain the articles needed at home. The Americans rapidly became serious competitors of the European merchants. These merchants, and their governments, began to take steps intended to hamper the American activities—which usually took the form of instigating the cruisers of some warring nation to seize and condemn American ships and cargoes on any flimsy excuse that could be devised.

The most useful tools for such purposes were the infamous Barbary corsairs of the Mohammedan regencies of Algiers, Tripoli, Tunis, and Morocco—Algiers being the most important. Long supported by the European maritime powers, these sea-rovers had looted without real hindrance for generations. They were small, weak nations—mere ports, in fact—ruled by adventurers whose tenure of power, and whose personal safety as well, was of short duration and generally uncertain. Hence negotiations with these rulers were very unsatisfactory, for the agreements stood only so long as the existing ruler remained on the throne. Not only were these Barbary rulers subject to violence from rivals; they were also the vassals of the Turks and were usually influenced by the turbulent political conditions in Constantinople. Being adventurers and seeking wealth and power, the Beys were readily controlled by foreign plotters, who used the corsairs to prey upon the shipping of enemies or competitors even when nominally at peace with such nations. This useful method of curbing the sea-borne trade of competing nations in the Mediterranean, and even out into the Atlantic, appealed to the maritime powers, and through treaties and subsidies they had preserved the corsairs from the destruction that would normally have been the lot of a group of pirates, and enabled them to maintain rather powerful fleets of cruisers whose only business was to prey upon helpless merchantmen.

With the appearance of American competition in the Mediterranean, the Barbary corsairs were encouraged to seize American ships, cargoes, and men. It had long been their practice to enslave all captives taken in their attacks on shipping, and it was their custom to release these captives only upon payment of ransom. By treating the captives cruelly it was possible to increase the willingness of the victim nation to pay large sums and pay them promptly. The Bey of Algiers took particular interest in the newcomers and was active in seizing American shipping as soon as it lost the protection of the British flag.

At the end of the Revolution the Continental Congress attempted to establish friendly relations with the Barbary corsairs and sent diplomatic missions to each. These were only partially successful; with each change in the occupant of the throne the Americans found themselves virtually at war with one or another of these troublesome powers. The loss of American shipping and the enslave-

ment of American seamen caused public indignation to mount. This in turn
became the motive for establishing the American Navy once the country had
a national government.

Until such a government was established there was no possibility of a
national navy, in spite of the need made apparent by the activities of the
Mediterranean powers. When the federal government came into existence, in
1789, the problem of the corsairs was immediately a matter of its concern. It
was widely recognized that the only practical way to deal with these pirates
was to employ force, but the country had many internal difficulties to settle
before reaching conclusions on its foreign problems. Economics was, of course,
the most pressing matter, and the establishment of federal taxation was necessary before anything could be done about a national force to protect American
interests abroad. When the new government had solved the most immediate
of the problems of internal affairs—or, at least, had settled on a workable procedure for handling matters—it could give attention to the needs of American
sea-borne trade.

Public opinion gradually brought the subject of an American naval force to
the top of the list of federal government projects. The matter was under consideration as early as 1791, and a congressional committee began investigating
the means to be employed in setting up such a force. In this investigation Congress utilized the aid of the Executive Branch, which had been established with a
War Office and secretariat, though no provision had been made for the equivalent Admiralty, or Navy, Office. President Washington therefore placed the
naval matter in the hands of the Secretary of War, General Henry Knox, who
had been a bookseller and a Revolutionary War army officer but had had no
experience in naval or maritime affairs. Like so many officeholders since, when
faced with responsibility for some problem which they are personally unequipped to solve, he was forced to depend upon the advice of friends and
chance acquaintances. Knox turned, naturally, to men who had been naval
officers either in the Continental or state navies during the Revolution. He was
in the position of a non-musician who was required to buy a piano; it seemed
to him that the advice of men who could play the instrument would be the
most necessary aid to correct choice.

With Congress demanding detailed estimates, his problem required extensive examination of the requirements in ships, armament, and personnel. These
were to be based on what was needed to meet the specific problem of the corsair
fleet—which, of course, varied as one or the other of the Barbary Beys agreed

to ransom or tribute or declared for peace. Under conditions such as these it was not strange that he became involved, during a period of about two years, in the highly technical problems of the exact dimensions of the ships considered best suited for a given gun power at the time.

Among his advisers were some officers who were acquainted with the *Confederacy*, the *Alliance*, and the French-designed *South Carolina*. There is no doubt that Knox heard much about these ships, particularly the last two, and their performance as compared with the smaller frigates built for the Continental and state navies. Though no detailed record has been found of the conferences held by Knox, the surviving papers and private correspondence show the general trend of thought that developed. It was felt that many of the Continental frigates were too small and too weak. Since the new ships would have to be few in number, it was considered vital that they be as powerful as possible, so that one would be a match for any vessel the corsairs were known to possess—and they were known to have ships carrying up to 44 guns, in service and building. Hence it can be seen why all estimates prepared by Knox for Congress contained references to 44-gun ships as the upward limit of power necessary; the lower limit fluctuated as the economic and diplomatic considerations of the moment indicated. In each estimate, the rates of the proposed vessels having been fixed, it became necessary to decide the probable dimensions of the ships in order to arrive at any reasonable idea of the cost involved. The ratings of the ships were a factor in the estimates for the number of men required to man the fleet. Since the estimates refer to ships between 24 and 44 guns, it is plain that Knox and his advisers had been forced to set up detailed dimensions and costs for all the rates within these limits. As a result, the War Office and Congress seem to have arrived at an agreement on the general dimensions of the ships long before the actual designs were ordered.

Knox's advisers cannot yet be wholly identified, though John Wharton was certainly very influential, as was also a Boston seaman named John Foster Williams. Captain John Barry, too, was relied upon by Knox for marine advice. It has not yet been discovered that any shipwright other than Wharton was consulted, though it is highly probable that Humphreys and others in the vicinity of Philadelphia were questioned informally. The national government was located in Philadelphia at this period, and local men were readily available for consultation. As a result, the influence of the Philadelphians was soon marked in all aspects of the federal Navy.

The Dey of Algiers proved extremely troublesome, and finally on March 27,

1794, Congress passed an act authorizing the construction of six frigates and their equipping and manning. This act founded the Navy of the United States. However, the act was not unconditional, for the ninth section permitted the stoppage of work authorized by the act if Algiers became peacefully inclined. Pains were taken to limit the new naval force so as to prevent the rise of a military or naval interest, which, at the time, was one of the fears of the American political leaders. It was intended that the new naval organization would be one of the responsibilities of the established War Office; the present idea of a consolidated armed-service administration is by no means an innovation in American theory of government organization.

The new act provided for three frigates to carry 44 guns and three to carry 36 guns, and Knox found himself with the responsibility of getting the ships designed, built, and manned. His first step was to procure the services of a shipbuilder and designer. He had become acquainted with the Philadelphia shipbuilder Joshua Humphreys through John Wharton, and he now hired Humphreys to prepare designs for the two classes of frigates. Humphreys apparently did not come into the picture until late in 1793, and by this time the size of the new ships had obviously been settled upon by the conferees at the War Office, as is evident from the various departmental estimates.

We have already examined the problem of Joshua Humphreys' part in the design of the Continental frigates and discussed his early career. Between the Revolution and 1794 Humphreys had become an established shipbuilder in Philadelphia. It is a matter of conjecture and opinion whether or not he can be said to have been a leading Philadelphia shipbuilder even in this period. His contemporaries did not refer to him in this manner, but Humphreys was at least fairly prominent in his community. It has been the fashion in more recent times to say that Humphreys was the leading shipbuilder of the time and that for this reason he was chosen to design the new ships. There is, of course, no real truth in this. He was chosen because he was a shipbuilder and had been available for consultation and also because he had shown great interest in the subject. He had, in addition, the support of his influential cousin, Wharton. His employment by the government was no more proof of prominence or unusual ability in 1794 than government employment today is certain evidence of prominence and extreme competence in a profession. It is evident that the same procedure was followed in selecting Humphreys and his associates that has so often been followed in solving the technical problems of a national government. First, the persons immediately responsible for the solution have neither experience in the particular field nor personal knowledge of the individuals who may be capable of the work; they are wholly dependent on chance and the helpful advice of friends, relatives, and acquaintances for recommendations as to who should be selected for the practical responsibilities. Next, after receiving such "competent" advice, the officeholder makes his appointment, but usually with strings attached; he appoints "assistants" whose advice has equal weight with that of the first appointee. Invariably the solution of the problems encompassed in the original responsibility becomes a matter of conflicting opinions by appointees and finally ends up as an administrative compromise or a group recommendation. This is exactly what finally happened in the design of the frigates. It is a conclusive answer to any claim that Humphreys was appointed because he was such an authority on ship design that his services were indispensable. The appointment had obviously been made simply because Humphreys had been available and was sufficiently interested to work for a time without certain compensation; he also had been recommended by one of Knox's advisers, Wharton. Being a resident of the then capital, Philadelphia, his advice could be obtained without delay, which was an added advantage.

Though Joshua Humphreys was appointed to design the vessel on June 28, 1794, his compensation was to begin May 1. This date did not, however, represent the beginning of his work on the design of the ships. He had apparently made a half-model to the dimensions given him by Knox sometime prior to April, 1794—147′ keel, 43′ beam, 14′ hold, 6′ between decks, 7′ waist, 30 guns on the main deck. This model he had submitted to the War Office as his design proposal. It is probable that his compensation was arranged to reimburse him for the time he had spent on the model earlier. There is no evidence yet available that Humphreys made a plan, as well as a model, at this stage in the proceedings.

In appointing Humphreys, Knox did not indicate that he was to be considered the chief or principal constructor, even though, as will be seen, it was soon considered necessary to furnish Humphreys with an "assistant," in the classic government manner. The reason why an assistant should be deemed necessary is not clear; perhaps it was soon found that Humphreys was overloaded with work, or it may have been apparent that he was not too well equipped professionally to supervise or plan work to be done at a distance.

Late in the fall of 1793 a young English shipbuilder named Josiah Fox came to the United States. He was then thirty years old, having been born in Falmouth, England, October 9, 1763. He was the seventh child of a wealthy Quaker, and his family had connections, relatives, and friends in Philadelphia.

His oldest brother, Charles, was a miniaturist and the son-in-law of an admiral of the British Navy. Through this particular connection Josiah Fox had been apprenticed to the master shipwright at Plymouth Dockyard. The apprenticeship had been completed October 9, 1786, and being independent of his salary as a shipwright, Fox had spent the intervening years in study at various dockyards and in voyages to study the action of ships of various models at sea. He also visited a number of foreign yards on the Continent, including the famous Arsenal at Venice. He had come to America to study timber and to visit his relatives and family friends, among whom was his cousin Andrew Ellicott, the then Surveyor General. Ellicott took him to members of the Administration, and he was examined by Knox and Captain John Barry. The latter appears to have been a family friend of Fox. As a result of the examination and recommendations, Fox was offered an opportunity to help in the design of the new frigates. While the appointment was still pending, Fox seems to have prepared, with some official sanction, a proposed design for a 44-gun frigate. That some sanction was given is evident from the fact that Knox accepted the plan when it was completed. There being no opening at the moment as a naval constructor, it was agreed that Fox should be temporarily appointed a clerk in the War Office. This does not appear to have been a menial position, for correspondence indicates that the "clerks" were really administrative assistants to the Secretary of War and each had a secretary or clerk of his own. In addition to the administrative duties, Fox was required to help with the design of the new vessels.

While this particular appointment was pending, Fox completed his design and, early in the spring of 1794, turned it over to Knox. The latter had Humphreys' model and, noting the differences in the two designs, turned both over to Humphreys' old partner, John Wharton, for his and others' comments. Humphreys, in the meantime, had shown Fox his model and had asked Fox to make comments and send them to the War Office. It seems obvious that Humphreys and Fox were then on excellent terms and that Humphreys had a high regard for Fox's education and ability.

Humphreys' model was destroyed when the Washington Navy Yard was burned in the War of 1812, so its lines do not exist. However, it is apparent from Fox's comments that the model was not on the lines of the vessels as built. One of Fox's objections to the model was the slight rake of the stem; he also objected to "any hollows in the Body; by no means to have any hollow in either her Waterlines or Timbers in the Fore Body." He objected, too, to the position of the wales (the thick belt of timber along the sides at and above the

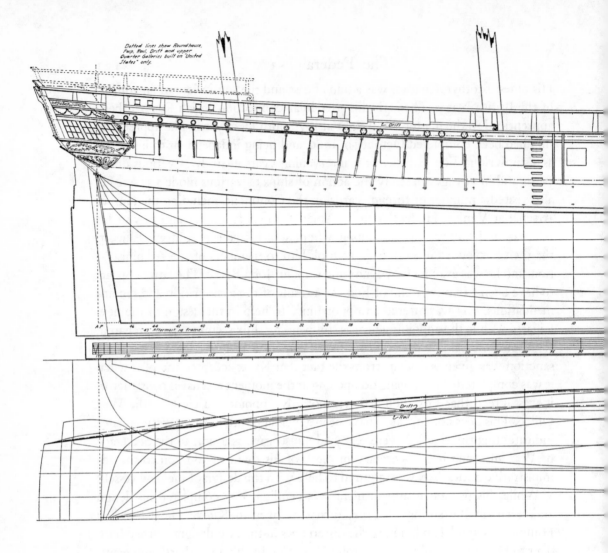

Dotted lines show Roundhouse,
Poop. Rail. Drift and upper
Quarter Galleries built on United
States' only.

L. Drift

AP   46   44   42   40   38   36   34   32   30   28   26   24   22   20   18   16   14   12   10
            "43" Aftermost sq frame

175 170 165 160 155 150 145 140 135 130 125 120 115 110 105 100 95   90

Drift
L. Rail

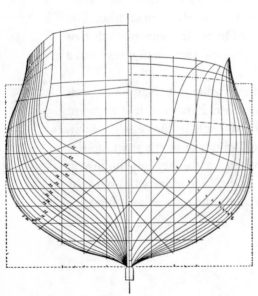

Particular Dimensions
○ is 70'9" from F.P.; 104'5' from A.P.
�○ is 3'.3'   "   "
"42 is 14'4' from A.P.
"X is 16'9'   F.P.
Room & Space 26"
Lowest waterline 4'6" above Base :- others spaced 3'0"
Buttocks spaced 4'0"

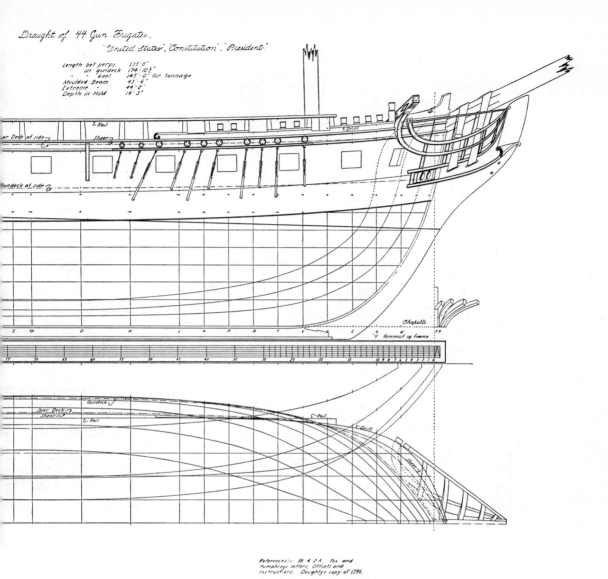

Plan 7. *Building draught for the 44-gun frigates* CONSTITUTION, UNITED STATES, *and* PRESIDENT.

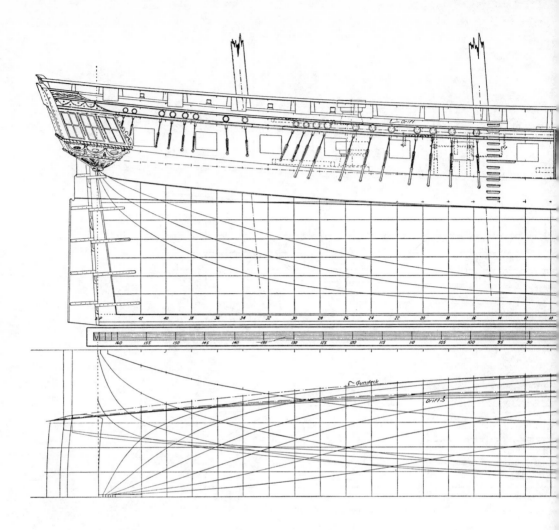

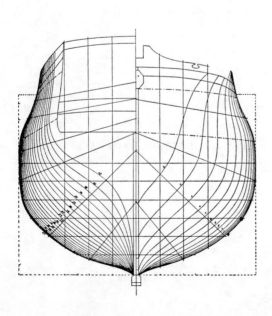

Particular Dimensions
a is 65'·11" from F.P.   b is 5'·1⅞" from F.P.
a " 97'·4 "   " A.P.   42 " 7'·3¾" " A.P.
2 " 3'·2½" "   O
Room & Space   26½"
Tumble Home   3'·0"
Lowest waterline 3'·3" above Base ; others spaced 3'·0"
Buttocks spaced 4'·0"

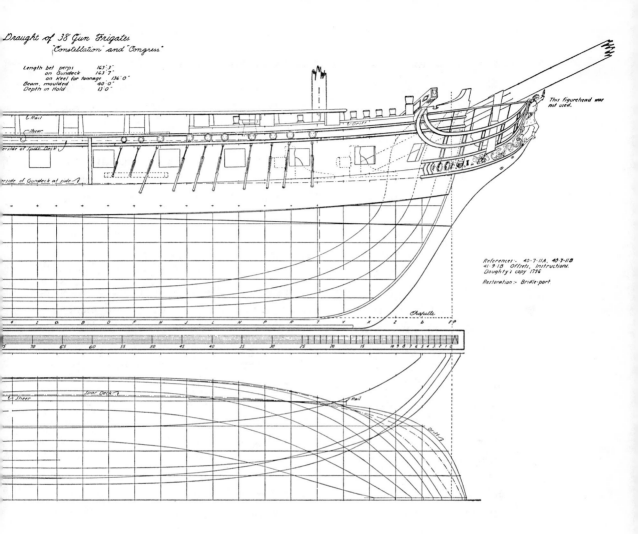

Plan 8. Building draught for the 38-gun frigates CON-
STELLATION *and* CONGRESS.

water line) and apparently thought the midsection was placed too far aft. In general, his strongest criticisms were directed to the size of the ships; he thought them so large as to be unwieldy and cumbersome. It is probable that Humphreys had an equal opportunity to comment on Fox's proposal, though his criticisms have not been found, if indeed they were ever committed to writing. It appears that Wharton and others made recommendations that were, in effect, a compromise between the two proposals. These have not turned up, but it is apparent from the correspondence that followed, and the redrawing of plans of the 44-gun ships, that a new basic design was to be prepared incorporating modifications of Fox's and Humphreys' proposals. It is obvious, of course, that the part played by these advisers in the proceedings answers any claim that Humphreys (or Fox either, for that matter) was so prominent that his opinions were authoritative and final. It is seen that Knox was not content with the judgment of either of his technical aides; he wanted a "majority vote" and called in other experts, among them Wharton, to obtain this. It is a curious condition of the historical records that Wharton, who seems to have established such a reputation as a shipbuilding expert, cannot yet be shown to have designed ships; however, it is apparent that he was considered highly competent. At the present time, about all that is known about his shipbuilding career is that he owned the shipyard and was associated with Humphreys in building the *Randolph* during the Revolution.

There is a good deal of mystery concerning the next step. Fox was to have worked as Humphreys' assistant in preparing the draughts and in the mould-loft work that would follow the preparation of the plans. It has never been established that Humphreys prepared the revised draughts (which were the basic designs, or "master draughts"), for the plans that Fox and Doughty made are the only surviving *building* plans of the two classes of ships. Perhaps it should be emphasized that Fox was far better trained than Humphreys in all respects, and was a far superior draftsman. From this it might be inferred that Fox now prepared the design of the 44-gun ships under Humphreys' verbal directions. The surviving correspondence offers conflicting evidence, for Humphreys is found writing letters to Fox, as though he were at a distance, requesting him to hasten the completion of the plans or draughts, which implies that they were not in the close personal contact required for directed designing. It is odd that in making claims that Humphreys was the responsible designer of the two classes of frigates his supporters have never attempted to produce the basic or "master" draught. If such a plan existed it seems reasonable that it would survive, for the naval plan files were, throughout the greater part of the sailing-ship period after the War of 1812, in the hands or under the supervision of Humphreys' son, Chief Constructor Samuel Humphreys. The latter would certainly have been careful to preserve as much of the evidence to support the claim that his father designed these frigates as he could produce, for in his time the controversy as to who was responsible for the design of the frigates had already started and was being given much public attention.

A careful search of the existing plan files in the National Archives has produced one plan that the writer believes to be Humphreys' "master draught" of the 44-gun frigates—the original drawing of their design, as built, and the only drawing that would support any claim that he prepared a basic design for any of the frigates. Plate VI is a photograph of the original draught in question. It will be seen that the draught is unsigned, but the claim that it is Humphreys' work is supported by a comparison of it with a draught that is known to have been made by him. This is his master plan for the proposed 74-gun ships of 1799, which is signed by him and also vouched for in competent contemporary documents still in existence; it is now in the National Archives (40–15–6 I). From this it is possible to identify Humphreys' draftsmanship with reasonable certainty. A careful comparison of the original draught of the 74-gun ship with that of the 44-gun ship shown in Plate VI shows that the workmanship appears to be the same. This is probably the strongest evidence that the plan of the 44 was the work of Humphreys.

The next step necessary is to attempt to establish that the plan was made after the initial designs were completed and therefore after the Wharton recommendations were made. Here the evidence is circumstantial and the supporting arguments become somewhat involved.

The drawing is identified by the name *Terrible* in an oval enclosure above the sheer elevation. This was one of the names for the 44's suggested by Humphreys prior to their building. Though one name he proposed, *Revolution*, was for a time under consideration, none of the names were finally adopted. The name on the plan not only gives some support to the idea that it was Humphreys' work, but it also indicates strongly that the plan was made before the building draughts were prepared by Fox and Doughty; for by the time these plans were made Humphreys' names had been rejected. A more substantial argument, however, rests upon the circumstances surrounding the preparation of the building plans of the ships and the method of their construction.

There is no logical reason for the existence of any plan of the ships in

Humphreys' hand, unless the plan is the basic design. In support of this statement it is argued that the records show that the building plans (and the offsets
made from them) were prepared by Fox and Doughty, and that the lofting
done in Philadelphia by these two men produced the moulds for all but one of
the ships completed under the authorization of the Act of 1794. Humphreys
was master builder of the 44-gun ship built at Philadelphia. He used the set of
moulds and patterns prepared from the basic mould-loft drawings, which du-
plicated those sent out to the other yards building the same class of ship. Hence
the fact that Humphreys built a ship was no reason for him to make a plan, after
the Fox and Doughty drawings were made, since a plan was not required for
any loft work in building his frigate. Furthermore, his poor draftsmanship and
his very apparent distaste for drawing plans make it reasonably certain that he
would not draw a plan of the ship for his own amusement. Since it is reasonable
to believe that he did not prepare the plan shown in Plate VI during or after
the construction of the Philadelphia 44, it can only be assumed that the plan
was made prior to the lofting of the ship. Now certainly he was not required
to prepare a draught, in competition with Fox and Doughty, for building.
Hence it appears reasonable that the plan must have been made sometime prior
to the starting of the building plans. The draught in question does not contain
the important features that Fox specifically objected to in Humphreys' original
model, but in fact does agree in these matters with the final building drawings
for the 44's, so it must have been made after the Wharton recommendations.
Thus, by a proceess of elimination, the conclusion is presented that the draught
was drawn as the "master draught" for the 44-gun ships and was the basis for the
final designs, prepared by Fox and Doughty, that were used for building the
ships.

    In attempting to show that Humphreys made the master draught, no claim
is made that he was, in a strict sense, the sole designer. It has been shown that
the size of the ships seems to have been established by the War Office in conjunction with congressional committees between 1792 and 1794. It is also quite
apparent that the model of the ships had been subject to much discussion. There
is evidence that Humphreys' original conception was altered by Knox as a
result of Fox's criticisms of Humphreys' model. By the same token Fox's
original plan was also rejected, and hence his part in the design was largely that
of a consultant. In short, the designs were what might be considered typical
of a government agency's solution of a technical problem of design: the plans
incorporated the ideas of everyone available but were the sole technical re-

sponsibility of no one person. It is mere speculation to attempt to judge which of the men who worked on the plans actually contributed the most. Both Fox and Humphreys naturally claimed credit, and this led to acrimonious debate which in turn clouded the issue by conflicting statements. Doughty seems to have shifted from first supporting Fox's claims to supporting Humphreys'. Were the papers of either Fox or Humphreys taken alone, it would be easy to conclude that the man whose papers were chosen was the designer; the papers of both, taken together, lead to confusion and a qualified conclusion. For example, the men do not agree as to who made the final draught of the *Constellation;* Fox in one statement says he made it but in another seems to give the credit to Doughty. Humphreys seems to have been under the impression that Fox was making the draught. The facts of the matter cannot be stated with certainty; probably Fox was supervising Doughty in the preparation of the plan. It appears that the men were working very hurriedly in an effort to complete the drawings in time to meet the needs of the various builders. In any case, the existing evidence is that the designs were the sole work of none but were, as has been said, the joint effort of Knox's advisers and the men who made plans or models—Fox, Humphreys, and Doughty.

Both Fox and Humphreys were supposedly members of the Quaker sect; both were subjects of action to expel them from their church as a result of the designing of war vessels. Neither seems to have been permanently separated from the sect, however. Humphreys is believed to have been reinstated, while Fox refused to accept the action of a Philadelphia group on the grounds that they had no jurisdiction over him since he was not a member of that particular group. No reason exists in this matter that would impeach the truthfulness of either. Since both claim credit for the designs of the frigates, the matter must remain for the present, at least, a matter of individual opinion as to which played the more important part. It is quite obvious that contemporary officials were not certain where credit should rest. This is shown by references to Fox and Humphreys in official correspondence and also by the expressions of appreciation and administrative recognition that were given to Humphreys and Fox in letters addressed to them in the same terms of commendation. Perhaps it would be proper, however, to look upon these as administrative acts rather than as technical evidence.

Though Humphreys was undoubtedly the principal constructor at the beginning, it was not long before Fox's superior training evidently permitted him to achieve ascendancy in technical matters. He seems to have introduced to

America the practice of complete lofting of the ship's stern and to have been the first to prepare a complete set of patterns or moulds for this portion of the hull. It is possible that he was also responsible for the introduction of buttock-and-bow lines (vertical planes parallel to the longitudinal center line of the hull) projected in the various elevations contained in the draughts, which appear in American naval ship plans, apparently for the first time, in this period. The trend of events gave Josiah Fox a great opportunity to become prominent in naval construction in the United States, and he eventually had great influence on the design of American men-of-war.

In the past it was the fashion to assume that the Americans copied the French in the design of their fast-sailing vessels. This has already been referred to, in regard to Revolutionary War ships, and the existence of a huge number of ship plans of the sailing-ship period now permits comparisons to be made that completely disprove any claim of French influence. Of course the Americans of the period now under discussion were acquainted with the hull forms used by the French and probably experimented with them, as they did with many other foreign ideas in shipbuilding. A comparison of the surviving plans of the American vessels of the period of 1785–1801 with those of contemporary foreign frigates shows very plainly that the American builders followed British hull models rather than French; only in the proportion of dimensions to gun power was there a similarity to the latter. It can be readily understood why this would be the case, for in the early ships there is reason to suppose that there had been a background of British Admiralty trained men and, in the later period, the Admiralty-trained Fox prepared the building plans of the 44's and of many other ships. He also supervised Doughty in the preparation of the plans of the 36's. His comments on the original Humphreys model of the 44's also had some influence, apparently, on the "master draught" for the 44's. In addition, a few of the War Office advisers had been in the Royal Navy and were acquainted with the British types of men-of-war; such men would naturally prefer similar vessels.

The third person connected with the design of these first frigates, William Doughty, has been mentioned. Little is known about his early years; he was a Philadelphian, and when Fox appeared he was the yard clerk in Humphreys' yard. Doughty was a trained shipwright and draftsman, according to Fox. His position in Humphreys' yard appears to have approximated that of a modern office manager. He was made available to Fox as an assistant and helped draw up the building plans and loft the ships. He is said by Fox to have drawn the building plans for the 36-gun frigates and to have made the necessary copies of these plans, and of the 44's drawn by Fox, to supply the builders. He was eventually to play a very important part in American naval construction, though at the time he first appeared in the work he was by no means a prominent professional. He was a far better draftsman than either Joshua or Samuel Humphreys but not as good as Fox, judging by surviving plans. He proved to be a very capable designer of ships and must have been well trained.

The final drawings of the two classes of frigates represented the joint ideas of many individuals, and as a result the designs combined elements of success and of failure. The ships were very large for their rates; the 44-gun ships were 175' 0" between perpendiculars, 174' 10½" on the gun deck, 43' 6" beam, 44' 2" extreme beam exclusive of wales, and 14' 3" depth of hold. They were 145' 0" on the keel for tonnage, or about 146' 0" straight rabbet. These dimensions were huge for a frigate at the time the ships were designed. These ships were actually 20 feet longer than the improved British 44-gun frigates laid down in 1797, and were also 2 to 3 feet wider. The contemporary French 40-gun frigates were 13 feet shorter and about a foot narrower than the American 44's. The latter had an innovation, also, that increased their power as frigates immeasurably. This was the use of what was practically a flush spar (or upper) deck, above the main deck. Frigates of the Revolution had detached quarter and forecastle decks, only the quarterdeck being armed. As the war drew to a close, foreign frigates were built with guns on the forecastle and light gangways, or bridges, along the sides of the ship, connecting the quarterdeck and forecastle. These gangways were narrow and were for convenience in getting fore and aft on the ships. There were no bulwarks along the gangways; a light rail and netting gave some security and masked the crew from sharpshooters to a limited extent. In the American 44's, the gangways were strengthened and widened to such a degree that the upper deck was practically unbroken, the survival of the open waist amidships being indicated only by a very long and rather narrow hatchway. In addition, the American ships were originally given rather substantial open rails on this deck, running flush and unbroken from the stern to abreast of the foremast. This rail was supported by heavy stanchions which also were arranged to form frames of gun ports. The rail was at first fitted with nettings and waist cloths, but later the rails along the forecastle and quarterdeck were planked up between the gun ports; those amidships were fitted to stow hammocks to form a breastwork proof against small-arms fire in action.

The model of the ships can best be described by plans. Plan 7 shows the final design of the 44's. For their type and period, the American 44's were considered unusually sharp. Compared with the noted California and China clipper ships of the 1850's, the frigates are full-ended indeed; but compared with the down-easters, which were built after the American Civil War, the frigates are at least equally sharp. It must not be supposed that these frigates were ever intended to be extraordinarily sharp; they were an attempt to combine capacity and displacement with fast lines. In this they were very successful. The design of these ships, so far as general arrangement and dimensions were concerned, influenced American frigates to the end of the sailing-ship period.

The design of the 36-gun frigates is shown in Plan 8. No master draught for this class has been found, and it is very probable that none was made prior to the building plan. The reason for this seems plain, for the lines of the 36-gun frigates are practically reduced copies of the 44's. Hence it is probable that Doughty or Fox worked from the plan of the 44's by changing the scale, and that the variations in the rake of the ends of the ships and in other details were the result of compromising the scale conversion, to suit the fixed requirements of space and headroom. The general design for the 36's was similar to that of the 44's, except for the dimensions and the number of gun ports on each deck. The 36's measured 163' 3" between perpendiculars, or 163' 7" from stem rabbet to after face of sternpost on the gun deck. The beam was 40' 0" moulded and 40' 6" over the plank, exclusive of the thick wales. The depth of hold was 13' 0", and the height between decks was 6' 9" on the gun deck and 6' on the berth deck. As in the case of the 44's, the 36's were far larger than ships of similar rates abroad; in fact, the American 36's were so large that they were re-rated as 38's while still under construction.

The plans of all the ships, and the final loft work, were completed in 1795–96, by which time arrangements had been made for building all of the vessels. It had been intended to build the three 44's at Philadelphia, New York, and Boston, and the three 36's at Portsmouth, New Hampshire, Baltimore, Maryland, and Norfolk (or Gosport), Virginia. It was also decided that the vessels were not to be built by contract; rather, yards were to be leased or purchased and the ships built under the supervision of their captains and government-employed naval constructors. The 44 to be built in Philadelphia was set up in Humphreys' yard, and he was retained as naval constructor. A yard was leased in New York, and the well-known New York shipbuilder Forman Cheeseman was appointed naval constructor. At Boston, space in the Hartt shipyard was leased and one of the three Hartt brothers, Edmund, was retained as yard foreman, but the naval constructor was a Col. George Claghorne or Claighorne. The arrangements for the 36's were somewhat similar: the Hackett yard at Portsmouth was taken over, and Col. James Hackett was made the naval constructor. At Baltimore, David Stodder was made the naval constructor, and at Gosport a Mr. Morgan was appointed to the post.

The number of each class of frigate to be built seems to have been subject to much uncertainty. The 36-gun frigate to be built at Gosport was often referred to as a 44, and even the Secretary of the Navy at a later date appears to have been uncertain of her rate and class. This was probably due to the fact that she was much delayed in getting started; Morgan was eventually sent to Georgia to supervise the cutting of timber. This delay and the lack of materials seem to have permitted a reconsideration of the size of the ship. In 1795 Fox was appointed an "assistant naval constructor," with an increase in salary, and was sent to take Morgan's place. He is known to have been one of the most active objectors to the idea of very large frigates, and it is possible that his objections, supported by some naval officers, led to the construction of a smaller ship than originally intended. It is also possible that a shortage of materials may have been a contributing factor; the supply of live oak proved to be disappointing. However, the rerating of all the smaller frigates built in this period makes the original rate of academic interest only.

The construction of the ships did not proceed very smoothly; many delays were caused by lack of materials, or by changes in specifications brought about as a result of such conditions. Then, in 1795, peace with Algiers was declared and all work was stopped until Congress passed a supplementary act which permitted the completion of the three most advanced ships—the 44's at Boston and Philadelphia and the 38 at Baltimore. The frigates building at New York, Portsmouth, and Gosport were left unfinished and the yards closed down. After a good deal of discussion over the names of the ships, it was decided that the frigate building at Philadelphia would be named the *United States,* the one at Boston the *Constitution,* the one at New York the *President,* the one at Portsmouth the *Congress,* and the one at Baltimore the *Constellation.* The frigate intended to be built at Gosport having been much delayed, no attempt was made to select a name for her when the others were assigned. This led to some confusion, but she was eventually named the *Chesapeake.*

The first ship to be launched was the *United States,* at Philadelphia, May 10, 1797. The launching ways were apparently very steep, for she went off too fast and was damaged. The *Constitution* was launched October 21, 1797, after two unsuccessful attempts brought about by insufficient inclination of the launching ways. The *Constellation* had been launched the month before, September 7, without untoward incidents.

These first ships were rather ornately carved, though little is known about the details of each vessel. The descriptions are largely allegorical and extremely florid, so that little can be judged from them. The *United States* had a figurehead representing the Goddess of Liberty, the *Constitution* a Hercules with club raised to strike, and the *Constellation* a female head representing Nature. The carvings were expensive to maintain and liable to damage, so it is not surprising that they changed rapidly in each ship, gradually becoming more and more simple and light.

The three ships were the subject of some criticism by many of the officers appointed to the new Navy. The great size and draft of the ships caused practical difficulties; many of the ports that had been intended to be used as bases were found too shallow or with too confined an anchorage, and this limited the usefulness of the new ships. One of the frigates, the *Constellation*, while at anchor in the Delaware tailed on to a bank or shoal, and when the tide left her she rolled over, filled, and sank.

The great length of the ships resulted in hogging, for Americans were as yet inexperienced in the construction of vessels of such great size. This, with their deep draft, which not only closed many ports to them but also prevented the use of many repair wharves in the harbors they could use, made repairs expensive. This condition of affairs was undoubtedly influential in the final establishment of navy yards. Another objection to the new ships was that they heeled too much under sail in strong winds, which was thought to be caused by their having too sharp a bottom. The same reason was advanced for the complaint that they lacked stowage space for the provisions and water required by the large crews assigned them. Some of the alleged faults were figments of the captains' imaginations; others were due to poor planning of the establishment rather than to ship design. In fact, the greatest faults of the new ships were not due to any failure of the group who advised Knox, or of the three men who were responsible for the plans of the vessels.

The ships really suffered most in being fitted out, or in finishing, to an extent that the naval constructors could not conceivably have estimated. The *United States*, for example, had a roundhouse added by her captain about as indicated in dotted lines in Plan 7. This added to her displacement and complicated trimming the ship with ballast. Every captain was also permitted to spar and rig the vessel to suit himself and to arm as he saw fit, or at least as available guns permitted. The quantity of ballast and stores placed on board was also a matter of the captain's judgment and opinion, rather than a matter of the constructor's estimates. No records were kept of the changes made in the ships, but it is evident that their appearance must have varied a good deal within the same rate, even if their lines did not. The effects of this condition on the sailing qualities and seaworthiness of the various ships can be imagined.

The relationship between the naval constructors and the ship captains was based upon the earlier idea that the man who played a piano was the best judge of the instrument. Hence the official correspondence, in the period under discussion, is marked by the freedom with which commanders of ships issued orders to the naval constructors and decided how the ships should be armed, fitted, rigged, and even built. From the perspective of the present, some of the American naval officers appear as surprisingly pompous and opinionated amateur ship designers, whose ill-judged decisions spoiled the reputation of many well-modeled ships. Oversparring and overgunning were chargeable to these officers and not to the ship designers.

It can be said, with some truth, that the theory Knox had introduced in selecting his naval advisers—that the best judge of a piano is one who can play the instrument—had now reached a stage where it was accepted that the player was competent to design and build the instrument. As a result, the constructors could produce hulls having all the elements of speed, but the resulting ships could be spoiled by the irresponsible changes of the officers supervising their construction or fitting them out for service. The correspondence of the Secretaries of the Navy in this and the succeeding period is full of complaints and suggestions of officers assigned to various ships. In most cases the officers made costly and unsound proposals for alterations. While no attempt was made to establish the proper relations between the constructors and commissioned officers, the Secretary soon became aware of the propensity of the captains to desire changes, whether necessary or not, and he acted accordingly in many cases—though much damage had been done before he awoke to the situation. The condition described explains why a vessel had a good reputation one year and the next is described as a "slug" or worthless. This makes judgments of the naval vessels at this distance somewhat questionable, if based on archives alone. In justice to the American Navy of the period it ought to be added that other navies had much the same attitude and suffered the same results. It is notable, in maritime history, that governments have the greatest difficulty in maintaining the proper balance between the alleged "practical knowledge" of the operators and the "science" of the designers; the player and the instrument maker are, in turn, in full control.

Overloading with guns aggravated the inherent weakness of the new ships; it increased their tendency to "hog" or become "humpbacked." It was not until nearly twenty-five years later that the American constructors learned how to design and build such long vessels successfully and to allow for any possible overloading. This difficulty led to the ships requiring extensive repairs when less than twelve years old: the *Constellation* was rebuilt and widened 14″, between 1805 and 1812, as she had in only eight years become severely strained by her armament, as well as by having gone aground in the Delaware. The uncontrolled loading of the ships with armament not only increased hogging, but it caused the whole upper portion of the hull to strain as the vessel rolled in the trough of the sea; this caused the structure to become loose and weak.

The armament of the new frigates was to be extraordinarily powerful; the 44's were to carry 30 long 24-pdrs. on the gun deck and from 20 to 22 long 12's on the quarterdeck and forecastle. In addition, they were to have 2 long 24-pdrs. on the forecastle as chase guns. The 38's were to have 28 24-pdrs. on the gun deck and 18 to 20 12-pdrs. on the upper deck. These proposed armaments were not employed, however, because it was decided to use carronades in place of the long 12-pdrs., and also the captains had their own ideas on how their ships ought to be armed. There was in addition the old trouble of getting the proper guns manufactured. The 24-pdrs. of the Federal Navy were not the same in model, weight, and dimensions in all of the ships carrying them. Some of the guns were on the British model, some were fortification cannon, and some were made on what was intended to be the standard model. However, the official establishment for the 44's was 30 long 24's on the gun deck and 20 to 22 carronades, 42-pdrs., on the upper deck. The *Constitution* seems to have carried 32-pdr. carronades instead of 42's in all of her early career. The 38's carried 28 long 18-pdrs. on the gun deck and 20 carronades, 32-pdrs., on the upper deck. The long guns and carronades followed the British pattern rather closely but had less windage and threw a slightly heavier shot. All of the American frigates carried long chase guns on the forecastle, as well as a number of cohorns on the rail. It will be noticed, perhaps, that both classes of frigates had far more ports than guns. The 44-gun ships could have mounted 60 guns, and the 38's 56, by filling all of their ports (exclusive of the bridle ports) on the gun deck. So far as is known, none of the ships ever attempted this, though some of the 44's mounted as many as 56 guns at one time. Such an armament seriously overloaded the ships and hurt their sailing and stability, as well as causing them to strain.

When the new ships were building, it was intended to arm them with long guns entirely, following the American practice in the Revolution. However, the advantages of the relatively new carronade, by now a favorite gun in the British Navy, were slowly becoming apparent, and the new ordnance was soon in demand. The carronade was a British invention, first produced by the Carron Foundry, from which it took its name. The American carronades appear to have been very close copies of the English guns in all respects. The advantage of the carronade over the long gun was in weight, the carronade firing more than twice the weight of shot fired by a long gun of the same weight of gun and mount. The carronade was short, and for this reason it was more quickly loaded than the long gun. Some American naval historians have been inclined to sneer at the effectiveness of the carronade, but the facts were that the carronade was often a more accurate cannon than the long gun, since the designers of the former had reduced the windage to overcome the objections of a very short gun. The long gun had the advantage of greater range, and, if properly bored, was relatively more accurate at extreme ranges of fire. The good features of the carronade resulted in its replacing the small long gun, of 4- to 12-pound shot, on the upper decks of nearly all American and British naval ships. Some ships were fitted out in both navies with an all-carronade armament, but this was found generally undesirable, as the long guns were found generally superior in range. The Americans usually retained the long gun for chase purposes in all ships and also used the long gun as the main armament when practical, employing the carronades as supplementary guns for rapid fire at close range. With the introduction of the carronade, the old swivels and howitzers went slowly out of fashion and were employed only as boat guns, or were relegated to the merchant marine. The Americans often used smoothbore muskets loaded with buckshot, shotgun fashion, in naval action. They also used rifles extensively. Americans cannot be said to have introduced any innovation in gun design in this period; they were following the best practices abroad in arming their ships, taking the carronade from the Royal Navy, and the idea of employing heavy long guns in the main battery from the French Navy. The latter were using long guns of large caliber at this time and had not adopted the carronade extensively.

Nevertheless, it will be seen that the Americans had introduced one innovation—the two-decked (or, as they came to be called later, "double-banked") frigates capable, at least, of carrying two almost fully armed decks (rather than one and a fraction, as had been the case in the standard frigate of that time). This eventually brought about a change in the large frigates of all the great powers, who finally adopted double-banked ships. Yet when the American vessels first appeared, they were not favorably received by foreign naval officers, and, as has been mentioned, some American officers thought them too large and clumsy to handle well in close action. Relatively great size was an essential feature of the spar-decked ships.

While the Americans were having difficulties with the Barbary corsairs, Europe was becoming disturbed. The French Revolution started while Congress was considering the establishment of a naval force. Soon the great powers were engaged in a destructive war, and the seas were full of privateers and cruisers. The French revolutionists had little respect for international law or relations. The French soon reached the point of seizing American shipping and condemning both vessels and cargoes. By 1798 this matter had reached the stage of an undeclared war, and Congress again found it necessary to consider a naval establishment and to ponder on the need of one far greater than had previously been thought necessary for the country. Congress made appropriations for more ships and for the completion of those started earlier. Doughty was made a naval constructor and sent to New York, and a young shipbuilder named Christian Bergh was made master builder to complete the 44-gun ship that had been started there. Doughty seems to have permitted some slight changes from the original plans, for the ship is known to have been more lightly built than the others of her class and to have had less sheer. It is possible that some liberties were taken with the timbers in the ends of this ship, the "cant frames," or this may have been accidental; at any rate this 44, named the *President*, became noted as the fastest of her class when put into service. She had a figurehead representing President Washington. She was delayed somewhat even after the fresh start and so was not launched until April 1, 1800.

The 38-gun frigate *Congress*, building at Portsmouth, was also completed with the new appropriations and was finally launched April 1, 1800. There is some evidence in existing dimensions of the ship that she was not wholly a sister ship of the *Constellation*, but the mode of measurement employed may account for the apparent difference, about 5 feet in length. The *Congress* had a relatively uneventful career and spent much of her life rotting "in ordinary," or laid up.

The frigate at Gosport was also reinstated. When work stopped on the frigates she was so little advanced that the order in effect canceled her construction. Fox had joined with Truxton and others in objecting to the size of the 44-gun frigates, and their arguments had much effect on the authorities. As a result Fox was permitted to prepare a new design for a 44, of reduced size, that would have the approval of Truxton and other objectors. The authorization for the revised design does not exist (at least it has not been found), but the correspondence shows that the Secretary of the Navy was aware that the new ship was smaller than the previous 44's, for he inquired as to her dimensions and tonnage while she was under construction. Among the Fox Papers there is a drawing, entitled *Congress*, which may be her building plan. The new ship was launched, under the name *Chesapeake*, on June 20, 1799. She was a rather unfortunate ship in the American service, though considered both handsome and fast. This was one of the three American frigates taken by the British in the War of 1812; she will again be referred to in Chapter Five.

While the ships authorized in 1794 were being completed and other vessels were being added to the Navy, a less attractive program of naval shipbuilding was forced on the Americans. The treaty with Algiers had called for the Americans to make a cash payment, which, for various reasons, had been delayed. In order to keep the peace the American diplomats had therefore agreed to present the Dey with a total of four "corsair" vessels, built particularly for the purpose. These ships were to be of naval design and of the best materials. The practice of giving the Barbary corsairs armed ships had long been common with many of the European powers, as part of the continuing conspiracy to employ the Mediterranean pirates against some commercial competitor. In our case, however, the ships were nothing more than a tribute—a sop to keep the peace.

The tribute vessels to be built were to consist of a 32-gun frigate, a brig, and two schooners. A good deal of care was taken to assemble all the information that could be obtained from former captives as to the exact requirements of vessels suited to the use of the corsairs and also their likes and dislikes in regard to ship decoration and arrangement. It was thought that the Dey would be pacified and his friendship purchased if the vessels were superior in every way to those he had received from the European powers. The frigate was, of course, the most important, and the most impressive, of the vessels. After some study the administration selected Josiah Fox to design the ship and James Hackett of Portsmouth, New Hampshire, to build her. She was deliberately made as small as her rate would permit, as can be seen by her dimensions: 122′ 0″ on the gun deck, 32′ 0″ moulded beam, and 10′ 2″ depth of hold. She was launched June 29, 1797, and was a very handsome ship, as was usual with Fox's designs. Though she has no particular bearing on American naval construction, the choice of her designer indicates how rapidly Fox had come to be recognized as a prominent ship designer in the United States. The plan and offsets of the frigate, named temporarily the *Crescent*, are among the Fox Papers in the possession of the Peabody Museum at Salem, Massachusetts.

The smaller vessels are of more interest, however, as they not only show the ideas of American naval constructors of the time, in small man-of-war design, but also because one of them had much influence on later American naval construction. The two schooners and the brig were contracted for at Philadelphia. One schooner, eventually named the *Lelah Eisha*, was designed and built by Samuel Bowers; she was the smallest and was to carry 18 guns, 4-pdrs. The larger of the two schooners was designed by Benjamin Hutton, Jr., and built by Nathaniel Hutton, Jr.; she was to carry 20 4-pdrs. and received the name of *Skjoldebrand* in honor of a Scandinavian diplomat who had been helpful to the Americans in the Mediterranean. The schooner's plan is of value in illustrating the American conception of a small cruiser for the Mediterranean in the period under discussion. Unfortunately there are very few plans of small American naval vessels in this particular period; this adds to the usefulness of the drawing of this "corsair" schooner, shown in Figure 17. Though the *Skjoldebrand* was of the approximate dimensions of some of the American naval schooners, such as *Enterprise*, she does not represent the model of the latter schooner. The "corsair" was an average-sized schooner of the time she was built—77′ 6″ between perpendiculars, 62′ 0″ straight rabbet, 23′ 0″ moulded beam, and 10′ 6″ depth of hold. She had a high raised quarterdeck, which had gone out of fashion in American war schooners at the time she was built. It is probable that this feature was desired by the Algerines, and also that it was intended to make this small ship look more impressive. This schooner is said to have rowed well—a necessity in a Mediterranean cruiser—and to have been a smart sailer.

The brig, or brigantine as she is sometimes called, was the most effective vessel of the lot; she was what was then a large naval brig, designed for speed and for carrying a heavy weight of armament. This vessel was designed and

British squadron on Lake Champlain, 1776, from a drawing made at Valcour Bay by a British officer. (Courtesy Kenneth Roberts.)

New England vessels at Valcour Bay, 1776, from a contemporary drawing. (Courtesy S. H. P. Pell, Esq.)

PLATE V

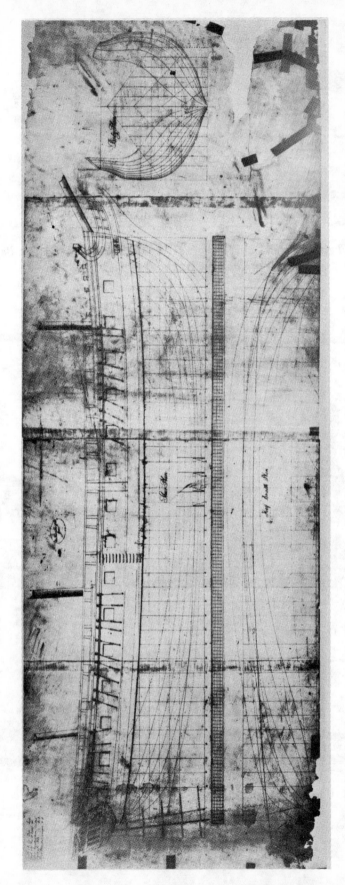

PLATE VI. Draught of TERRIBLE, *probably the "master drawing" for the 44-gun frigates* CONSTITUTION, UNITED STATES, *and* PRESIDENT.

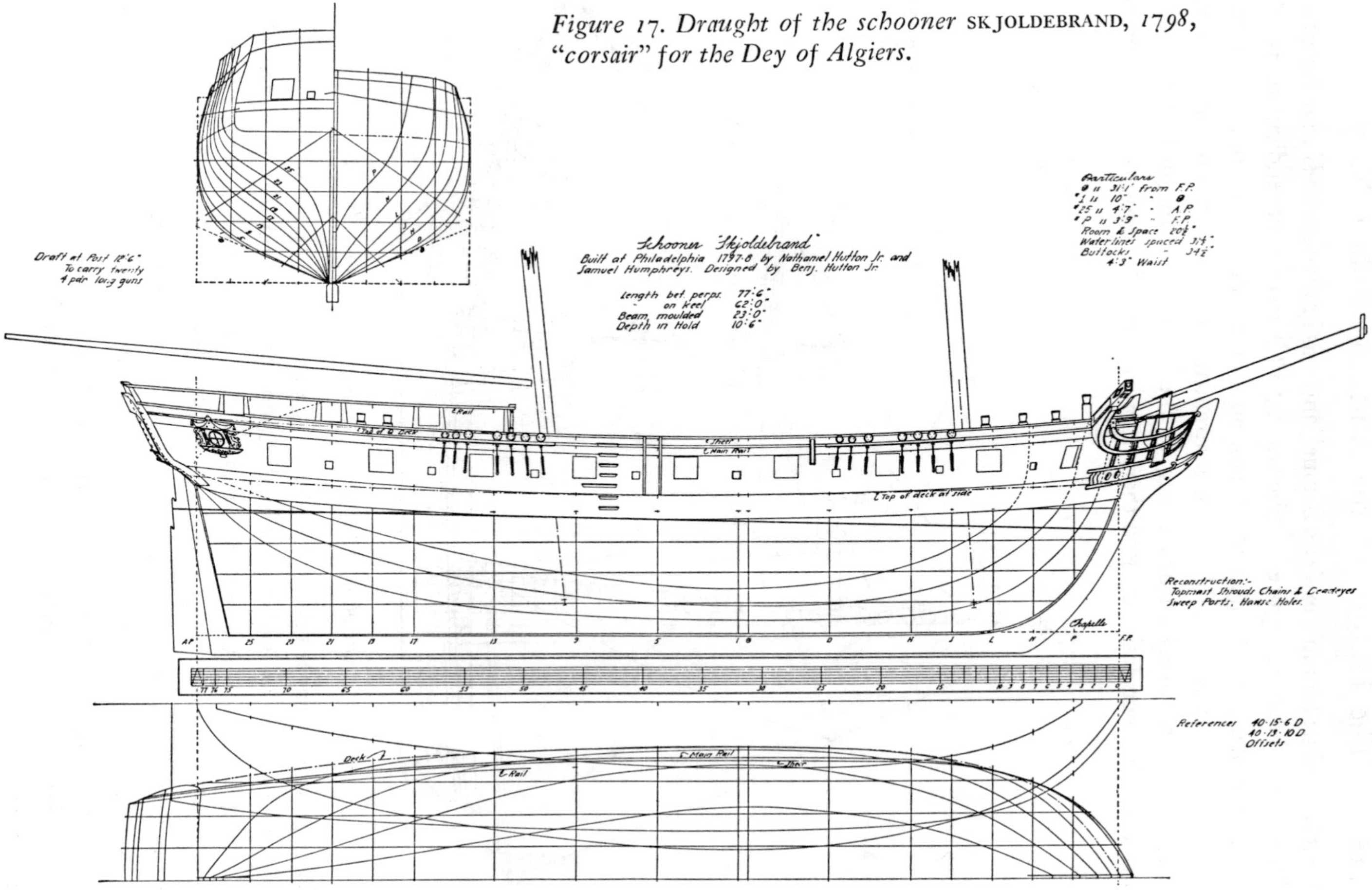

Figure 17. Draught of the schooner SKJOLDEBRAND, 1798, "corsair" for the Dey of Algiers.

137

built by Joshua Humphreys' son Samuel, and was known as the *Hassan Bashaw*. Her plan is shown in Figure 19. She was 93′ 2″ between perpendiculars, 75′ 0″ straight rabbet, 27′ 0″ moulded beam, and 11′ 6″ depth of hold; she measured 287⁴²⁄₉₄ tons customhouse measurement. This brig represents a good example of an American naval brig of the period; her original plans show evidence that her designer used them as a basis for the designs of two much

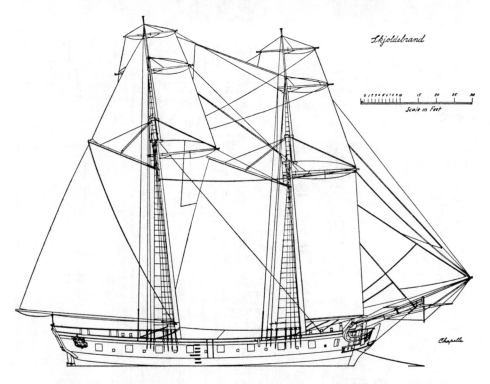

Figure 18. Sail plan of the SKJOLDEBRAND *from spar dimensions.*

later American naval vessels. On the body plan of one of the surviving drawings of the *Hassan Bashaw*, the midsections of the sloop of war *Peacock* as "rebuilt" (actually redesigned and an entirely new hull constructed) in 1828 and of the schooner *Enterprise*, built in 1831, have been laid off. This shows that Humphreys used the brig as a basis for the design of the latter vessels—the reason being that the *Hassan Bashaw* had proved unusually fast. She was a moderate "clipper," on the model, somewhat modified, of the famous American "pilot-boat construction" schooners then coming to the attention of the maritime world.

Figure 19. Draught of the "corsair" brig HASSAN BASHAW, presentation vessel to the Dey of Algiers.

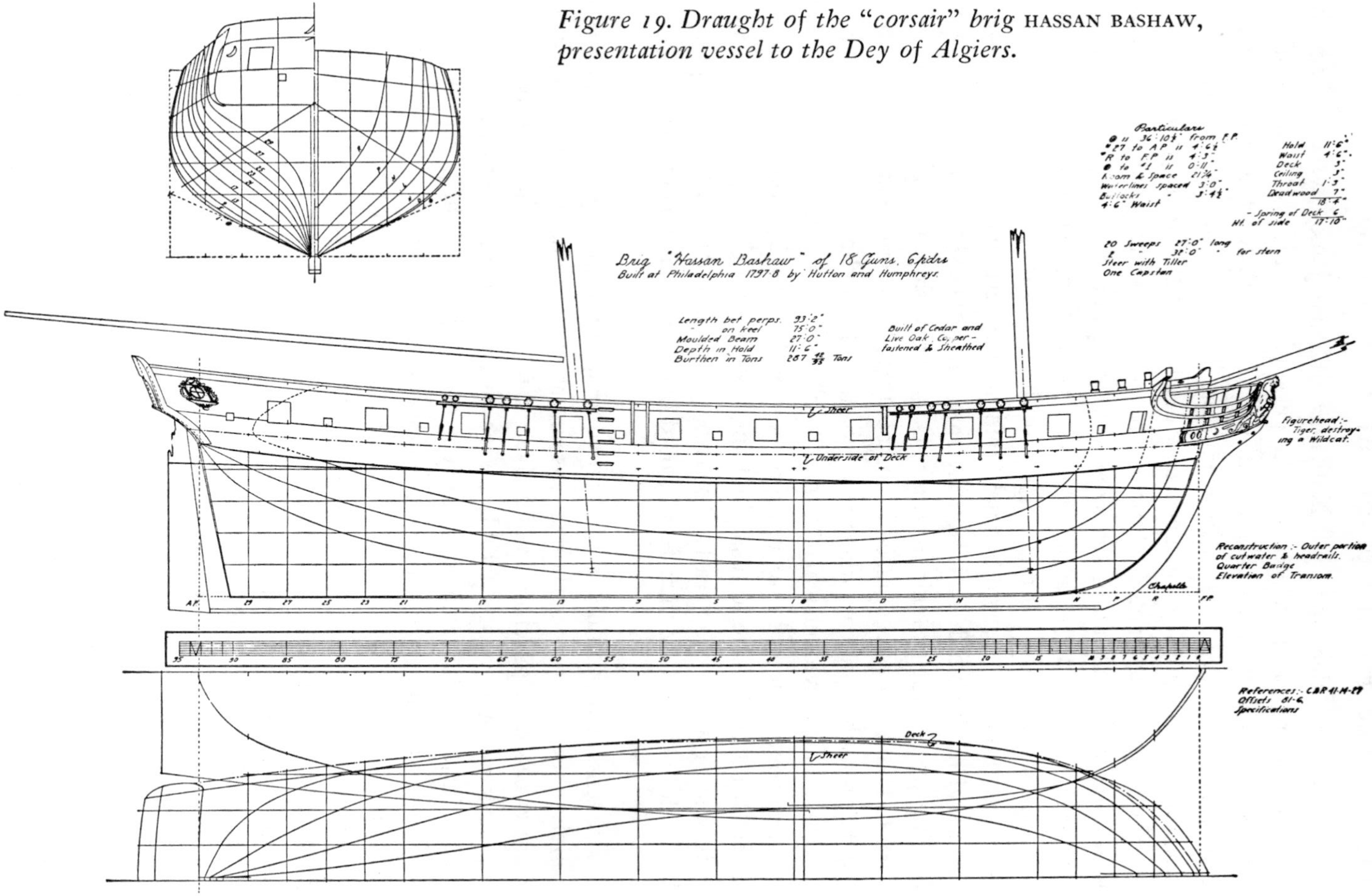

The Huttons, Benjamin, Jr., Nathaniel, Jr., and James, were perhaps the most competent naval architects of the period in Philadelphia. Unfortunately little is known about their careers and work, other than a few plans of naval craft that have survived. Benjamin Hutton, Jr., seems to have specialized in designing and lofting; Nathaniel was a designer and builder. James seems to have been a younger member of the family; he too was a very competent draftsman. The draftsmanship of Benjamin, Jr., and James was superior to that of Fox or Doughty and was, in fact, the equal of the finest work of the European naval architects of the period, judging by the few plans that have been found. Nathaniel Hutton, Jr., and Samuel Humphreys were close friends and were associated in shipbuilding. It appears that the *Skjoldebrand* and the *Hassan Bashaw* were actually built by the two in partnership, though this does not seem to be officially recognized in the contracts. It is apparent, however, that the Huttons had much influence on Samuel Humphreys' later work as a designer. This is evident when Humphreys' plans are examined, for a number of them contain notes in reference to Hutton designs. It is one of the unfortunate features of American shipbuilding history that the papers of the Huttons, and of a few other early American naval architects, have disappeared. Were this not the case their fame would have been far greater than it is.

The tension with France steadily mounted, and so the new Navy increased rapidly under the new authorizations and appropriations. A number of merchant vessels were purchased and converted to cruisers. While a marked effort was made to obtain vessels suitable in every way—fast and able to carry guns—the results proved far from satisfactory in nearly all cases. The purchases began in 1798 and continued on into 1799. They consisted of six ships and two brigs, the latter being new vessels purchased either on the stocks or soon after launching. The need for small, fast cruisers in the West Indies, to suppress French privateers operating against American shipping, placed much emphasis on brigs, schooners, and small, fast ships.

The building program consisted of ships built by contract for the federal government and of "subscription" vessels, built by the merchants of various ports and presented to the government. The government built two 28-gun frigates and three smaller ships of 20 to 24 guns. In addition, two schooners and seven galleys were built. Eight revenue cutters (seven schooners and a sloop) were turned over to the Navy. The merchants built five frigates of rates from 28 to 44 guns, four ships of from 18 to 24 guns, and a brig of 18 guns. A 36-gun frigate and a 14-gun schooner, taken from the French, were also added to the Navy.

The administration of the naval force now passed from the War Office to the newly established Navy Department, which came into existence in the middle of 1798. Benj. Stoddert, a merchant marked by initiative and force of character, was the first Secretary of the Navy. The Navy owed much to his zeal, for he attempted to establish a well-disciplined and superior officers' corps and to bring some order into the management of naval affairs. The old methods set up under the War Office, of utilizing local navy agents as civil officers of the Navy, was continued. The only criticism that might be leveled at Stoddert was his reliance upon certain favorites among the officers for advice and his compliance with political interests in some matters. In justice to Stoddert, however, it must be said that he often brought political favorites and his own advisers to heel when he thought they had imposed upon him. In short, his errors were due to inexperience rather than to any weakness in character or intentions. The navy agents were either prominent merchants or else local men with sea experience and maritime interest.

The position of the naval constructors is, however, of more concern here than the administrative organization of the Navy. As has been stated, at this period the relations between the constructors and the commissioned officers placed the latter in the ascendancy in making technical decisions. There is no evidence that Stoddert was ever conscious of any weakness in this situation. He looked upon the construction organization as a mere convenience in building and fitting out ships. In making inquiries about ships to be purchased he was inclined to consult a captain, rather than the constructors. It was not until some of his purchases were criticized that he finally utilized Humphreys and Fox for this work. Even then the constructors were usually placed in the position of having to receive orders from commissioned officers.

In completing the ships authorized in 1794 the federal government had purchased property, at Gosport, Virginia, and Portsmouth, New Hampshire, either for building shipyards or as storage locations. This led to the eventual establishment of navy yards in these locations, though these facilities came into existence more by the natural trend of events than by a planned development. The deep draft of the new ships played a part in this, as well as the need of fitting out ships, as has been noted previously. When naval hostilities began in mid-June, 1798, the need of localities for repair of ships became a matter of immediate concern. The Gosport Yard (or, as it came to be called, the Norfolk

Navy Yard) and building site became particularly important because it was conveniently situated to service the ships going to or from the West Indies. Fox had been placed here as constructor and was left independent of a commandant. He was engaged in building the *Chesapeake* and in repairs of naval ships until his discharge in the reduction of 1801. The lack of both navy yards and suitable private facilities began to be seriously felt in 1799, and soon the subject of locating a number of navy yards reached the stage of official recognition. Joshua Humphreys was sent along the coast, from New England to Virginia, inspecting possible sites. Throughout the difficulties with France, however, the Gosport site was the only one actually employed as a navy yard.

In addition to Fox, Joshua Humphreys continued to serve as a naval constructor and was utilized also as a navy agent for individual ships. He advised the Secretary occasionally and supervised repairs in the Philadelphia area. His honesty and his capabilities as a practical shipbuilder made him very useful to the Department. In spite of his ability, he was given relatively little design work, compared to Fox. It is probable that his activities in repairing and fitting out ships and in the business of the Department was the main reason for this.

The first two merchant vessels purchased were a Baltimore ship named the *Adriana* and one found at Philadelphia, named the *Ganges;* these were bought May 3, 1798. On the 5th of May another Philadelphia ship was purchased, the *Hamburgh Packet.* On June 15 the merchant ship *Herald* was bought at Boston, the *Montezuma* was obtained June 26 at Baltimore, and the *George Washington* was bought at Providence, Rhode Island, in September, 1798. The two brigs purchased were both obtained at Norfolk, Virginia, and were particularly selected for fast sailing. One was bought in 1798 and the other in June, 1799.

The *Adriana* was renamed *Baltimore;* her customhouse measurements were 103′ 9″ length, 30′ 8″ beam, depth not given, 422 32/95 tons; she had quarter galleries and a "Woman figurehead" and was fitted to carry 20 9-pdrs. She was a new ship launched at Baltimore early in 1798, built by Joseph Caverly. She soon had the reputation of being a slow ship, and in 1801 she was sold.

The *Ganges* retained her old name. She had been built in 1795 at Philadelphia; her customhouse measurements were 116′ 4″ length, 31′ 4″ beam, depth 15′ 8″, 504 tons. She had double quarter galleries (indicating a ship with a high quarterdeck or poop), a stern gallery and a roundhouse, and a figurehead not described; she was fitted with 26 9-pdrs. Her original merchant-ship captain, Richard Dale, who had served with John Paul Jones, took her over as a

Navy captain. This vessel was one of the best of the purchased ships; she too was sold in 1801.

The *Hamburgh Packet* had been built at Philadelphia in 1794; her custom-house dimensions were 94′ 9″ length, 28′ 0″ beam, 14′ 0″ depth, 321^{64}⁄$_{95}$ tons; she had quarter galleries and an Indian figurehead. She was renamed *Delaware* and was armed with 20 guns—16 9-pdrs. and 4 6's. She too proved slow and was sold out in 1801.

The *Montezuma*, which retained her original name, was a 347-ton ship with quarter galleries and a figurehead. She carried 20 guns, apparently 9-pdrs.; her dimensions have not been found. She was a very unsatisfactory cruiser, and was sold at Baltimore in 1799.

The *Herald* also retained her original name. She had been built at Newbury in 1798, and her customhouse dimensions were 92′ 8″ length, 26′ 3½″ beam, 13′ 1¾″ depth, 279^{75}⁄$_{95}$ tons. She had quarter galleries and a "man figure-head." Though commonly referred to as an 18-gun ship, she carried 22 guns —16 6-pdrs. and 6 4's. She was supposed to be a fast ship when offered to the government, but she seems to have suffered from an officious captain; the Secretary of the Navy maintained that she had been spoiled by alterations after purchase. At any rate she proved to be overloaded and an unsatisfactory cruiser; she was sold out in 1801, but had been inactive for some time previous.

The *George Washington* was a 624-ton ship, 108′ 0″ long on the keel, 32′ 6″ beam, and 15′ 8″ depth in hold. She had quarter galleries and a figurehead. Built at Providence, Rhode Island, in 1793 as a merchant ship of the largest class, she was well built but slow. She seems to have been very roomy and was fitted with 32 guns, but was rated as a 24-gun ship. She carried 24 9-pdrs. and 8 6's. She was retained in service for a longer time than the other purchased ships and was not disposed of until 1803. She was sometimes referred to as a frigate because of her size and appearance.

The brig *Norfolk* was purchased at the city she was named after, and was selected because she was thought to be fast. She was built at Gosport by Nash and Herbert, and was new at the time of purchase; she carried 18 6-pdrs. on a flush deck and was a sharp vessel. She was a good sailer and a useful brig, but, said to be rotten, she was sold at Baltimore late in 1800.

The *Augusta* was the second brig purchased at Norfolk. She too was a new vessel, a little smaller than the *Norfolk*, and carried 14 guns—10 6-pdrs. and 4 4-pdrs. She was sold at Norfolk in 1801.

Both brigs were lightly built; the *Norfolk* was about 200 tons, or roughly

88′ on deck; the *Augusta* was about 175 tons and around 75′ on deck. The *Augusta* caused the Secretary of the Navy some annoyance after her purchase in 1799. He sent her to Boston to be fitted out with stores removed from the *Herald*, which had been laid up as an unsatisfactory cruiser. Upon the *Augusta*'s arrival at Boston, her captain expressed his dislike of taking over a smaller vessel and, together with the local ship carpenters, requested permission to change the vessel—to cut down the spars, which were considered too light for their length, to remove the rudder irons and replace them, and to add to the bulwarks and cabins. By this time the Secretary had learned that the captains were never satisfied with a vessel as she was built and had lost patience. He refused to grant permission to change the vessel in any way; finally becoming disgusted with the Boston clique's insistence that only they were competent to judge a ship, he had the brig sent to Philadelphia and ordered Humphreys to pass on her. Humphreys made a few minor repairs and fitted the brig out; she proved very fast and a good seaboat. She was very stiff, carrying her lee guns two feet above the water in a reefed topsail breeze, and was noted as a weatherly vessel in all conditions, well suited to the West Indies.

In general, the purchased ships were too small to carry the armaments placed aboard them; when they were ready for sea their guns were so close to the water line that they could not be used in heavy seas, or when under sail in a fresh breeze. Some undoubtedly had poor lines for speed, but, judging by the correspondence, a good deal of the difficulty in the ships could be traced to their captains' insistence on changing the ships and on overgunning them. In only rare cases, such as that of the *Augusta*, were the constructors consulted in preference to accepting the captain's verdict. The *Ganges* is another exception. She was taken out as a cruiser by the same captain who had her as a merchantman; therefore there were few changes, and these were partly made under Joshua Humphreys' supervision. As a result, she seems to have been a very useful ship, with a reasonable turn of speed, even when she was under other captains. Once a ship got to sea on her maiden cruise as a Navy ship, the Secretary was usually adamant about making any more alterations.

These purchased vessels were obtained by an authorization of Congress dated April 27, 1798, which was followed by another on May 4. Congress, by the Act of June 30, 1798, also permitted the acceptance of vessels built by the citizens. Nevertheless every effort was made to prevent the construction of unnecessarily expensive ships. The federal government contracted for the construction of two frigates, the *Adams* and *General Greene*. The *Adams*, of 28

guns, was built at New York by Jackson and Sheffield. The latter also designed
her; at least he supplied a plan and a model. She was about 113' on the gun
deck, 108' straight rabbet, 34' moulded beam, 10' 9" hold, and about 530 tons.
She carried 24 12-pdrs. and 4 6-pdrs. This small ship was launched in 1799 and
remained in the Navy. At the outbreak of the War of 1812 she was rebuilt as
a flush-decked corvette and lengthened about 15'. She was burned in the
Penobscot on September 3, 1814, to prevent capture by British boats. The
General Greene, also a 28, was built by contract at Warren, Rhode Island, by
Benjamin Talman and James de Wolf. Measuring 124' 3" on the gun deck,
34' 8" beam, and 17' 4" depth in the hold, she was 654 tons and carried 24
12-pdrs. and 6 6's. Launched January 21, 1799, she remained in service after
the reduction of 1801 and in 1805 was converted to a sheer hulk at Washington Navy Yard, where she was burned when the city was captured August 24,
1814. Her plan was indexed in the Navy plan files but cannot now be found.
It is not known who designed her, but it was probably Talman.

The smaller ships contracted for were the *Portsmouth*, built at Portsmouth,
New Hampshire, by Hackett, 590 tons, 24 guns; the *Connecticut*, built at
Middletown, Connecticut, launched June 6, 1799, from the Overton yard;
and the 20-gun ship *Warren*, contracted for at Newburyport, Massachusetts,
but actually built at Salisbury by an association of builders. The *Warren*, a
385-ton ship, was sold at Boston in 1801. The *Connecticut* leaked after her
launch and sank in the river, which caused much delay in getting her commissioned. She rated as a 24-gun ship of 492 tons, carrying 26 12-pdrs., and was
one of the fastest ships in the Navy on the West Indian Station.

Two schooners, the *Enterprise* and *Experiment*, were also built by contract,
handled entirely by the Baltimore Naval Agent, Henry Yellot. The *Enterprise*,
built on the Eastern Shore of Maryland by Henry Spencer, was a square-tuck-
stern schooner, 60' on the keel, 84' 7" on deck, 22' 6" beam, 9' 6" depth of hold,
135 tons. She was said to have been 23' beam over the thick wales. No plan of
the vessel has ever been found, and the only information on her form, as
originally built, is contained in the letters of her commanding officer when she
was "repaired" and almost entirely rebuilt at Venice in 1805. He noted that she
was almost completely rotten, had a square-tuck stern and a good deal of
tumble home in her sides above the water line. It is apparent that she was a
typical pilot-boat schooner of the period, fitted with deeper bulwarks than
usual. She carried 12 long 6-pdrs. when originally fitted out. This schooner
became a noted vessel and was retained in service. She was again rebuilt from

the floor timbers up in the fall of 1811 at the Washington Navy Yard, and was then rerigged as a brig with her tonnage increased to 165 tons. About 1806 Fox measured her and found her to be 92' 9" on deck, 80' 6" between perpendiculars, 23' 9" extreme beam, 22' 11" moulded beam, and 10' 10" depth of hold at the mainmast. This was after the first rebuilding, which undoubtedly accounts for the variation in the dimensions.

The *Experiment* was a schooner of the same rate and ordered to the same dimensions: keel 60', moulded beam 22' 6", depth of hold 9' 6", 135 tons. Whether she was built in Baltimore or on the Eastern Shore is uncertain. In an official paper of 1802 William Price of Baltimore was said to have built the *Enterprise*, although this may refer to the *Experiment*. It is possible, of course, that the schooners may have been originally let to Price, who contracted them out to other builders on subcontracts.

Like the *Enterprise*, the *Experiment* was a very successful cruiser, but she was one of the vessels sold in 1801. The swiftness of these schooners, and the fact that their size rated junior officers as commanders, soon made them noted vessels. Commanded by young, bold, and ambitious officers, the two schooners naturally had eventful careers.

The revenue cutters were all new vessels. Not all the existing cutters were to be transferred to the Navy, so it was possible to limit the selection to vessels of recent build. The Revenue Service had been established in 1790, and between 1791 and 1793 nine small schooners and one sloop had been built. These had been found too small, and so larger cutters were laid down in 1797. These were double-topsail schooners, or "jackass brigs," with fore and main square topsails. Much confusion exists in the records of these vessels, since some of them carried the names of the earlier and smaller cutters. The cutters taken into naval service included all but two of the new schooners. Those chosen were the *Diligence*, built at Philadelphia, the *General Greene*, built by Price at Baltimore, the *Governor Jay*, built at New York, the *Pickering*, built at Newburyport, the *Scammel*, built at Portsmouth, New Hampshire, the *Eagle*, built at Philadelphia, the *South Carolina*, built at Charleston, South Carolina, and the *Virginia*, built at Norfolk. One other, the *Pinckney*, or *General Pinckney*, built at Charleston and taken over on the stocks, was apparently the largest of the cutters. All of the cutters except the *Pinckney*, *General Greene*, and *Virginia* were listed as being 58' 0" straight rabbet, 20' 0" moulded beam, 9' 0" depth of hold, and 187 tons; the last seems to be an error. The *Greene* was 98 tons, and the *Virginia* is noted as being 50' 0" straight rabbet, 18' 10" moulded beam, 8′ 6″ depth of hold, and fitted with a poop flush with the top of the bulwarks to form a cabin aft. These cutters were armed with 4- and 6-pdrs., usually brass. Fox designed the *Pickering, Eagle,* and *Diligence;* possibly the others were sisters, but this cannot be proved. All the cutters except the *Scammel, Eagle,* and *Pickering* were returned to the Treasury in 1799. The first two were sold out of the Navy in 1801, and the *Pickering* was lost at sea with all hands in the fall of 1800.

No plans that can be identified with certainty as one of these cutters has yet come to light. However, among the plans formerly in the Navy plan files in the Washington Navy Yard, and now missing from the National Archives, were a number of schooner and ship plans without identification—some without an index number. These plans were mostly those from the personal files of some of the constructors and assistants—Humphreys, Doughty, and Rhodes. The writer traced some of these plans before they were removed from the Navy Yard, among them a schooner design that he first supposed to be of the 1797 cutters. This plan, redrawn, is shown in Figure 20. It does not appear that it was the plan used to build the cutters, for the beam is one foot less than that given in the register of the vessels, though the length on the keel, or of the straight rabbet, and the depth in hold can be seen to correspond. The original plan, which has disappeared, was in pencil and seems to have been either a preliminary design or a rather hasty copy of a working drawing. The drawing, though less valuable than it would be if it could be identified, is useful in showing the approximate size of the cutters, as well as the extremes reached, in the period under discussion, in the design of fast schooners. The plan was noted as being of a 14-gun schooner to carry 6-pdrs. but it is doubtful if her displacement was anywhere enough to permit such an armament. It will be seen that she was 77′ 0″ between perpendiculars, on a length of 58′ 0″ of straight rabbet; this shows that the cutters must have been approximately the same length—say 70 to 80 feet on deck. The plan also permits a rough idea to be formed of the appearance of the larger schooners, *Enterprise* and *Experiment.* The schooner not only had the square-tuck stern of these vessels, but also had the same tumble-home topsides that seem to have characterized these cruisers. The "round-tuck" stern consisted of what was really two transoms, the lower one square across along the bottom, or "cross seam," with the bottom and lower side planking "tucking" up in a round full curve to the cross seam. The "square-tuck" stern had three distinct transoms, the lower one a V (or heart shape), to which the bottom and lower side transom ran "square," as in the stern of a modern powerboat. The round-tuck stern can be seen in the draw-ings of the other ships of this period. The square-tuck stern had pretty well gone out of fashion in large ships by 1790, but it was retained in many small craft until the modern counter stern appeared in the first half of the nineteenth century.

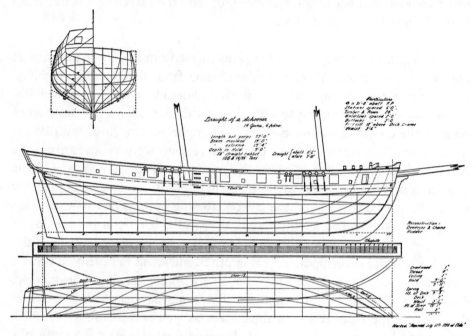

Figure 20. Draught of an unidentified 14-gun schooner showing an extreme de-sign of the period.

It has been the custom to suppose that the designers of the latter part of the eighteenth century were incapable of designing very sharp-ended sailing ves-sels, but this is a fallacy. Usually the constructors of the period were limited in the use of sharp-lined hulls by the necessity of carrying guns and a large store of provisions. The Secretary of the Navy, for example, usually in-structed the navy agents and citizens' associations that the ships they were to have built were to carry a given number of guns, to be strong, and to sail well, but that they must carry, say, six months' provisions for a crew of a stated num-ber. This last specification usually prevented a naval vessel from being as sharp as the privateers or those vessels built for illegal trades. The need of having fast cutters to stop smuggling often produced revenue vessels that were very sharp, in both England and the United States, in this period. As has been seen in Fox's criticism of Humphreys' model for a 44-gun frigate, very hollow sharp lines in the bow were usually looked upon with disfavor. However, some of the designers of sharp schooners and pilot boats employed such lines because of the fine ends they desired in their craft. Only rarely did the load water line show any hollow, but the lines below often show a good deal, as in this example. This was an incidental feature of design brought about by a combination of a sharp bow and marked forefoot. The same thing occurred later in the design of the California and China clipper ships of the 1840's and 1850's; most of their designers disliked a hollow load water line, but they were forced to hollow lines below by the very sharp entrance and angular forefoot they employed in the ships. The "long hollow bow" of the clipper ships was a mere figment of journalistic imagination on the part of a newspaperman attempting to describe a ship. Even today, the hollow load water line at the bow is rarely seen in sailing yachts, and few designers place any value on the feature. A sharp entrance can be obtained without hollow water lines only by employing extreme rake in the stem, as in most modern sailing yachts, but this was not always desirable when vessels carried square sails or were very heavily canvased.

The difference between the length on the keel and the length on deck, in American schooners and other vessels of this period, is deserving of attention. The American designers usually employed a good deal of rake in the stem and sternposts, though less in the latter than in the former. The rabbet of the bow in many American vessels was on a large radius, with its axis over the forward end of the straight of the rabbet. In small vessels like schooners this radius was usually about three-quarters of the beam, though it is apparent that this was not a rule or set proportion. In large vessels the radius was usually less—say four-sevenths of the beam. Actually, of course, the rabbet of the stem usually departed somewhat from an arc of a circle, as the designers commonly straightened the curve in profile as it approached the deck line. It is found that, as a result, the American schooners and small craft had a measured bow rake ranging from about three-quarters of the beam to the full beam, and large vessels from about three-sevenths to four-sevenths. The measured stern rake was often small; the post usually raked about one-fourth of the beam in schooners and about one-seventh in large vessels. There were, of course, variations in rake, with a great many vessels falling between the two extremes. Schooners and small craft built in the South and on Chesapeake Bay commonly had more rake than those built at Philadelphia or New York or in New England. It is quite noticeable that small vessels to be fitted with a square rig—brigs, for example—commonly had less fore-rake than schooners with square topsails only. In this matter of rake the Americans were quite consistent, and their design practice differed from that followed in England and France. The English revenue and naval cutter of the period was the British equivalent of the sharp American schooner; this type usually had greater rake to the sternpost than to the stem, or, occasionally, the rakes of stem and sternpost approached equality. The French equivalent of the American schooner of pilot-boat construction was the lugger and some small brigs; these commonly employed less rake to the stem and sternpost than either the American or British fast-sailing craft. The French, however, were less consistent, particularly at the end of the eighteenth century, for they designed some vessels with great rake in the ends and with a variety of midsections whose forms were not employed in either American or British small craft. While the British copied some French ships, they did not use any French features in the design of their very fast cutters, as can be seen by the existing plans in the National Maritime Museum at Greenwich, England. In fact, there is some reason to suppose that the French copied English cutters in some of their fast luggers of the period under discussion.

The schooner in Figure 20 is less extreme in the rake of her stem and approaches the practice of some English constructors. This was probably brought about by the need of gaining displacement without increasing the beam, which could be accomplished by reducing rake. Fox seems to have proposed building an English cutter, and it is probable that he employed its features in some of the schooners he designed. It is possible that the schooner in Figure 20 shows the influence of his ideas in this respect. While there is no evidence to support the idea, the writer believes it is possible that this schooner design was a proposal for a revenue vessel that was not built. It does not appear to have been the work of a Philadelphia designer, judging by an endorsement of the date of receipt on the original drawing.

Schooners of this class were in great demand, particularly in the West Indies. From 1792 to the end of the Napoleonic Wars there was a very active export trade in new American schooners. During the quasi war with France the sale of sharp schooners to French agents was a matter of official concern, and some effort was made to apprehend foreign agents as well as to stop the transfer of such schooners abroad by means of sales of "ships and cargoes" under the guise of regular trade. As early as 1795 the sharp American schooners had achieved enough notoriety abroad to make them much sought after, not only as privateers and illegal traders but also as regular light naval ships. Three-masted schooners appeared, and the average size of the sharp-model schooners increased somewhat. During the years of the French troubles there was much speculative building of schooners, and the model rapidly became more and more extreme, judging by the plans that have been found.

One of the congressional appropriations produced a peculiar class of small craft, the galley. By the Act of May 4, 1798, the Navy Department was authorized to purchase or build up to ten small vessels of the galley type, to be manned by what might be termed naval militia. The personnel was under the control of the War Office, but the boats were to be built and fitted by the Navy. This act produced not only some curious shoal-draft craft but also a confusion in the records. Joshua Humphreys was commissioned to prepare the plan for the first galley; however, the plan seems to have been the work of his son, Samuel. The first design was modified, and finally four designs appear to have been used. Two or three galleys were built by private subscription; these seem to have been designed by their builders. In addition the revenue cutter *Pinckney*, which had been taken over incomplete, was completed by use of the galley funds, the Secretary of the Navy "considering" her a galley for administrative purposes to permit the diversion of funds. Because of this she is usually noted as a "galley," whereas it appears that she was actually a brig or brig-schooner of some size.

One of the designs used to build the galleys has survived, and Figure 21 probably shows the first one built at Pittsburgh. This is for a boat 50′ 6″ between perpendiculars, 13′ 6″ moulded beam at the level of the top of the wales, or 14′ 4″ at plank-sheer, and 6′ 8½″ total depth. The plan shows that the galley in general model was almost a much-reduced copy of Arnold's galley on Lake Champlain in the Revolution. The armament was an 18-pdr. in the bow and four howitzers or swivels (3-pdrs.) of brass, mounted on stocks along the after rail and on the stern. The crew slept in berths under the side decks and under the center-line gangway; a tarpaulin covered each of the hatchways at night. The officers had a small cabin or cuddy aft. Cooking seems to have been done in a small fireplace on the gun platform forward or ashore if the opportunity arose.

The surviving building instructions by the Humphreys show that a second

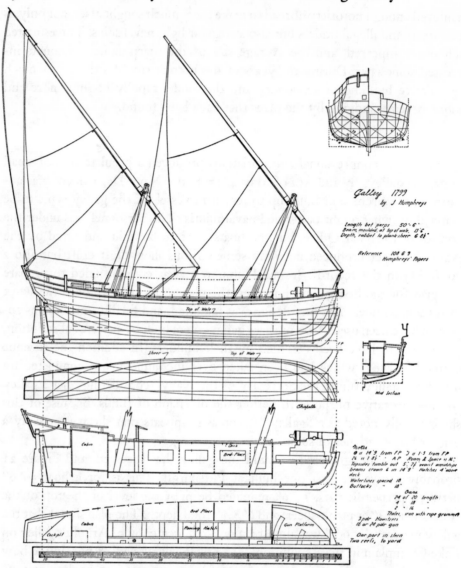

Figure 21. Galley of 1799, designed for river and harbor service.

design intended for use on the Mississippi was 45′ 0″ between perpendiculars and 13′ 0″ moulded beam; a third was 51′ 9″ between perpendiculars, 15′ 3½″ moulded beam at rail, or plank-sheer, and 5′ 1″ depth of hold; and the fourth design called for boats 56′ 0″ between perpendiculars, 14′ 6″ moulded beam, and 5′ 8½″ depth of hold. This last design was to be used for three western

Bow gun of a Mediterranean gun vessel.

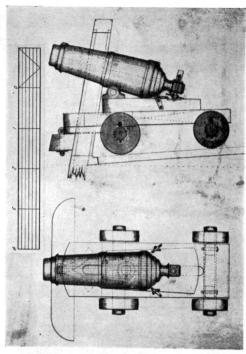

Admiralty carriage mount for an 18-pdr. carronade, 1808.

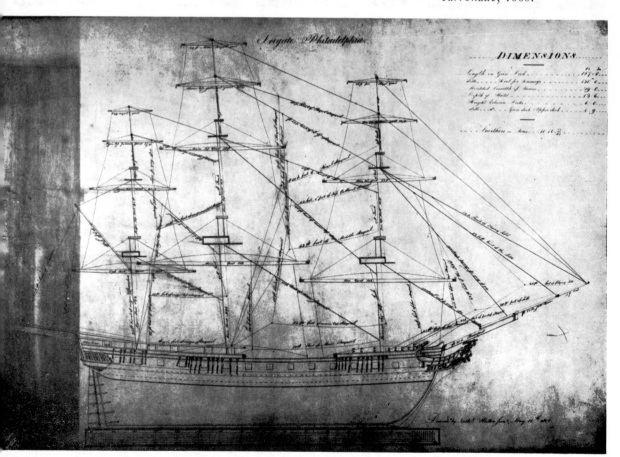

Builder's sail plan of the frigate PHILADELPHIA.
PLATE VII

Master sailmaker's plan of the ship of the line INDEPENDENCE.

Master sailmaker's plan of the ship of the line COLUMBUS.

PLATE VIII

river galleys to be built at Pittsburgh, Louisville, and Marietta. The galleys built on the coast appear to have been usually on the 51′ 6″ design, to carry one 24-pdr. long gun and six 3-pdr. swivels, manned by twenty-five privates or seamen and a commander, lieutenant, and boatswain. The larger galleys had the rail raised above the main sheer line from the bow gun port aft to the forward end of the rowing hatches; their gun port was much higher above the water line than in the galley shown in Figure 21. The coastal galleys were the *Savannah*, built at Savannah, Georgia, the *St. Marys*, built at St. Marys, Georgia, the *Charleston* and *South Carolina* built at Charleston, South Carolina, the *Beaufort* built at Beaufort, North Carolina, and the *Governor Williams* and the *Governor Davie* (or *Governor Davies*), both built at Wilmington, North Carolina. The known galleys built on the rivers were the *Marietta* and the *Senator Ross;* the names of the others have not been found. The galleys *Beaufort, Charleston,* and *South Carolina* may have been the ones built by subscription; the *Charleston* was first called the *Mars,* and the *South Carolina* the *Protector,* apparently. The first galley built in the West was one at Pittsburgh, contracted for by John Taylor. Joshua Humphreys received twelve dollars for the design shown in Figure 21. There was some objection to the rig of the galleys; some officers wanted to use square sails, but Humphreys very properly objected. Though the galleys were eminently suited for river service, they were of little value on the coast, except perhaps for harbor defense.

The plan of operation for the galleys proposed in the congressional act did not work out. The interest of the War Department in the boats was nil, and the Navy not only built and fitted the boats but eventually manned them as well. The coastal galleys were disposed of in 1801–2, some going to the Revenue Service and the others being sold. In 1800 the Secretary of the Navy wrote that in his opinion one 12-gun schooner on the naval establishment was worth a thousand galleys under the Act of May 4, 1798. In spite of the uselessness of the galleys for naval service the boats built in 1798–99 were to mark the beginning of an era of gunboat construction in the American Navy.

One of the modes of increasing the Navy in this period is interesting in the light of the modern theory that the protection of all groups within the national sphere is a matter of government responsibility. The popular concept was quite different in 1798. Since the merchants who owned ships were the chief sufferers from the seizures of American shipping by the Barbary powers and other nationals, it seemed reasonable to Congress that they should make a special contribution to the defense of the merchant marine. As a result, they provided, in the Act of June 30, 1798, that ships would be accepted by the Navy which were to be built by public subscription. The act authorized the President to accept a limited number to be paid for in bonds of 6 per cent interest and an unlimited number that might be voluntarily presented. In the event the first quota was not filled, the remaining portion of bonds, or "stock," could be paid on the second category. The intention was, of course, to encourage the merchants of the large ports, and the maritime interests in general, to contribute to the naval establishment, with partial repayment, at least, in interest-bearing notes. Of course, the possibility of the outright gift of ships by individuals or groups of citizens was to be encouraged by the government under this particular plan. Great efforts were made to call upon the patriotism and pride of the large maritime towns and cities to accomplish this and to make them outdo one another. Events showed that this procedure of the government seemed reasonable and fair to the general public and to the merchant class. As a result the Navy received a number of fine ships, from frigates down to brigs, some by bond payments and some as gifts.

The only drawback to the plan was that it required much time to raise funds for such a purpose in a community and to get the ships started. As a result, the frigates built by those ports financially able to handle such construction were slow in being completed and few were ready in time to play any part in the trouble with France. The smaller ships, however, got to sea early enough to be of some use.

One of the ports or areas that might have been able to build one large ship chose instead to produce two small ships. Baltimore built two 20-gun ships to carry 20 9-pdrs. on the main deck and 6 6-pdrs. on the quarterdeck. One was to be called the *Maryland* and the other the *Chesapeake*. The latter name, however, had been chosen for the frigate building at Gosport, so the Secretary of the Navy ordered the ship building at Baltimore to be renamed *Patapsco*. The *Maryland* and the *Patapsco* were both launched in June of 1799, and both were sold out of the Navy in 1801. No plans of the vessels exist, but from correspondence of Yellot, the navy agent at Baltimore, it appears that the vessels were 87' 0'' on the keel, 29' 0'' moulded beam, and 12' 0'' or 13' 0'' depth of hold, measuring "380 tons" and sharp-built. From a letter written by James Buchanan about the *Maryland* and a letter written to the navy agent by Truxton, it is known that the vessels had a spar deck, or rather forecastle and quarterdeck with gangways, and carried their guns too low. They were, however, good sailers, and the *Maryland* was said to be very fast in light weather.

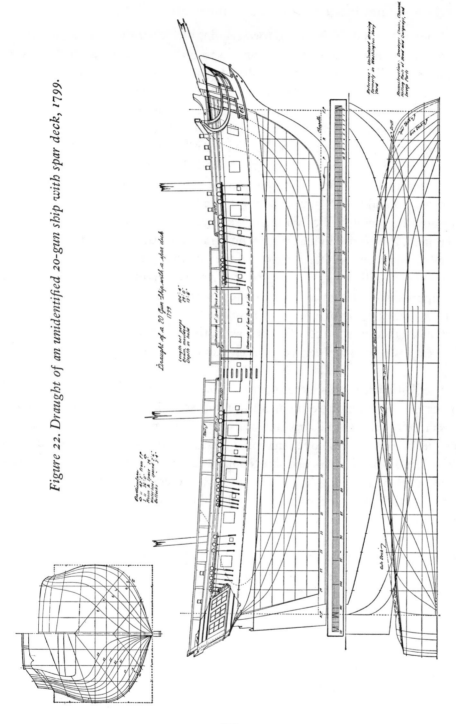

Figure 22. Draught of an unidentified 20-gun ship with spar deck, 1799.

155

Among the unidentified plans formerly in the files of the Washington Navy Yard was a rather incomplete drawing of a 20-gun ship much like the Baltimore-built vessels. Figure 22 shows this drawing of a spar-decked sloop of war to carry 20 guns on the lower deck and 4 on the quarterdeck. Such a vessel could have carried the six guns on the quarterdeck noted in the description of the Baltimore ships. The plan shows a miniature frigate, 106' 4" between perpendiculars, 29' 0" moulded beam, and 13' 6" depth of hold. The plan was dated 1799 and so cannot be a design for the Baltimore-built ships. It is possible that the plan was intended for an improved 20-gun ship based on them, with a deeper hold and fewer guns to permit more freeboard. The original plan cannot now be found in the National Archives, so the draftsmanship cannot be identified; the writer, in making a pencil tracing of the original in 1934, made no effort to accomplish this. In view of the fact that the drawing is another that cannot be identified with any degree of certainty, it is of value only in showing the approximate design and appearance of some of the 20-gun ships of the period. The design is of a rather sharp-ended vessel with the midsection placed farther aft than was the practice, at least in the larger ships. The appearance of the vessel would have been very much like that of the frigates of the 32-gun class.

The Baltimore vessels were apparently originally intended to have detached upper decks; Truxton recommended a full spar deck. When the *Maryland* was criticized it was said that this was one of the causes of objection and that spar decks were not employed in similar vessels abroad. This is an error, for both French and British navies had ship sloops with spar decks, or very wide gangways, as early as 1795. Buchanan wrote the Secretary of State, repeating the earlier criticisms of the spar deck and adding the more just comment that the ship was overgunned for her size. Comparing the ship in the plan and the known dimensions and armament of the *Maryland* and *Patapsco* with a British sloop of the period illustrates the mistake made in arming the American vessels. The British sloops of war built on a similar plan between 1795 and 1798, named *Termagant, Bittern, Cyane, Plover,* and *Brazen,* will serve to illustrate the point. The *Cyane* later fell into American hands and was taken into the United States Navy. The British ships were 110' 0" between perpendiculars, 29' 0" moulded beam, and 13' 8" in the hold, using the American system of measurement. They originally carried 16 6-pdrs. on the gun deck, 6 12-pdr. carronades on the quarterdeck, and 2 12-pdr. carronades on the forecastle— 24 guns all told against the Americans' 26 guns of heavier weight. Though rhe

British sloops had sharper bows than the ship in Figure 22, the greater area of the British ship's midsection and her slightly greater length gave her more displacement on slightly less draft.

Overloading with armament became as much a fault in the British Navy as in the American, as can be illustrated in the case of the *Cyane*. This ship carried a total of 32 guns in 1809—22 32-pdr. carronades on her main deck and 8 carronades, 18-pdrs., and 2 long 6's on her quarterdeck and forecastle. The effect of this on the ship was to damage her sailing qualities to a ruinous extent. In both the American and the British Navy the captains were trying to make frigates out of even the smallest ship sloops. If the Baltimore ships were anything like the plan shown here, they were far handsomer ships than the British vessels, and would probably have been faster sailers if they had been properly gunned and rigged. The builders of the two Baltimore ships are not given in government records, but the *Patapsco* is reported in a contemporary newspaper account to have been built in De Rochbrune's yard. She had a Neptune figurehead; the *Maryland* had a figure of the goddess of "commerce and plenty."

Another 20-gun ship, the *Warren*, already mentioned as built by contract at Newburyport, was 385 tons according to the official statements. Taking the dimensions of the ship shown in Figure 22, calculation of the tonnage in accordance with the method then in force shows her to be only a little over 360 tons; it is highly probable, then, that all tonnage in these small naval vessels was grossly overestimated and that the two Baltimore-built ships as well as the *Warren* were only about 350 tons burden. Tonnage statements in this period seem to have been based on varying local practices and are therefore unreliable.

It is apparent from the official correspondence that the Secretary of the Navy sent out dimensions and, in some cases at least, plans of 20- and 24-gun ships for the information of the sponsors of subscriptions. In a letter to Charleston he enclosed a plan of a 24-gun ship, to measure about 538 tons and to carry 24 guns on the main deck and 4 or 6 more on the quarterdeck, the lower-deck guns to be 12-pdrs. His letter indicates that he sent a plan of the ship *Portsmouth*, designed by Josiah Fox, but the plan was not used, as a larger vessel was finally built. In another letter he gives the navy agent at New York an idea of what he considers to be the dimensions of a 20-gun ship: 93' 0" keel, 31' 0" beam, and 13' 6" depth of hold; to carry 20 guns on the main deck, exclusive of the bridle ports, and 2 guns on the quarterdeck. In a letter to Connecticut he asks about the possibility of building an 18-gun ship or brig, and then indicates the desire for a ship of from 300 to 360 tons to carry 18 long 9's. The tenor of his correspondence was to give the sponsors of the subscription vessels an idea of the desired size, leaving it to the local groups to choose a designer and builder and to judge the proper model and proportions.

In this manner he was able to induce the citizens of Newburyport to build the 24-gun ship *Merrimack*, with 20 9-pdrs. on the main deck and 8 6-pdrs. on the quarterdeck. Built by an association of shipwrights, among whom was Cross, this ship was launched October 12, 1798, and was sold at Boston in 1801. He also succeeded in getting the people of the Norwich, Connecticut, area, which included New London, to build the 18-gun ship *Trumbull* of 400 tons, carrying 18 12-pdrs. on one deck. He obtained the 200-ton brig *Richmond* from the citizens of Richmond, Petersburg, Manchester, and Norfolk, Virginia, in 1798. Both the *Trumbull* and the *Richmond* were sold in 1801. A number of other small vessels were projected but failed to be brought forward. The two Baltimore vessels and the *Merrimack, Trumbull, Richmond*, and the frigate *Boston* were the only subscription-built vessels to see active service in the French troubles.

The Secretary's desire to utilize the shipbuilding knowledge of as many communities as possible and the lack of technical supervision by the government's naval architects, or other central authority, that was inherent in the subscription method of obtaining ships (as well as the disorganization of the newly established Navy Department) all created a confusion of records, and it is not surprising to find that few plans of the ships have survived. While it was plainly the intention of the Secretary to obtain plans of each ship built, he was too burdened with duties and responsibilities to be able to follow the matter up and to complete the plan files. The latter, in fact, were at that time of little practical value; because of the newness of the ships, their maintenance had not yet become a serious matter, and so there had been no particular demand for the information that was contained in the plans. About the only purpose they served was to guide the proposals for new vessels.

The Secretary's desire to employ the shipbuilding knowledge of as many areas as possible appears to have arisen from a realization that naval ship design and construction was becoming concentrated, to an undesirable degree, in certain Philadelphia shipyards. The small clique of Philadelphia shipwrights not only dominated the design of new ships to a great extent, but their advice had been accepted to the exclusion of all others. Even Fox could be placed among

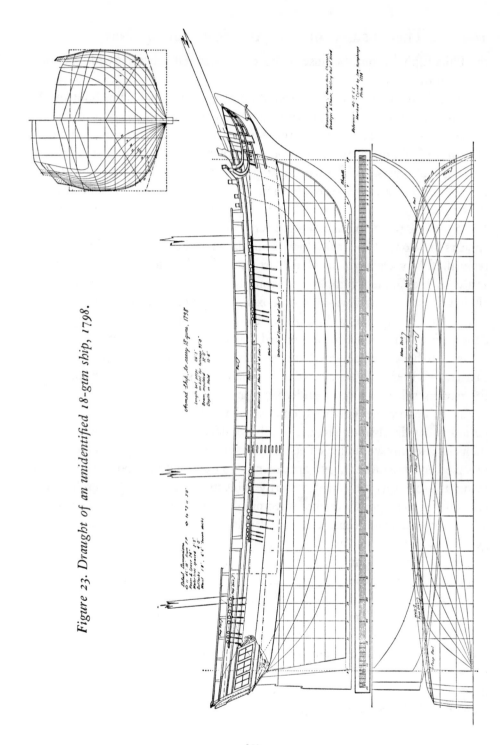

Figure 23. Draught of an unidentified 18-gun ship, 1798.

159

the Philadelphia group because of his close personal relations with the merchants of that city.

It is unfortunate that we have found no plan of the small ships built by the government or by subscription that can be identified as the design of any individual vessel. In fact, so far as the Navy plan files are concerned, the only plan of a small armed ship of the period, other than the 20-gun ship last described, is of a vessel whose nature cannot be determined with certainty. The design of this vessel is presented in Figure 23, redrawn from a pencil tracing of the original when it was in the Washington Navy Yard files. Though indexed (40–15–6 E), the plan has not yet been found in the National Archives and appears to be one of the many lost or misplaced in the transfer of the drawings from the Navy Department. This particular drawing, dated 1798, was noted as a copy by Samuel Humphreys. From the appearance of the stem it is concluded that the design was one of Fox's, but as yet no identification can be made. The ship appears at first glance to be a merchantman, but study of the design shows the model to be unusual for a vessel employed in trade. She is too large to have been designed as a fast illegal trader, and too sharp to be a good carrier. It is therefore possible that this plan represents either a ship proposed for naval service, or one intended as a merchant-cruiser. The design might be said to be intermediate between a merchant ship and a sloop of war of the period under discussion. The use of a berth deck in this ship was indicated on the plan, and this would have been needless in a merchant ship. The vessel also was pierced for a rather heavy armament—18 guns, with the possibility of carrying 22—but this did not necessarily indicate a naval vessel; merchantmen carrying up to 22 guns were not uncommon in the American merchant marine at the end of the eighteenth century. A ship of this design would have made a good convoy guard and an effective cruiser. It is possible that the plan may be that of one of the 18-gun ships, but in the absence of the dimensions of these vessels identification is wholly impractical. The design was for a ship 95' 0" on the keel for tonnage, 32' 0" moulded beam, 13' 6" depth of hold, and 116' 3" between perpendiculars. The tonnage was not given, but it works out at about 430 tons. She would have been somewhat similar in appearance to some French-built sloops, except for carrying her guns on the upper deck. It is to be observed that the Americans had accepted the basic model and arrangement of the 44-gun ships as the ideal for all classes, from ship sloops upward. This can be seen not only in the 20-gun ship design shown in Figure 22 and in the ship just described, but also in the greater part of the frigate class of the United States Navy.

Though most of the large ships built by subscription were completed too late to be of any real service in the trouble with the French republicans of the Directorate, they were excellent additions to the Navy and were of value in the events that followed the quasi war with France. Five new frigates resulted from the efforts of the merchants of the important ports: the *Philadelphia, New York, Essex, Boston,* and *John Adams;* all were well-built ships on what were then considered very good models.

The merchants of Philadelphia went to Josiah Fox for the design of the frigate they wished to build. The wealth of the port and the pride of the merchants had decided the type of ship to be built; she was to be an "improved" 44-gun ship. Now, Fox was not satisfied with the large 44's, as we have seen, and was convinced that ships of this class somewhat smaller than the *Constitution* type were the most desirable. He was given freedom to design the new frigate as he thought best, and he produced a ship much like the earlier frigates in appearance but differing in dimensions and model. Like the earlier 44's, she was to have what constituted a spar deck. The final dimensions of the *Philadelphia,* or as she was sometimes called, *City of Philadelphia,* were 157′ 0″ between perpendiculars, 130′ 0″ on the keel for tonnage, 39′ 0″ moulded beam, and 13′ 6″ depth of hold. Samuel Humphreys, Nathaniel Hutton, and John Delavue were selected to build the ship. They completed her in the spring of 1800. This fine frigate is shown in Plan 9; the differences between this drawing and the one in the National Archives (reprinted in *Barbary Wars, Personnel and Ships' Data,* as part of the Naval Documents printed under the supervision of the Office of Naval Records and Library, U.S. Government Printing Office, 1945) require explanation.

The drawing of the ship in the above-mentioned publication is an exact reproduction of the existing draught, with such additions as were necessary to restore a very damaged plan. This drawing of the *Philadelphia* shows a ship with what appears to be a solid spar-deck bulwark, running flush and unbroken from stem to stern. One of the oddities of the plan was that the cutwater and head seemed remarkably modern and more like the frigates built during and after the War of 1812 than like the earlier frigates. Another plan of the ship existed, however; this was a carefully drawn sail plan dated May 16, 1800, which was made by Nathaniel Hutton, Jr., one of the builders. This plan, part of the papers of John Lenthall, constructor of the U.S. Navy and a former apprentice of Samuel Humphreys, is in the Franklin Institute, Philadelphia. It showed a vessel having the apparent lines and dimensions given in the plan in the National Archives, but with an entirely different cutwater and headrail arrangement, as well as extensive departures in the rail on the spar deck. In examining the plan of the *Philadelphia* in the National Archives, it was noticed that the draftsmanship was not that of Fox, but that it was very much like

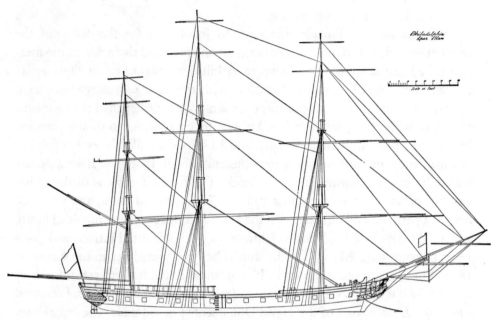

Figure 24. Spar plan of the frigate PHILADELPHIA *after spar dimensions. (See Plan 9.)*

that in the plan of the frigate *New York*, also in the National Archives and reproduced in *Personnel and Ships' Data*. In searching for the plan of the *New York*, which also showed what appeared to be a solid spar-deck bulwark, the inboard-works drawing of the *New York* was found. This showed that the draught of the *New York* was incorrect in the spar-deck rails and other details. In addition it showed that the *New York*'s draught was not the original, but rather a plan drawn by an apprentice named Henry Allen. Additional search brought out the evidence that the plans of both the *Philadelphia* and the *New York*, as well as a drawing of the brig *Syren*, had been made by Allen from offsets and building directions in the years 1816–21. This seems to explain the comparatively modern appearance of the plans now in the National Archives. Accepting the lines shown in Allen's drawing of the *Philadelphia* as correct, since they were made from the offsets, the headrails and spar-deck rails have been taken from Hutton's plan. However, the vessel was intended as a 44, so the draught in Plan 9 shows the probable appearance of the ship as originally designed.

While the ship was building she was referred to as a 44, but before she was commissioned she was rerated as a 36-gun ship. This seems to have been accomplished, in fact, by the omission of the spar-deck rail and gun ports, from just forward of the mainmast to the bow, and the shifting of some of the gun ports on the quarterdeck as well as a reduction in their number. She first carried 28 guns on the main deck, 18-pdrs., and 10 guns on the quarterdeck, type and caliber unknown. In 1803 she carried sixteen 32-pdr. carronades on her quarterdeck and forecastle, which is evidence that her spar-deck rails had undergone another alteration. The sail plan of the ship shown in Figure 24 shows the ports and spar-deck rails arranged approximately as in Hutton's sail plan. Both drawings of the *Philadelphia* presented here have the figurehead shown in Hutton's plan, as well as the same headrail and stem profile. The extensive reconstructions in the plans of the *Philadelphia* are made necessary by the unintentional anachronisms contained in the draught in the National Archives reproduced in *Personnel and Ships' Data*. The quantity of documentary material, and the two plans, relating to this ship, make the reconstructions reasonably accurate, though the figurehead shown is open to question.

The *Philadelphia* was not on the same model as the earlier 44's and 38's, as has been mentioned. She was fuller in the cross sections, near the keel, which gave less deadrise to the bottom. This was apparently typical of Fox's designs for frigates, for it also appears in the plan of the *Crescent*. The design of the *Philadelphia*, by showing radical departures from both the model and the dimensions of the *Constitution* and *Constellation* classes, obviously disposes of any claim that might be made that Fox was solely responsible for the earlier designs.

It might be a matter of surprise that the Philadelphia merchants went to Fox rather than to their fellow townsman, Joshua Humphreys, for the design of the local frigate, but there is no reason to believe that this was a reflection on the ability of the Philadelphian. The fact of the matter appears to be that Humphreys rejected the commission as he was very busy with repairs and the supervision of fitting out vessels for the Navy and was at work on the design of a 74-gun ship while the *Philadelphia* was building. Fox's connections with Philadelphians and his known ability and experience made him a natural choice under the circumstances.

The *Philadelphia* was considered a fast and beautiful frigate. Her end at Tripoli is well known, and the events that surrounded her final destruction produced some of the most inspiring acts in American naval history. In spite of having been considered a very fine frigate, neither her model nor her size and rate had much influence on later design. The Americans were fully committed to ships of great size for their rate.

The next largest frigate built by private subscription was the *New York*, designed by Samuel Humphreys, probably with the help of Nathaniel Hutton, Jr., with whom he was then closely associated. The original plan of the *New York* cannot be found; the drawing made from offsets by Henry Allen, now in the National Archives, and published in *Personnel and Ships' Data*, has been mentioned. While the lines of the ship in Allen's plan are correct, the head and cutwater are not only anachronisms but also are technically incorrect, since they would require the hawseholes to be placed in an impossible position. Plan 10 shows the drawing of this ship, based on the lines preserved in Allen's plan but with the spar-deck rails and other details in accordance with the only original plan that survived, her inboard profile. The headrails and cutwater are conjectural and are based on partial measurements that were given in Samuel Humphreys' memorandum in his offset book (indexed in the National Archives as C & R 81–6), now missing.

The *New York* seems to have been intended as a comparatively small 38; she had ports to permit mounting 50 guns, though of course she could not have borne their weight. She was rerated when placed in commission as a 36. The *New York* was 144′ 2″ between perpendiculars, 37′ 0″ moulded beam, and 11′ 9″ depth in the hold. She was to carry 26 18-pdrs. on her main deck and 14 9-pdrs. on her spar deck, but the 9-pdrs. were apparently replaced by an unknown number of carronades, late in her active service. The ship was built at New York by Peck and Carpenter, in the latter's yard, and was launched in April, 1800. She spent the greater part of her life laid up in the Washington Navy Yard and was burned there when the British took the capital in 1814. She seems to have been a satisfactory sailer as a frigate, but there is little else on record as to her qualities. Her model was somewhat like that of the *Constellation* class, with a rather marked hardness in the bilges and slacker bottom.

Nothing has been found on her carving, but she undoubtedly was heavily orna-
mented.

The third frigate in size was the famous *Essex*. This vessel was built with
funds raised at Salem and in Essex County, Massachusetts, and was built by
Enos Briggs of Salem on a design prepared by William Hackett. She was to
be a 32-gun frigate and large for her rate—140′ 0″ between perpendiculars,

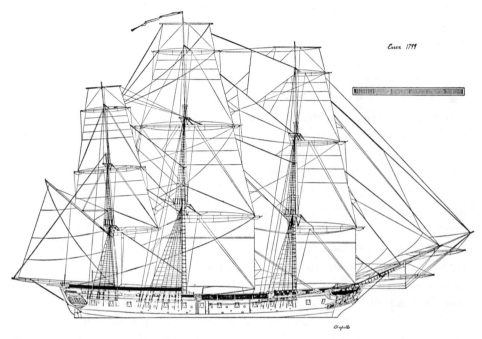

Figure 25. Spar and sail plan of the frigate ESSEX, *typical of the rig in the smaller
American frigates of her period.*

36′ 6″ moulded beam, and 12′ 3″ depth in the hold. Her design is shown in
Plan 11, redrawn from the original plan preserved in the National Archives
(41–9–1 L), with the head and the stern elevation restored. The head is from
the well-known painting of the ship, and the elevation of the stern is wholly
conjectural. The *Essex* was unlike the other American frigates in model; the
sections do not show the rather marked "knuckles" below the water line to be
seen in the other frigates, and they follow approximately the general section
design shown in the unidentified ship plan in Figure 23 and in the unidentified
design of a 20-gun vessel in Figure 22. She was designed with detached fore-

castle and quarterdeck, which were connected by means of the usual gangways along the sides, not quite flush with these two decks. She was somewhat like the Revolutionary War frigates in appearance, but had guns on her forecastle. She was designed with a solid bulwark on her quarterdeck, which seems to have gone out of fashion in the American frigates, but which again became the general practice early in the 1800's. Hackett's drawing of the ship was hurried and very rough; a reproduction of the original plan will be found in *Personnel and Ships' Data*. The *Essex* was a very fast frigate, but by the time the War of 1812 began the changes made by her various commanders and by navy yard commandants had spoiled her sailing. The ships that were easily overweighted, because of sharp lines, were invariably those first spoiled by the "improvements" of their commanders.

The fourth frigate in size was the *Boston*, 32 guns. This ship was designed by Edmund Hartt and built in the Hartt yard, operated by Edmund, Edward, and Joseph Hartt, at Boston, Massachusetts. The ship was launched in May, 1799, and was finished during the summer following. The *Boston*, shown in Plan 12, was a frigate somewhat like the *Essex* in appearance, though different in model, being less sharp. The *Boston* also had her gangways flush with the quarterdeck and forecastle deck and carried 24 guns on her main deck, 12-pdrs., and two 12-pdr. chase guns on the forecastle, with 12 9-pdrs. on the quarterdeck and forecastle. In 1801 12 32-pdr. carronades either were added to 6 9-pdrs. on the upper decks or replaced the 9-pdrs. entirely—which seems more probable. The ship was rerated as a 28-gun frigate when placed on the Navy list. The *Boston* was 134' 0" between perpendiculars, but owing to the way these were established she was actually 136' 6" on the gun deck. Her moulded beam was 34' 6", and her depth of hold 11' 6". She was originally built with an open rail on her quarterdeck, but in her first commission this was planked up to form a bulwark, as in the *Essex*. The *Boston*, as can be seen, was a very handsome frigate, but her plan in the National Archives did not do justice to her beauty—having been drawn, as her designer noted on the plan, without instruments. If the *Boston* and *Essex* are sufficient evidence, the New Englanders employed longer and lighter heads, or cutwaters, on their ships than were popular at Philadelphia. The *Boston* was the only presentation frigate to see action against the French; she captured the small French frigate *Berceau*, which was later returned to France. Captain Little of the *Boston* was not as fortunate as Truxton and did not receive comparable praise and publicity for the capture of the French frigate. The *Boston* was laid up in the Washington

Navy Yard in 1802 and allowed to rot. She was burned when the yard was destroyed in 1814, having by then become unfit for repair.

The rerating of the frigates, to lower rates than designed, was a fashion that seems to have been brought about by a desire to establish a standard relation between rates and dimensions, as existing in the frigates authorized in 1794. Another factor involved was the jealousy of commanding officers regarding the perquisites of seniority; it would have been "disgraceful" for the senior officer to command a 44 that was actually smaller than one commanded by a junior in rank, even though the ships were of the same rate. The squabbles over rank during this period were continuous and violent.

The smallest of the frigates built by subscription was the 28-gun *John Adams*, designed by Josiah Fox and built by the merchants and citizens of Charleston and vicinity, South Carolina. Paul Pritchard was the builder. The frigate's dimensions were variously given in official papers, owing to the fact that her plan was never turned over to the Navy Department. James Marsh, a noted shipbuilder of Charleston, was foreman of Pritchard's yard when the *John Adams* was built, and writing in 1820 to the Navy Department, he stated that the ship was designed to be 86' 0" on the keel or straight rabbet, 32' 0" beam, 12' 0" lower hold, 6' 0" berth to gun deck, and 5' 10" waist. He said also that the keel timbers were of such length and quality that the committee of the association building her decided to lengthen the ship 5 feet and she was given one more port to the side on the main deck than called for in Fox's draught. Marsh thought she had but 10" deadrise and said she was a flat-floored ship of light draft that would permit her being taken across the bar at Charleston. Another official set of dimensions shows her to have been 127' 9" on the gun deck, 33' 3" extreme beam, and total depth from ceiling to gun deck 16' 10". Carvings were by William Rush of Philadelphia. She stuck on the ways on the first attempt to launch but got over on the second attempt, June 5, 1799. It was either this ship or the *Adams* whose two sides, according to tradition, were unlike, so that she sailed better on one tack than on the other. From the alleged circumstances supporting this tradition it appears that the ship having this curious feature was the *Adams* after her rebuilding as a corvette, rather than the *John Adams*. The *John Adams* spent much of her life laid up and was permitted to rot; she was finally broken up at the Norfolk Navy Yard in 1829, a new ship of the same name being constructed in the guise of "rebuilding" the old ship.

It can be seen by the ships' plans that have survived that American designers had established what might safely be called a "standard" appearance. The cutwater and its supporting headrails followed a standard practice; the "seat" or "middle" rail (known to shipwrights by a far less polite but more expressive name) was carried up, at the after end, to fair into the knee supporting the cathead; the upper or "hair" rail also turned up at its after end approximately parallel to the "seat" rail, to end outside the bow chock rail, or to form a decorative timberhead. Above the upper rail was a light, straight rail, either of timber or of iron rod, used to support the nettings and weather cloths masking the crews' toilet facilities, which were located on a grating platform contained within the headrails. No troughs or discharge pipes were employed at first, though most frigates were fitted with these improvements by 1810. The lack of these plumbing fixtures often made the ship's bows anything but attractive at close range.

The construction of all the new ships was intended to be very strong, with the hope of producing vessels of a very long life. The problem of finding a species of American shipbuilding timber comparable to English oak was thought to be solved by the use of southern live oak, and this timber was therefore used very extensively in the new ships. However, it did not live up to expectations. In addition, it was found that the available supply was more limited than had been supposed. Other timber was therefore resorted to—white oak, yellow pine, cedar, and various hardwoods. The ships soon showed evidences of rot in spite of the efforts made—but the trouble was probably due more to improper seasoning than to poor timber.

The American preference for a spar deck, or at least for very wide gangways connecting quarterdeck and forecastle, in the frigates and larger ship sloops was based on the desirability of having a clear working space for handling the sails and rigging in action. The spar deck, being at most only partially armed, was very useful for this purpose. However, the administrative system which permitted officers to change the armament almost at will made the temptation great to place additional guns on the spar deck or along the gangways.

The ships were commonly overcanvased and oversparred, as has been mentioned; the desire to obtain speed was at odds with the equally great desire to carry an impressive number of guns, which materially increased displacement and reduced speed. Often, after increasing the number of guns in his ship, the captain felt it necessary to increase sail area by getting longer spars. There are numerous cases where ships were placed in jeopardy by this vicious circle of "improvement." The overcanvasing of American naval ships was eventually to become notorious; it was probably the cause of the loss of a number of small vessels at sea.

In most of the frigates the designers had intended to save weight high in the hull by using open rails on the quarterdeck or along the greater part of the spar deck. Pictures of some of the ships a few years after they were placed in service show that this aim was defeated by the closing in of the quarterdeck rails and the eventual raising and closing in of the forecastle rails to the same height. The original open rails were intended to be covered with netting and painted canvas, or weather cloths, to mask the crew working on this deck from enemy sharpshooters and musketmen; the rails were intended to be strongly built to provide for temporary gun ports along the middle portion of the length of the spar deck, or gangways. With the closing in of the forecastle and quarterdeck rails, the rails amidships on the gangways were replaced by light iron stanchions supporting a light wooden handrail, which was soon made double to support a deep hammock netting. When hammocks were placed in this and covered with a heavy tarpaulin, a light breastwork was created. The low bulwarks of the forecastle and quarterdeck were gradually increased in effective height by adding hammock nettings along their tops, a fashion which had developed gradually in European navies during the previous seventy-five years.

Though the original plans of most of the frigates show the old "rule-joint" rudders, it is evident from the correspondence that some of the ships were built with the "plug-stock" rudders that were gradually becoming common. In the old style of "rule-joint" rudder, the head had to swing in an arc owing to the shape of the stock and the position of the gudgeons and pintles in relation to the vertical center line. In this style the rudder and its head swung after the manner of a door, and so the opening through the transom for the stock had to be very large. This opening was covered by a greased rawhide "boot," or by a heavy canvas "coat," but was nevertheless a source of leakage and weakness. In the "plug-stock" rudder, the stock was offset forward so that its axis was in a vertical line with the center line of the pintles and gudgeons; this permitted the stock to revolve when the rudder was swung and resulted in a small, snug opening in the ship's transom for the rudderstock. The only difficulty with the "plug-stock" rudder was that the offset in the stock could be a source of weakness and many rudderstocks failed because they were improperly built. Though there was some prejudice against the new style of rudders, it

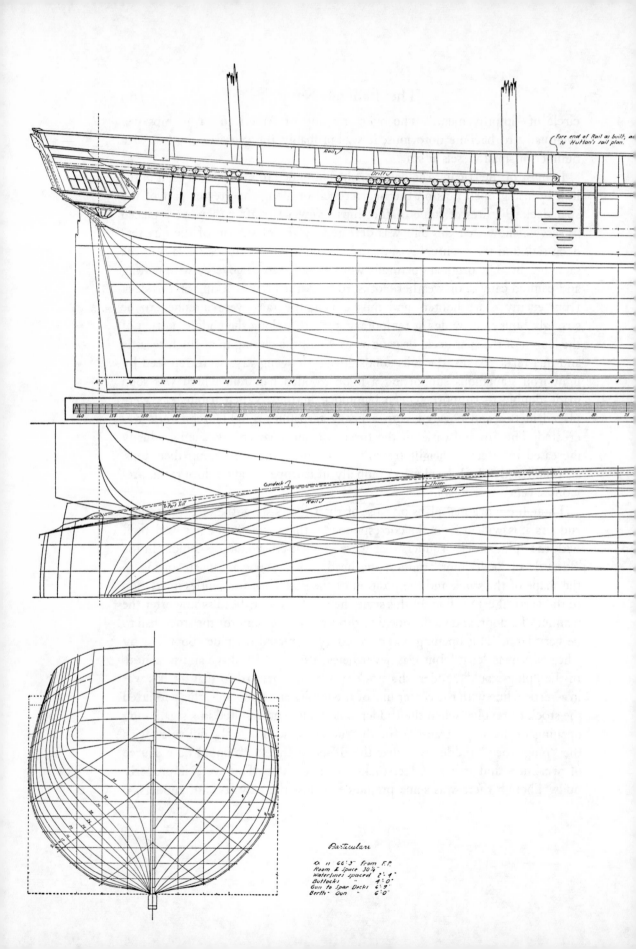

Fore end of Rail as built, a[...]
to Hutton's sail plan.

Rail J

Drift J

A/P   34   32   30   28   26   24   20   16   12   8   4

160   155   150   145   140   135   130   125   120   115   110   105   100   95   90   85   80   75

Gundeck J   E:Tier
                Rail J   Drift J
2.Port Sill

Particulars

O " 66'3" from F.P.
Room & Space 30½"
Waterlines spaced 2'4"
Buttocks 4'0"
Gun to Spar Decks 6'9"
Berth· Gun 6'0"

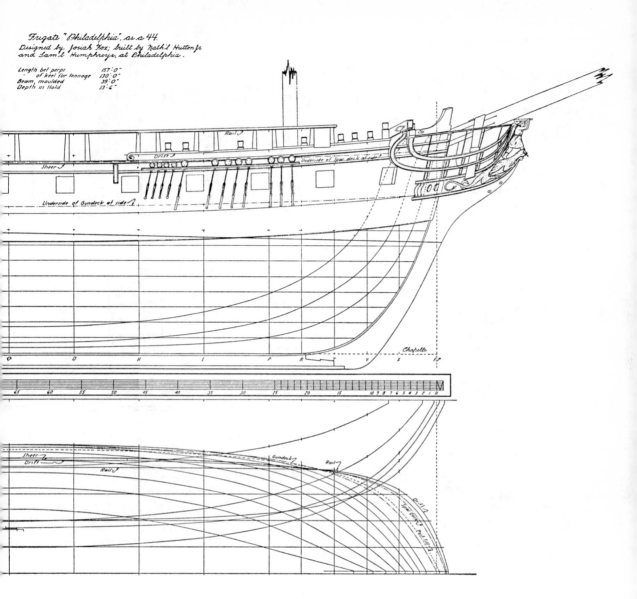

Frigate "Philadelphia", as a 44.
Designed by Josiah Fox; built by Nath'l Hutton Jr
and Sam'l Humphreys, at Philadelphia.

Length bet perps.   157'0"
  " of keel for tonnage 130'0"
Beam, moulded   39'0"
Depth in Hold   13'6"

References - Restoration
Lines from Allen's draught, made from Offsets
Headrails, Cutwater Figurehead Bridle port,
Sheer-mouldings, from Nath'l Hutton's Sail Plan
of 1801. Spar Deck Rail & Gunports forward of
mainmast believed probable for original draught
as a 44 gun frigate

Plan 9. Draught of the 44-gun frigate PHILADELPHIA, after Allen's drawing and builder's sail plan.

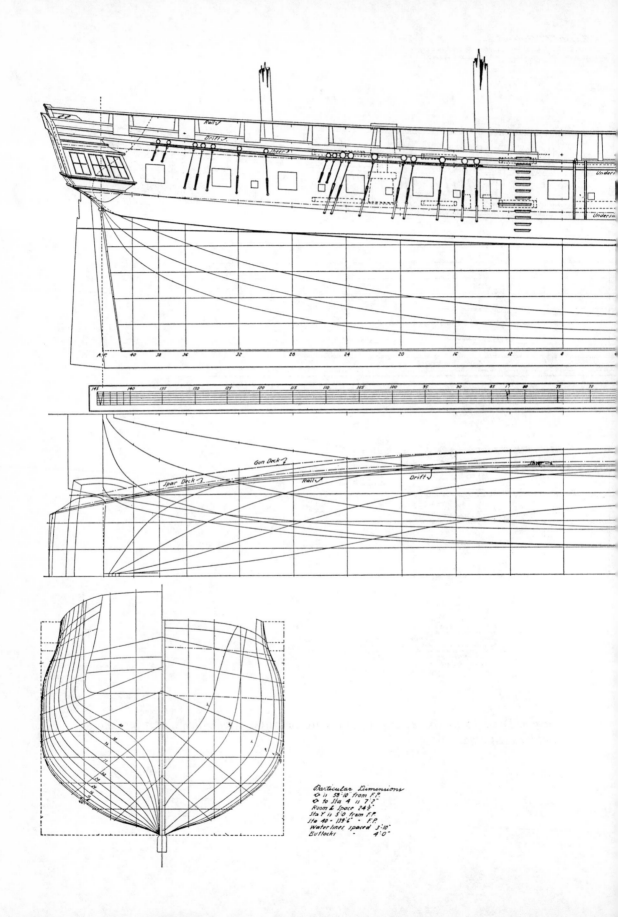

Particular Dimensions
○ is 58'10 from F.P.
○ to Sta 4 is 7'2"
Room & Space 24½"
Sta Y is 5'0 from F.P.
Sta 40 = 139'6" " F.P.
Water lines spaced 5'10"
Buttocks " 4'0"

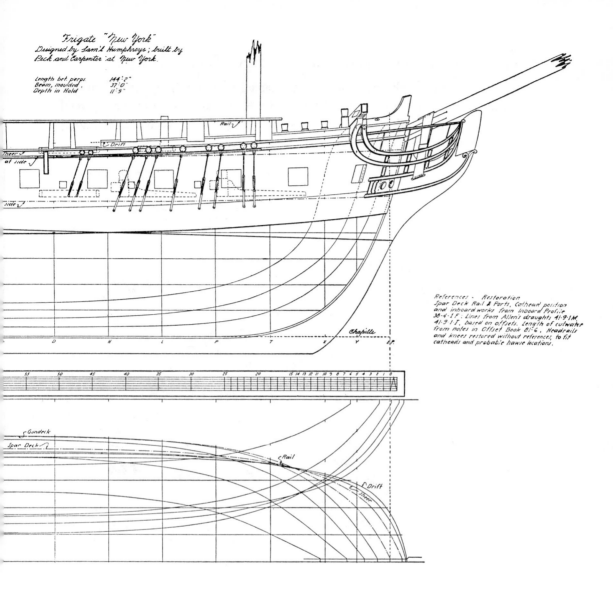

Frigate "New York"
Designed by Sam'l Humphreys; built by
Peck and Carpenter at New York.

Length bet. perps.   144'2"
Beam, moulded   37'0"
Depth in Hold   11'9"

References - Restoration
Spar Deck Rail & Ports, Cothead position
and inboard works from Inboard Profile
38-4-1 F. Lines from Allen's draughts 41-9-1M,
41-9-1 T, based on offsets. Length of cutwater
from notes in Offset Book 81-6. Headrails
and knees restored without references; to fit
catheads and probable hawse locations.

Plan 10. Draught of the 36-gun frigate NEW YORK, after Allen's plan and inboard
works plan.

was not long after the new ships were started that the "plug-stock" rudder became a standard fitting in naval ships. The Americans seem to have replaced the "rule-joint" rudder with the new style by 1801 or thereabouts, changing over the ships already fitted with the older type.

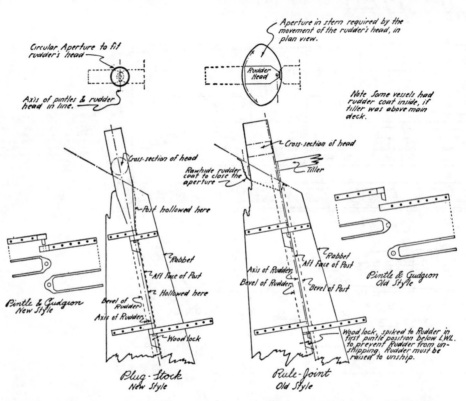

Sketch showing difference between "rule-joint" and "plug-stock" rudders.

The frigates were all fitted with air scuttles on the berth deck. These are shown in the plans of the *Essex* and *Boston*. The scuttles had solid covers hinged at the fore side. The American style was similar to the British; the hinge was horseshoe- or U-shaped, with the open end forward on the cover to give two hinge eyes. These rested on two eyebolts driven into the wale or side of the ship, or else there was another U-shaped hinge plate on the hull, with bolts for pins, one in each eye. The glass was recessed into the hull to permit the cover to close; the glass could be unshipped from the inside.

The scuppers were of the standard type used abroad—lead pipe through the waterways and sides of the ship—and some vessels apparently had leather valves on lower-deck scuppers. These valves were leather strips weighted with lead so that the outside pressure of water closed them; to permit this, the strips were secured at the fore side of the scupper only.

The general design of the frigates and other ships had produced a rather low and long hull. This was considered desirable in windward sailing, since it reduced windage in proportion to size of hull and gave greater sail-carrying power than would be possible in a short, high-sided ship. The gradual changes in the upper rails and bulwarks of the ships had the effect of raising the apparent freeboard, and some of the smaller frigates were undoubtedly harmed by this change in fashion.

It was gradually recognized both by naval officers and by the office of the Secretary of the Navy that frigates and ship sloops, while very useful and highly necessary, were insufficient to create an effective Navy. As early as 1797, Secretary Stoddert suggested to congressional groups the need of 74-gun ships, and late in 1798 he recommended the construction of such vessels. During the preliminary discussions, proposals had been made that 74-gun ships be purchased abroad. The Secretary now pointed out that it was improbable that a foreign power would part with a first-class 74, and that in any event the expenditure of funds abroad would act as an unfavorable balance of trade on the national economy. He consequently recommended that twelve ships of this class be constructed and that the timber for them be acquired at once. He also suggested that, if the ships were not built at once after the timber was procured, the latter could be preserved in storage in wet decks for an indefinite period until needed. In 1799 Congress authorized the purchase of six sets of frames for 74's and authorized funds to "purchase timber for naval purposes." The funds authorized were in excess of those actually required; as a result some islands in the South with live-oak timber on them were bought, and altogether eight sets of ship frames were contracted for by the Secretary of the Navy.

Stoddert had carefully worked out a plan for building up the new Navy. His recommendations in 1799 proposed not only the construction of twelve 74's but also the maintenance of twelve frigates and twenty to thirty smaller vessels as the requirement to protect American interests abroad. The following year he also suggested the purchase of timber for a frigate and for twelve 24-gun ships; in doing so he found it opportune to point out in general terms the increasing need for navy yards or other suitable facilities for the storage of naval materials—though it must be admitted that this was done without much conviction.

In the winter of 1798–99, Joshua Humphreys was employed in assisting the Secretary with advice on the 74's, and in the spring—March 20, 1799—he completed the initial draught of this class. The ships were to be 178′ 0″ between perpendiculars, 48′ 6″ moulded beam, and 19′ 6″ depth of hold, armed with 28 32-pdrs. on the gun deck, 30 24-pdrs. on the upper deck, 12 9-pdrs. on the quarterdeck, and 4 more on the forecastle. Humphreys' plan was rather poorly drawn, but the first design served for discussion purposes. After numerous consultations between the Secretary and his advisers, including naval officers, it was decided to make all the guns 32-pdrs. This required more displacement than Humphreys' draught permitted, and a new drawing was necessary. Samuel Humphreys redrew the design under his father's direction, lengthening the ship 5 feet amidships and altering the position of the gun ports accordingly, but with no change in number. Hutton and Doughty made copies of this plan, all of which survive. The plan by Doughty has the name "Independence" written on its back. The Hutton drawing was dated February 7, 1801, and was the last one made.

The revised design is shown in Plan 13, with the length increased to 183′ 0″ between perpendiculars. Unfortunately, in the light of later events, the 74's were never built and the timber acquired for them either rotted or was used for small craft and shore construction. The design of the ships is of value, however, as it shows the most advanced ideas in America on what a line-of-battle ship ought to be, at the end of the eighteenth century. Had the 74's been built, they would have been among the most powerful ships of their class in the world, and about the same length as the largest French ships. Having slightly less beam and depth, but with 6 inches greater length, they would have had a tonnage slightly less than that of the French 74's built in the same year that the American ships were designed. The larger of the two ships of the class built for the Royal Navy in 1800 was the *Spencer*, 180′ 10″ between perpendiculars, 49′ 3″ extreme beam, and 21′ 10″ depth of hold; but neither the French nor the British ships were intended to carry the armament proposed for the American design.

The plan prepared by Humphreys, and the lengthened copies by his son and by Doughty and Hutton, show that Joshua Humphreys had an excellent grasp of hull form. The 74's would have been sharp-ended for their class and would undoubtedly have been comparatively fast sailers. They retained the beakhead bulkhead of earlier ships, and in this followed general practice in 74-gun ship design abroad. They were spar-decked in the American fashion, though not intended to carry guns on the wide gangways amidships that were, in reality, the continuations of the forecastle and quarterdeck, which constituted the spar deck in fact, if not in name. Had the ships been built, it would have been found that they were unable to bear the armament proposed for them, but even with a slightly reduced weight of guns they would have been most formidable vessels. If the six proposed ships had been either in commission or ready for fitting out, their existence might have been sufficient to prevent the events that finally led to the War of 1812.

A great deal of preliminary work was done on the 74's; they were lofted and moulds for their timbers were made; rough copies of these were sent to the contractors to get out timber to the required shapes and sizes. Humphreys prepared rather complete specifications for the ships, and it is obvious that the design of the class, and the timber contracts, were seriously considered as a realistic step in establishing a navy of effective force.

The only ships left unaccounted for are those captured from France during the quasi war. Only two of the ships taken were placed on the Navy list, though one small schooner, the *Bon Père*, was taken into the Revenue Service as the *Bee*. She had been captured from the French by the cutter *Eagle* while the latter was in naval hands. The frigate *L'Insurgent*, a good 36-gun frigate, had been captured by Truxton in the *Constellation* after a very hard encounter, February 9, 1799. An almost new ship, *L'Insurgent* was taken into the Navy as *Insurgent*, and the survey of her shows that she measured 148' 0" on the gun deck, 37' 5" beam, and 11' 9" depth of hold. When captured she had 24 12-pdrs., 2 18-pdrs., 8 6-pdrs.—all long guns—and 4 36-pdr. and 2 24-pdr. carronades, or 40 guns all told. Since she was the first capture of a regular man-of-war by a ship of the new Navy, much was made of Truxton and the battle. It was claimed that she was superior in force to the *Constellation*, and both her size and power were reported in exaggerated terms. Actually, she was smaller and was a less effective ship than the big American frigate. The *Insurgent* had a very short career in the American service, being lost at sea with all hands in the fall of 1800. No plan of this ship has yet been found. A small frigate, the *Berceau*, was taken by the *Boston*, as mentioned earlier, but this ship was one of those returned to France at the end of the quasi war. The schooner

Retaliation was a 107-ton, 14-gun schooner carrying 6-pdrs. taken as the French privateer *Le Croyable* by the *Delaware* July 7, 1798. She was purchased into the Navy on the 30th of the same month. One account states that she was a Maryland-built schooner. As the *Retaliation* she was taken by the French frigates *L'Insurgent* and *La Volontaire*, November 20, 1798, and taken into the French Navy as *La Magicienne*. Then she was recaptured by the *Merrimack* on June 28, 1799, and was sold as a prize to private owners. She seems to have been either a very unlucky vessel or a poor sailer.

While the various acts had stated the types of vessels to be acquired, in some cases at least, the Secretary of the Navy seems to have enjoyed a good deal of freedom in departing from the exact terms of the authorization. He was, of course, required to stay within the sums authorized. In one case the Secretary writes about six brigs authorized by Congress in 1798–99, but none of these were built. It is not possible to determine under what authority the Secretary acted in specifying the type of ship to be acquired, but reference to some of the acts shows that the understanding as to the exact type of ships must have been an informal one between the Secretary and members of the congressional committees, rather than a decision of Congress to be complied with in full.

The records of the individual naval constructors cannot be accounted for as completely as might be desired. Fox and Doughty could not be hired as naval constructors. As has been mentioned, Fox was officially listed as a "clerk" in the War Office; Doughty was therefore listed as a "clerk" in the Treasury Department while he was employed in drafting and laying down the frigates. Doughty's papers, which are believed to have been burned in a fire at Baltimore while being moved by a descendant, might have shed additional light on some of the questions that have been discussed. Humphreys' and Fox's papers have been preserved; the greater part of Joshua Humphreys' papers are now in the Pennsylvania Historical Society, and a large proportion of Fox's material is now at the Peabody Museum in Salem, Massachusetts. Existing papers of some of the politicians and officeholders of the period add some supporting evidence, but all these contain insufficient evidence to permit an unqualified assignment of credit for the design of all the naval vessels, and particularly to allow final conclusions as to the predominant personalities in the design of the first frigates authorized in 1794. Samuel Humphreys' papers are very incomplete and scattered. The disappearance of many of the plans once in his possession, in the transfer of the plan files from the Navy to the

National Archives, is an irreparable misfortune. The additional loss of many of his notebooks and offset books, which apparently occurred at the same time, is equally unfortunate. Because of these gaps in the technical history of naval shipbuilding, a great many matters of importance must remain in the field of conjecture, at least for the present.

The end of the quasi war with France led to a reduction in the new Navy and its reorganization on a peacetime establishment. This was accomplished by the Congressional Act of March 3, 1803. The wisdom of the act proved somewhat questionable, to say the least. Though the Secretary of the Navy had presented a series of carefully worked-out recommendations for a proper peacetime establishment, his ideas were largely disregarded and Congress decided that the Navy was to be reduced to the thirteen frigates—*United States, Constitution, President, Chesapeake, Philadelphia, Constellation, Congress, New York, Boston, Adams, Essex, John Adams*, and *General Greene*. All the other vessels were to be stripped of naval gear and sold. The ships retained were to be laid up except for six, which were to be manned with crews two-thirds of the war complement. Economy was the watchword, and the sale of the ships was gradually accomplished, except that the schooner *Enterprise* was retained because of the criticism her intended sale had produced in the newspapers and among the maritime population.

Though some of the ships obtained to build up the new Navy had undoubtedly been either unsatisfactory in design or unsuited for naval purposes, there were a few at least that were very fine cruisers. The reduction disposed of these, as well as those not wanted for the service, because of the severity of the slash in ships and personnel. Generally, the small ships had proved very useful, but Congress took the attitude that only the large ships were of sufficient importance to be retained—a position that had unfortunately been taken to some extent by the Secretary's office in making its recommendations. As a result, the Navy not only lost some very fine small vessels, but also lost practically all of its cruisers that had proved so valuable in suppressing the West Indian privateers and marauders. The short-sightedness of this was soon apparent.

The reduction also brought about the discharge of all the naval constructors, as well as a great reduction in the number of commissioned officers and enlisted men. Fox remained at Norfolk and engaged in private business. Joshua Humphreys also returned to his private affairs. Occasionally each was consulted about some minor naval matter. With the new peace establishment, however, all naval construction had ceased and there was little to require obtaining their advice. Humphreys disappears from naval affairs at this time, but Fox and his co-worker Doughty will appear again.

The peace establishment, by the severity of the reduction it entailed, destroyed the greater part of the administrative and operating organization and to an equal extent the progress already made in setting up construction and maintenance facilities of the new Navy. Many capable officers left the service, though an effort was made to retain the most capable and to discharge those that had been inefficient or incompetent. Of the thirteen captains retained under the act, Thomas Truxton (fourth in seniority) was perhaps the most interesting from the shipbuilding point of view. Truxton had been the lieutenant of the Revolutionary War privateer *Congress* at the age of twenty-one, and from 1777 to the end of the war had commanded the *Independence, Mars,* and *St. James* with great success. A Philadelphian, he settled there when the war ended in 1783 and became a merchant, and in 1785 he took over the command of a China trader. With the building of the Federal Navy, he was appointed as one of the first six captains and was supervising officer in the building of the *Constellation.* Made commander of the ship, he fought *L'Insurgent* and took her, and also fought the heavier *Vengeance,* which escaped him. Truxton became involved in many difficulties over seniority, particularly in the case of the appointment of Captain Silas Talbot over his head, as a result of which he threatened to resign. Finally, during the Barbary Wars, he was ordered to command a small squadron in the Mediterranean and finding that he was not to have the perquisites of a flag officer, particularly a captain for his ship, he resigned from the service. He held a few political offices and appointments, and died in 1822.

Truxton was a highly intelligent officer, much interested in the technical side of his career. He had prepared and published a book on navigation, which also contained an appendix (or "annex") giving, in great detail, a rule for the masting of ships. This was illustrated by Josiah Fox with a well-drawn plan of the spars and rigging of the 44's, in accordance with the hull design of the new ships and with the spar proportions as set forth by Truxton. This book was completed shortly after Truxton became captain, and for some time he carried on a friendly correspondence with Fox on matters of naval construction and mutual interest. Truxton was a martinet aboard ship and, like many officers with this characteristic, was often overbearing and officious. The latter characteristic was heightened in Truxton by his friendly relations with Stoddert, who relied upon him for advice on all naval matters, even to the selection of officers and their promotion. However unpleasant Truxton may have been as a commanding officer, his ideas of strict discipline were undoubtedly very desirable in the new Navy. To Truxton, and to one or two other captains, perhaps, the new Navy owed its concept of the high standards of competence expected in its officers' corps. With the capture of *L'Insurgent* and the resulting public praise, Truxton seems to have become overly conceited and very sensitive of his own importance because of which he gradually lost influence. Through attempting to usurp the powers of Fox at Gosport, his friendship with the constructor ceased. This closed his connection with naval shipbuilding. During the time Truxton was supervising the *Constellation*, he was influential in establishing Fox's position and in supporting his views; Fox and Truxton were perhaps the outstanding objectors to the huge American frigates, while Humphreys, Barry, and others supported the new ship concept. The latter, as events were to show, had the best of the dispute.

Though the organization of the new Navy received a serious setback in the Congressional Act "Providing for a naval peace establishment, and for other purposes" of March 3, 1801, the groundwork had been laid for the national Navy, based on the idea of ships superior in size, power, and speed to classmates in foreign navies, and on an officer corps having a high sense of duty and responsibility. The administrative organization was as yet inadequate, though much progress had been made in comparison with the Continental Navy. The events of the period had placed the Secretary of the Navy in firm possession of a recognized authority over the whole naval establishment. As yet there was no conception of a strategic or technical control of the service by a professional staff or a board of officers and technicians. Power rested entirely with the Secretary, not only in the technical field of naval construction and equipment but also in the strategic and tactical control of naval operations. As a result, political considerations often predominated, operations were controlled by clamor at home rather than by war strategy, and construction programs were governed by pressure groups or by the preferences of influential individuals, officers, or politicians.

In the process of building up the new Navy, the design and construction of its ships had not been reserved to a small group of government employees. Private designers had competed, and ships had been built by, or under the supervision of, men who had been trained in merchant yards. The only constructor who can be said to have been fully trained in the exclusively governmental field of naval construction was Fox, and, as has been shown, his influence, though somewhat marked, was nevertheless circumscribed. The Revolution had created a number of men who had some experience in the problems of the design of vessels for naval purposes. These men were civilian constructors when the new Navy was created, and were therefore inclined to compete for superiority. The results can be seen in the individual ships of the Federal Navy, even though they had not been produced in the stress of a serious war, or in a great national emergency.

★ ★ ★ ★ ★ ★ ★ ★ ★

CHAPTER FOUR

The Gunboat Navy
1801-1812

THE ACT "Providing for a naval peace establishment," passed March 3, 1801, was the first historical illustration of a type of national error that Americans seem prone to commit—the liquidating of their armed might before peace is firmly secured. In view of the numerous repetitions of this mistake, there is no particular use in attempting to account for the mentalities of a Congress or an administration that would reduce the Navy so laboriously built up for the quasi war with France while still faced with the predatory Barbary regencies and the national disgrace of making tribute payments and presents to a group of minor naval powers who made no pretense of observing their treaty obligations. The same error that was made in 1801 has been made in more recent times. The very recent examples of the flight of common sense that seems to occur when the state of open warfare is officially declared at an end offer far better opportunities for study of the excessive optimism of the American people than the relatively minor occurrence in Jefferson's administration; then the price paid was small, but it has steadily risen with each repetition.

At the end of 1801 the new construction facilities were either liquidated or made inoperative. The property intended for navy yards was utilized entirely for storage; in some cases portions of the properties were sold. The frames of the 74's contracted for in 1799 were placed in these storage yards, but in most localities little was done to preserve the material. The frigates not sent to the Mediterranean were usually laid up at Washington, under the eye of the Administration, and repairs and upkeep were niggardly attended to. The theory on which Jefferson intended to operate the Navy visualized the frigates laid up "in ordinary" as being in storage and capable of being made serviceable in a very short time. Economy was intended, and by this means the cost of maintaining the ships in cruising service was avoided, since neither crews nor rations were needed in the ships laid up. While it was supposed that the ships could be maintained in ordinary in good condition for a long period with the minimum of expense, this assumption was not fully investigated, and many of the precautions that should have been taken were omitted. The official correspondence shows why this was the case. The administration had to depend upon the advice of naval officers as to the proper means of preserving the vessels, since all of the constructors had been discharged. While many of the officers gave good advice, there was a widespread difference of opinion about preservation methods, and there was now no one in the Navy Department competent to decide which opinions were sound. As a result, most of the vessels laid up deteriorated rapidly; the frigates not placed in service once in four years soon decayed and finally became wholly unserviceable. In this way the Navy lost some fine and valuable vessels.

While the naval peace establishment was being put into operation, in 1801, and the new Navy was being reduced in effectiveness, the relations with the various Barbary regencies, particularly with Tripoli, continued to be most unsatisfactory. By the end of that year the Bey of Tripoli had, in fact, ordered attacks on American merchantmen. In expectation of this the Americans had maintained a squadron of four frigates in the Mediterranean throughout the summer and fall of 1801. Early in the winter of 1801 a relief squadron was organized consisting of two frigates, which were to replace two ordered home from the Mediterranean, and in addition the sole small man-of-war left in the Navy, the schooner *Enterprise*. Tripoli was blockaded by one or two of the American frigates, while another lurked near the Straits of Gibraltar to prevent corsairs from getting into the Atlantic. The Spaniards also made a habit of seizing an occasional American ship, so the frigate at Gibraltar thus served two useful purposes. Congress recognized that a state of war with Tripoli existed and, on February 6, 1802, passed an act authorizing the Navy to attack and seize Tripolitan shipping. Congress also authorized the fitting out of privateers against the Tripolitans. The obvious lack of incentive to fit out privateers against the Barbary regency, which had no real merchant marine, makes this proposal of Congress appear strange. Actually, the explanation is very simple: it was the American naval policy to maintain only the minimum national navy and to depend upon privateers in time of war, paralleling the national military practice of maintaining a very small regular army and placing reliance in an emergency on the state militia regiments and on volunteers. The Tripolitan incident showed the inherent weakness of the policy, but, as will be seen, there was no change in the American attitude toward an effective navy. Jefferson became President in 1801, and the attitude of his administration was violently anti-naval and anti-military. Doctrinaire in judgment, Jefferson was not influenced by the international state in his time and, in spite of the plain warning of future trouble given by the numerous incidents, including outright attacks on American ships by foreign men-of-war, could not bring himself to prepare for war. Rather, he sought some cheap method of defending the country, even at the sacrifice of the merchant marine.

The lack of judgment of his administration in naval affairs was soon apparent. In August, 1802, his Secretary of the Navy, Robert Smith, wrote that a few gunboats were necessary at Gibraltar to protect American shipping from Spanish interference. Just how small vessels were to be maintained on such a station, without a base, was not apparent, and the Secretary was soon forced to give up the idea. Though many suggestions were made for the use of small men-of-war in the Mediterranean, in lieu of the expensive and rather ineffective frigate squadron, the administration did nothing. Only the *Enterprise* (or *Enterprize*, as her name was usually spelled) was available, and a plan for employing small vessels would require new construction or the purchase of suitable craft. This was not an attractive idea to the administration, and some time was wasted before the proposal was finally accepted. Throughout 1802 and well into 1803, a frigate squadron was maintained in the Mediterranean which carried on a desultory blockade of Tripoli. It was not until Captain Edward Preble took command in 1803 that the squadron became efficient, though it was still handicapped for some time by the lack of small cruisers.

By early winter of 1802 the administration had reached the decision that a few small cruisers were needed, and the Secretary of the Navy began to make inquiries among experienced naval officers regarding the most suitable types of vessels for the purpose. On February 28, 1803, the Seventh Congress passed an "Act pertaining to the Navy" which authorized the construction or purchase of four vessels of war, not to exceed 16 guns, and appropriated funds for the purpose. The same act provided for the construction of fifteen gunboats, with funds segregated for this purpose alone.

The Secretary of the Navy, having no constructors available, was forced to utilize the existing establishment in obtaining the new vessels authorized by the act. He examined the recommendations of the naval officers regarding the craft most suitable for service in the Mediterranean, and in the early spring of 1803 he selected three naval officers to supervise the construction of the new vessels—Captains William Bainbridge at Philadelphia, Edward Preble at Portsmouth, New Hampshire, and Samuel Barron at Norfolk, Virginia. At each of these places he intended to construct a vessel. Another vessel was to be built at Baltimore, and Bainbridge was to supervise this also. The navy agents were requested to enter into suitable contracts, and the naval officers were instructed to obtain suitable designs.

It was found that vessels could not be constructed at Norfolk and Portsmouth because both places would require more time to build a vessel than the government intended. It was finally decided to build two brigs, one at Philadelphia and one at Boston, and to build two schooners at Baltimore.

The 16-gun brigs were ordered to meet the definite specifications recommended by the naval officers who had been consulted. They were to be flush-decked brigs, designed to row fast and to have long lower masts and rather short yards; the rig was to be light, high, and narrow to be suited to the sailing conditions met in the Mediterranean. Weight was to be kept out of the ends of the ships; this was to govern the location of the gun ports, which were to permit carrying 16 24-pdr. carronades, one long 18-pdr. gun in the bow, and another in the stern. The bulwarks were to be solid and of suitable height for the guns. It was decided that the vessels were to be 94′ on deck, 76′ straight rabbet, 25′ 6″ beam, and 12′ 6″ depth in the hold. The frames were to be 14″ deep at the keel, 8″ at the floor heads, 7″ at the wale, and 6″ at the rail. One of the superintendents, Barron, found fault with the specified beam, and the Secretary agreed to allow it to be increased.

The schooners were to be built to the same dimensions as the *Enterprise*, to carry 14 6-pdr. guns, and to be 84′ on the gun deck, 60′ on the keel, 22′ 6″ beam, or 23′ to outside of wales, and 9′ 6″ depth of hold. Bainbridge was particularly instructed to obtain the plan of the *Enterprise* if possible, as the Secretary wished to build to it rather than to a new design. However, the plan was not obtained.

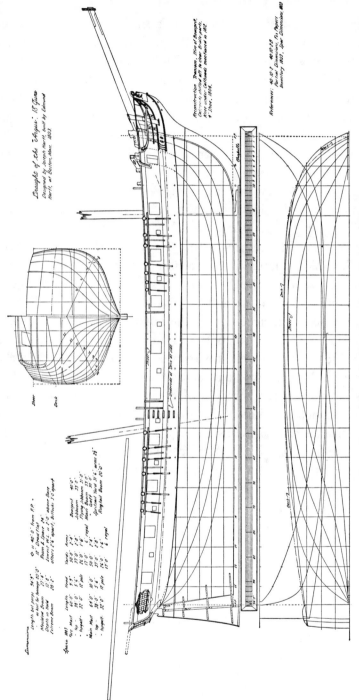

Figure 26. Draught of the brig ARGUS, *full-model hull.*

The brig built at Boston under Preble's supervision was first called the *Merrimack*, then the *Argus*. She was designed by Joseph Hartt and built by Edmund Hartt, master builder of the *Constitution*. A plan of her survives; two copies, in fact, made by Edward Hartt, are in the National Archives. The plan, which is shown, redrawn, in Figure 26, probably represents with reasonable accuracy the ship as built. In the redrawing it was necessary to lower the head and reduce the steeve of the bowsprit, since that shown in Hartt's drawings was much too great, as was indicated in the spar dimensions. Hartt showed so much steeve that the bowsprit would have had to pass through the deck in order to "bury" inboard enough. No deck arrangement has been found. A portrait of the ship exists in the well-known painting of the attack on Tripoli, August 3, 1804, part of which, showing the *Argus*, is reproduced on page 254 of Naval Documents, Vol. V, *Barbary Wars*, U.S. Government Printing Office, Washington, D.C., 1944. The plate is wrongly captioned in the reference as *Nautilus*, which is actually shown as *Argus* on page 72, *ibid*. In this portrait, the vessel is shown to have a figurehead and the quarter badges are omitted. The accuracy of the portrait is open to question, however, by the omission of one gun port on a side; nine are shown in the painting, including a bridle port, whereas it is recorded in both the plan and elsewhere that the vessel as built showed ten ports on a side, with the bridle port. The *Argus* was 94′ 9″ between perpendiculars, 27′ 4″ moulded beam, 80′ on the keel, and 12′ 8″ depth of hold. The plans show her to have been calculated at $298^{63}/_{94}$ tons. As can be seen, she was a full-bodied vessel, rather full forward and quite fine aft, with an attractive sheer, and rather low in the water. Her design seems to have followed that of a fast merchant brig of her period in order to give the displacement necessary, within the specified dimensions, to permit her to carry her guns and a large quantity of stores. In spite of her rather full lines, the *Argus* was a notable sailer and was a favorite vessel with her officers. She was launched in August, 1803, and went into commission in September. In her early years her armament was 16 24-pdr. carronades and 2 long 12-pdrs.

The second brig was on a different model. Named *Syren*, she was designed at Philadelphia by Benjamin Hutton, Jr., and built by Nathaniel Hutton. The plan of this brig has also survived; a handsome copy of the original design, made by Nathaniel Hutton, Jr., in 1803, is in the National Archives. This plan, redrawn, is shown in Figure 27. The figurehead is as shown on the original, but it is questionable in view of the fact that this brig, when taken by the

Portrait of William Doughty, Naval Constructor 1813 to 1837. (Courtesy Howard N. Doughty.)

Sketch of the SARATOGA, *Lake Champlain. (Study for a painting by George C. Wales.)*

PLATE IX

PLATE X. (*Top*) *Sail plan of schooner* LYNX. (*Bottom*) *Sail plan of brig* PROMETHEUS.

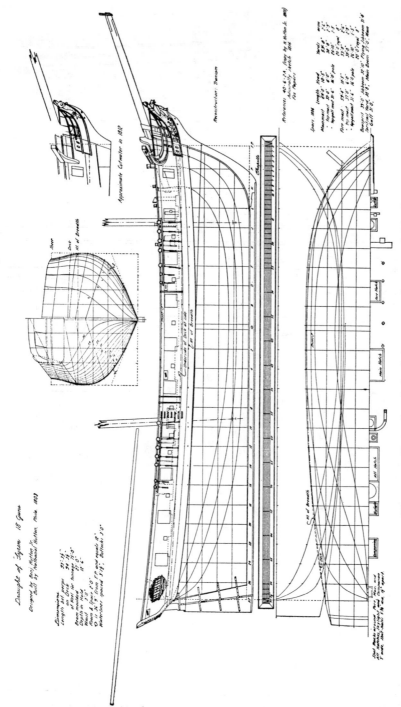

Figure 27. Draught of the brig SYREN, sharp-model hull.

185

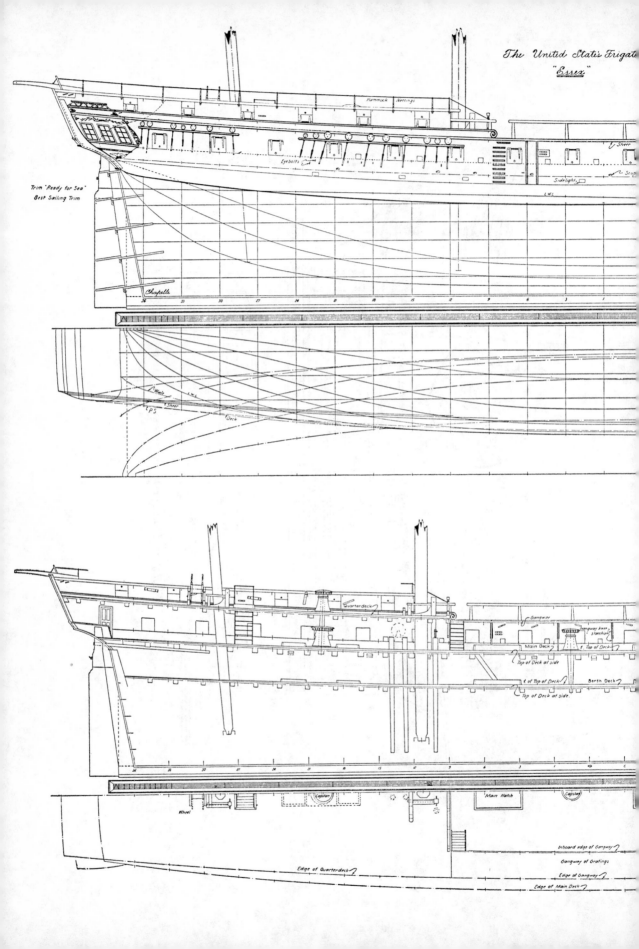

The United States Frigate
"Essex"

Hammock Nettings

Sheer

Eyebolts

Sidelight

Scup

Trim "Ready for Sea"
Best Sailing Trim

LWL

Chapelle

36 33 30 27 24 21 18 15 12 9 6 3 1

Wale LWL
CPS Sheer
Deck

Quarterdeck

Gangway
Gangway knee
stanchion
Main Deck
Top of Deck at side
Top of Deck at side
Berth Deck
Top of Deck at side

36 33 30 27 24 21 18 15 12 9 6 3 C

Wheel
Capstan
Main Hatch
Capstan

Inboard edge of Gangway
Gangway of Gratings
Edge of Gangway
Edge of Main Deck

Edge of Quarterdeck

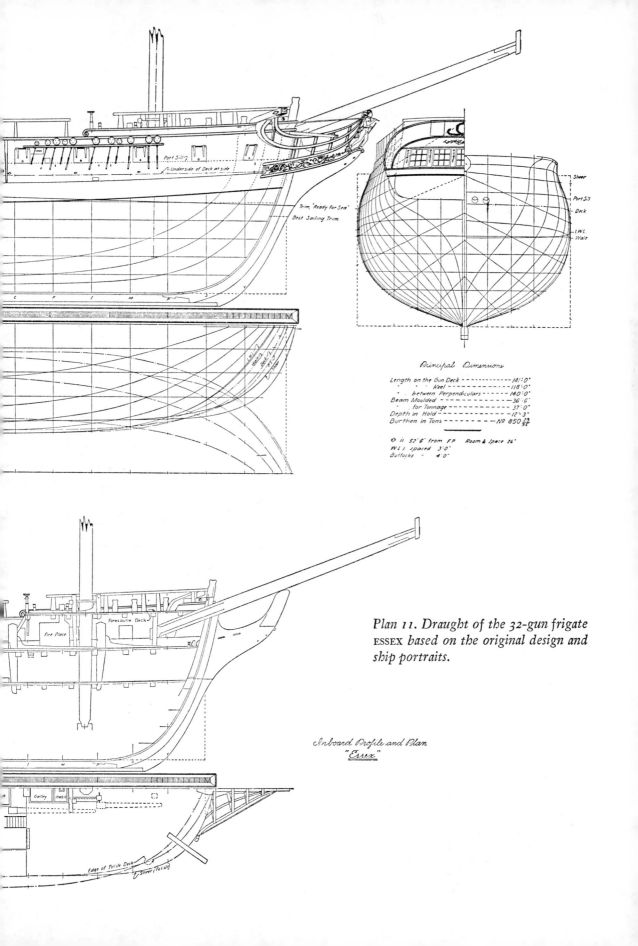

Port Sill

Underside of Deck at side

Trim, 'Ready for Sea'
Best Sailing Trim.

Sheer
Port Sill
Deck
L.W.L.
Wale

Principal Dimensions

Length on the Gun Deck ----------- 141'-0"
" " Keel ----------- 118'-0"
" between Perpendiculars ----- 140'-0"
Beam Moulded ------------- 36'-6"
" for Tonnage ----------- 37'-0"
Depth in Hold ----------- 12'-3"
Burthen in Tons ------- N⁰ 850 ⁵³/₉₅

O ii 52'-6" from FP   Room & Space 26"
WL i spaced 3'-0"
Buttocks " 4'-0"

Forecastle Deck

Fire Place

Plan 11. Draught of the 32-gun frigate
ESSEX based on the original design and
ship portraits.

Inboard Profile and Plan
"Essex"

Galley

Edge of Fo'csle Deck
Sheer (Fo'csle)

Frigate "Boston", 32 Guns

Designed by Edmund Hartt; built by Edmund, Joseph and Edward Hartt
at Boston.

Length bet perps   134' 0"
Length on Gundeck   135' 6"
Beam, moulded   34' 6"
  "   over plank   35' 0"
Depth in Hold   11' 6"

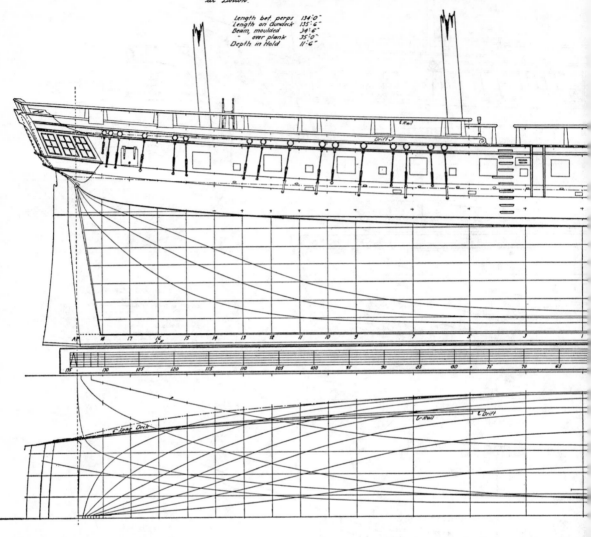

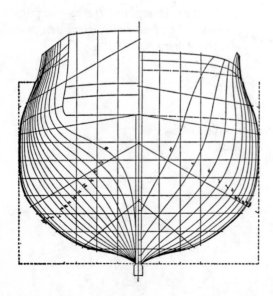

Particular Dimensions
O is 56' 6½" from F.P.
1 is 61' 7"   F.P.
Numbered frames spaced 48½" (Room & Space 24¼")
Lowest Waterline 2' 0" from Base, others spaced 2' 6"
Buttocks spaced 3' 0"

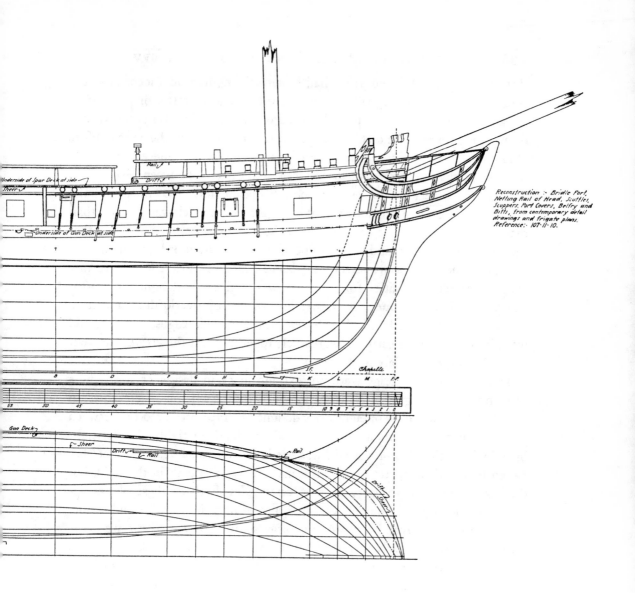

Reconstruction :- Bridle Port,
Netting Rail of Head, Scuttles,
Scuppers, Port Covers, Belfry and
Bitts, from contemporary detail
drawings and frigate plans.
Reference:- 107-11-10.

Plan 12. Draught of the 32-gun frigate BOSTON, *after the builder's plan.*

British during the War of 1812, had a mermaid figurehead (according to a rough plan of the vessel made when fitting her as a lazeretto, or prison vessel, after her capture). The probable head of the vessel in 1812 is shown in a detail in Figure 27. The quarter badges were removed from the *Syren* before 1812, apparently—if indeed they were ever placed on her. She was a slightly smaller ship than the *Argus*; the *Syren* measured 93′ 3½″ between perpendiculars, 75′ on the keel for tonnage, 27′ moulded beam, and 12′ 6″ depth in hold. She carried the same armament as the *Argus*. Her model was sharper than that of her classmates; she had much deadrise and a slack bilge. She was rather full forward, however, and was less fine aft than *Argus*, in order to obtain displacement enough. She was a very handsome brig and an excellent performer in light weather, a condition for which she was particularly designed. Unfortunately her model was one that was readily harmed by overloading, and from this she eventually suffered. The *Syren* was launched August 6, 1803, and went into commission early in September; together with the *Argus* she went to the Mediterranean late in that year.

These two 16-gun brigs were not extraordinary in design or size. There were numerous 16-gun brig classes in the British Navy that were equal in size. The *Diligence* class of eight brigs designed in 1795 measured 95′ between perpendiculars, 27′ 6″ moulded beam, and 12′ depth in the hold. The eight brigs built on the plan of the *Dispatch,* designed the same year, were 96′ between perpendiculars, 30′ moulded beam, and 12′ 9″ depth in the hold, but these were designed to carry 32-pdr. carronades. Both of these classes approached the *Argus* in model, yet were not exactly like her in midsection. A later class of Royal Navy 16-gun brigs somewhat like *Syren* were the seven brigs designed early in 1805 as the *Challenger* class. This class measured 96′ between perpendiculars, 25′ 4″ moulded beam, and 11′ 6″ depth of hold, and were to carry 24-pdr. carronades and two long 6's as chase guns. Their model was sharp in section but somewhat full in the ends. In this period the French built many brigs of 14 to 16 guns that were larger than the American vessels. Examples of French brigs taken into the Royal Navy will serve to illustrate the size of some of these: *La Victorieuse* of 12 guns and 12 swivels, captured in 1795, was 103′ 1″ on deck, 28′ 6″ moulded beam, and 12′ 10″ in the hold; *La Jalouse* of 14 guns, taken in 1797, was 102′ 10″ between perpendiculars, 27′ 4″ moulded beam, and 12′ 11½″ depth in the hold; *L'Arrogant* was a 10-gun brig but was 91′ 9″ on deck, 25′ 6⅜″ beam, and 11′ 2″ in the hold. These French brigs were much alike in model, with sections very full

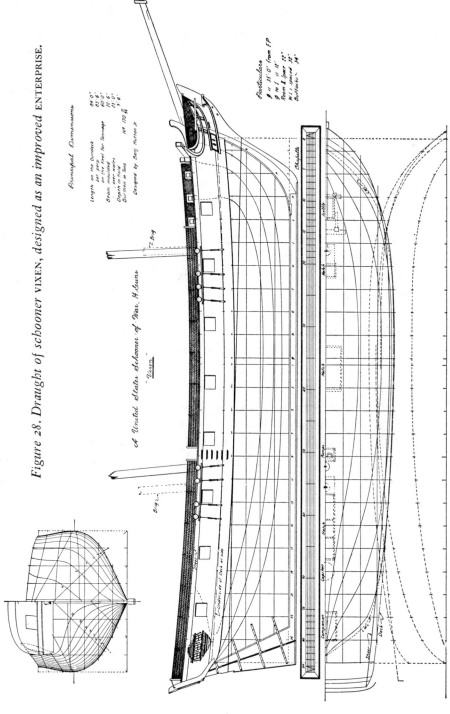

Figure 28. Draught of schooner VIXEN, designed as an improved ENTERPRISE.

187

and round on the bottom and the topsides remarkably wall-sided. Yet these vessels sailed well enough to be purchased for the Royal Navy, in spite of their ugliness in model and appearance.

The two schooners authorized were to have been sisters, but the difficulty in getting them both built led to the decision to build only one and to purchase the other. The vessel built was named *Vixen*. Her plan, redrawn, is shown in Figure 28. Her design was prepared by Benjamin Hutton of Philadelphia, and she was built by William Price of Baltimore. Her launch took place June 25, 1803; she was commissioned in August. *Vixen*'s dimensions were exactly those given officially for the *Enterprise*—84' 0" on the gun deck, 83' 5" between perpendiculars, 22' 6" moulded beam, 60' on the keel, and 9' 6" depth in the hold—yet her tonnage is given as $170^{37}\!/\!_{95}$, as against 135 or 165 tons officially given for *Enterprise*. Either there had been an error in the tonnage of the earlier schooner or the official dimensions were in error. After a year as a schooner, the *Vixen* was altered to brig rig, and it was said that this spoiled her speed. In spite of the expressed desire of the Secretary of the Navy that the *Vixen* be on the model of the *Enterprise*, and also the similarity of the dimensions, it seems probable in the light of what is known about the latter vessel that there was very little similarity in model.

The purchased schooner, named the *Nautilus*, was obtained at Baltimore. She was a vessel built on the Eastern Shore of Maryland, apparently by the same man who had built the *Enterprise*, Henry Spencer. No plan of the schooner has been found, but she measured 87' 6" on deck, 23' 8" beam, and 9' 10" depth of hold. Lieutenant Richard Somers was her first commander, and in a letter to his brother, written when he first saw his new command, he gave some description of her. He said that she was very sharp in section, "like a wedge." He thought she was too sharp in the topsides around the bow and, because of her rake, she had too little room in her forecastle. Also her bulwarks were very light, the planking being only ½" thick. Her run was so sharp that she had to have a cabin trunk aft. Her bowsprit had very little steeve, and Somers wanted this altered. Captain Bainbridge had reported adversely on her, prior to purchase, stating that in his opinion she was too sharp and too low in the water, and had too much rake in the bow and stern. The picture of her in the painting of the attack on Tripoli indicates that she had no head, or knee, in the bow, if the portrait is to be trusted. The *Nautilus* was a very fast schooner, particularly to windward. Her spar dimensions of 1806 indicate that she was rigged as a fore-topsail schooner crossing a fore royal, whereas the painting just mentioned shows a two-topsail schooner. She too was eventually rerigged as a brig, and the change in rig hurt her sailing qualities, as it had done in the case of the other schooners.

By the construction of the two brigs and one schooner and the purchase of another schooner, the very effective small cruisers lost through the naval peace establishment were partly replaced. No sloops of war were yet contemplated, and the new vessels were obtained for a particular service, rather than as a normal development of the Navy list.

The gunboats authorized by the Act of 1803 were intended as harbor defense craft. The steps by which Congress was led to authorize the new gunboats are not wholly clear from available records. It appears that the action was taken independently of the Mediterranean problem, and that the supposed value of this class of naval vessel was enhanced in official quarters by the requirements for such craft in the subsequent operations off Tripoli.

It has been usual to connect the plan for building American gunboat flotillas with the success of this type of craft in Europe. However, there is some doubt as to the validity of this connection. While gunboats were employed by all the navies involved in the War of the French Revolution, they had not been outstandingly successful, and they attracted little attention until 1804, in which year Napoleon had accumulated enough small craft on the French coast opposite the British Isles to arouse the fears of the British government. The French plan for the invasion of Britain had been drawn up by Napoleon as early as 1798 and was based on employing a huge quantity of small craft carrying troops, supported by heavily armed gunboats and a powerful fleet of seagoing vessels. The final plan involved the use of about two thousand small craft, and these were not ready until 1804–5 in enough numbers to cause concern in Great Britain. By this time the Americans were well committed to the gunboat theory. Owing to the relations between France and the United States before 1801, and to the secrecy that surrounded the French plans for the invasion of the British Isles, it is not probable that they were particularly aware of what the French were doing.

The French gunboats and auxiliary craft included a range of types and sizes from large open boats rigged as luggers, about 60' long, to ship-rigged prames 100' long. There were also brigs and ships having round-bottomed hulls but of lighter draft than seagoing vessels. A huge number of large and well-designed shoal-draft luggers were built, armed and fitted with bow ramps, for landing infantry, cavalry, and artillery on beaches in the same manner that landing craft were used in World War II. The German plan for the invasion of England during that war was on exactly the same tactical concept as Napoleon's—employing "invasion barges" in huge numbers with what support was to be available from naval vessels—but with the addition of supporting aircraft. Of course, the Germans would have had another advantage, the use of motor-propelled barges that could operate regardless of the direction and force of the wind. Both the French and the German plans failed to be put into operation because of the final loss of the necessary support. The French "invasion flotilla," often called the "Boulogne Flotilla" after its most important base, was a highly specialized organization employing craft particularly designed for a definite purpose and entirely different from anything visualized in the American ideas for the employment of gunboats.

The Danes also employed gunboats extensively in the Napoleonic wars. They had lost the greatest portion of their naval force in the fall of Copenhagen in 1801 and had replaced the loss as soon as possible with a fleet of powerful gunboats and heavily armed brigs and schooners. However, their gunboats were apparently not ready to accomplish much until after 1804. There is no evidence available to support a theory that the Americans were aware of the Danish plans, or were influenced by foreign gunboats and tactics.

Both the French and the Danes had prepared their gunboat flotillas with a well-defined plan in view, for which gun vessels appeared suitable. The Americans, on the other hand, seem to have had no more than a very general objective in view and prepared no plan of operation for their gunboats. A close search of the correspondence relating to the gunboat flotillas has so far failed to produce any operational justification for the American gunboats except on the western rivers, where row galleys would have been very effective in a day when large craft could be propelled only by sails. As has been seen, the row galley had been introduced on the western rivers in 1799, and similar craft had been built on the coast for harbor and coast defense.

The Jeffersonian plan was at first a repetition of the plan of 1799, to build gunboats for river and harbor service. By chance, events placed emphasis on the type, and this seemingly produced the Jeffersonian theory of employing gun vessels in place of normal naval craft. The trend of events that apparently gave support to the gunboat theory can be readily traced in the archives.

In October, 1803, the Navy suffered a grave disaster in the Mediterranean. The fine frigate *Philadelphia* ran aground at Tripoli, while in chase of a blockade-runner, and was captured by the Tripolitans. This incident led to active operations against Tripoli to destroy the frigate and to avenge the capture of so large a national vessel.

In November and December, 1803, the Secretary of the Navy wrote to

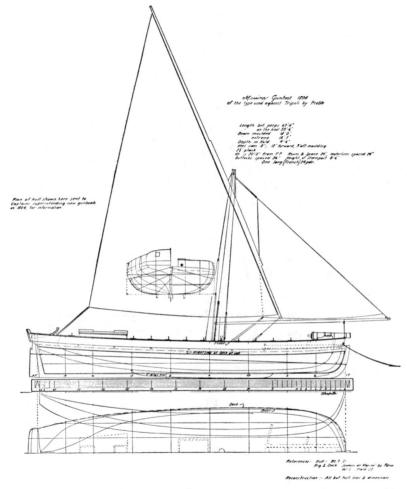

Figure 29. Plan of a Messina gunboat, parancelle rig, employed to guide the design of the first American gunboats.

Captain James Barron and Captain John Rodgers, asking if they were willing to supervise and help design a gunboat. In the fall of 1803 Preble had begun to search for suitable gunboats in the Mediterranean, for use against Tripoli. He had investigated the possibility of getting boats from Naples and had secured a model, or plan, of one of the Neapolitan types of gunboats, which he sent home. This plan (or model) was made available to Barron and Rodgers, but was not to control the design of the new gun vessels. There is no evidence available that any extensive investigation was made as to what was required. The letters of the Secretary indicate only that two experimental gunboats were to be designed and built; they do not outline any of the desired characteristics other than what might be surmised from the data on the Neapolitan boat. In February, 1804, Preble received two plans of proposed gunboats from James L. Cathcart, the American agent at Leghorn, who had been U.S. Consul General successively at Tripoli, Algiers, and Tunis. In one of these plans, Cathcart proposed the use of a schooner rig, the foremast of which was to be a "sliding gunter," which will be seen in the plans later. Cathcart seemingly directed the drawing of the designs he proposed and gave Preble information on the various types of gunboats and bomb vessels that could be purchased, and were suitable, for use against Tripoli. Cathcart visualized the use of mortars in the gunboats, in addition to long guns. He also recommended that bomb ketches like those used in the Royal Navy be employed.

In May, 1804, Preble secured six gunboats, each mounting a long 24-pdr. in the bow, from the Neapolitan government. The boats were actually obtained from Messina. The official dimensions of these boats were 56′ 6″ on the keel, 18′ 0″ beam, and 4′ 6″ depth. The types of gunboats then in use in the Kingdom of the Two Sicilies were what were called "parancelles"—beach boats 40′ to 65′ in length rigged with a single-masted lateen rig, with a jib, and armed with a single gun in the bow, on a slide. The gun could be trained only ahead; though the slide was pivoted at the forward end, its traverse was limited to about 30 degrees. Some of the boats were sharp-sterned, others had square sterns. They were decked and had a small hatch abaft the mast and a small trunk cabin right aft with a hatch and skylight. The boats had bilge keels and were capable of being hauled ashore with a capstan, or "crab," staked out on the beach. The jib was set not on a bowsprit but on a sprit, or temporary spar, having its heel lashed to the mast and its forward end secured with vangs or tackles. It was placed well above the deck to clear the bow gun and could be squared off like a spinnaker pole on a modern yacht. Rowing was usually done by the crew standing on deck; some of the boats had a rowing frame laid on the deck, but this was apparently rather unusual. The deck of the Mediterranean boats usually had a great deal of crown. The Neapolitan boats sailed very fast; their bilge keels acted as leeboards, so they were weatherly in spite of their shoal draft. The six boats obtained by Preble, numbered *1* to *6*, took part in the attacks on Tripoli in August and September, 1804. In October of that year all six boats were returned to the Neapolitan government.

The plan of the Sicilian gunboat sent to the United States has survived. It is shown redrawn, with the rig reconstructed, in Figure 29. The drawing shows the rig of the parancelle and the manner of mounting the gun. This is apparently the hull design sent to the supervisors of the experimental gunboats. Although the letters mention a draught of a Messina gunboat and a draught or model of a Naples gunboat, it seems probable that this single plan is referred to and not two distinct designs.

Preble also borrowed two "bombards" from the Neapolitan government, at about the same time he obtained the Messina gunboats. The bombards were rigged as bomb ketches, square-rigged on the main and with a gaff sail on the mizzen. This Mediterranean type usually had a strong sheer, low raised quarterdeck, and good lines, and was used for convoy guard by the French during the Napoleonic Wars. The bombards were used as bomb ketches at Tripoli and returned to Naples with the gunboats in 1804. They were numbered *1* and *2*; *No. 1* was damaged in action August 24. No dimensions are on record, but these ketches were probably about 90′ in length.

Three gunboats were taken from the Tripolitans, numbered *7*, *8*, and *9* in the American service. Little is known about them, but they seem to have been very small, for *9* was only 31′ 1″ long, 14′ beam, and 5′ in the hold; the length measurement must have been on the keel. The boats were lateen-rigged with one mast and carried a long gun, an 18- or 24-pdr., and two or three swivels. The Americans rerigged them as sloops. *No. 9* blew up August 7, 1804, and the others were sold in Sicily that fall.

Though the records of the gunboats built in the United States are very extensive, there is much confusion in them, and it is almost impossible to establish the various designs used. Of the first two experimental boats, *No. 1* was built under the supervision of Captain John Rodgers at the Washington Navy Yard by master carpenter Peter Gardner. Nothing has yet been found on her design, which is believed to have been made by Captain Rodgers. *No. 1* had one long 32-pdr. and two 6-pdr. swivels. She went into commission in July, 1804. She was considered unfit for ocean work and was placed in the coastal defense flotilla.

No. 2 was built by George Hope of Hampton, Virginia, under Captain James Barron's supervision and was launched in August, 1804. She had a single long 32-pdr. in the bows and seems to have had swivels also. Her dimensions are uncertain, but she was rigged with a single lateen sail and a bowsprit in which a jib was set. Rerigged as a "dandy," or yawl, for crossing the Atlantic, she was sent to the Mediterranean in 1805. Returning home in 1806, she was laid up for a time and finally was lost off St. Marys, Georgia, in 1811.

A plan of a gunboat exists which was apparently sent to the Office of the Secretary of the Navy by Captain Barron. A redrawing of the design is shown in Figure 30. On the original is the following note: "The gunboat to be built under the superintendency of Captain James Barron will be materially different from this draft." This is signed by the initials Ch. W. G., Charles Washington Goldsborough, the Chief Clerk of the Navy Department, who evidently filed the plan. The accompanying letter has not been found. In spite of Goldsborough's note, however, it is possible that the plan represents Barron's gunboat in hull form and dimensions. What the differences were between the plan and the finished boat cannot be established. Correspondence, however, shows that Barron's boat had her gun below the bowsprit somewhat as shown in the plan, for at a later date it was desired to raise the bowsprit to permit the gun to be elevated, but this was found impractical. The gun was so mounted that it could be slid aft and lowered on inclined skids. The design called for a hull 64′ 5″ between perpendiculars, 16′ 10″ moulded beam, and about 6′ 6″ depth in the hold. The vessel was to have an open rail, with the oars working on top of the plank-sheer. The design was for a double-ender and was well planned for sailing and rowing. The plan indicates that she was to have sixteen swivels. The gun apparently could not traverse and could be trained only by lining up the boat on the target. The original sketch shows the bow gun much too low, with the gun platform on the load water line. In redrawing it has been raised to bring the muzzle above the plank-sheer. The correspondence indicates that the finished boat was considered faulty in the mounting and position of the long gun.

In the spring of 1804, William Doughty was appointed naval constructor at the Washington Navy Yard, but on May 4, 1804, he was replaced by Fox, who now received the title of "Head Ship Carpenter and Navy Constructor." In June Fox prepared a gunboat design from which a number of boats were built, but neither the plans nor the dimensions of all the boats can be established with certainty. The design appears to be the one shown in Figure 31, calling for a double-ender, to row and sail in either direction and armed with two long guns, one at each end, on pivots. The boat was shoal-draft and was

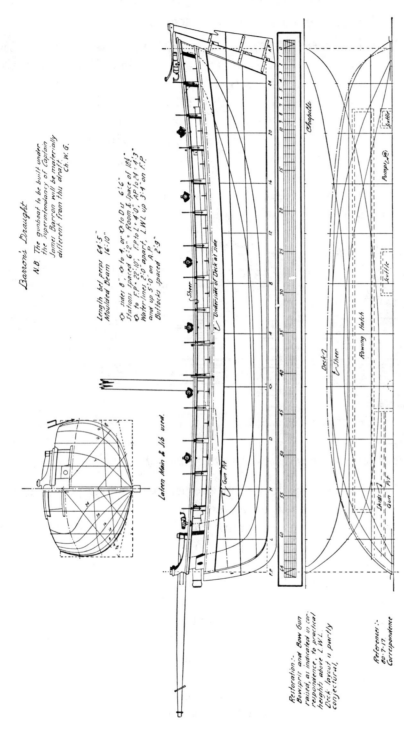

Figure 30. Barron's first design for a gunboat.

fitted with bilge keels to beach; she was better designed to row than to sail. The rig was to be two lateen sails, and the rudder could be shifted from stern to bow whenever desired. This design was 71′ 0″ between perpendiculars, 18′ 0″ moulded beam, and 4′ 8½″ depth in the hold. The drawing shows the details of the arrangement of the deck and construction. It seems safe to assume that *No. 3* was built on this design by Nathaniel Hutton at Philadelphia and launched in December, 1804. She had two long 24-pdrs. She was never rigged with lateen sails, however, but was fitted with the dandy rig used in *No. 2*, and had leeboards fitted. She went to the Mediterranean in 1805 and returned home in 1806. *No. 4* was built by Fox in the Washington Navy Yard

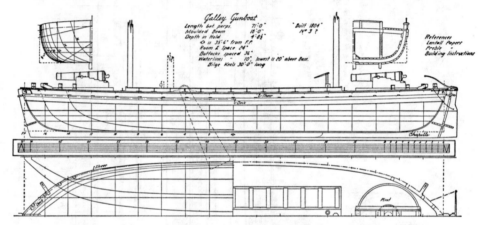

Figure 31. Fox's first design of a galley gunboat, shoal-draft model.

and may have been on this design; but she had two long 32-pdrs., and it is therefore possible that she was on another plan.

Soon after Fox had completed his first gunboat design he prepared another on the same general model, but deeper than the first. This design is shown in Figure 32, with the lateen rig originally proposed for this class of boat. The new design was on the same dimensions as the first boat, but with more depth— 5′ 6″ depth of hold instead of 4′ 8½″. The second design had some deadrise and was better suited for sailing than the first; it also had more displacement because of greater depth and slightly fuller ends, and so could carry heavier guns. On the basis of the larger guns placed on *No. 4* it is very possible that the second design was used for her rather than the first. *No. 4* was launched on March 5, 1804, and was sent to the Mediterranean in 1805.

In September, 1804, Fox proposed a gunboat to carry three pivot guns, but the plan has not been found. He made a plan for Captain Barron in 1805, but it has not been identified. It may be that the following gunboats were built on one of the two designs by Fox shown in Figures 31 and 32: *No. 5* at Baltimore by William Price, launched March 1, 1805; at New York, *No. 6*, launched February 4, 1805, and *No. 7*, launched February 6, 1805; at Boston, *No. 8*,

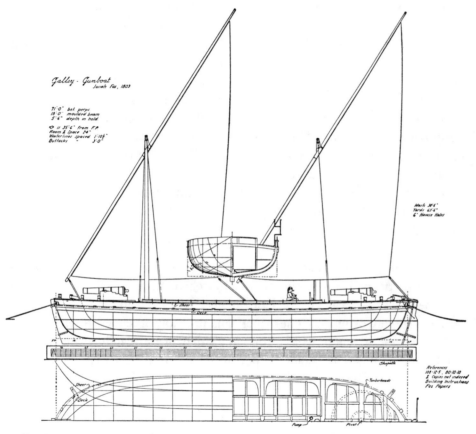

Figure 32. Fox's second design of a galley gunboat to improve seaworthiness.

launched April 24, 1805; and at Washington Navy Yard, *No. 10*, launched April 30, 1805. All these boats were armed with long 32-pdrs.

No. 9 was built at Fair Bank, Charleston, S.C., by Paul Pritchard and was launched in March, 1805. She seems to have been originally on Fox's double-ender model, 71′ 0″ between perpendiculars, 18′ 0″ moulded beam, and 5′ 6″ depth of hold, but her builder and superintendent were given permission to alter the design, and she was built to the following dimensions: 71′ 0″ between perpendiculars, 21′ 0″ extreme beam, and 6′ 2½″ in the hold, with her deadrise increased from 9″ to 12″. She was rigged as a fore-and-aft ketch and had a square stern and a single rowing hatch along the center line. This boat was therefore on a design distinctly different from that of any of the others; no plan exists other than a rough deck-arrangement layout.

Gunboats *5, 6, 7, 8, 9,* and *10* were all sent to the Mediterranean. *No. 7* was lost at sea with all hands on the passage out. The boats had to be prepared especially for the crossing: *3* had leeboards fitted as noted; the rest, except *9,* had false keels added, 20″ deep (*8* had only a 14″ keel added); and all were given the dandy rig. It is probable that *6* was the only one launched with the original lateen rig. None of the new boats saw active service, as Preble had been replaced by Captain Samuel Barron, whose illness, combined with extraordinarily poor advice from a State Department representative, Tobias Lear, had led to stagnation in naval operations in the Mediterranean and finally to a highly unsatisfactory peace settlement.

While Barron was in command of the Mediterranean squadron, he and Master Commandant Thomas Robinson, Jr., purchased four gunboats at Ancona and two trabacolos in the spring of 1805. These vessels were not in combat and were first laid up at Syracuse and then sold in 1807. No dimensions have been found, but a plan of a trabacolo was found in the plan files of the Navy Department (now in the National Archives). This is shown in Figure 33. The trabacolo was an Adriatic lugger, very full and burdensome but excellent in seaworthiness. The Americans probably intended to employ the two trabacolos as bomb vessels, for which they were readily made suitable. While there is no documentary support to the claim that the plan in Figure 33 is one of these vessels, it is of the proper period, and it is probably safe to assume that the plan was sent home to show the boats being purchased.

Early in March, 1804, Preble reported to Secretary Smith at Washington and apparently discussed the need of gunboats and bomb vessels in the Mediterranean, and in April he wrote the Secretary at some length about the matter. Preble put much emphasis on the subject and was ordered by the Secretary to supervise the construction of two gunboats and four bomb vessels; the latter were to be either built or purchased, as found most practical. Preble commissioned Jacob Coffin, a Newburyport, Massachusetts, shipbuilder, to prepare designs. It is apparent that the two gunboats to be built under Preble's supervision were much influenced by Cathcart's earlier recommendations, for in many respects the new boats showed many of the ideas mentioned in Cathcart's letters to Preble. The correspondence indicates that at least four, and perhaps five, designs were prepared.

The first design was for a boat 50′ between perpendiculars, 17′ 0″ moulded beam, and 4′ 6″ depth of hold. The original plans for this boat have not been

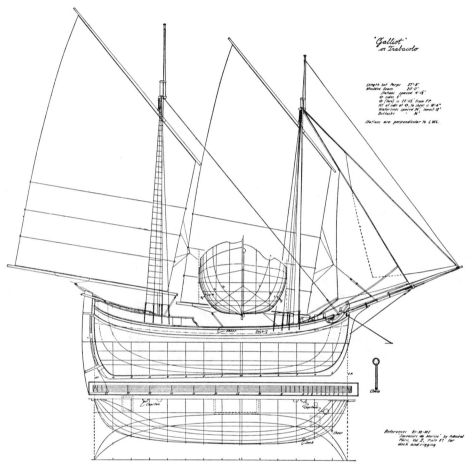

Figure 33. Draught of a trabacolo, probably one of those purchased for a bomb vessel by the Americans.

found. The second design was a modification of the first, but particulars are not known. No drawing of this design has yet been identified. The third design was for a boat 55′ between perpendiculars; this is shown in Figure 34. The drawing, made by Coffin, was rather sketchy and was probably a proposal rather than a working drawing. The boat would measure 55′ between perpendiculars, 17′ 6″ beam, and 4′ 6″ depth of hold. The specifications accompanying this plan mistakenly give the moulded beam as 17′ 0″. The design was for a well-shaped boat much like an enlarged ship's launch in model, primarily designed to sail rather than to row fast. The gun mounting was a curious one.

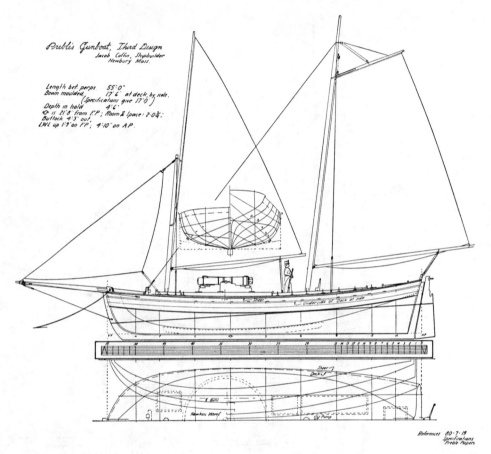

Figure 34. Drawing of Preble's third design for a gunboat, showing Hawkins' method of mounting two guns.

Preble had become acquainted with an inventor named Hawkins, who proposed to mount two cannon, pointing in opposite directions, on a horizontal wheel. When one gun was fired its recoil would turn the wheel, so that the opposite gun would be brought to bear on the target. The advantages claimed for this was that the effect of the recoil on a boat would be much lessened and that two guns could be served very rapidly. Preble had a model made and

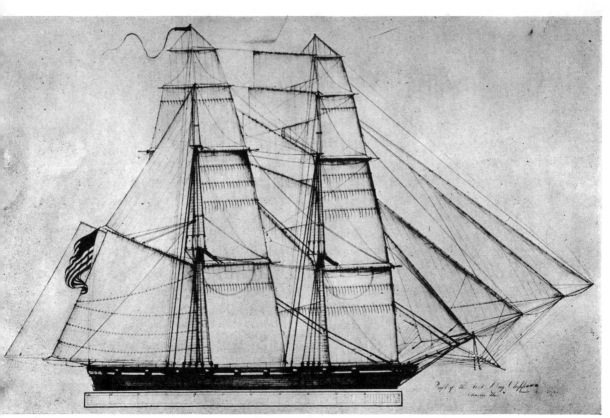

PLATE XI. (*Top*) *Sail plan of corvette* GENERAL PIKE. (*Bottom*) *Sail plan of brig* CHIPPEWA.

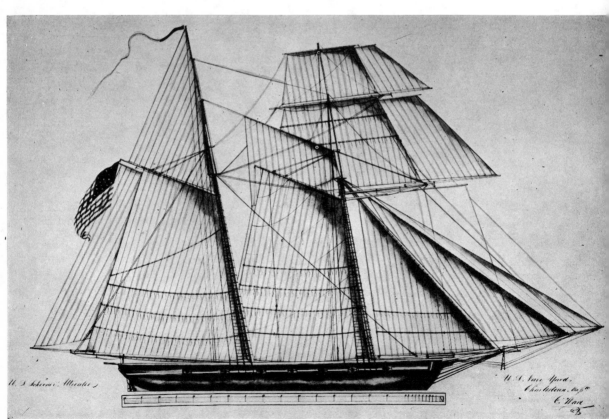

PLATE XII. (Top) Sail plan of brig SPARK. (Bottom) Sail plan of schooner ALLIGATOR.

tested it, as did one of the commanders assigned to the boats, and it was claimed that the arrangement was satisfactory. The complete details of the mount are not described, but it was said that the guns were secured to the platform or wheel with a pin or "hinge" which permitted the gun fired to recoil 4″ before it moved the platform. This was supposed to prevent the circular move-

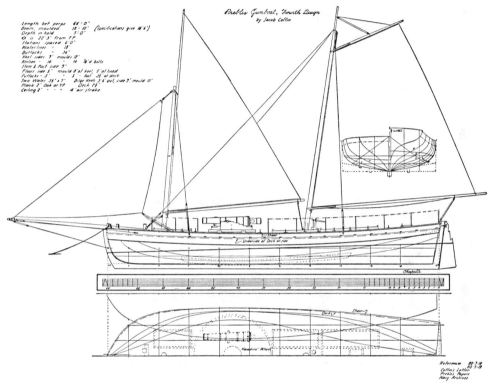

Figure 35. Preble's fourth design for a gunboat, gunter mast forward.

ment of the gun, when the platform on which it was mounted began to revolve, from affecting the accuracy of the shot. The method by which the guns were trained is not clear; perhaps they could pivot slightly on their individual pins, or possibly the platform had to be moved with handspikes. The brackets of the gun carriage may have rested on rollers or casters attached to them; this is not clear in the references to the mount. The shipbuilders were not responsible for the mount, but constructed only the foundation and the bed on which the platform or wheel was mounted; therefore the specifications go no further. The mount was certainly considered practical by all who

tested it, and at least three gunboats were fitted with guns on revolving platforms. The design in Figure 34 seems to have been used for contract plans in
a number of gunboats; these will be referred to later. The fourth design was
an enlargement of the third, and Figure 35 shows a redrawing of the original
rough plan. The boat was somewhat similar to that of the third design, but,
owing to changes in proportions, she was longer and lower in appearance.
The fourth design was 66′ 0″ between perpendiculars, 18′ 10″ moulded beam,
and 5′ 0″ depth of hold.

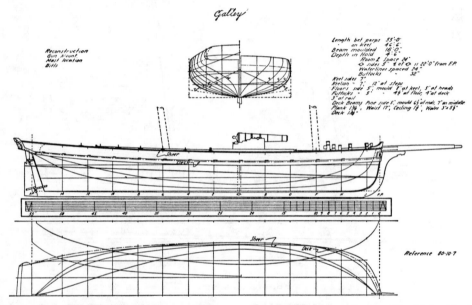

*Figure 36. Draught of a galley gunboat, probably an improvement on Preble's third
design.*

There is evidence that a fifth design was made, apparently to the same dimensions as the first one. No plan has been identified as the fifth design, but there
is reason to be uncertain as to whether all the designs were made by Coffin,
as will be shown.

The proposals made by Preble in his first, third, and fourth designs seem to
have been approved by the Secretary of the Navy and were utilized in the contracts for a number of gunboats. However, the Coffin drawings were rather
crude and incomplete. It is stated that copies were made in the Navy Department, probably by Fox. Two drawings survive that may be these "copies"—
which in fact, were independent designs.

Figure 36 is a careful redrawing of a gunboat or "galley" design which may
be the adaptation of Preble's third design used by the Department. The original
drawing is unsigned but appears to have been the workmanship of Fox. The

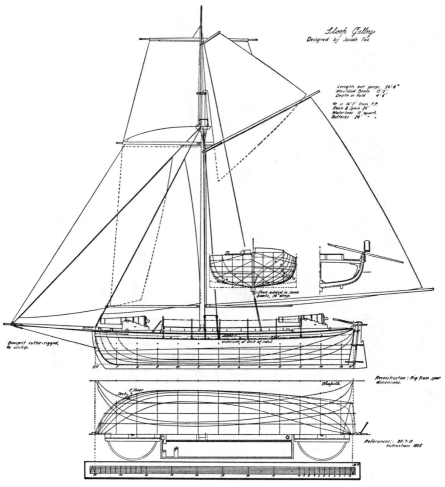

Figure 37. The small galley fitted with a sloop rig and two guns.

plan was not wholly complete, as the masts were shown by light pencil lines
that had apparently been added later. These indicated that the boat had been
rigged in three ways—sloop and two schooner rigs. This plan, though following Preble's third design in a general way, was a wholly distinct one. It called
for 55′ 0″ between perpendiculars, 16′ 0″ moulded beam and 4′ 6″ depth in

the hold. Whereas Preble's proposals had square-tuck sterns like a rowboat (at least his designs that survive show this), the plan under discussion had a round-tuck like a large vessel and had, in addition, a knee on the bow.

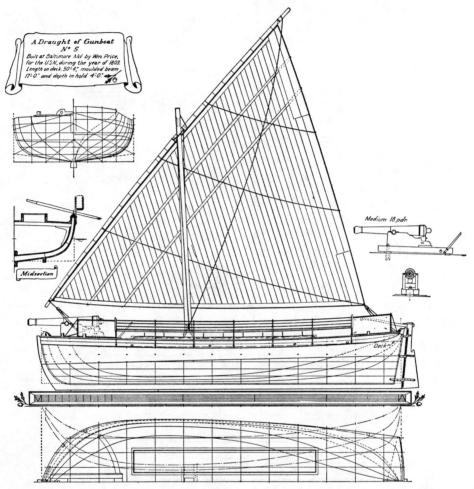

Figure 38. Fox's design for a small galley carrying one gun.

Another design that may perhaps be traced to Preble's proposals is shown in Figures 37 and 38. This is for a boat 50′ 4″ between perpendiculars, 17′ 0″ moulded beam, and 4′ 6″ depth of hold—approximately the dimensions of Preble's first design. The length on the original plan is given as 50′ between perpendiculars in fact, but the frame spacing indicates that the boats on this design would run a few inches over the stated length. This design was also prepared by Fox, and the boat was originally intended to be rigged with a single lateen sail, as shown in Figure 38. However, it appears that most, if not all, the boats supposed to have been built to the design were finally sloop-rigged, about as in Figure 37. The original drawing was marked as having been sent to William Price, at Baltimore. Since he built Gunboat *No. 5*, it may be that the plan is of this boat, though the correspondence indicates a strong possibility that *No. 5* was built to the double-ender design, as previously indicated. In any case, the original design was intended to mount a single gun forward, a long 18- or 24-pdr. This was mounted on skids pivoted at the forward end and traversing in a limited sweep, as in the Messina gunboats. However, the deck arrangement and the heavy displacement of the design permitted the mounting of two guns fully pivoted, and accordingly many of the boats built to the design were fitted with two medium or long 24- or 32-pdrs. on pivots and full circles.

The double-ended designs by Fox were considered a useful type of gunboat, but the commanders and crews seem to have disliked the lateen rig proposed. The boats also were low in the water and were quite wet. It was soon apparent that a modified design was wanted, and so Fox made the design shown in Figures 39 and 40. This was simply a modification of the design shown in Figure 32, with 6″ more depth and the topsides altered. The idea of the boats being capable of working either end foremost, under sail or oars, was given up, and the rudder was permanently located on the stern. The bulwarks were raised fore and aft and more sheer was employed. This design was prepared to utilize the standard rig proposed by Captains Preble and Tingey for the dandy-rigged gunboats that crossed the Atlantic in 1805 and 1806. Some of the boats were sloop-rigged, and in these the mast was placed forward of its location in the dandy rig and a longer bowsprit was employed. The bowsprit in both rigs was fitted to unship, and its heel was secured to the pivot bolt of the bow gun which was locked in fore-and-aft train. Before the gun could be traversed the bowsprit had to be removed. The rigs were modified a number of times with the apparent desire to improve sailing qualities at the expense of rowing ability. This can be seen in the development of the double-ender, where the designs were progressively more seaworthy and better sailers, but became less suitable for operations in shoal and confined waters.

It will be noted that there had been an attempt to produce a number of standard designs. However, there is little evidence that any consideration was given to establishing the characteristics that would be desirable for any particular field of operation. On the contrary, the designs were made to fit the personal opinions of a selected group of captains and of Constructor Fox. The ruling factor otherwise appears to have been economy. Though the original

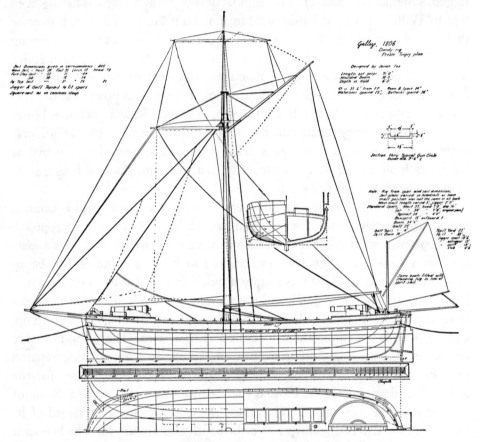

Figure 39. Galley gunboat with "dandy rig."

intention was to build gunboats suitable for harbor and coast defense, the Mediterranean adventure had placed emphasis on seaworthiness and sailing ability because the boats were required to cross the Atlantic. The apparent importance of sea-keeping qualities had not been modified by experience in action, as the boats arrived too late to be of service in the attacks on Tripoli. Hence the original idea was lost sight of completely, and the gunboats were being designed more as substitutes for regular naval vessels than as craft for special service.

It is impossible to draw any definite conclusion as to the importance of Preble in the development of the visionary gunboat theories of the Jeffersonian

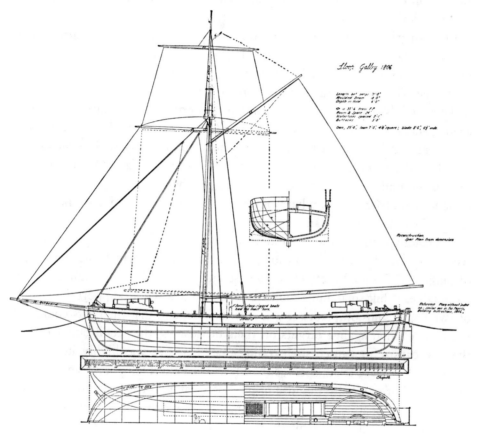

Figure 40. Fox's design to improve seagoing qualities of a galley gunboat.

administration. Certainly he contributed something to the idea. In this period naval officers were fanatical party men, and it was not uncommon for them to place their professional opinions and acts within the framework of a political platform. This seems to have been done by many officers in the Mediterranean and probably accounts for the very uneven performance of the Americans in the Tripolitan war. It is certainly possible that Preble had permitted his political partisanship to override his professional judgment, and he may have encouraged the administration to put its faith in gunboat flotillas rather than in a sound naval construction program. However, no real evidence has yet been found to support such a conclusion. Rather, the indications are that Preble put excessive emphasis on gun vessels, which the administration seized upon to develop a political naval policy of its own.

In comparing American designs for gunboats with those in Europe it is apparent that the former gave very little attention to craft required to land on, or to operate from, beaches and that there was no intention of producing boats that would be operated in support of a military movement, as Napoleon had planned. Nor was there any definite plan for gunboats operating in flotillas against enemy naval vessels, for if there had been there would have been more large gun vessels and more types carrying heavy armaments, such as the Danes, Dutch, and French produced during the Napoleonic Wars. On the basis of the correspondence and the gunboat designs that have survived it is very difficult to understand just what was intended to be the operation of the American gunboats in time of war.

It is readily seen that the predominant American designs in the gunboat class were very small craft. The problem of arming such small boats with guns of sufficient size to be effective against enemy shipping was almost insurmountable. While small hulls could be produced that would support the weight of two heavy guns on pivots, it was eventually found that the boats could not use their cannon against targets on their broadsides; the recoil either caused them to capsize or caused such rolling that their fire was highly inaccurate. Various ideas were tried, such as the Hawkins Wheel supported and utilized by Preble, but gradually the idea of gunboats having broadside fire was given up in favor of boats with limited traverse ahead and astern, as will be shown. In the process of development the American gunboats grew first in displacement, and finally in length.

The gunboats that immediately followed the first ten were still to a great degree experimental types. Preble placed two contracts in 1805—one on March 15 with Nathaniel Dyer at Portland, Maine, for *No. 11*, and one on July 1 with Jacob Coffin at Newburyport, Massachusetts, for *No. 12*. It is not clear on what plan *No. 11* was to be built, for she measured, when completed, 73' 10" on the rabbet, 18' 11" extreme beam, and 5' 3" depth in the hold. Preble's correspondence reveals that she had some carving on a knee on the bow and on parts of the stern. It seems probable that Preble's fourth design was the basis for the boat and that it was altered by the builder. The boat was schooner-rigged. *No. 12* was built to the fourth design, shown in Figure 35, for the contract is for the exact dimensions of that design. The finished boat differed slightly, however, for she was 67' 8" on deck, 18' 11" extreme beam, and 5' 4" depth in hold.

Preble employed the sliding-gunter rig on the foremast of the gunboats, as shown in Figures 34 and 35. This rig had been popular in some ship's boats and gave short spars that were easily stored inboard. It is difficult to see what advantages were expected from the gunter rig in these gunboats, however, except that they might lay head to the wind very quietly with sails furled, as the windage on the foremast was much reduced. It may be concluded that the advantage of the rig was slight, for it appears to have been abandoned in the later schooner gunboats. *No. 11* and *No. 12* were sent to the New Orleans station and were condemned about the time the War of 1812 began, by which time their odd gun mounts had been removed.

Gunboats *13* through *16* were built on the western rivers in 1805–6, and all went to New Orleans. *No. 13* and *No. 14* were built by John Smith at Cincinnati, Ohio, and *15* and *16* by Matthew Lyon at Eddyville, Kentucky. Henry Carberry was agent for these. The boats are listed as having been 60' on the keel, 18' 6" beam, and 5' 0" in the hold. Apparently all were on Fox's design, shown in Figure 40, according to building directions, but the correspondence seems to imply that Preble's proposals were used, and one of the boats, *13*, had the Hawkins Wheel gun mount. The boats were sloop-rigged and had a 16' boat, two anchors of 700 lbs., and a kedge of 100 lbs. The armament was two 24-pdrs. It seems highly probable that the cause of confusion in the plans used was that while Preble's proposal, the fourth perhaps, was used in negotiations, the final design used to build the boats was Fox's double-ender.

In addition to the fifteen gunboats authorized February 28, 1802, twenty-five more were authorized March 2, 1805. It appears that only sixteen were built with the funds appropriated by the second authorization, and the balance of the money available under the two Acts was used to obtain the four bomb vessels mentioned earlier. No plans of the bomb vessels have been found other than a few arrangement sketches. One of the vessels, named the *Etna*, was designed by Jacob Coffin and built by William Moulton at Portland, Maine. This bomb ketch was hurriedly run up and was launched in June, 1806. She measured 83' 6" on deck, 24' extreme beam, and 8' depth of hold. The *Etna*, or *Aetna*, was rigged like the English bomb ketches and crossed a royal on her main, but had only a square topsail above her spanker on the mizzen. The *Vesuvius* was a similar vessel built by Jacob Coffin from his own design and launched in May, 1806. She was probably a sister ship of the *Etna*, though there is a slight variation in their dimensions. These vessels carried a 13″ mortar and ten guns on the broadside—9-pdrs.—and either two 24-pdr. carronades or two howitzers, 8″ bore. The register dimensions of the *Vesuvius* were 82′ 5″ on deck, 25′ 5″ extreme beam, and 8′ 4″ hold; this is close enough to those of the *Etna* to indicate both were on the same design. The rigs were similar in all spar lengths, and both had a cutwater, headrails, and some carving. Neither one was a very good sailer because of faulty balance, and the mounting of the mortars was very unsatisfactory. Both were completed too late to go to the Mediterranean, and they were sent to New Orleans. The two remaining bomb vessels were purchased merchantmen. The *Spitfire* was a Connecticut merchant sloop built in 1803 and purchased by Preble at Boston in April, 1805. She was converted to a bomb ketch and was in the Mediterranean in 1805–6. The *Vengeance* was a Connecticut merchant schooner built in 1804 and purchased at Boston at the same time as the *Spitfire*. She was converted to a bomb ketch at the Boston Navy Yard by Rhodes and Page. Rhodes had built Gunboat *No. 8*. The work on the *Vengeance* was done between April 27 and June 19, 1805. The ketch was then sent to the Mediterranean, and it returned in 1806 to be laid up at New York. Both the *Spitfire* and the *Vengeance* were poorly balanced under the ketch rig, and their mortars were not properly mounted. The *Etna* was struck from the Navy list just before the War of 1812; the *Vengeance* was broken up in 1818, the *Vesuvius* in 1829, and the *Spitfire* in 1820. All appear to have been used as receiving ships for the greater part of their lives.

In following the development of the gunboats, we have omitted mention of two seagoing vessels added to the Navy in 1805–6. By an Act of Congress dated March 26, 1804, two more 16-gun vessels were authorized. Fox was ordered to prepare a design for these on July 6, 1804, and seems to have been given complete freedom in selecting characteristics. According to Fox's own statement, the design was "on the principles of an English cutter," though the design, which has survived, shows very little evidence of this influence unless the statement was intended to indicate that the new design was to have more deadrise than the earlier brigs, and possibly a little more "drag" to the keel. The original design called for brigs to measure 105′ 0″ between perpen-

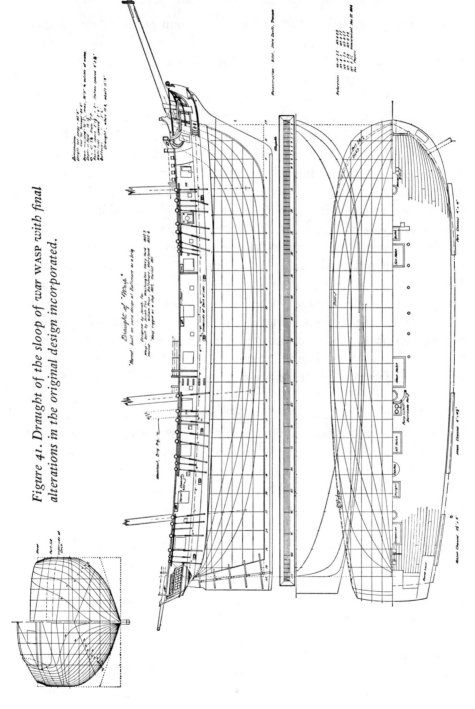

Figure 41. Draught of the sloop of war WASP with final
alterations in the original design incorporated.

211

diculars, 105′ 7″ on deck, 84′ 0″ on the keel for tonnage, 30′ 0″ moulded beam, 30′ 11″ maximum beam, 13′ 9″ depth of hold, and $387^{35}\!/_{95}$ tons carpenter's measurement. The depth of hold was changed to 14′ 1⅝″ by raising the deck in construction of the brigs.

Fox began the construction of one brig, the *Wasp*, at the Washington Navy Yard. The other was built by William Price, at Baltimore, Maryland, and was named the *Hornet*. Both vessels were launched as brigs, but the *Wasp* was altered to the ship rig of a sloop of war before being placed in commission. At this stage Fox made additional sketch plans showing the alterations to make her a ship and detailed her spars and new deck arrangement. In addition he made extensive deck measurements of the vessel as built and noted the alterations necessary to convert her to the ship rig. The original design had placed the channels just below the port sills, where they would have been in the way of sweeps and would have been endangered in boarding. In revising the *Wasp* the channels were raised. Figure 41 is a redrawing of the original plan incorporating all the changes made during construction and conversion to a sloop of war. The original drawing by Fox has suffered damage and was mounted on linen, which so distorted the plan that it was very difficult to correct the projections. The redrawing has been done with great care in an attempt to obtain as accurate a representation of this noted vessel as is possible with the data available.

The *Hornet* was commissioned as a brig and was not rerigged as a ship until 1811–12. The builder had made some errors in setting up the frames of this ship, and as a result she measured 106′ 9″ on deck, 29′ 7″ moulded beam, 31′ 5″ extreme beam, and 14′ 0″ hold. Apparently the rake of the stem had been increased slightly and the beam had been reduced 5″ either in fairing up the frames or in putting them together. As designed, neither the *Wasp* nor the *Hornet* had quarter galleries, but they were added to the former when she was rerigged as a ship: this may also have been the case with the *Hornet*. The latter was not very satisfactory as a brig, as she lacked stability, and so when her rig was changed her planking was doubled at the bilges and up to the top of the wales, adding 10″ to her extreme beam. Both vessels appear to have had billets throughout their careers, but nothing has yet been found about their carvings.

The *Wasp* was launched April 21, 1806; her rig was ordered changed in January, 1807, and she was commissioned late in April of that year. The *Hornet*, which cost a good deal less than the *Wasp*, was launched July 28,

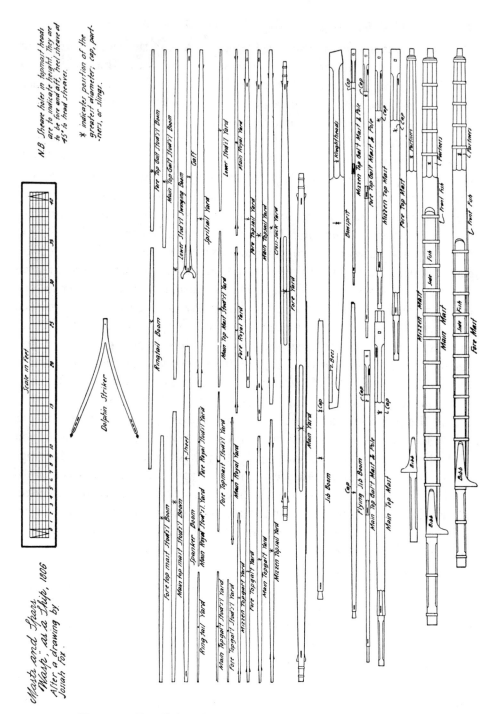

*Masts and Spars,
"Wasp", as a Ship, 1806
After a drawing by
Josiah Fox.*

Figure 42. *Detail drawing of masts and spars of* WASP, *as a ship.*

213

1805, and went into commission in October, 1805, so she was the first completed. The *Hornet* never had her channels as high as the *Wasp*'s, as it was found structurally impractical to raise them. Her builder had placed them higher than the original design called for, however, to clear the rowports, about mid-height of the gun ports. The curved knee under the cathead in *Wasp* was replaced by a vertical one in *Hornet* and the bridle ports were 2' farther aft in the latter, so that the catheads were forward of the bridle ports, rather than aft as in *Wasp*. The masts were also located differently. The foremast of the *Hornet* was about a foot farther forward, the main two feet farther forward, and the mizzen about eighteen inches farther forward than in the *Wasp*. When the *Hornet* was rebuilt and altered in 1811 she had her gun ports placed closer together and one added on each side, giving her eleven ports, including the bridle port, on each side. This arrangement placed the aftermost port one foot ahead of the foremost end of the quarter-gallery moulding, at the level of the port sill, and must have resulted in a rather crowded gun deck. Both vessels were to be armed with long guns, but only the *Hornet* appears to have been so fitted; she carried 16 long 9-pdr. guns in her first commission. The *Wasp* carried 16 32-pdr. carronades and 2 long 12-pdrs. in 1807. When rebuilt, the *Hornet* carried 18 carronades, 32-pdrs., and 2 long 12's. This was the armament of both sloops in the War of 1812.

The *Wasp* and *Hornet* represented Fox's ideas of what a fast man-of-war should be. He prepared the design with unusual care both in the preparation of the lines and in details. Figures 42 and 43 show his detailed spar drawings for the *Wasp*, which illustrate the attention he gave the matter. It seems probable that the design lacked sufficient stability to carry the brig rig first intended. After being changed to a ship the *Hornet* was considered a very good sailer, and the *Wasp* was deemed a fast vessel throughout her career in the American Navy. The hull form Fox employed in these vessels was somewhat similar to that he had used in the frigate *Philadelphia*, but it was somewhat more extreme in deadrise. The midsection was made rather full at the top of the floor timbers, and then the rise of the bottom was sharply increased. The bilges were rather hard and on a short radius. The advantages of this form were obviously that it made it possible to stow the inside ballast low, that it gave sail-carrying power without spoiling the lines for speed, and that it added to the capacity of the vessels. These two sloops were looked upon as superior vessels of their class, and though their designs were never repeated

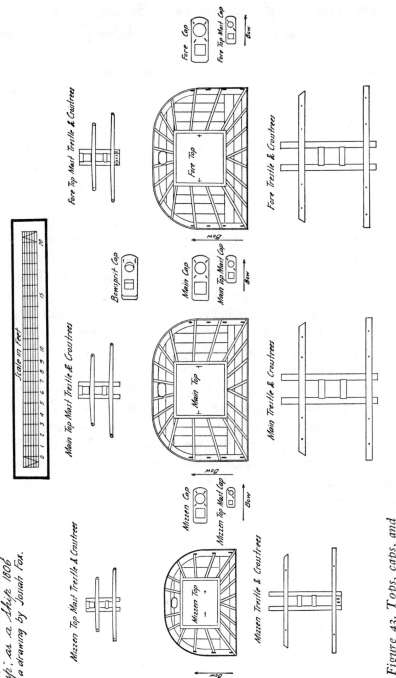

Tops, Crosstrees and Caps
"Wasp," as a Ship 1806.
After a drawing by Josiah Fox.

Scale in Feet

Fore Top Mast Trestle & Crosstrees

Main Top Mast Trestle & Crosstrees

Mizzen Top Mast Trestle & Crosstrees

Bowsprit Cap

Mizzen Cap

Mizzen Top Mast Cap

Fore Cap

Fore Top Mast Cap

Main Cap

Main Top Mast Cap

Fore Top

Main Top

Mizzen Top

Bow

Fore Trestle & Crosstrees

Main Trestle & Crosstrees

Mizzen Trestle & Crosstrees

Figure 43: Tops, caps, and crosstrees for WASP.

N.B. Drawing shows upper-side of Tops and Crosstrees; Underside or Fore of Caps.

they influenced the characteristics of the big ship sloops built in the War of 1812.

The two brigs designed by Fox were not greatly dissimilar in size to the favorite design of brigs of similar rate in the Royal Navy. As the American vessels were to fight brigs of the favored Royal Navy design in the War of 1812, it is desirable to make a comparison. In January, 1797, Sir William Rule supervised the preparation of a design for a brig and two ships, to carry 18 guns—16 32-pdr. carronades and 2 guns, 6-pdrs. This design was to be an improvement on earlier attempts to produce a satisfactory 18-gun vessel. That year the new design was used to build the brig *Cruizer* and the ship sloops *Victor* and *Snake*. These vessels proved very successful, particularly the brig *Cruizer*, and the design was made the standard for Royal Navy 18-gun brigs for nearly twenty years. The design called for a vessel 100′ 0″ between perpendiculars, 30′ 0″ moulded beam, and 12′ 9″ depth in the hold. The model was very good, a rather round midsection with slightly hollow floors, moderately fine entrance and run, and rather raking ends. The vessels had a square-tuck stern. This design, with slight modifications in sheer and head, was also used in the 16-gun brigantine class of 1812. The *Epervier*, of this class, was carried as an 18-gun brig in the American Navy after the War of 1812. Her plan will be seen later. One member of the experimental brig squadron tested by the Royal Navy between 1832 and 1845 was built to the lines of the *Cruizer*. The vessels built on this noted design were generally fast sailers and fine sea-boats. They failed in action against the Americans because they were rather ineffectively armed and, to a greater extent, because their crews were not good gunners. There is no evidence that Fox had seen any vessels of the *Cruizer* model, but he was certainly well acquainted with some of the vessels of similar model that had preceded her. It cannot be said that he copied the Royal Navy brigs, however, as the Fox design was for a sharper model. It has been common for American naval historians to describe the British 18-gun brigs of the War of 1812 as greatly inferior to American vessels in design. But the American *Argus*, *Wasp*, and *Hornet* all fought brigs of the *Cruizer* class, which were equal to them in model, as can be seen by comparing the plans of the American vessels with that of *Epervier*.

During the Tripolitan operation the Navy acquired a few unimportant craft by purchase or capture, the most famous of which was the ketch *Intrepid*. This was a Barbary vessel referred to as the *Mastico*, but whether this was the name of the craft or the name of her type is not clear. She was captured by the

Enterprise and *Constitution* on December 23, 1803, and was purchased as a bomb vessel. Her dimensions are given as 60′ length and 12′ beam; either the beam dimension is an error or she was really a smaller boat than her length indicated. It is probable, from surviving descriptions, that she was a small "bombard," with Tripolitan modifications of the galley type. She was no more than a gunboat, of course. This boat was employed to destroy the frigate *Philadelphia* in Tripoli harbor on the night of February 16, 1804, which was accomplished by boarding the frigate and setting her on fire at her anchorage. Later the *Intrepid* was fitted as a fire ship and sent into Tripoli harbor on the night of September 4, 1804, under the command of Lieut. Richard Somers. She blew up prematurely, killing all of her crew and officers.

A sloop named the *Traveller*, a Massachusetts-built trader, was bought at Malta in the winter of 1804–5. She was a new vessel, having been built only two years before, and was described as being 71 tons, but her dimensions are unknown. She was renamed *Hornet* and remained in the Mediterranean until 1806, when she came home and was sold at Philadelphia in September.

A brig named the *Scourge* was also obtained in the Mediterranean. She was an illegal trader or pirate originally named the *Transfer*, either American or Bermudian built, and was captured by the *Syren* March 18, 1804. She was taken into service as a 16-gun brig and remained in the Mediterranean until well into 1805. She was then brought home to Norfolk and laid up, and was sold as unserviceable in 1812. No dimensions are known, but she was probably a small vessel, since her sixteen guns were only 6-pdrs.

A 10-gun schooner, the *Revenge*, carrying 6-pdrs., was purchased at New Orleans in December, 1806. She was wrecked off Newport, Rhode Island, February 2, 1811. This schooner, about 70′ on deck, was said to be so sharp that she could not stow enough provisions to be of use as a seagoing cruiser. Her spar dimensions indicate that she was a fore topsail schooner, very lofty and crossing a fore royal.

Another vessel obtained in this period was the brig *Franklin*, 8 guns, a merchant vessel bought at Trieste in April, 1805. She had been built at Philadelphia in 1795, and measured 72′ 4″ on deck and 22′ 4″ beam. She was not intended to be employed as a cruiser, but rather as a supply ship, to transport tribute stores particularly. She came home in November, 1805, and in 1806 made two cruises to New Orleans, where she was sold the next year.

By the Act of April 21, 1806, Congress authorized the construction of fifty additional gunboats, and by another authorization the following year, Decem-

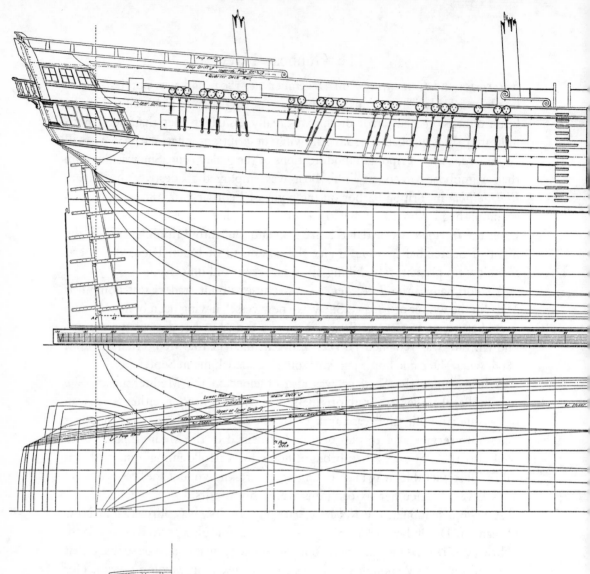

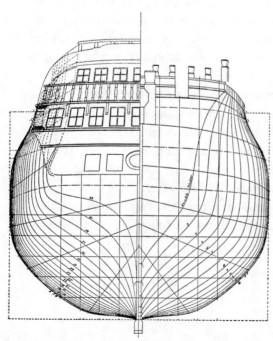

Particular Dimensions
Foreside of M.F. is 73·6½ from F.P.
M.F. sided 1·4"
"41 to "43 is 4·4"
"43 to A.P. is 3·5⅞"
Knuckle Timber is 5·0" from F.P.
Room and Space 2·5⅝
Lowest waterline 4·0" above Base; others 3·0½" apart
Buttock 3·0½" apart.

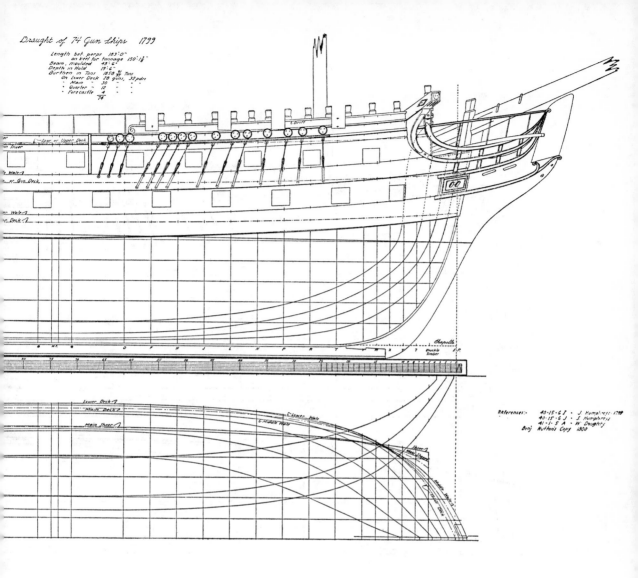

Draught of 74 Gun Ships 1799

Length bet perps 183'0"
on keel for tonnage 150'1⅝"
Beam, moulded 45'6"
Depth in Hold 19'6"
Burthen in Tons 1850 ³⁴⁄₉₅ Tons
On Lower Deck 28 guns, 32.pdrs
  " Main " 30
  " Quarter " 12
  " Forecastle 4
                    ——
                    74

References:-   48-15-6 J - J. Humphreys 1799
              48-15-6 J - J. Humphreys
              41-1-5 A - W. Doughty
    Benj Hutton's Copy 1800

Plan 13. Draught of the proposed 74-gun ship of the line, 1799.

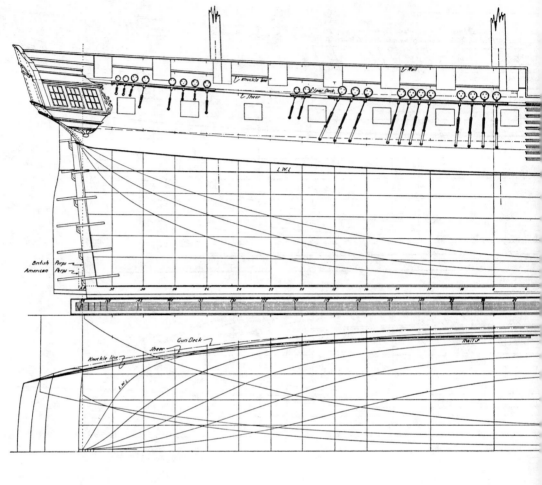

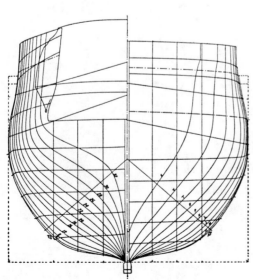

Particulars

O 11 66'0" from F.P.
O to Sta 1 11 6'6"
Stations 5'1" apart
LWL 11 16'0" above Base on F.P
" " 18'0" " " A.P.
Other Waterlines parallel and 1'4" apart.
Buttocks spaced 4'0" apart

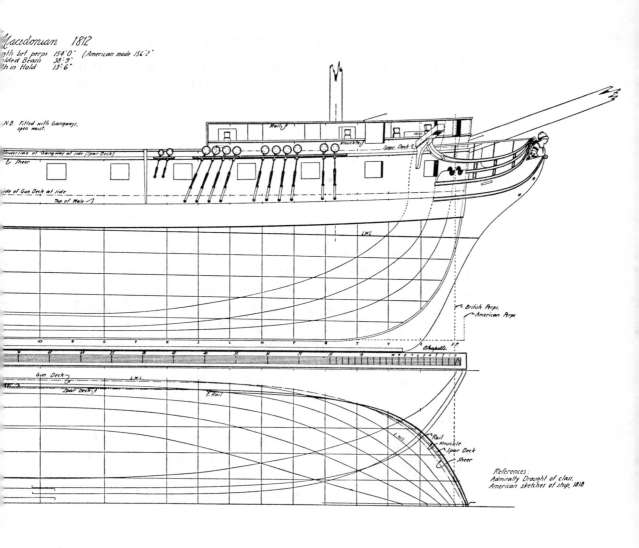

Macedonian 1812
...gth bet perps 154'0" (American mode 156'2")
...lded Beam 38'9"
...h in Hold 13'6"

N.B. Fitted with Gangways,
open waist.

Underside of Gangway at side (Spar Deck)
& Sheer

...ide of Gun Deck at side
Top of Wale

Nail

Knuckle
Spar Deck 2

LWL

British Perps.
American Perps.

Chapelle

Gun Deck
L.W.L
Spar Deck
& Nail

LWL

Rail
Knuckle
Spar Deck
Sheer

References:
Admiralty Draught of class.
American sketches of ship, 1818

Plan 14. Draught of the prize frigate MACEDONIAN, *a British design for a fast frigate,*
1812.

ber 18, 1807, one hundred and eighty-eight more. The boats built under these appropriations varied in design and size, ranging from small sloops or galleys up to sizable sloops and schooners. The designs employed in most of the contracts cannot be readily identified, and some of the plans that have survived are probably no more than proposals. The records of the boats are generally incomplete, and there is a doubt as to the exact number built, for the number authorized in the two congressional acts were not constructed. Lieutenant Commander M. V. Brewington has made an extensive study of the gunboat records and has compiled a list of all boats which he could find any references to either in contracts or in official lists. This information, with a great deal of material on contracts and specifications of various boats, he very kindly loaned to the writer. This has made it possible to assemble more information on the boats than could have otherwise been done. Nevertheless, the material available is both incomplete and unsatisfactory, so far as establishing the plans used in many contracts is concerned. This is due to the practice that had grown up, with the use of naval officers as building superintendents, of referring to plans in correspondence as "Captain Preble's draught" or "Chauncey's plan." These plans, with few exceptions, can no longer be identified with certainty. The best way to assemble the mass of material available seems to be to trace the boats by number and contract.

Gunboats *Nos. 17* through *27* were built on the western rivers and were on the Fox design used for the earlier boats, *13* through *16*, shown in Figure 40. *Nos. 17, 18,* and *24* were built in Cincinnati, Ohio, the first two by John Smith and the last by Thomas Reagan. *Nos. 19* and *20* were built in Kentucky—it is uncertain whether at Lexington or Louisville—by J. Jordan and James Morrison. *Nos. 21* and *22* were built at Marietta, Ohio, by Edw. W. Tupper and Thomas Vail. *No. 23* was built by John Connell and Peter Mills at Charleston (West Virginia?), and *25, 26,* and *27* were all built by Matthew Lyon at Eddyville, Kentucky. These boats, which seem to have been completed in 1807–8, were armed with two 24-pdrs. and sent to New Orleans. Carberry was the navy agent for these boats, and the contracts were let to western politicians who sublet to the actual builders; of the latter Commander Brewington could establish only Thomas Vail of Marietta. *No. 28* was built at the Washington Navy Yard, where work began early in 1808. The correspondence indicates that she was on "Preble's model."

A new 7 was also built, to replace the one lost at sea. The second 7 was built, on a contract let in November, 1806, at Havre de Grace, Maryland, by Bennett Barnes, who was a subcontractor for Gabriel Christie. According to the contract the boat was to be 60′ on deck, 16′ 6″ beam, and 6′ 6″ depth, but she actually measured 59′ 6″ on deck, 16′ 6½″ beam, and 6′ 1½″ depth. She was square-sterned and schooner-rigged.

The plans on which these boats were built are in question. In the first place, there were often errors in the contract dimensions, as the length on deck given in some was actually the length on the keel. Errors also exist in the beam measurements, where moulded and extreme beam are confused. The depth was also subject to error, and the final dimensions given when the boat was accepted are not trustworthy. The superintendents often ordered the boats building under their eye to be made deeper than planned. The variation between what was called for in the contracts and what was built is shown in a study Brewington made of the customhouse registers of the gunboats that were later sold as merchant craft. In these it could be seen that boats built under one contract in a yard often varied in depth, length, and beam so much that the design used became doubtful, regardless of the contract stipulations.

In examining the surviving plans and the data in the various contracts it seems possible, at least, that the boats shown in Figures 36, 37, and 38 were among the designs that were called "Preble's," in spite of the fact that they were the work of Fox. The design shown in Figure 36 seems to have been substituted for the third Preble design, shown in Figure 34, while the boat shown in Figures 37 and 38 seems to have been considered Preble's first design. *No. 7* was not on either of these designs, it is certain, and it is probable that she was merely a pilot-schooner model designed by her builders. *No. 28* was probably as shown in Figure 37, since it was said she was on Preble's model.

Nos. 29 through *33* were built at Portland, Maine, by William Moulton, who built three boats, and Eleazer Higgins, who built two. These boats were designed by Coffin and are supposed to have been on Preble's third design (Figure 34). Preble was the agent, and the contracts were let August 25, 1806. Contracts for three other boats on the same design had been let by Preble a few days earlier at Brunswick, Maine, to Ephraim Hunt and Robert Giveen— *34, 35,* and *36. No. 37* may have been built by the same builders, but this cannot be stated with certainty.

Nos. 38 through *41* were built at Middletown, Connecticut, by William Van Deusen, contractor, and James & Thomas Childs, builders. Captain Isaac Hull and Lieut. Thomas Macdonough were the superintendents. The design used is unknown. *Nos. 42* and *43* were built at Newport, Rhode Island, by

Benjamin Marble, with Captains Hull and Stephen Decatur, Jr., as super-intendents. These boats were on "Preble's model"—either his third design or Fox's copy (Figure 36). *Nos. 44* and *45* were built under the supervision of the same officers at Greenwich, Rhode Island, by John Glozier. These were also on "Preble's model." Gunboats *38* through *45* were all let in August and September, 1806.

Contracts were let in New York State in 1806, and a number of young ship-builders who afterward became noted received orders for boats. Captain Charles Stewart acted as supervisor and let contracts to Adam and Noah Brown for four, *46* through *49;* four to Eckford and Beebe, *50* through *53;* and four to Christian Bergh, *54* to *57* inclusive. These boats were all apparently on one design, 47′ 4″ on the keel, 18′ 0″ moulded beam, and 5′ 6″ depth in the hold. They were to carry one long gun on a pivot, a 24- or 32-pdr., and two car-ronades, 12-pdrs., one on each side. Now, Stewart does not seem to have had a plan prepared, but used one that Chauncey had suggested in reply to a query sent him by the Secretary of the Navy in March, 1806. Both Chauncey and Barron had then made new suggestions, and Chauncey had Bergh prepare a plan which he forwarded to the Secretary, accompanied by a set of speci-fications. The plan proposed by Chauncey is in existence; a redrawing of the original is shown in Figure 44.

This design was entirely different from the ones that had preceded it. Bergh produced a boat modeled to sail well, without much regard to rowing qualities. In order to carry a large gun, the boat, though small, was made wide, deep, and burdensome, yet there was a very great effort to obtain as fast a sailer as possible. The design first called for open bulwarks, but it is probable that these were filled in by plank in most of the boats. With the armament as originally planned the trunk cabin shown in the plan could not be used, and this made the boats very cramped for their crews. The two small carronades were looked upon as being of no particular value, so they were omitted in later boats, and in these the trunk cabin was employed. The rig was to be the "Periagua," popularly known about New York as the "perry-auger." This was a type of boat that was a descendant of the early dugout canoes which had developed a distinctive rig—two-masted schooner without a jib. In the "perry-auger" the masts did not have the same rake; the foremast raked sharply forward and the main sharply aft. The rig was a handy one in small craft and was used in the sailing ferryboats and some lighters in New York Harbor. The sail plan was undoubtedly based on the early Dutch two-masters, which also had no

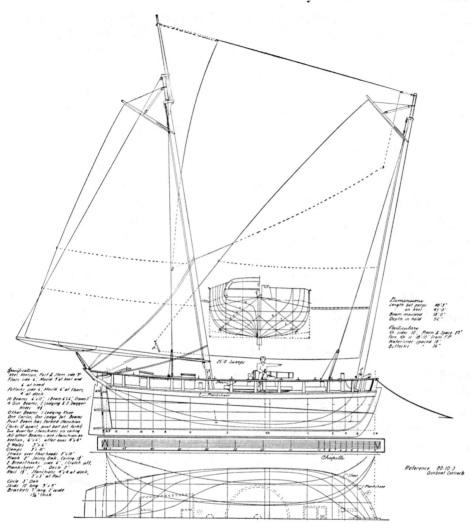

Figure 44. Bergh's design for a gunboat with a Periagua rig, used in building Nos. 50 to 57 and 99 to 104.

bowsprit or jib. The New York boats had short gaffs, and the foresail was loose-footed and "lug-rigged"—that is, without a boom. The New York rig, with its crazily raked masts, may have stemmed from the same source as the old Chesapeake Bay "stick-up" rig, which employed a short foremast raked forward sharply in lieu of a bowsprit; this rig has only recently disappeared from the Bay. The "perry-auger" had some similarity to the "chebacco" and "dogbody" of Massachusetts Bay, which were also schooners without jibs or bowsprits and with the foremast placed right in the eyes of the boat. Basically the same rig was used in the later "Block Island boats," but in all the New England craft the masts raked aft.

The advantages of the "perry-auger" rig were very great, in spite of the unorthodox appearance of the boats. They were really sloops, with the jib set on a mast rather than on a stay. By raking the mast forward the same effect was obtained that would be found in a jib set on a bowsprit; in the "perry-auger" the bowsprit was not required, and this was an advantage in working in crowded waters or close quarters, in slips and around wharves. By the use of the foremast, a straight luff was obtained in the foresail; this was and still is difficult to maintain on a jib set on a stay. As a result, the "perry-auger" was considered more weatherly than a sloop. It had still another advantage. The widely spaced mastheads permitted the use of a huge staysail, after the fashion of the modern schooner's "fisherman staysail" (which was at one time properly called a "pilot-boat staysail," as the sail was first widely used in American pilot schooners rather than in fishermen). Though the efficiency of the "perry-auger" rig was readily proved, the appearance of the sail plan was shocking to conventional sailors, and the rig finally disappeared in New York waters about the time of the Civil War. The related Chesapeake Bay "stick-up" rig became extinct as late as 1936, and one example may have been in use even more recently. These rigs went out of use because of their unusual appearance rather than because they were faulty. However, they were best suited for small craft under 50′ in length; when the work required a larger vessel than this the schooner rig was easier to work. This is also the explanation of the disappearance of the "chebacco" and "dogbody" boats in the New England fisheries; like the "perry-auger," they became finally extinct by the time of the Civil War. Some of the New York "perry-auger" ferryboats were scows, and many of the rig had leeboards.

Chauncey, Stewart, and Bergh were closely associated in interest, and they had looked upon the new boats as primarily for the defense of New York waters. It was natural that they would select a type that was useful around New York and particularly suited for the local requirements. Bergh's design and Chauncey's defense of it are the only gunboat proposals that mention suitability for local use. A few of the commanders assigned to the boats objected to the rig, and so some of the boats were given the standard schooner rig of the 55′ gunboats, shown in Figure 45, which has been drawn on Bergh's design with the bulwarks closed in. When some of the Bergh-designed gunboats were sold for the merchant service, the customhouse clerks were at a loss to describe the rig, so they are often listed as "sloops, two masts." Later such rigs were classed as "cat-schooners."

There appears to have been a similar design prepared, somewhat shoaler

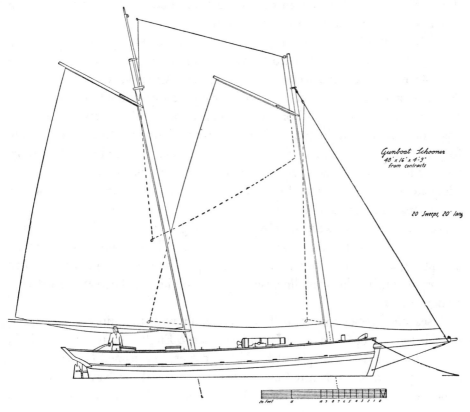

Gunboat Schooner
45' x 16' x 4'-9"
from contracts

20 Sweeps, 20' long

Figure 45. Sail plan of a gunboat, schooner-rigged.

and narrower—45' on the keel, 43' straight rabbet, 16' beam moulded, and 4' 9" deep. These are close to the dimensions given for the modification of Preble's design in Figure 36. However, it appears evident that another design existed which has not been found.

Captain James Barron made a number of proposals for gunboats, but only the design shown in Figure 30 has been found. In 1807 George Hope also made suggestions through Barron, that river gunboats be 50' on deck, 15' beam, and 5' in the hold, but no plan of such a boat has yet been found. In 1806 Barron apparently proposed a plan that was widely used. The design called for a boat 60′ between perpendiculars, 56′ on the keel, 48′ straight rabbet, 16′ 6″ beam and 6′ 6″ in the hold. This was a square-stern sloop, though it appears that many were rigged as schooners with their hulls on this design. This is another design that has not been found. The boats must have been much like the Norfolk sloops of the period, which in turn were much like the small schooner pilot boats, but shoaler and flatter on the bottom.

On Barron's plan of 1806 Hope built two boats at Hampton, Virginia—*58* and *59*. John Pool and Richard Servant of the same town built *60* and *61*. *Nos.* *62* to *65* inclusive were built in Mathews County, Virginia, by John Patterson and Hunley Gayle. *Nos.* *66* through *69* were built at Portsmouth, Virginia; John and Joseph Forster built *66*. It appears that forty-three of the boats built under the foregoing contracts were charged to the appropriation for fifty boats authorized April 21, 1806. From July, 1806, to December, 1807, no new gunboat contracts were let, as it was feared that funds would be inadequate. With the passage of the Act of December 18, 1807, authorizing 188 new boats, gunboat building was resumed.

Nos. *70* through *78* were built by the Washington Navy Yard, work starting in February, 1808. The design appears to have been the one shown in Figure 37, except *73*, which was built to an enlarged plan and was given a very lofty rig, as shown by the spar dimensions given for her in the Navy Yard correspondence.

A seagoing vessel appears to have been built with the gunboat appropriations between 1806 and 1809. This was a large English cutter, 73′ on deck, 23′ 8″ beam, and 7′ 6″ depth of hold. The cutter, first named *Ferret*, was designed by Fox. She was fitted out with funds granted the Navy January 31, 1809, and was ordered to be rerigged as a schooner. Soon after this order was given, her name was changed to *Viper* and she was rigged as a brig. It is therefore probable that she never went to sea as a schooner. She rated as a 12-gun vessel when commissioned. The depth of hold given seems very shallow for a cutter of her length and beam. No plan of this vessel has been found. A number of cutter hulls were rerigged as schooners and brigs in the Royal Navy between 1778 and 1800. These were cutters which were thought too large for the one-masted rig, or which lacked the stability necessary in a cutter. One such vessel, the *Spider*, became a well-known cruiser in the West Indies, and many of the other converted cutters were very fast vessels as schooners or brigs.

Gunboats *79* through *88* were built by David Green at Portland, Maine, on a contract made December 30, 1807. These boats had either a single 32- or 24-pdr. on a pivot. They were probably built on the design shown in Figure 37, as it was noted that they were sloop-rigged. The superintendent for the boats, William Bainbridge, wanted to rig them as schooners.

Nos. 89 to 92 inclusive were built at Norwich, Connecticut, and at Westerly, Rhode Island. Amos Cross built two of the boats at Westerly, and Elisha Tracy built two at Norwich. These boats were on the design shown in Figure 37; one of the four had been schooner-rigged by 1815.

Another lot of gunboats was now let in New York, numbered from 93 to 115 inclusive. Six builders were chosen: Eckford and Beebe were to build five, Christian Bergh five, Adam and Noah Brown five, Charles Browne five, Robert Jenkins two, and Thomas Bell one. All were built at New York City except the boats built by Jenkins, whose yard was at Hudson, and the one built by Bell, at Schanks, Long Island. These boats were on two plans: Bergh, Adam and Noah Brown, and Charles Browne used Bergh's design, shown in Figure 44, while the remaining boats were built to the plan mentioned earlier—45′ keel, 16′ beam, and 4′ 6″ or 4′ 9″ depth. Commander Brewington's examination of the customhouse records brought out the fact that one of the boats supposed to have been built to this design actually measured 49′ on deck, 14′ 10″ extreme beam, and 4′ 10″ depth, which indicates how much departure was made from the designs in building.

Gunboats 116 to 135 were built at Philadelphia; seven of these were built outside the Navy Yard. All of these boats were apparently on the design shown in Figure 37. Nos. 136 to 145 inclusive were built by Price and others at Baltimore on Barron's plan, 60′ on deck, 16′ 6″ beam, and 6′ 6″ depth. According to the tenor of the correspondence they were sloop-rigged, but there is some indication that the plan in Figure 37 may have been used. The designs referred to in the official correspondence are not readily identified, and often, as in this case, the letters indicate that another design, rather than the one mentioned in the contracts or initial reports, was used to build the boats. No. 143 was certainly on a smaller plan than Barron's, for Brewington discovered her customhouse measurements to be 51′ x 17′ 6″ x 4′ 2″. Nos. 146 to 155 inclusive were built at Norfolk, Virginia, by Theodore Armistead—dimensions not found. Nos. 156 through 165 were built by James Marsh and Francis Saltus at Charleston and Beaufort, North Carolina. Marsh built five at his yard in Charleston. Marsh, originally from Philadelphia, had been foreman on the frigate built by the citizens of Charleston. He established a yard after that vessel was launched and for some twenty-five years was the leading builder in that section. All of the gunboats built in North Carolina were on Barron's plan. Another North Carolina builder, Amos Perry, constructed three boats, *166* through *168*, at Wilmington, North Carolina. The boats were supposedly on Barron's plan but were schooner-rigged. *No. 166* was renamed *Alligator* in the War of 1812. The remaining numbered boats were *169* through *176*. No contracts or data have been found on these, but it appears that a total of 177 boats may have been built.

Before leaving these boats, it should be noted that there are other designs that may have been used for some of them, but there is no basis on which to connect them with the known contracts. For example, it is known that the United States Navy possessed some "block sloops" in the War of 1812 which were built before the war started, and which were part of the gunboat flotillas. At least two of these sloops saw action; one, named the *Scorpion*, was part of Barney's flotilla on the Chesapeake, and another was in action on the lower Delaware. No record has been found of the building of the *Scorpion*, and it is highly probable that she was part of one of the many gunboat contracts. The design of a single "block sloop" has survived—apparently a proposal—and a reconstruction of the plan is presented in Figure 46. The boat was to measure 48′ 8″ on deck, 17′ 8″ moulded beam, 18′ 2″ extreme beam, and about 4′ 6″ in the hold. It can be readily seen that this design could be substituted for the one in Figure 37 without its being made apparent by the original contracts. The "block sloops" were no more than self-propelled floating batteries, in which speed under sail or oars was sacrificed to the ability to carry heavy guns. The "block sloops" also had high bulwarks to protect the crews from small-arms fire and to aid in resisting boarders. They were, in fact, a small edition of "block ships" used in many European navies. These were often old ships, too old to go to sea, made into hulks and used for harbor defense. There were, however, a number of "block ships" that were designed and built for the purpose. These were very powerful floating batteries fitted with some sail power. In November, 1806, Captain Stewart and Bergh made a proposal to construct "block ships" for the protection of New York harbor. Bergh's plan, which still exists, called for a three-decked ship, very short and wide, 100′ on the keel, 46′ beam, and 10′ in the hold, to carry 40 guns, 32-pdrs., and 14 carronades, 42-pdrs., on a draft of 10′ aft and 9′ forward (Figure 47). The vessel was never built, but a "block ship" was finally started at New Orleans during the War of 1812, and other proposals for such floating batteries were made during the war.

Another plan of a gunboat is shown in Figure 48. She is a small schooner designed by Bergh as a dispatch boat. This is a pilot-boat schooner 47′ 8½″ between perpendiculars, 49′ 5″ on deck, 12′ 0″ moulded beam, and 4′ 3″

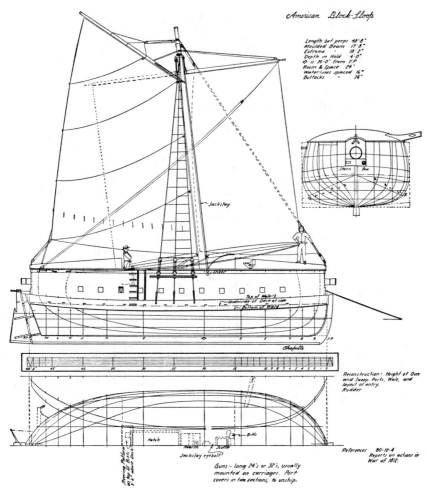

Figure 46. Draught of an American block sloop showing characteristics of this type.

depth in the hold. The schooner was too small to carry a large gun, and it is probable that she was to carry a small carronade on a pivot amidships. The date of the plan is uncertain, but it appears to have been made between 1806 and 1810.

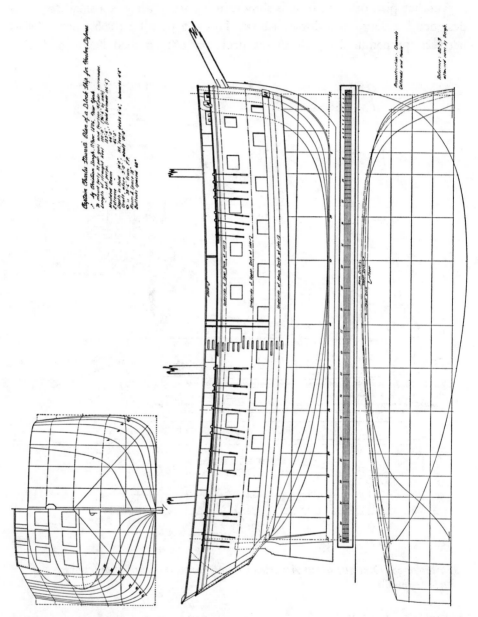

Figure 47. Captain Charles Stewart's and Christian Bergh's proposal for a block ship for the defense of New York.

On the 2nd of July, 1808, the Secretary of the Navy wrote to Captain
Rodgers and ordered that a "gunboat be built on Lake Ontario, equal in dimensions to one of the ketches at New York built by Commr. Preble, and two
small gunboats be built on Lake Champlain sufficiently large to carry one
long 12 pound cannon each." Lieut. M. T. Woolsey was ordered to superin-
tend the construction with Lieut. Haswell and four midshipmen to assist. Captains Rodgers and Chauncey were to furnish the plans and specifications and
with Navy Agent John Bullis were to make the building contracts. The large
gunboat "must be calculated to carry one large 32 pdr. iron cannon in the bow,

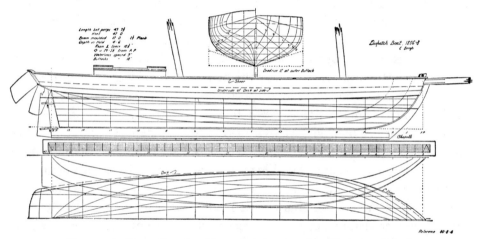

Figure 48. Draught of a dispatch schooner by Christian Bergh.

and 12–18 or 24 pdr. carronades,—or 12 long 9 pdrs.—in the waist. I want
her to be made sufficiently large and armed to cope with any vessel of war now
in Lake Ontario or with a small sloop of war," wrote Secretary Smith. Contracts with Eckford and Bergh and with John Winans were made by the end
of July, 1808. Bergh designed the "large gunboat" to be built on Ontario; her
plans are shown in Figures 49 and 50. The design called for a brig 85' 6" between perpendiculars, 77' 6" on the keel for tonnage, 22' 6" moulded beam,
23' 0" extreme beam, 8' 0" depth in the hold, 262 tons carpenter's measurement. The brig carried the long gun, required by the Secretary, on a pivot
mounted on a raised forecastle, 2' 9" above the gun deck. Bergh made a mistake in drawing the lines, in that he allowed only 14 carronades on the main
deck, but he corrected this in his spar plan, showing the correct number and
the spacing as shown in Figures 49 and 50. The brig was very loftily sparred

and was very powerful for her tonnage. She was built within five miles of the garrison at Oswego and was launched March 31, 1809. Incidentally, her contract price was $20,505 and 110 gallons of spirits. Her carronades were mounted on carriages, and she had a 32' launch and a 20' boat. The brig was fitted with sweeps and had a sheet anchor of 1,500 lbs. weight, one bower of 1,300, another of 1,200, a stream anchor of 800 and two kedge anchors, one 400 and one 200 lbs. She carried four cables 5", 12", 13", and 11" in circumference. The captain, Woolsey, objected to the raised forecastle and wanted to replace it and the pivot gun with two more carronades, but he was overruled. The brig was named the *Oneida*. She served through the War of 1812 and was sold out of service in May, 1815, but was repurchased. The final fate of the brig has not been discovered. The *Oneida* was a fast brig, according to early reports on her, but at the beginning of the War of 1812 her bottom was in poor shape and her speed was affected. Late in the war she was repaired, and her speed was again favorably reported. Bergh's drawings do not show the head built on her, but by 1812 she had a short cutwater and a billet, with only one headrail, about as shown on the two plates of the vessel here. The position of her bowsprit made the head rather low, and Woolsey said she could not have head netting. The gunboats built by Winans do not appear to have been numbered and were not among the boats already listed. No data on the boats has been found, though there is material on the Lake Champlain gunboats built later.

One gunboat plan that cannot be accounted for is shown in Figure 51. This is an undated plan of a galley 74' 10" between perpendiculars, 15' 0" moulded beam, and 3' 9" in the hold. The boat was to be armed with a long gun forward, an 18- or 24-pdr., and a carronade could be mounted aft. A pencil note on the original plan indicated that the positions of the gun and carronade should have been reversed. The boat shows a strong Mediterranean influence in her bow and stern and was about the size of the gunboats built on the Great Lakes in 1813-14, as will appear later. The spur cutwater and "pink" stern served no useful purpose and did not appear on the War of 1812 galleys. It is possible that this plan is for the boats built on Champlain by Winans, but this is mere guesswork. It is apparent that the boat was unsuited for coastal work and only seaworthy enough for relatively protected waters. The galley was alike in lines at the two ends, like Fox's double-enders, but was a much lighter and faster model than the earlier galleys. Pencil drawing on the original indicated that the forward gun was to be removed from the full pivot and remounted lower on slides pivoted at the forward end with limited traverse. It was found,

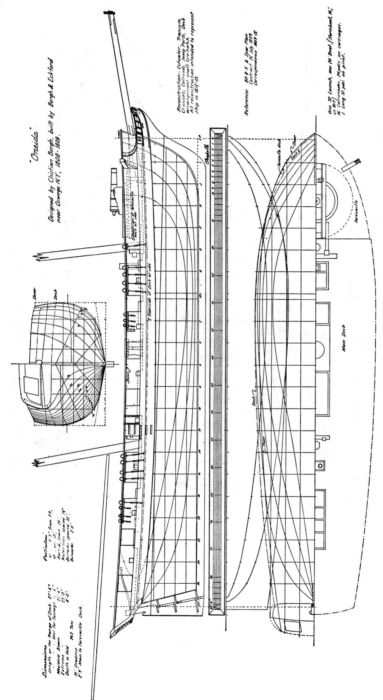

Figure 49. Draught of the brig ONEIDA *built for use on Lake Ontario.*

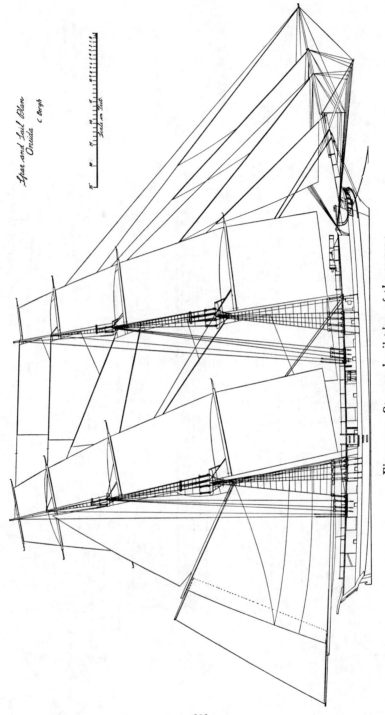

Spar and Sail Plan
Oneida
C. Bergh

Scale in Feet

Figure 50. Spar and sail plan of the ONEIDA.

perhaps, that the boat could not withstand the recoil of the gun when fired on the broadside.

By the end of 1808 the gunboat program ceased, so far as new contracts were concerned, and no new work was authorized from this time to the beginning of the War of 1812. The only undertaking in this period, aside from the completion of the gunboat contracts, was the rebuilding of some of the seagoing

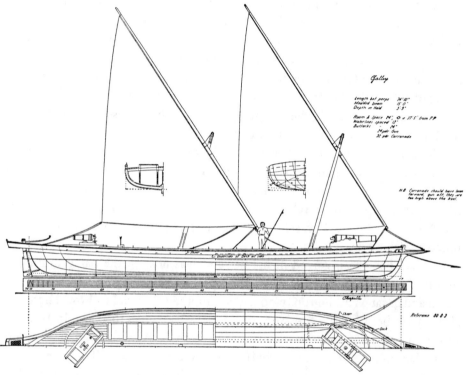

Figure 51. Plan of a galley gunboat showing Mediterranean influence.

vessels. In 1807 Fox had proposed the cutting down of the frigate *Adams* into a flush-deck corvette. This was approved that year, and the work proceeded in a leisurely manner at the Washington Navy Yard. The *Adams* had been considered too sharp on the bottom for a frigate and drew too much water loaded, but she was reported to be a very fast sailer. Fox apparently thought the change would produce a very useful sloop of war of great size. The rebuilding was not completed until after the beginning of the War of 1812. In the process the vessel was lengthened 15′, and so must have been over 132′ on deck.

The *Constellation* was also rebuilt, with the result that her beam was increased 14″ and her appearance much changed. It is not known whether the increase in beam was accomplished by doubling her planking or whether her frames were padded out; at any rate the change in the ship appears to have been very extensive. Under the lash of economy, the ornate carvings on naval craft were removed and replaced with simple billets and stern embellishments. The intricate curved headrail arrangement of the cutwater was simplified by replacing the two upper curved rails with one or two straight rails, and the knees under the catheads were now made straight and vertical in many vessels. On the brigs the hawse holes were considered too low, and some of them, *Syren* among the lot, had the hawse raised so that it was above the trail knees. Some of the small vessels also had short topgallant forecastles added, to aid in working the anchor, and the rail in the wake of this was sometimes raised to the level of the top of the hammock nettings.

The schooners *Vixen*, *Enterprise*, and *Nautilus* and the cutter-schooner *Ferret* were all rerigged as brigs between 1806 and 1811, and some of these craft were extensively rebuilt. The *Enterprise*, which had been rebuilt in the Mediterranean, was again rebuilt, and this time both her model and her dimensions were changed. The schooner was not popular with American naval officers, it seemed.

Fox had become involved in politics and was now in the party in opposition to the administration. He was also at odds with Tingey, the Navy Yard commandant at Washington, who had attempted to dictate to Fox. There was also trouble between the constructor and the workmen in the yard. In July Fox was dismissed by the new Secretary of the Navy of Madison's administration, Paul Hamilton, and no new constructor was appointed. If anything, the handling of naval affairs during Madison's administration was more inept than it had been under Jefferson. Since Madison was a member of the Jeffersonian clique, there was, of course, no change in naval policies in 1809. The Mediterranean became relatively quiet, but relations with England became increasingly disturbed. In spite of this, however, the administration does not appear to have made any preparation for the coming war.

The relation between commanding officers and the naval constructor had not changed. The former were still supreme in technical matters, as evidenced by the power given the captain-superintendents in the gunboat program. Commandants in the various areas had full power to make technical changes at will. Tingey, at the Washington Navy Yard, instigated the changes in rig of the schooners *Enterprise, Nautilus, Vixen,* and *Viper* (ex *Ferret*) to make them brigs, in spite of the objections of Fox. The normal growth of the construction departments of the Navy had been stultified by Jefferson's and Madison's administrations. The navy yards at Norfolk, Washington, Philadelphia, New York, Boston, and Portsmouth had come into real existence, however. Much of the timber purchased for the proposed 74's of 1799 was used in the yards for constructing gunboats and buildings. With his dismissal, Constructor Fox disappears from naval construction history; he eventually settled in Ohio and died there.

While the Navy was declining in effectiveness, commercial shipbuilders in America were making great strides. Ships were gradually becoming larger, and fast brigs and schooners were being built. The sharp vessels increased in average size, so that many two-masted craft exceeded 95' on deck. Three-masted schooners were coming into use, and the "pilot-boat" model so popular with Americans was being improved and also made more extreme in proportions. Rigs were also in process of development; spars and rigging were becoming stronger and lighter. The period between 1800 and 1812 was one of rapid advances in ship design in both America and Europe.

While the Americans had undoubtedly taken the lead in the design of schooners, and of frigates also, it should not be assumed that they had no competition as ship designers. While there can be no doubt that the Americans did remarkable work in ship design in this period, it is a mistake to assume that they were alone in this or that they had a monopoly on radical designs and new ideas. It does not detract from American accomplishments to find that foreign designers were also progressive and were in fact presenting the Americans with sharp competition for the palm of leadership in design of fast ships. The advances of the French in this period in the design of fast men-of-war and privateers were remarkable. The French were experimenting with hull forms of many types, and some of their large vessels were very sharp both in sections and in water lines. French constructors seem to have been given great freedom and were permitted to try any hull form they believed might have possibilities. The Spanish also experimented with fast-sailing craft, and there was hardly a maritime nation in this period that did not seek increased speed for at least some of its craft.

In spite of the predominance Americans were to take in the development of shoal-draft sailing craft, they were not the inventors of the centerboard, but were rather its developers. The centerboard first appeared as a "drop keel" and, as has been said earlier, was the invention of Captain Schank, while a lieu-tenant in the Royal Navy, stationed at Boston, Massachusetts, in 1774. Schank was a very ingenious officer. He also developed a method of mounting guns that permitted a single battery to be used on either side of the ship, and he was the leading proponent in the introduction of the "drop keel" into large vessels. It is really doubtful, however, whether he should be called the "inventor" of the drop keel, for a similar fitting seems to have been in use in some Chinese junks and in South American sailing rafts long before his time.

The drop keel introduced by Schank was first a long single plank in a case like that of the modern rectangular centerboard. This was controlled by a tackle at each end and for this reason was not very satisfactory in large craft. This objection Schank overcame by introducing two or more single narrow boards each in an individual case, along the center line of the hull, and each independent of the others. This gave a stronger hull and permitted adjust-ment of the boards to shift the center of lateral plane that was desirable in a square-rigged vessel. By 1798 he had succeeded in getting the British Ad-miralty to build a number of drop-keel vessels of some size. These not only included a large cutter, 65' long, the *Trial*, but also a ship sloop named *Cynthia*, 113' 2" on deck, 28' 7" beam, and 12' depth of hold. In addition there were two classes of gun brigs fitted with drop keels: one the *Hasty* class of 16 ves-sels, 76' 0" on deck, 22' 6" beam, and 8' 0" in the hold; the other, the *Assault* class of 17 brigs, 75' 0" on deck, 22' 0" beam, and 7' 11" depth of hold. One or two small tenders were also fitted with drop keels.

One of the most advanced naval constructors of the period was Samuel Bentham, of the Admiralty staff. This English designer was very radical in his ideas; in 1796 he designed and built two advice (dispatch) schooners for the Admiralty, first called *No. 1* and *No. 2*, but later named *Redbridge* and *Eling*. These were 80' on deck, 21' 0" moulded beam, 11' 6" in depth, and 158 tons. They had diagonal bulkheads and very cutaway ends and were, so far as has yet been discovered, the first sailing vessels to employ outside ballast. This outside ballast was cast in short sections, just under 4' in length, which were placed in line along the bottom of the keel. Each had two lugs at the top which tenoned into the keel and were secured by pins passed through keel and lugs athwartships. The outside ballast was cast so that it was markedly wider on the bottom than at the keel. These schooners also steered with a wheel, geared to a quadrant. They had iron windlasses and mast winches, iron stoves, and other improvements. Both schooners were considered good sailers. Two others, the *Milbrook* and the *Netley*, were built, but on different models. Each was an experiment in hull form. The *Milbrook* was 81′ 8″ on deck, 21′ 0″ moulded beam, and 9′ 8″ depth of hold, and the *Netley* was 86′ 7″ on deck, 21′ 0½″ moulded beam, and 11′ 3″ in the hold. Bentham also designed the strange ship sloops *Dart* and *Arrow*, which had whaleboat sterns, built-in water tanks, diagonal bulkheads, and many innovations in construction, rig, and fittings. They were 128′ 8″ on deck, 33′ 10″ beam, and 7′ 11″ depth of hold; each had three drop keels. Bentham's hull form was cut away at bow and stern and the sections were either V-shaped or U-shaped.

It is a sad turn of fate that Bentham's genius has been forgotten while the reputation of other men, such as Symonds, Humphreys, and others, of less technical accomplishment has been lauded. In addition to his many experiments in construction methods and ship design, Bentham introduced improvements in the Admiralty dockyards—steam sawmills, improved drydocks, and other mechanical aids. His personality appears to have been a somewhat unpleasant one, and there are indications that he was cordially disliked by many of his contemporaries. Henry Peake, a noted Admiralty naval constructor, was impressed by Bentham's ideas in hull design and produced a number of vessels, largely schooners, employing some of Bentham's ideas. The schooner *Rapid*, designed and built in 1808, was one of these; she was 107′ on the range of deck, 22′ 6″ moulded beam, and 12′ 0″ depth of hold. She had raised forecastle and quarterdeck and was to be armed with 14 18-pdr. gun-carronades in the waist, four ordinary 12-pdr. carronades on the quarterdeck, one 12-pdr. gun carronade on the forecastle, and one 24-pdr. gun carronade in the waist as a mortar. She could fight 12 guns on a side.

The pivoted centerboard was apparently first worked out by an English officer named Shuldham, while a prisoner of war of the French at Verdun, in 1809. The American patent for a pivoted centerboard was issued to Joshua, Henry, and Jacocks Swain, April 10, 1811. The Schank drop keel was used in some American schooners and sloops as early as 1806, but the centerboard did not become common until after 1820.

Mention of these matters will serve to bring into proper perspective the state of naval architecture in the United States in the period just preceding the War of 1812. Americans were by no means the most advanced and scientific ship designers and builders; they had as yet produced only their huge, fast schooners and their great frigates. The Navy had no constructor comparable to Bentham, and the most radical American vessels were to be found among the small pilot-schooner types. There was apparently nothing in the American merchant marine approaching the sharp lines used in the British four-masted vessel *Transit*, designed and built by Captain Richard Hall Gower in 1799–1800. The American fast-sailing vessels were not so much radical departures in design as natural developments of the then existing theories of design of fast-sailing vessels. Large, sharp, fast-sailing craft, particularly schooners, undoubtedly made up a greater proportion of the American merchant marine at this time than sharp vessels did in the foreign merchant services. This was due not to American progressiveness so much as to the unprotected state of their trade abroad, which, with the troubled international situation of the period, placed emphasis on speed in many classes of merchant craft.

It has become somewhat common to assume that the controversy over the advantages of a rather full, flat-bottomed midsection, as compared to the sharp midsection of the pilot-boat model, began with the building of the clipper ships in the late '40's and '50's. This was certainly not the case, for there were two schools of thought in the United States as early as 1800. This can be illustrated in the naval vessels built in this period. The *Argus*, by Hartt, and the *Oneida*, by Bergh, combined full, flat-floored midsections with fine ends, while the *Syren* and *Vixen*, by Hutton, and the *Wasp* and *Hornet*, by Fox, had sharp bottoms. The New York and New England builders, in general, seem to have favored the hull form employing very moderate deadrise amidships combined with sharp, well-formed ends, while the builders south of New York preferred the "pilot-boat" section with fine or moderately sharp ends.

The period between 1801 and 1812 produced few changes in naval guns. In America the carronade had become popular, and the long gun on a pivot had now reached its height in professional popularity, which it was to maintain for sixty years or more, until it was replaced by the turret mount. The pivot mounts of long guns were gradually employed in carronades also. The mount most commonly used consisted of a metal ring, or "circle," of from 9′ to 12′ in diameter, on deck and brought level athwartships by a wooden foundation. This circle was usually of iron, though copper and brass were also employed. The section of the circle was a shallow U shape, hollow side up, about 5½″ wide and 1″ thick. The inside and outside rims of the top were raised ½″ and were about ½″ wide. Rollers traveled in the track thus formed. These were on the bottom of two horizontal timbers, 8″ to 12″ square, called "skids," which were secured together by three or more blocks, or "chocks," and bolted. The skids were parallel and usually a couple of feet apart. On the top inside edge of each there was a rabbet running the full length of the skid. In this the bottom of the gun mount could slide. The skids were pivoted at the middle, or thereabouts, by a heavy pivot bolt, or pin, which passed through the center chock of the skids and thence through deck and a heavy timber below. The pivot bolt was further supported by a cast-metal socket and plate in the deck and was often heavily bushed in the skid-chock, since the strains of recoil were largely concentrated on this structure. The gun mount consisted, as a rule, of the standard broadside carriage without trucks, the bottom of the side brackets of which rested in the rabbets on the upper and inner side of the skids. Sometimes there were rollers on the underside of the brackets, or the trucks were retained and traveled in the grooves in the skids. The gun was trained by prying the skids around by means of handspikes. Recoil was controlled by breechings—heavy rope secured to the breech of the gun and fastened either to ringbolts in the deck about the gun, or on neighboring bulwark stanchions. Small guns had breechings secured to the skids, but this put a greater strain on the pivot bolt than was desirable, so when the gun was brought to bear on a target the breechings were commonly hooked onto ringbolts in deck and rail. Neither gun nor mount was particularly suitable for firing on fast-moving targets.

There were a great many variations in pivot mounts. Some had pivots at one end of the skids and traversed on an arc rather than a circle; some so pivoted could traverse a full 360 degrees. The rollers on the bottom of the skids went out of use gradually, as the guns grew heavier and longer, and the top of the track was then rounded. In such mounts, the casting at the pivot bolt was carried slightly higher than the track, and the skids balanced in the pivot casting. This made it easier to train the skids and gun quickly, as the skids could be lifted off the track to traverse. With the gun brought to "battery" or in the firing position, the weight of the gun and carriage brought one end of the skids to rest on the track, or circle. The details of many mounts can be studied on the plans of the gunboats and other vessels, where their general arrangement can be seen. The need of shallow bulwarks where pivot guns were employed was looked upon as a disadvantage, as the gun crews were thus unprotected from small-arms fire. As in the *Oneida*, the gun on a pivot could be mounted on a raised forecastle or quarterdeck, but the same disadvantage existed. The pivot gun should not be confused with the famous "Long Tom" of the privateers; the latter was a shifting long gun on a broadside carriage and not, as a rule, a pivot gun.

Carronades were mounted on both carriages and pivoted beds; some of these weapons had trunnions, and some were without. Bentham had introduced a non-recoil carronade into the British Navy; it was loaded outside its port and had other disadvantages but was capable of being loaded and fired very rapidly. This carronade did not become very popular in the Royal Navy, where only a few ships were armed with it, and it was never employed in the United States Navy, so far as is known. The Americans did not attempt any innovation in gun design, though, as noted, they did experiment with sights and mounts. Their cannon and carronades were gradually cast without the numerous mouldings and ogees that had marked the earlier guns. In spite of their preference for long guns, it is to be noted, most of the American naval vessels were armed with what was later called a "medium" gun; the length of cannon now ranged from 18.4 to 20.6 times the diameter of the ball. The length was gradually being increased, however, during the period under discussion. Small arms placed aboard the gunboats and other craft were muskets, pikes, boarding axes, cutlasses, and pistols. Dirks and swords, as well as pistols, were regulation for the officers. Rifles were also issued to marines in some cases. The American boarding ax was the same as that issued to the Royal Navy, a tomahawk-shaped ax having a spike at the back.

The gunboats and the brigs laid down in the period under discussion were not important additions to the Navy, with the possible exception of *Wasp* and *Hornet.* Their designs were not unusual, and the governmental construction program added nothing to the advances then being made in the design of American commercial craft. Though conventional in design, the small vessels built for the Navy were usually of good model for their size and limitations. This could be said of most of the gunboats, in fact, though they were wholly inadequate in dimensions for the required armament of this class of naval vessel.

It seems strange today that Americans gave so little thought to building up the Navy in the years preceding 1812, when it must have been obvious to all that war was approaching. The attacks on American shipping by British cruisers, culminating with the *Chesapeake-Leopard* affair in 1809 and the *President–Little Belt* incident in 1811, should have been sufficient warning.

It seems probable that the Jeffersonian policy that looked upon war at sea as primarily an attack on the enemy merchant marine (which could be carried out by privateers) explains the neglect of the national Navy in these years.

As the War of 1812 approached, the gunboat program slowly came to a halt. The discharge of Fox had left the Navy without a constructor, and Madison's Secretary of the Navy made no attempt to replace this technician. Only the gunboats which had been contracted for earlier, but which had not been delivered, were under construction in 1811. Many of the ships in ordinary were decayed and were rapidly becoming entirely useless. The vessels in commission were generally in a poor state, and many were in need of extensive repairs. Though the big schooner had now become almost the national type of fast-sailing vessel and was to be the mainstay of the privateer type, the Navy had now discarded the rig entirely under the influence of a few pompous officers; only a few large schooners in the Revenue Service were in government hands. The navy yards were inactive, and most of them were, in fact, mere storage plants. The abysmal ignorance of both the American politician and the public regarding the function of a navy was about to be corrected in a sharp and highly unpleasant manner.

★ ★ ★ ★ ★ ★ ★ ★ ★

CHAPTER FIVE

The War Navy
1812-1816

I T WAS FULLY apparent by the beginning of 1812 that war with Britain was fast approaching. The western and southern congressional members were hot for beginning hostilities, but the New England states and the larger part of the maritime interests were less enthusiastic. The objections of the seafaring groups to war with the greatest naval power on earth were partly a matter of economics and partly political animosity. Seamen and merchants had no feeling of friendliness for the British, for the impressment of American seamen and the seizure of American ships and cargoes by the cruisers of the Royal Navy caused strong resentment. However, France had also been active in arresting American vessels and mistreating their crews, and public opinion in most maritime communities was almost equally unfriendly to both of the contending powers. The agrarians of the Jeffersonian party had never been friendly to sea-borne trade, and the party's "Long Embargo," initiated by Jefferson in his second administration and continued by Madison, had not only effectively ruined legal sea traders but, by its nature, had created a vested interest in illegal trade. The merchants ruined by the embargo, and seamen or officers out of employment because of the embargo, naturally joined the party in opposition to the administration. On the other hand, those engaged in the highly profitable illegal trade viewed with the utmost distaste any act of the administration that would interfere with these activities. The southern states were politically the partners of the western states in the Jeffersonian party, and their maritime interests benefited; the embargo was less rigidly enforced in the South, and so seafarers and merchants of the Chesapeake and of the southern ports were sympathetic to the administration and, on the whole, willing to follow party leadership into war.

The shipbuilding trades had been depressed by the "Long Embargo," and this, with the administration's neglect of the Navy and lack of any preparation for war, alarmed those thoughtful enough to appreciate the danger of war with the greatest of naval powers. Lack of business had closed many shipyards and the skilled labor had drifted away, and many good vessels from Philadelphia northward had sadly deteriorated while laid up during the embargo. Only on the Chesapeake and in a few southern ports was there any shipbuilding, and this was confined almost entirely to the construction of fast schooners for the illegal trades and for West Indian adventures. It seemed, therefore, that if war came it would be difficult to get fighting ships to sea with half if not more of the potential shipbuilding facilities of the United States inactive. This seemed particularly important because both the Jeffersonians and the opposition placed reliance on privateers in naval warfare and had little knowledge of the uses of a regular naval force on the high seas.

The difference of opinion regarding the national Navy was quantitative rather than basic. In public opinion it was part of the coast-defense system; to the administration it was a relatively unimportant part to be used only as floating batteries in support of fortification. The opposition, however, wanted the naval ships to function not only as a mobile coast defense but also in defense of sea-borne trade, particularly coastal. Neither party seems to have had a clear concept of naval tactics, and, as in the Revolution, there was widespread doubt that Americans could possibly cope with the British Navy at sea. It was thought that success would be obtained by assault on British maritime trade by means of privateers, combined with land operations against Canada. This suited the diverse groups of the Jeffersonians. The westerners wanted to put a stop to British help to the Indians and to punish both Canadians and British for alleged incitement of Indian warfare. The opportunity to loot Britain's sea-borne trade appealed to southern maritime interests.

The Jeffersonian gunboats had been created in accordance with the party's theory of a coast-defense Navy. The inadequacies of the gunboats were, of course, fully apparent to seafarers and shipbuilders of both the Jeffersonian and Federalist parties. The Jeffersonians deprecated the matter because they felt they would have to rely upon privateers anyway, and the Federalists complained because the gunboats obviously would not be able to defend even the coasters, to say nothing of the sea traders. Only a few private citizens and the naval officers had any idea of sending naval vessels to sea to fight as well as to destroy commerce. So well fixed was the idea of the uselessness of the Navy that, as the War of 1812 approached, it was the government's plan to lay up the frigates in harbors, to strip them, and to use the vessels as floating batteries and as receiving ships for the recruits being trained for gunboat service.

The state of the Navy in 1812 was certainly not encouraging to those who thought the national ships ought to fight at sea and not be kept in port. The periodical "laying up in ordinary" of the frigates and the economically minded insistence on putting off repairs had caused practically all of the vessels to deteriorate, and many were, in fact, wholly unserviceable. The fine frigates *New York* and *Boston* in the Washington Navy Yard were now so rotten as not to be worth repairing. The *John Adams* was in need of extensive repairs, as were the *Constellation* and *Chesapeake*. The *Congress* was in commission but also needed extensive repairs. The *Constitution* was fitting, but was without crew or stores, and only the small vessels—the sloop of war *Wasp* and the small brigs, *Enterprise*, *Vixen*, *Syren*, and *Viper*—were at sea. A squadron at New York, comprising the *President, United States, Congress, Hornet,* and *Argus*, was fully manned and ready for sea. The *Oneida* was at Sackett's Harbor on Lake Ontario, and there were only six gunboats on both the coast and the lakes that were not either laid up or unmanned. Only the *Adams* was having any work done. She was at Washington being lengthened and cut down into a flush-decked sloop of war. Only the Washington Navy Yard was manned; the other yards were in the hands of watchmen and were inactive. Supplies and munitions were lacking, the Navy was without a naval constructor, and the administrative staff of the Navy Department had been reduced to ineffectiveness. There was no reserve of trained naval seamen, and naval funds were lacking. One thing alone the Navy possessed, a fine officers' corps, well disciplined and trained, spirited and aggressive.

It was the officers of the Navy who pressed the reluctant politicians to risk getting ships to sea when war was declared against Great Britain, June 18, 1812. The successes in single-ship actions that followed raised enough confidence and pride in the general public to force the creation of a wartime Navy.

Two of the naval captains, Stewart and Bainbridge, had gone directly to President Madison at the moment war appeared inevitable and had pressed him for authority to permit the naval ships in commission to cruise against the enemy. Immediately on the outbreak of war, one captain, Hull, took his frigate to sea without waiting for orders. The defeat of three fine British frigates by American ships in the first months of the war not only created confidence and tremendous pride on the part of the American public, but also horrified the British public and established American naval prestige in Europe.

Yet, in justice, it must be said that the splendid officers' corps could not, unaided, have been successful. Though most of the American ships were in poor condition, they were better designed and manned than the general run of Royal Navy vessels of the same classes. In addition, the American craft were better armed. Possessed of superior vessels, the American officers had quickly trained the hastily collected crews, and in a few weeks the naval captains had highly efficient fighting machines which proved far superior to the British frigates they met in the early months of the war. It would be inspiring to recount the various frigate and small-ship actions, but this would be outside the scope of this discussion. It was the early victories, however, that led to naval shipbuilding history in this war.

In the period from June to December, 1812, the Navy was slightly increased. It gained one frigate, the *Macedonian*, taken by the *United States* in October, and a 16-gun sloop of war, the *Alert*, taken by the *Essex* in August. Two other British frigates, the *Guerriere* and *Java*, had been captured, but were too much damaged to be preserved and so were destroyed by their captors. One 18-gun brig, the *Frolic*, was also taken, by the sloop of war *Wasp*, but both ships were taken by a British 74 immediately after the action. The *Wasp* was brought into the Royal Navy under the name *Peacock*, to replace a brig of this name that was captured by the Americans, but was lost with all hands off the Virginia Capes in 1813. The Navy lost two of its small brigs this year. The *Nautilus* was taken by the British frigates *Shannon* and *Aeolus* and the 64 *Africa*, July 17, 1812, and the *Vixen* was taken by the frigate *Southampton* November 22, 1812.

Three new vessels were added to the Navy, all of which were apparently bought on the stocks in the builders' yards. The schooner *Carolina* was obtained from the yard of James Marsh, at Charleston, S.C. She was 89′ 6″ long on deck, 24′ 4″ beam, and 11′ 4″ depth of hold, and was armed with 12 carronades, 12-pdrs., and 3 long 9's. The schooner *Nonsuch*, a former Baltimore privateer, was bought at the same port; she was 86′ on deck, 21′ 0″ beam, and 9′ 0″ depth of hold; she carried 12 12-pdr. carronades and one long 12. A small ship, named *Louisiana*, was bought at New Orleans; she was only 99′ 6″ on deck, 28′ 0″ beam and 14′ 0″ depth in the hold. The *Louisiana* was rated as a 16-gun sloop and seems to have been a rather sharp merchant vessel in model.

Further additions to the Navy were made by taking over some of the larger revenue cutters. They were *Surveyor, Active, Jefferson, Mercury, Vigilant, Gallatin, Madison, Eagle,* and *Commodore Hull.* All were schooners; some were large craft and quite new. Except for the *Madison*, little is known about these beyond their names. The *Jefferson* was a schooner purchased for the revenue service a few years before the war, the *Surveyor* was a Baltimore-built schooner bought in 1807, the *Madison* (properly the *James Madison*) was built at Baltimore in 1807–8, the *Mercury* and *Gallatin* were bought the same year, and the *Active* and *Hull* were chartered schooners. The *Vigilant* was built in 1811 by Benjamin Marble at Newport, Rhode Island. The *Eagle* was a purchased vessel bought at New Haven, Connecticut, in 1809.

Another schooner, named *Norwich*, appeared on the Navy list in 1812. No record of her construction or purchase has yet been found, so it is highly probable that the *Norwich* was a hired schooner. A number of small vessels were also purchased in the South; the 8-gun schooner *Ferret* was bought at Charleston, South Carolina, and the 16-gun brig *Troupe* at Savannah. Two small craft were obtained at New Orleans, the 1-gun schooner *Sea Horse* and a dispatch sloop named *Tickler*. A block sloop, the *Scorpion*, was also added to the Navy list, but nothing has been found about her origin; she was probably one of the boats built under the gunboat contracts.

The Great Lakes and Lake Champlain became scenes of naval activity as soon as the war started. In the Great Lakes there were two theaters of operation, Lake Ontario being independent of the others because it was separated from them by Niagara Falls. Except for Lake Erie the remaining lakes were without important settlements, and the few posts on the western lakes could be reached by vessels from Lake Erie. Champlain was independent of the upper lakes and so represented a third theater of operations. These three naval theaters were of immediate importance in the grandiose plans of the Americans for the invasion of Canada. Except for a few galleys, the British forces on the Lakes consisted of three ship sloops and three schooners of the Canadian Provincial Marine, on Lake Ontario. On Lake Champlain the Provincial Marine had a few large galley gunboats and one or two unserviceable vessels. There

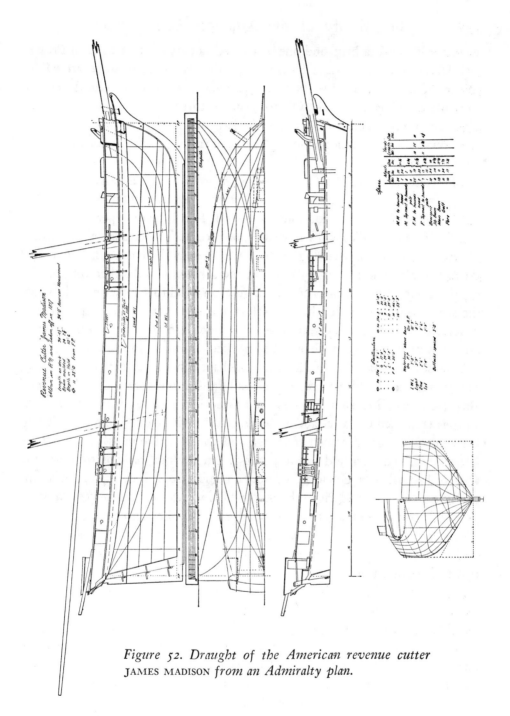

Figure 52. Draught of the American revenue cutter
JAMES MADISON *from an Admiralty plan.*

247

were a ship sloop, a brig, and one or two schooners of the Canadian Provincial Marine on the western lakes. In addition there were some armed fur traders. These vessels made their headquarters in Lake Erie. The Americans had only the *Oneida* on Lake Ontario, two or three small gunboats on Champlain, and no naval craft of any kind on Erie or the western lakes. On all the lakes there were a number of small American trading vessels—sloops, schooners, and a rare brig.

The commander of the *Oneida*, Lieutenant Woolsey, as senior officer on Lake Ontario, was ordered to obtain additional vessels as soon as possible. He had been on the station for some years (in fact he had superintended the building of the *Oneida*) and was well acquainted with the available lake vessels. He went about the purchasing of these with care and seems to have obtained the best craft. The lake was deep, and the schooners were therefore on the clipper model. Since navigation was largely confined to summer months when the winds were moderate, the lake schooners were very heavily sparred and canvased. As a result, they were fast sailers but were not very safe and, when armed, were prone to capsize or to be knocked down and swamped.

Woolsey purchased the following merchant schooners: *Elizabeth*, 2 guns, as a transport; *Fair American*, 2 guns and 82 tons measurement; *Charles and Ann* (renamed *Governor Tomkins* and fitted out with 6 guns); *Experiment*, 53 tons (renamed *Growler* and armed variously with from 2 to 6 guns during her career); *Diana* (renamed *Hamilton* and armed with 9 guns); and the *Collector* (renamed *Pert* and given 3 guns). On the outbreak of the war, the *Oneida* had taken a Canadian schooner named *Lord Nelson*, 12 guns, apparently a Provincial Marine schooner, which was renamed *Scourge*. Another prize, named *Julia*, was armed with 3 long guns. Woolsey also obtained a packet schooner, *Genesee Packet*, 82 tons, which he renamed *Conquest* and armed with 2 or 3 long guns. Many of these schooners had no bulwarks and so carried their guns on pivots.

In November, Captain Isaac Chauncey took command on Lake Ontario and brought with him the New York shipbuilder, Henry Eckford, who immediately laid down a large corvette, the *Madison* of 593 tons, at Sackett's Harbor, New York. Eckford, it will be remembered, had been a gunboat contractor under Chauncey's supervision. He had been born at Kilwinning, a small town near Irving, Scotland, and had come to Quebec when he was sixteen to learn his trade under his uncle, John Black, a noted Canadian shipwright. In 1796, at the age of twenty-one, he came to New York and worked in a boat shop.

Three years later he married, and in 1800 he opened his own yard. This was located in the vicinity of the present Brooklyn Navy Yard. Eckford was an intelligent designer and a man of tremendous energy and industry, as will be seen. In 1808 Eckford joined Lester Beebe in a gunboat contract, and later in the same year he also went into partnership with Christian Bergh to build the *Oneida* on Lake Ontario. When he came to Sackett's Harbor with Chauncey he was not a stranger to the lake. Here he was to show his genius as a designer and builder, as an organizer and manager, and as a master of the art of high-speed production of ships. Eckford and Bergh were close friends, and it is probable that Eckford received much help from the older man, who was a noted shipbuilder as early as 1806. Perhaps the explanation of Eckford's success in shipbuilding can be attributed to a characteristic of his, mentioned by a contemporary: he could and did tell the men how and why the work was to be done.

The British Navy had taken over the Canadian Provincial Marine, and Captain James Yeo, an officer who had an excellent record, was placed in command of all the lakes. He immediately began to bring in ship carpenters and materials and established yards at Kingston and York (now Toronto) to build up his squadron. Late in 1812 he had two ship sloops laid down, one in each of his new yards. His master shipwrights appear to have been Canadians who were eventually displaced by Admiralty men, about 1814. Yeo also strengthened his squadron by enlisting Canadians and by bringing in drafts of men taken from ships of the British Navy at Quebec. He also purchased a few small vessels on Lake Ontario, but it appears that there were fewer commercial craft on the Canadian side than on the American, for Yeo employed few such vessels, even though he was often in great need of small craft.

The building race on Lake Ontario was now begun, each side striving to out-build the other under the most trying difficulties. The two Canadian bases were poorly equipped and insufficiently manned, and the American base, Sackett's Harbor, was even worse situated. Both sides suffered from the difficulties of getting materials and equipment in from the coast, and there was much sickness among the workmen. The British had so much difficulty that they went to the extreme of having the frames of some new ships prepared in England.

On Lake Erie the British assembled a small squadron of eight craft, schooners, sloops, a brig, and a ship sloop, of the old Provincial Marine or converted trading vessels. One of these was an armed vessel of the Northwest Fur Company, the brig or brigantine *Caledonia*, with three guns on pivots. They soon added another brig, the *Adams* of 14 guns, which had been bought by the American Army at Detroit, Michigan. This brig fell into British hands when Detroit was captured in the first months of the war and was taken into the Provincial Marine as the *Detroit*.

Commodore Chauncey, as commander on the lakes, sent Lieut. Jesse D. Elliott to Lake Erie to establish a squadron to meet the British on the western lakes. He succeeded in capturing the *Caledonia* and *Detroit* by a daring boat attack late in 1812. He also purchased some rather small merchant craft at Buffalo, Erie, and other lake settlements; these were the 1-gun schooner *Amelia* (renamed *Tigress*), the *Catherine* (renamed *Somers*), 2 guns, and the sloop *Contractor* (renamed *Trippe*), 1 gun. Preparations were also started to build more powerful craft at Presque Isle, now Erie, Pennsylvania. Late in 1812 or early in 1813 a small 2-gun schooner was laid down which was launched as the *Scorpion*.

On Lake Champlain American Lieutenant Sidney Smith was ordered to buy suitable vessels, and the best he could find were shoal-draft sloops about 60 feet in length. One of these was named *Growler* and was armed with 10 small guns; another was the *Bull Dog*, renamed *Eagle*, also of 10 guns. The third was the *President*, a 12-gun sloop originally bought by the War Department but turned over to the Navy late in 1812. These, with the gunboats on the lake that had been built before the war, gave the Americans temporary dominance on Champlain. The American base was on Otter Creek, Vergennes, Vermont, where there was a small arsenal. The British base was at Isle aux Noix, where the British had maintained a small shipyard since the days of the American Revolution, though few vessels had been built there in the intervening years.

Returning to seagoing vessels, there are no plans, that can be identified, of the American vessels added to the Navy in 1812, except for a revenue cutter captured by the British. She was the revenue cutter *James Madison*, taken into the Royal Navy after her capture under the name *Alban*. Her lines were taken off after the war, in 1817, by Admiralty draftsmen, and her plans are shown in Figure 52. The *Madison* was a large clipper schooner, 94′ 4½″ on deck, 24′ 2⅝″ moulded beam, and 10′ 6″ depth of hold. In model she was about the same as the privateer schooners of the War of 1812. Like most of her type, this schooner was plainly finished, and no money or time had been wasted on decoration.

The writer has an unidentified plan of another schooner of the same period

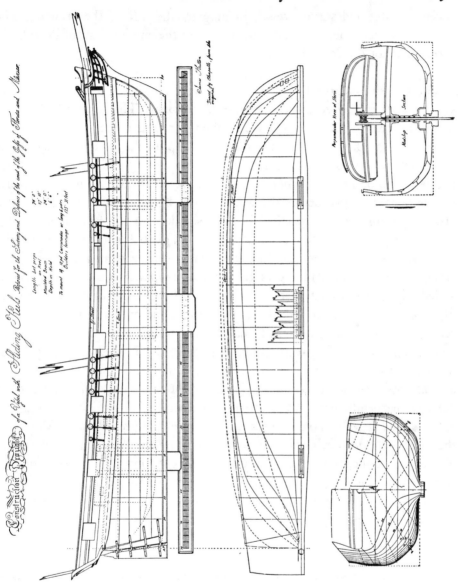

Figure 53. An American plan for a schooner with sliding keels.

as the *Madison*, but on an entirely different model. The plan, shown in Figure 53, is of a drop-keel schooner 74′ 0″ between perpendiculars, 24′ 0″ moulded beam, 6′ 6″ depth of hold. The design was prepared by James Hutton, of Philadelphia, sometime before the War of 1812, and was evidently intended as a revenue cutter and survey vessel, judging by the title of the drawing. The plan is of some value, as it shows the details of the employment of drop keels, forerunners of the centerboard.

The two ships of the Royal Navy that were purchased into the American service were the *Alert* and the frigate *Macedonian*. The former had been a merchant vessel—some accounts described her as a collier—that had been bought for the British Navy and rated as a sloop. In the American service she was employed as a supply ship rather than as a cruiser. No plan of the *Alert* has been found. The *Macedonian* was a new vessel at the time of her capture, having been built just before the war. She was built of oak and was one of a class of 38-gun frigates that had become standard in the British Navy. No Admiralty plan of the *Macedonian* appears to exist, but Plan 14 shows the lines of a sister ship, the *Bacchante*, which in turn was on the lines of the frigate *Lively*. The plan shows that the *Macedonian* was a rather sharp-ended frigate, somewhat narrow for her length. American references to the *Macedonian* show her to have been a fast sailer and an excellent vessel in all respects, though she was deemed small for her rate. In view of the numerous comparisons of this frigate with her opponent, the *United States,* by naval historians, the dimensions given on the design may be of interest. The *Macedonian* class is shown to have been 154′ 0″ on the lower deck, or about 156′ 0″ between perpendiculars, American measurement, with a moulded beam of 38′ 9″, and a depth of hold of 13′ 6″. Her figurehead was a bust of Alexander the Great of Macedonia, which was later used on the American-built frigate of the same name. It will be readily seen that the *Macedonian* was a smaller frigate than most of her American counterparts and, in size at 'least, was comparable to the *Chesapeake*. The *Macedonian* was rather hastily repaired when put into the American service, and this shortened her life.

No plans of the vessels obtained for the American service on the lakes have been found. In view of the circumstances this is not surprising; the lack of any construction organization in the Navy Department in 1812 and the methods employed in getting new vessels built on Lakes Ontario and Erie effectively prevented any plans that may have been used from being retained. On the British side this was not the case, and some few plans of lake vessels have survived. On the British plans alone it is possible to show that the vessels em-

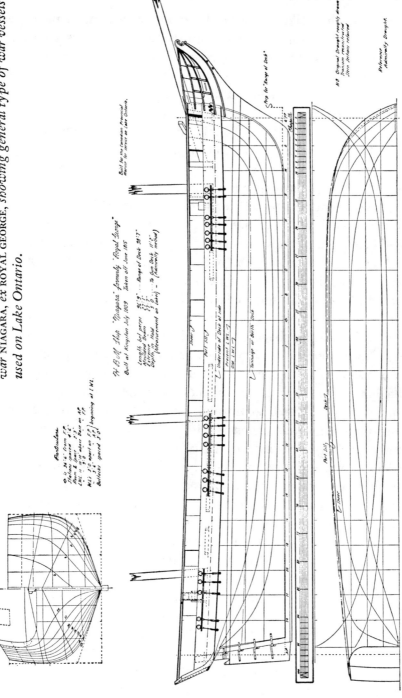

Figure 54. Draught of the Canadian Provincial Marine sloop of war NIAGARA, ex ROYAL GEORGE, showing general type of war vessels used on Lake Ontario.

253

ployed in the three lake theaters of operation were of two basic types, which were in turn the result of geographical conditions. As has been mentioned, the vessels on Lake Ontario were relatively deep and sharp and were of the seagoing type in nearly all respects. The plan of one of the British ships will suffice to illustrate this. Figure 54 shows one of the ships of the original squadron on Lake Ontario—the *Niagara*, formerly the *Royal George*, built at Kingston on the Canadian side of the lake in 1809, for the Canadian Provincial Marine. She was a small ship sloop 96′ 9″ on the lower deck, or about 98′ 6″ on the main deck (American measurement), 27′ 1″ moulded beam, and 27′ 7″ extreme beam. Her depth of hold was given as only 5′ 0″, but the plan shows that this was from the lower deck and that she was 11′ 6″ from ceiling to main deck. Her model was much like that of a seagoing ship sloop of her size and date, though lighter in displacement, and she drew about 11′ 9″ service trim. The *Niagara* was considered a good ship, and she sailed well. She remained in service throughout the war as a cruising vessel. Another ship of the British squadron whose plan has survived is the *Wolfe*, later named *Montreal*. This ship was 101′ 9″ on the lower deck, 30′ 0″ moulded beam, 4′ 6″ hold (but actually nearly 12′ from ceiling to main deck) and on a sharp model that required 12′ 3″ draft. This is sufficient to show that the Lake Ontario ships and small craft were of the seagoing type and that their tonnage was fictitious, being obtained by hold measurement to the lowest deck rather than to the main deck.

On Lake Erie, and on Lake Champlain too, the vessels were rather shoal and very small. Some of the schooners on Erie were of the pilot-boat model, apparently much like that used in the Norfolk pilot boats of the Chesapeake, but the lake was too shoal, particularly on the American side, to permit the use of such deep vessels as were possible on Lake Ontario. The small craft on Champlain were almost flat-bottomed, but in the War of 1812 none of the vessels were as shallow as the Champlain gondolas and the radeau of Arnold's time. The sloops bought by the Americans in 1812 were shallow-keel craft; one was 60′ on deck, 19′ beam, and 5′ 8″ depth.

With the outbreak of the war, American privateers began to get to sea and soon were creating great destruction and loss to British shipping. The first privateers to get to sea were hastily fitted schooners and small craft that operated close to home. Some were pilot boats and fishing schooners having but one gun. Larger schooners, carrying up to 14 guns, began to appear in the fall of 1812, and these were suited for more distant cruising. The effect of these first vessels was to cause the British to bring out a large number of small naval cruisers, schooners, and brigs to protect trade, particularly in the West Indies, and finally to resort to the convoy system almost entirely. The activities of the privateers could be countered only by stopping such vessels from getting to sea, and the British Navy soon began to blockade those ports sending out large numbers of raiders. The strict blockade and the swarm of British light cruising vessels made the American coasts unsafe for small privateers. This soon led the American builders to produce a type of large privateering vessel that had previously been unknown.

The blockade eventually affected naval shipbuilding, but in the early years of the war the danger of national strangulation by the blockade was not realized by either the American public or the incompetent administration. Hence no preparations were made to combat the blockade with suitable naval construction. The victories of the small American Navy at sea actually caused the blockade to become increasingly effective, for, by the end of 1812, British naval prestige had been seriously damaged by the Americans, and the Admiralty tried to make it certain that no more American cruisers got out of port.

As 1812 drew to a close, the American public felt great pride in their Navy, and an aroused public opinion forced a reluctant government to increase naval effectiveness with new construction. The sea victories stood out all the more because of the disgraceful failures on the Canadian border in the early months of the war, when the militia army and incompetently led regulars were unable to carry out the administration's and western politicians' plans for the invasion of Canada and suffered one disaster after another.

When the war began, William Doughty was at Georgetown, in the District of Columbia, operating a small shipyard of his own. He had not been active in politics, like Fox, nor had he influential connections with the opposition party like Joshua Humphreys. The administration therefore found him acceptable and now appointed him naval constructor at the Washington Navy Yard. The Secretary of the Navy, and the administration as a whole, still had no idea of creating an efficient naval establishment. The number of officers and enlisted personnel was rapidly increased to man the newly purchased ships and those employed on the lakes, but the increase was brought about by expediency and not by plan. No administrative organization was set up, and this portion of the naval establishment as well as the construction organization was permitted to grow up aimlessly and without plan, controlled only by the needs of the moment. One by one, the navy yards had been put into use, to repair ships and to act as shore stations. Doughty received his commission February 8, 1813, and his appointment was not as chief constructor but only as the Washington Navy Yard constructor. In January of 1813 Congress authorized the construction of three 44-gun frigates and six 18-gun sloops of war, and Doughty at once began work on the design of these. He prepared one frigate design for the three 44's and two designs for the six sloops.

The three plans were completed, and the necessary copies made, by June, 1813, and contracts were let for some of the vessels. One frigate and one sloop were to be built under Doughty's personal supervision in the Washington Navy Yard, but all others were to be built by contractors. One frigate was given to Joseph and Francis Grice at Philadelphia (*Guerriere*) and the other to Flannigan and Parsons at Baltimore (*Java*). The frigate to be built at Washington was to be named *Columbia*. The ship sloop to be built at Washington was finally named *Argus*, when the brig of that name was captured by the British. Two sloops, later named *Erie* and *Ontario*, were built by Thomas Kemp, at Baltimore. The *Argus*, *Erie*, and *Ontario* were on the same design. The three remaining sloops to be built were on an entirely different model. The *Wasp* was built by Cross and Merrill at Newburyport, Massachusetts, the *Peacock* by Adam and Noah Brown at New York, and the *Frolic* at Boston. The record is conflicting as to whether the last-named sloop was built in the Boston Navy Yard or whether she was built by contract, by Josiah Barker. It is probable, however, that Barker built her under contract, as he was not appointed constructor at the Boston Navy Yard until after the War of 1812. Barker and Edward Hartt were in partnership in 1813–14 and built on the site of the present Navy Yard at Boston.

Doughty was given complete freedom in the designs of the new ships, apparently, as the scanty correspondence indicates that no extensive directions were given him. It is highly probable that the designs of the sloops were intended to be improvements of the earlier *Wasp* and *Hornet*, of increased size and power. As a result, the two sloop designs of 1813 were on the same dimensions—117′ 11″ between perpendiculars, 31′ 6″ moulded beam, and 14′ 6″ depth of hold—but were not of the same model. The *Argus*, *Erie*, and *Ontario* drew 4′ 8″ more water at the sternpost than at the stem, while *Wasp*, *Peacock*, and *Frolic* had a difference of but 1′ 9″. As designed, the two classes had the same appearance above the water, except that the *Argus* class had no quarter galleries or quarter badges. The ships were capable of carrying 22 guns with ease and were to be armed with 20 32-pdr. carronades and 2 long 18's. The *Argus* class, of which two were completed, were on the Baltimore Clipper

Figure 55. Draught of ship sloops ARGUS, ERIE, *and* ONTARIO, *1813, showing pilot-boat schooner influence, in sections and profile.*

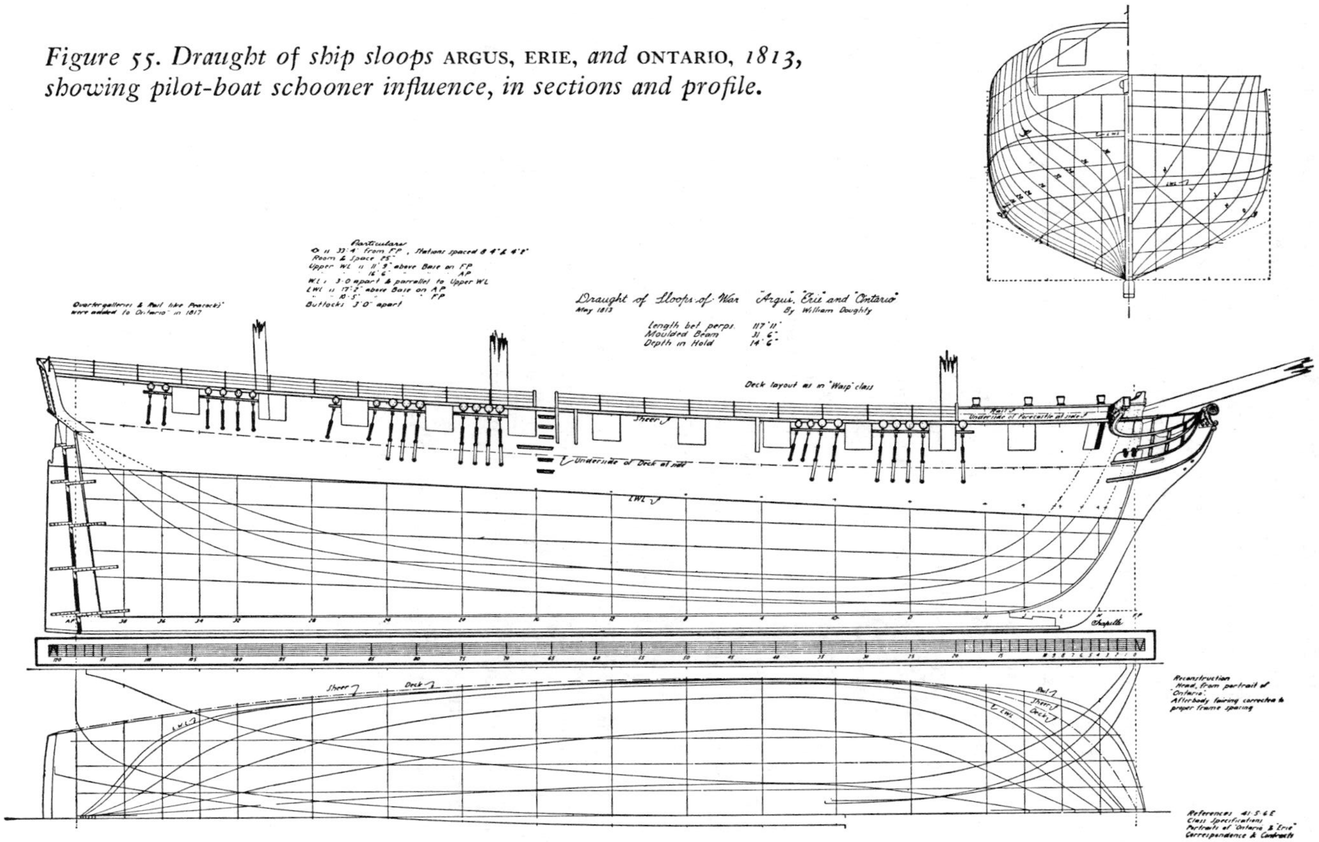

model. They were fast ships, but they were said to have steered wildly when first commissioned and so their rigs had to be altered.

Figure 55 shows the design for the *Argus* class. It has been said that the two ships of this design that were finished, *Erie* and *Ontario*, were built closely to the plans. This statement is supported by later plans of *Erie*, made when the ship was lengthened and rebuilt, which show that the contractors had followed the lines very carefully. The *Argus* was burned on the stocks at Washington, August 24, 1814, when the British took the city. The *Erie* and *Ontario* were completed during the war, but the Chesapeake was too closely blockaded for the sloops to get to sea. Thomas Kemp, who was the builder of the ships, was a noted designer in his own right and a builder of privateers and fast schooners. He was responsible for the famous *Chasseur*.

The *Wasp* class were to have been built on the design shown in Figure 56, but there was much variation in the three ships when built. The *Wasp*, constructed by Cross and Merrill at Newburyport, was reported to have been built "quite closely" to the design; the other two ships were not, as is evidenced by plans made from the ships afterward. The *Wasp* was lost at sea in 1814 after making a great name for herself and her commander, Blakeley. Her builders, Cross and Merrill, were noted New England shipbuilders. Cross was the business head of the firm; Merrill was the master builder and boss carpenter of their yard. William Cross was the oldest of the twelve children of Ralph Cross, the builder of the Revolutionary ships and, though trained as a shipbuilder, had held a number of civil appointments and also a commission in the state militia.

Orlando B. Merrill was also a member of a shipbuilding family and had a local reputation as a designer as well as a builder. He was one of the early proponents of the use of the "lift" half-model in designing hulls; indeed, some have claimed that he invented this method, but the credit is open to question. Merrill built privateers and revenue cutters on his own account. One of his half-models has survived which is represented to be the first made on the "lift" system. It has been said that the model is of the *Wasp*, but this is in error.

The builders of the *Peacock*, Adam and Noah Brown, had interesting careers. Noah Brown was born in northern New York, one of a large family, in 1770. His father and three brothers were captured by Indians in 1780, and his father was murdered. One of the brothers escaped, and the other two returned home at the end of the war. Two other brothers served in Washington's army; one was killed. His mother, with five small children, Adam and

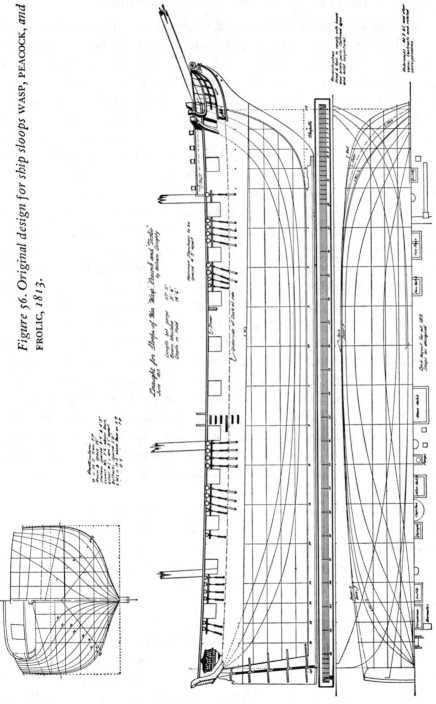

Figure 56. Original design for ship sloops WASP, PEACOCK, *and* FROLIC, *1813.*

259

Noah among them, moved to Stamford, Connecticut, at the end of the Revolution. When Noah was fifteen he left home and learned the house carpenter's trade, at which he worked until 1792. In that year he went to New York as a joiner and was employed there in house building until 1804, when he and his brother Adam went to Newark, near Fort Niagara, on the Canadian border and built a schooner named *Work* for the N. W. Fur Company. Later that year they returned to New York and worked a year as ship carpenters for Cheeseman. In 1805 they went to Sag Harbor, Long Island, and built a whaling ship. Then, until 1807, they worked for George Peck, a shipbuilder, in New York. In 1807, Noah went south to cut oak for the frigate *New York* and returned in the fall. Adam and Noah Brown then worked on this frigate until March, 1808, when the two went into the shipbuilding business for themselves. They engaged in building and repairing merchant vessels and constructing gunboats until the outbreak of the War of 1812. By this time they were well established as builders, and with the coming of war they went into the construction of privateers. They built the very noted privateers *General Armstrong*, *Prince de Neufchatel*, and *Paul Jones*. They also cut down a ship named *China* into the privateer *Yorktown*. In 1813 they started work on the *Peacock*, apparently before they had received a contract, for on June 29, 1813, they wrote the Navy Department asking for it. There is no evidence that the Browns ever served a formal apprenticeship as shipwrights. Their performance as ship designers and builders is therefore all the more remarkable, particularly as the ships designed by them were usually noted for speed—*Neufchatel* and *Armstrong*, for example. It is known that one of them made plans, but nothing else has been discovered about their designing methods or how they learned this work.

Figure 57 shows the *Peacock* as built, from lines taken off the ship in 1828 while she was hauled up at New York to be taken to pieces. The *Peacock* was a fast ship in heavy winds and was considered an ideal sloop of war. She had the same armament as the *Argus* class except that long 12's were carried instead of long 18's. The Browns had built two brigs on Lake Erie the winter of 1812–13 and had then returned hurriedly to New York to build *Peacock*, which they seem to have completed in about four months.

The *Frolic* was built by Josiah Barker, a Revolutionary War veteran born at Marshfield, Massachusetts, in 1763. He had learned his trade on the North River, not far from his birthplace, and had set up a yard in Charlestown about 1795. Barker was a successful builder and later a naval constructor. He launched

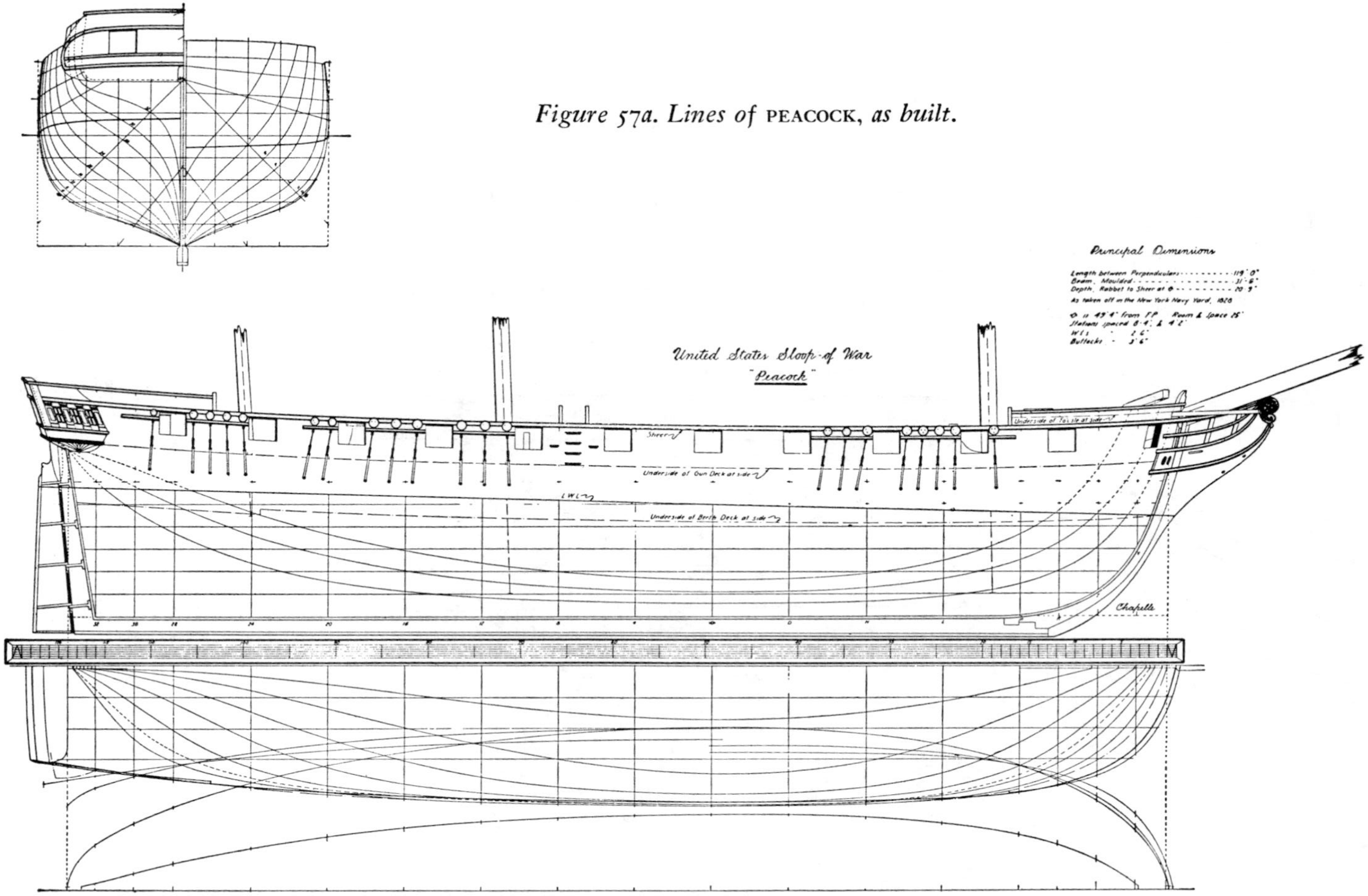

Figure 57a. Lines of PEACOCK, *as built.*

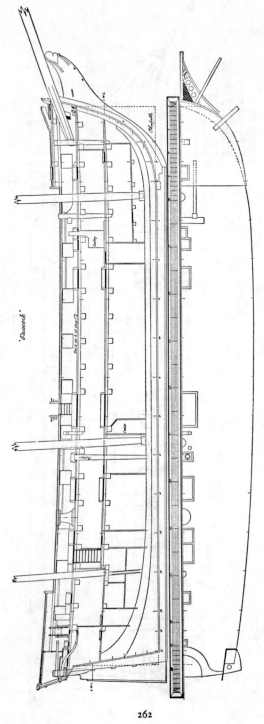

Figure 57b. Inboard arrangement of PEACOCK.

the sloop in September, 1813, and on April 20, 1814, she was captured after a 60-mile chase by H.B.M. frigate *Orpheus*, 36, and the ex-American privateer schooner *Shelbourne*, 12, off the coast of Cuba. The *Frolic* was taken into the Royal Navy as the *Florida* and was broken up in 1819. Her lines were taken off by the Admiralty, and her plan is shown in Figure 58. The dimensions of the *Frolic*, as taken off, were 119′ 5½″ between perpendiculars, 31′ 5½″ moulded beam, and 14′ 2″ depth of hold, which may be compared with *Peacock*'s 119′ 0″ by 31′ 6″, and 14′ 6″ hold. It will be seen that two of the vessels were longer than designed, as the builders were not held strictly to the official plans. Probably this was due partly to the lack of supervision given the contractors. This class of ship sloop was more powerful than the majority of European classes and was to have a lasting influence on American naval designing.

Though the new frigates were never to get to sea during the war, their design is of importance in showing the development of the American frigate that was now taking place. In the preparation of the new design, Doughty seems to have been influenced to a moderate degree, at least, by his experience at Georgetown before the war. While a designer and builder of merchant craft, he had become well acquainted with the schooners and brigs built on the Chesapeake and had become a convert to the very sharp model employed on the Bay. His liking for the type is shown in the ship sloops of the *Argus* class, in which he had gone to what was then an extreme design for a ship-rigged vessel. In the *Wasp* class he had been more moderate, and with the same restraint he incorporated the sharp model in the new frigate design. Holding closely to the dimensions of the 44's of 1796, he produced quite a different model. The new ships were given less tumble home and slightly more deadrise. The ends of the ships, particularly the bows, were sharpened. Doughty had to proceed rather cautiously in refining the lines of the new frigates, as he well knew that the ships would have to carry a very heavy armament. Too great a loss of displacement due to sharp lines would be disastrous.

The new frigates were given less sheer than the older vessels, following a change in style that had gradually taken place since 1806. While the ships were to have a complete spar deck, it was decided that the waist was not to be armed, as experience with the double-banked 44's and 36's of 1796–99 had shown that the ships were strained by such an arrangement and, in fact, were overloaded by the additional guns. The *Columbia*, started on the new design, was burned with the sloop *Argus* at the capture of the city of Washington, so only two ships of the new design were completed, *Guerriere* and *Java*, named after the British frigates captured and destroyed in the first six months of the war. The design of the new frigates is shown in Plan 15. They were plainly finished as befitted men-of-war built in time of war and in haste. The blockade of the Chesapeake and Delaware was too strict to permit the new frigates to escape to sea during the war, but both ships were good sailers. Flannigan, one of the builders of the *Java*, became a noted designer and builder of fast vessels at Baltimore after the War of 1812. One of the Grice brothers, Francis, who was a builder of the *Guerriere*, was afterward a naval constructor in the United States Navy. The *Guerriere* and *Java* were armed with 33 long 24's on the main deck and 20 carronades, 42-pdrs., on the forecastle and quarterdeck. Their dimensions were 175′ 0″ between perpendiculars, 44′ 6″ moulded beam, and 13′ 8″ depth of lower hold, or 31′ 1″ height of side, rabbet to planksheer.

The new frigates should be compared with the *President*, whose plans are shown in Plan 16, as taken off the ship by the British Admiralty after her capture. It will be seen that the *President* had been altered in appearance since her launch, and the drawing shows the general appearance of her sisters *Constitution* and *United States* during the War of 1812. It can be seen how standardized the appearance of the American frigates had become.

In 1813 a few vessels were obtained for the Navy on the coast. A sloop named *Asp*, of 56 tons, was purchased at Alexandria, Virginia. She was armed with a long 18-pdr. and 2 12-pdrs. The *Helen*, a dispatch schooner carrying four 4-pdrs., was bought at Philadelphia in the fall of 1813. A more effective purchase was the 14-gun brig *Rattlesnake*, built at Medford, Massachusetts, as a privateer. Another brig, the 14-gun *Vixen*, was bought at Savannah, but this vessel was not in the American service very long, as she was captured on her way north, without armament or stores aboard, by H.B.M. frigate *Belvidera*, on December 25, 1813. In this year the frigate *Essex* made her famous cruise into the Pacific and manned three prizes which were temporarily on the Navy list: the *Essex Jr.*, 20 guns, 355 tons; the British letter of marque *Atlantic*; the *Georgiana*, 18-gun ship, a whaler; and the *Greenwich*, 338 tons, 20 guns, also a former British letter of marque. These prizes were employed as tenders to the *Essex* rather than as cruisers; only the *Essex Jr.* ever reached the United States, and she came as a cartel carrying the officers and crew of the *Essex* home on parole. In this year the gunboat *No. 166* was renamed *Alligator* and

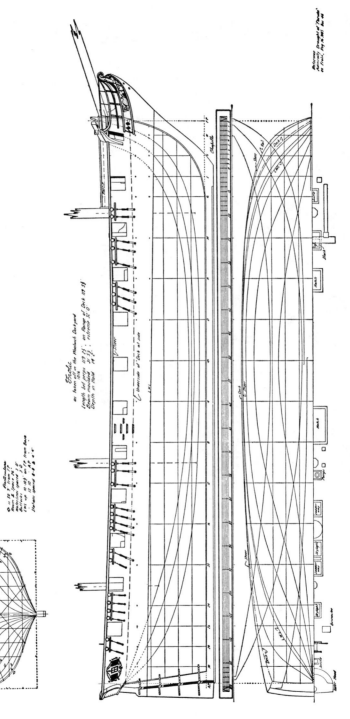

Figure 58. Lines of FROLIC, *as built.*

265

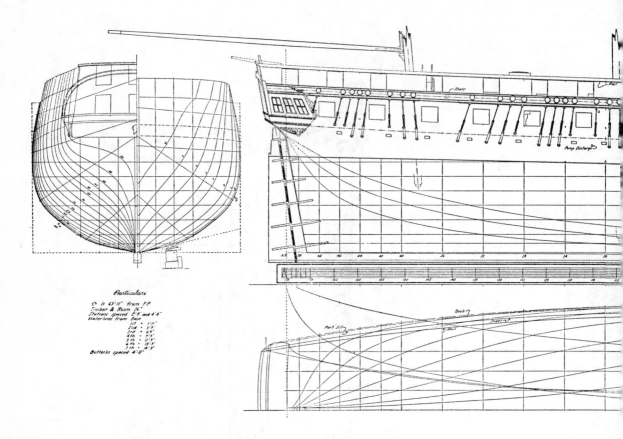

Plan 15. Draught of the improved 44-gun frigates COLUMBIA, JAVA, *and* GUER-RIERE, *1813.*

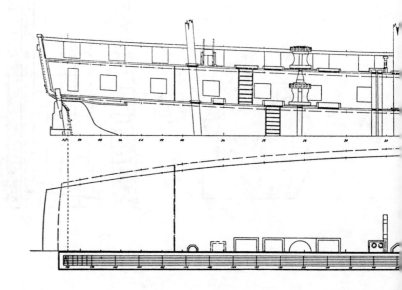

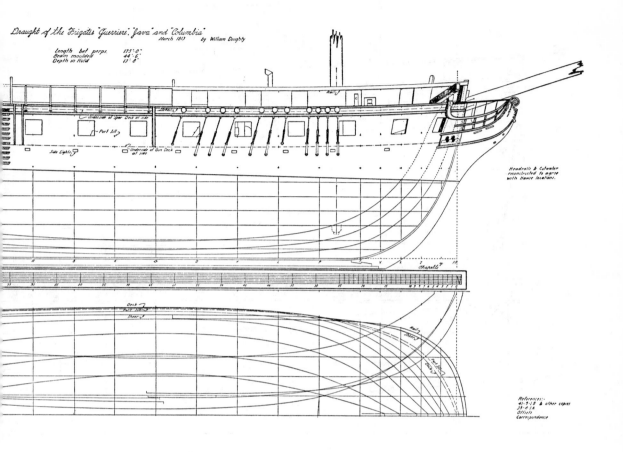

Draught of the Frigates "Guerriere", "Java" and "Columbia"
March 1813   by William Doughty

Length bet. perps.   175'-0"
Beam moulded   44'-6"
Depth in Hold   13'-6"

Headrails & Cutwater
reconstructed to agree
with Hawse locations.

References:-
41-9-18 & other copies
13-4-1A
Offsets
Correspondence

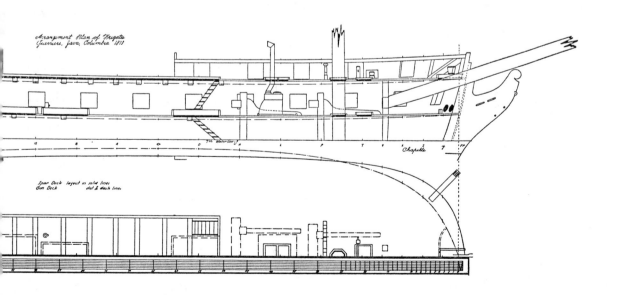

Arrangement Plan of Frigates
Guerriere, Java, Columbia 1813

Spar Deck   layout in solid lines
Gun Deck   dot & dash lines

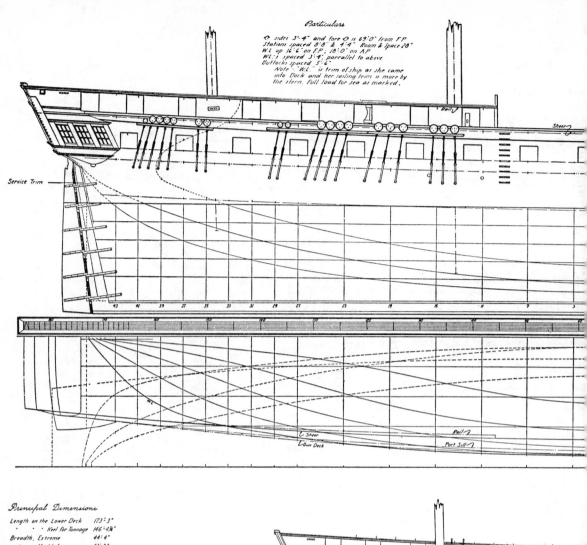

Service Trim

Rail
Sheer

Sheer
Gun Deck

Rail
Port Sill

Principal Dimensions

Length on the Lower Deck	173'-3"
" " Keel for Tonnage	146'-4¾"
Breadth, Extreme	44'-4"
" Moulded	43'-8"
Depth in Hold	13'-11"
Burthen in Tons	Nº 1533 23/94 ths

As taken off at Portsmouth, England,
in 1815.

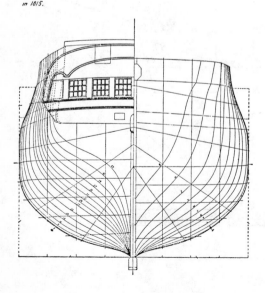

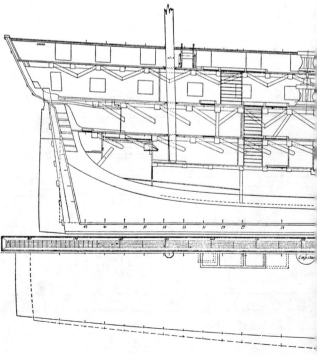

Capstan

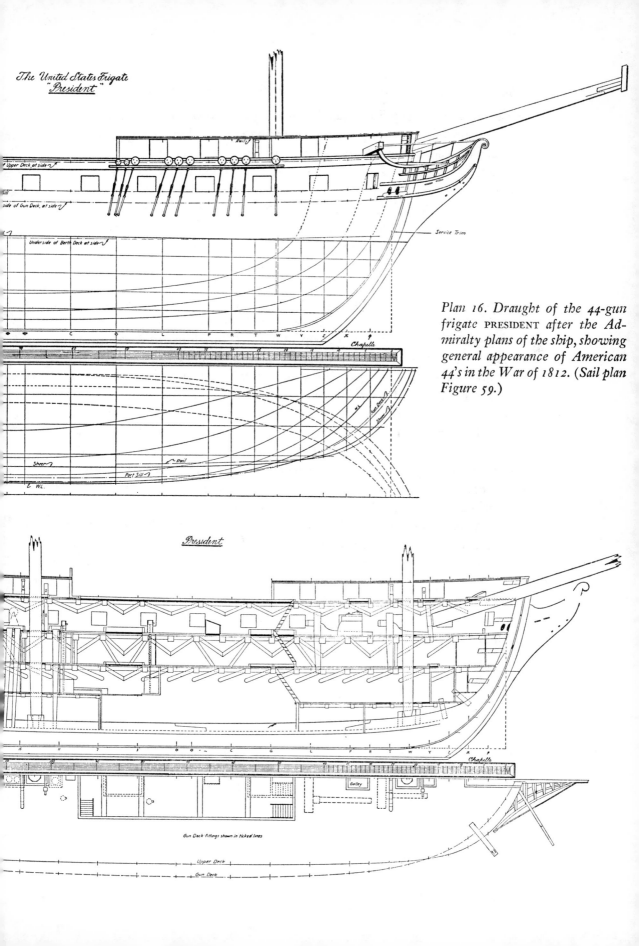

The United States Frigate
"President"

Plan 16. Draught of the 44-gun frigate PRESIDENT after the Admiralty plans of the ship, showing general appearance of American 44's in the War of 1812. (Sail plan Figure 59.)

President

so carried on the Navy list. A ketch was bought at New Orleans, the *Etna* or *Aetna*, a vessel listed as being 220 tons, carrying 11 guns. This ketch apparently replaced the earlier bomb ketch of the same name. A schooner of 5 guns was purchased at Georgetown, D.C., as a dispatch boat and named *Hornet*, and a few privateer schooners, bottled up in the Chesapeake by the blockade, were hired as lookout vessels in the lower Bay, to warn of British raids and to aid the gunboats in discouraging small British cruisers from attacking local craft. These were the armed schooners *Revenge*, *Comet*, *Patapsco*, and *Wasp*. The *Revenge* was 102′ long, 23′ beam, and 12′ hold, customhouse measurement, built at Baltimore in 1812. The *Comet* was 90′ 6″ x 23′ 3″ x 10′, built at Baltimore in 1810. The *Patapsco* was 101′ x 25′ x 11′ 5″, built at Baltimore in 1812. The *Wasp* was 59′ x 17′ 3″ x 6′ 3″, built at Baltimore in 1810.

This year the American ship sloop *Hornet* captured and sank the British 18-gun brig *Peacock*, of the standard *Cruizer* design. The American brig *Enterprize* captured the British gun brig *Boxer*, a new vessel built in 1812. The *Boxer* was one of a class of twelve brigs of the *Contest* class, all 84′ 0″ between perpendiculars, 21′ 6″ moulded beam, and 11′ 0″ depth of hold and designed to carry 10 18-pdr. carronades and 2 long 6-pdrs. The prize was not taken into the Navy, as she was considered inferior in size and model to the privateers that might be readily purchased. The former American privateer schooner *Highflyer,* which had been taken into the British Navy as a tender, was also taken but was sold to private owners.

The Americans suffered the loss of three cruisers this year, the most serious being the fine frigate *Chesapeake*, taken by the *Shannon* off Boston. It will be remembered that the *Chesapeake* was not built to the design of the *Constellation* and *Congress,* but to an independent design by Josiah Fox. The original plan of the ship was not retained in the American Navy files, but may be the plan marked "Congress" in the Fox Papers. However, after her capture the lines of the ship were taken off and drawn by Admiralty draftsmen, so a record of her design exists. Plan 17 shows the lines of this beautiful though unfortunate frigate. She was quite different from her sisters in model; in fact, she was somewhat like the *Philadelphia,* which had been lost at Tripoli. The *Chesapeake* was a sharp frigate, compared to the others built before the War of 1812; she had the reputation of being very fast, but her reputation for being unlucky had been firmly established by the *Chesapeake-Leopard* affair. The *Chesapeake* measured 152′ 6″ between perpendiculars, 40′ 4″ moulded beam, and 13′ 9″ depth of hold. Though Fox intended her to be a small 44,

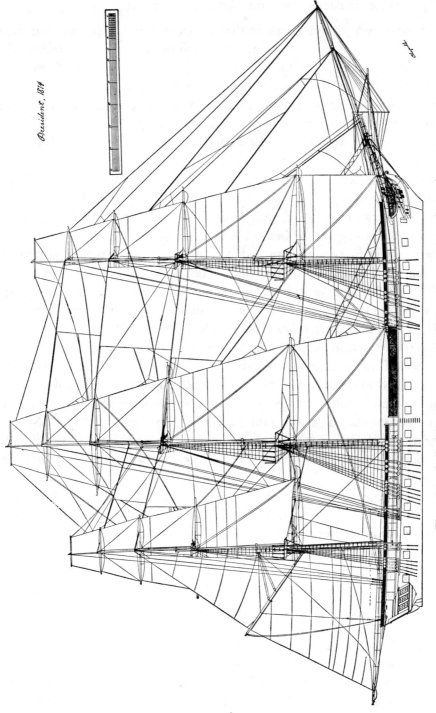

President, 1814

Figure 59. Sail plan of PRESIDENT in War of 1812. (See plan 16.)

267

she was rated as a 36-gun frigate in the American Navy. Her armament was 28 long 18's on the main deck, 16 32-pdr. carronades on the quarterdeck, and 4 carronades, 32-pdrs., on the forecastle. The *Shannon* was 150′ 1½″ between perpendiculars, 39′ 3″ moulded beam, and 12′ 9″ depth of hold. She was a sister ship of the *Tanais*, on the design of the *Leda*, 38 guns; this class was one of the few frigates having square-tuck sterns at this date.

The brig *Argus* was taken in the Channel by the British brig *Pelican*, another of the numerous *Cruizer* type. The British brig rated as 18 guns, and was 100′ 0″ between perpendiculars, 30′ 0″ moulded beam, and 12′ 9″ depth of hold—altogether a larger and more powerful brig than her American opponent, as may be seen by comparing the dimensions of the *Pelican* with those of the *Argus*, given on her drawing.

The *Viper*, ex *Ferret*, was captured in January of 1813 by the British frigate *Narcissus* after a chase in strong winds. The sloop *Asp* was taken in a boat attack in the Chesapeake and set on fire, but her crew got aboard her again in time to save the sloop. The revenue cutter *Surveyor* was also taken by a boat attack in the Chesapeake. Gunboats had been largely employed in defending coastwise trade in protected waters, such as the Chesapeake and Long Island Sound, or were used for harbor defense, and occasionally one was captured by British boats. Attempts to attack British ships with small gunboat squadrons were wholly unsuccessful, owing partly to the lack of training of the gunboat crews and partly to the small size of the boats employed. Nevertheless, the gunboats were often useful in preventing the boats of the British blockading squadrons from raiding isolated towns and farms for provisions and loot.

The Americans were more successful on the lakes in 1813, owing to the efforts of their builders to produce enough vessels to meet their opponents. Lake Erie was the center of much naval activity in this year. When navigation ended in 1812, the Americans had but one small brig, the *Caledonia*, which, with the brig *Detroit*, ex *Adams*, had been captured by an American boat attack. The *Detroit*, however, had gone ashore after the attack and had been destroyed. Their other vessels were the three small purchased craft, *Somers*, *Tigress*, and *Trippe*, 1 gun each, and the new schooner *Scorpion*, 2 guns. Lieut. Oliver H. Perry had been ordered to Lake Erie, and being senior to Elliott he was now the commodore. In January of 1813, the Navy Department sent Adam and Noah Brown to Lake Erie with instructions to build two large brigs. Noah Brown left New York February 14 with a small gang of carpenters and arrived at Presque Isle on the 24th. Brown went to work at once, but having few men he could make little progress until early March, when more carpenters arrived from New York. Adam had remained at home to procure men and to operate the yard in New York. By this time Noah Brown had most of the timber and framing cut for the two brigs, as well as for three schooners. In April another draft of men from New York reached Brown, and in May some more carpenters came from Philadelphia. In all Brown finally had two hundred men, but he was short of caulking material and iron. A British schooner was found, frozen in the ice in the lake, so Brown and his men went to her, getting provisions, rigging, and cables; they then burned her to get what iron they could. By scouring the near-by posts and settlements, Brown obtained enough iron to complete his task. Finally, late in the spring, he received oakum and iron which the government had been unable to forward earlier because of bad roads. Brown also had great difficulty in getting provisions, which led to strikes that Brown had to settle by convincing the men that he was getting all the food possible. Noah Brown returned to New York in July, leaving his foreman, Sidney Wright, later a noted New York shipbuilder, and sixteen carpenters to finish up. Brown had designed and built two large brigs, the *Lawrence* and *Niagara*, the 75-ton schooner *Ariel*, the gunboat schooner *Ohio*, the *Porcupine*, and probably the *Scorpion*, and had rebuilt the *Tigress*. He was not paid for this work, by the way, until March, 1814.

Brown also built a blockhouse 30′ square, a guardhouse 40′ x 20′, a cook and mess building 100′ x 20′ (with a loft which was used as a barracks for the carpenters), a blacksmith shop 80′ x 16′, a barracks for fifty men, an office for Brown and Perry (18′ x 18′), four camels or floats to get the brigs over the bar, fourteen boats for the fleet, and all the gun carriages. In building the vessels, Brown was responsible for all woodwork from hull to spars, tops, boats, and gun carriages; the rigging and the sailmaking were done by the crews that were being slowly collected by Perry. The amount of work that Brown accomplished with about 200 men, without power tools, and in a wilderness during the worst winter months, makes some of the modern wartime production feats something less than impressive. The man was tireless and ingenious.

No drawings of the Erie squadron appear to have reached the Navy Department. At the end of the War of 1812 the serviceable vessels were stripped and the hulls sunk to preserve them. The two brigs were thus preserved for many years, but unfortunately no accurate record was made. The hulk of the *Niagara* was raised in 1913, under the supervision of Captain W. L. Morrison of the

Wolverine (ex *Michigan*). The state of the wreckage required extensive research in order to make a restoration. With the limited information then
available, the brig was rebuilt. In 1939, it was again necessary to rebuild the
Niagara, and the writer was commissioned to prepare the new plans. With
the assistance of Captain Morrison and Captain Stephen C. Rowan, U.S.N.,
another attempt at restoration was made. The results are shown in Figure 60.
It should be observed that this drawing cannot be accepted as wholly accurate,
as the topsides of the original brig had rotted so much that little could be
preserved when she was raised in 1913. The ends of the ship were particularly
difficult to determine; the writer therefore assumes the responsibility for the
revised drawing presented here. The reconstructed brig, as built by the Com-
monwealth of Pennsylvania (now exhibited at Erie), differs slightly from the
plan shown in Figure 60. According to what could be determined from the
remains of the original brig, and the dimensions given in contemporary papers,
the two brigs were each 110′ 0″ between perpendiculars, 29′ 0″ moulded beam,
and 9′ 0″ hold. There is a wide difference of opinion as to whether the brigs
had a gammon knee, a plain raking stem, or a cutwater and headrails. In view
of the speed with which Brown ran up these vessels, the writer leans toward
a belief in a plain stem or a gammon knee. The deck arrangement is wholly
conjectural and is based on British war brigs of approximately the same
date. Figure 61 shows a design of a British man-of-war brig, designed in 1815
for Lake Champlain, which gives some support to the writer's restoration and
is the authority for the greater part of the doubtful details included in the
reconstruction drawing of the *Niagara*.

The two brigs were launched in May and by means of the two "camels,"
or floats, were carried over the sand bar into the lake. The "camels" were two
rectangular barges, with one side shaped to fit closely under the hull of the
brigs, which could be submerged and secured to each of the brigs in turn, and
then pumped out and raised. This would lift the brig and reduce her draft
enough to cross the bar that separated the building site from the open lake.

The *Ariel* was a clipper schooner with low bulwarks and had her four long
12-pdr. guns mounted on pivots—one forward of the foremast, two between
the masts, and one abaft the main. She was designed for speed, and Brown
claimed that nothing on the lake could sail with her. The *Porcupine* had one
long 32-pdr. on a pivot and two 12-pdr. carronades. The *Ohio* had one long
gun on a pivot, and the *Scorpion* seems to have been a sister ship of the *Porcupine*. Some accounts indicate that the *Tigress* was not a purchased vessel but

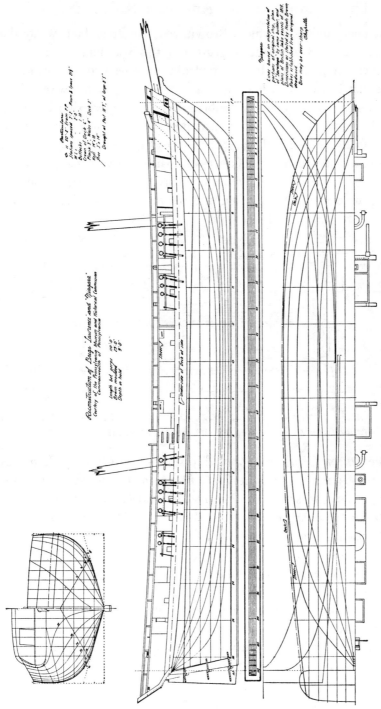

Figure 60. A reconstruction of the brigs LAWRENCE *and* NIAGARA.

271

was a "gunboat" built by Brown. Brown, as a matter of fact, wrote that he
.built *Porcupine*, *Scorpion*, and *Tigress*, but this was long after the event,
when his memory may have been at fault. With respect to *Scorpion*, it seems
reasonable that Brown built her and that the record that she was built in the
fall of 1812 is an error, for it is doubtful that there were ship carpenters at
Presque Isle before Brown arrived. It is possible, of course, that the *Tigress*
was also built by Brown and was not the *Amelia*, renamed, as there is much
confusion in the records of the lake vessels, particularly as many had changes
of name. Perry's victory in September liquidated the British squadron on Erie,
and the captured vessels were taken into the American service—the *Detroit*,

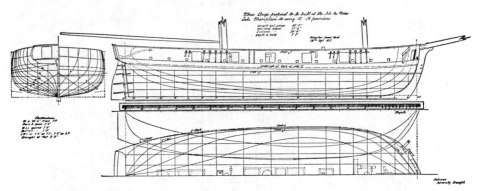

*Figure 61. An Admiralty design for brigs to be built on Lake Champlain, 1815,
showing characteristics of brigs used on the American lakes.*

18, and the *Queen Charlotte*, 16, as ship sloops, the *General Hunter* as the
brig *Hunter*, 10 guns, the schooner *Lady Prevost* as a 10-gun schooner, and the
Little Belt as a 3-gun schooner. The *Detroit* and *General Hunter* had been
built at Malden, now Amherstburg, in 1806, and the *Queen Charlotte* had been
built in the same place the following year. The *Lady Prevost* was also built
at Malden, in 1810. These British-Canadian vessels were somewhat deeper
draft than the American brigs built on Lake Erie, as the former's designs
were not controlled by the shallow channel at Presque Isle.

By 1813, the building race on Lake Ontario was well under way. The winter
of 1812–13 was a severe one, and both sides were greatly handicapped by deep
snows and extreme cold, which made the movement of supplies, materials, and
munitions in from the coast a very uncertain matter. Lack of shelter and poor
food, as well as unsanitary living conditions, created much sickness among the
carpenters on both sides of the lake, and this caused unforeseen delays. How-

ever, Henry Eckford was on the same mould as the Browns; he rushed the *Madison* to completion; hurriedly designed and built a small sharp dispatch boat, the schooner *Lady of the Lake*, 89 tons and 5 guns; and started the *General Pike*, a very large 24-gun ship, and a large sharp schooner, the *Sylph*. The *General Pike* was launched 63 days from the day her keel was laid; she was a flush-decked corvette 145′ 0″ between perpendiculars, 37′ 0″ beam, and 15′ 0″ depth, armed with 26 long 24's and 2 pivot guns, probably 24-pdrs. also. The *Sylph* was built in 23 working days, to launching, and was variously armed. At one time she seems to have had 4 long 32-pdrs. on pivots, with 12 long 6-pdrs. on broadside carriages; a year after her launch she was rerigged as a brig and carried 2 long 7's and 16 carronades, 24-pdrs., so apparently her original rig and armament were not considered satisfactory. She must have been a large vessel, as her tonnage is given variously as 300 and 350 tons. Except for a sail plan of the *Pike*, no drawings have been found of these vessels.

On August 24, 1813, the Secretary of the Navy wrote the New York Navy Agent to ask the Browns if they would proceed to Sackett's Harbor and build three sloops exactly like *Peacock*. The Browns agreed, and it was also suggested that they join with Eckford or that he build one sloop. Nothing seems to have come of this, but the incident suggests the possibility that the designs of the 1813 ship sloops and frigates may have been used as the basis of some of the Lake Ontario vessels. However, it is highly probable that Eckford prepared plans for most of the ships built on the lake. The exact relation between the Browns and Eckford is not clear. From official correspondence it would appear that Eckford was in charge of all shipbuilding on the lakes; on the other hand, the contracts with the Browns were independent of Eckford's contracts. For example, the Browns had a contract for building two ships of the line and a frigate at Sackett's Harbor dated December 15, 1814. On this the *New Orleans*, *Chippewa*, and *Plattsburg* were started, and there is no evidence that Eckford had anything to do with them.

In addition to the new vessels built on Ontario, three more schooners were purchased, the *Asp* of 57 tons and 2 guns, the *Ontario*, 2 guns, and the *Mary*, 50 tons. The last was renamed *Raven* and was fitted with a mortar but was usually regarded as a transport and supply vessel. The combination of large vessels of the seagoing type—*General Pike*, *Madison*, *Oneida*, and *Sylph*—with lake schooners created a very unhandy squadron. Effective in smooth water, the squadron was difficult to manage in strong winds, as the small lake vessels were prone to capsize. The *Hamilton* and *Scourge* foundered in a squall in the early morning of August 8. Two days later the schooners *Growler* and *Julia* were captured by the British in the face of the American squadron, through Chauncey's mismanagement and the failure of the two schooners to obey the commodore's signals. The two schooners were recaptured the same season, however, so they were not lost to the Americans.

In the winter of 1812 the British had started the construction of two sloops of war, one at York named *Sir Isaac Brock* and one at Kingston, named *Wolfe*. Yeo had difficulty in getting his building program started, and the two vessels were much delayed. York was weakly defended, and in the spring of 1813 Chauncey attacked the place and captured it with the aid of some troops. He destroyed the *Sir Isaac Brock* on the stocks and carried away a small brig, the *Gloucester*, 10 guns, which he found in the harbor. The *Gloucester* does not appear to have been a serviceable craft, for she was not employed as a cruiser in the American service. The remaining ship sloop, *Wolfe*, was launched at Kingston early in the spring, making the British temporarily superior in force to the Americans. The British fighting squadron now consisted of the *Wolfe* and *Royal George*, ship sloops, the *Earl of Moira*, *Prince Regent*, *Sydney Smith*, and *Lord Melville*, brigs, and the schooner transports *Seneca* and *Simcoe*, as well as a few gunboats. When the Americans launched the *Pike* they again became superior in force. Throughout the remaining years of the war Ontario was the scene of very cautious warfare. As either side launched a powerful ship the other retired from the lake, until his builders again made him apparently superior in force. The British ships on the lake in 1813 were relatively small: the *Wolfe* and *Royal George* have been described; the *Prince Regent* was a 71' brig built in 1812, the *Melville* was about 73' long, and the *Moira* 70'. The end of the year saw the British shipwrights at work on two frigates, the *Prince Regent*, carrying 58 guns, and the *Princess Charlotte*, first named *Vittoria*, carrying 42. They also laid down a large ship of the line, the *St. Lawrence*. The Americans, hearing of this, prepared to build additional ships, but they were later in getting started on their program than the British.

Lake Champlain was the scene of some activity. Here Lieut. Thomas Macdonough was now the American commander with a force of two sloops, the *Eagle* and *Growler*, and two one-gun row barges. He also had the sloop *President* awaiting men. Late in June he sent the *Eagle* and *Growler* up to the head of the lake to harass the British. The two sloops chased three British gunboats into the Sorel and were ambushed. The *Eagle* sank in shoal water, and the

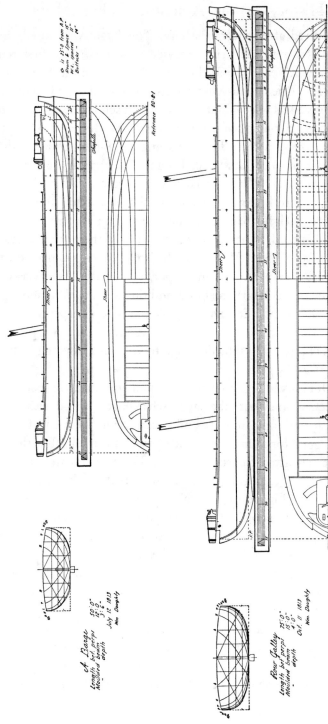

Figure 62. Plans of barges and row galleys in the American Navy, 1813–14.

Growler was captured after she ran ashore. The *Eagle* was raised, and the two sloops were taken into the British service. The *Eagle* was first renamed *Broke*, then *Finch* (or *Tench*), and the *Growler* became the *Shannon*, then *Chub* or *Chubb*. The British thus won control of the lake, and Macdonough set about obtaining vessels to regain it. He bought a schooner, or sloop, named *Montgomery*, to carry 7 long 9's and 2 carronades, 18-pdrs., and a sloop named *Preble*, which he armed with 7 long 12's and 2 18-pdr. columbiads. The columbiads were forerunners of the shell guns that appeared after the War of 1812. They were apparently short large-bore cannon, sometimes made by reboring old guns to fire hollow shot and bombshells. They appear to have been much lighter in weight than the regular naval gun and were intended as improvements on the standard naval carronade; most of these guns were classed as 18-pdrs. in the War of 1812. Macdonough also hired a sloop named *Frances* and armed her with 4 12-pdrs. and an 18-pdr. columbiad. As it was obvious that it would soon be necessary to build additional craft, Macdonough applied to the Navy Department for a builder. With the few carpenters available, the barge *Alwyn*, one gun, was built at the American base, Vergennes, Vt. A small sloop was chartered by Macdonough to serve as a dispatch boat on the lake; this was the *Wasp*, 5 guns.

During 1813 Doughty designed a new class of gunboat, the barge. These were double-enders, somewhat like large whaleboats, armed either with a single gun or with one long gun aft and a carronade forward. The barges were sometimes rigged for sailing with one or two lateen sails, but the smaller boats were sometimes fitted for rowing only. The first design was for a 50' barge, made in June, 1813, and building began on the plan in July or August. This design, shown in Figure 62, is probably the one used for the *Alwyn*, built that year on Champlain. The new design called for boats 50' long, 12' moulded beam, and 3' 6" total depth. In September Doughty made another design, this time for a barge 75' over all, 15' beam and 4' 0" depth. This is also shown in Figure 62, and the boats built from it were usually rigged with one or two lateen sails. Late in the year a third barge design was made, for a boat only 40' long, 10' beam, and 3' depth and fitted to row only. This plan is shown in Figure 63. These barges were intended for Lakes Champlain and Ontario, the Chesapeake, and rivers, and were not in any way seagoing coast-defense gunboats. The American barges were, in fact, the counterparts of the large launches carried by some British blockading ships for boat attacks and raids inshore.

Doughty was now acting as the chief naval constructor, with his station in the Washington Navy Yard. Henry Allen was either his apprentice or his assistant. Nearly all of the plans of new ships prepared by Doughty in the war years are preserved only in the working copies made by Allen; the originals cannot now be found. On April 17, 1813, Samuel Humphreys was ap-

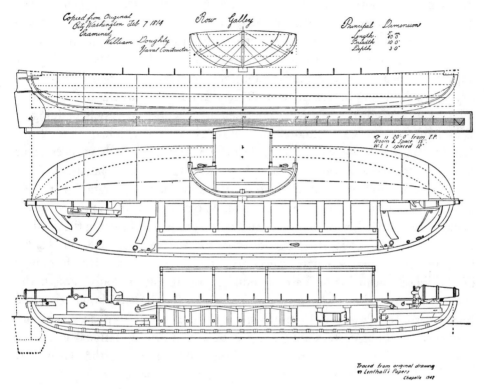

Figure 63. Plans of a small row galley by William Doughty.

pointed naval constructor at the Philadelphia Yard. He spent a good part of the year getting the neglected navy yard into working order. Samuel Humphreys, unlike his father, was a competent draftsman and a very able ship designer, rather more conservative than Doughty, but he appears to have designed only one ship during the War of 1812. He had been born in Philadelphia, November 23, 1778, and had worked with his father until the frigate *United States* had been completed, after which he went into business for himself and had a number of associates or partners. Samuel Humphreys, like Doughty, was a strong adherent to sharp-floored small vessels, and Humphreys had designed a number of very sharp schooners before his appointment to the Philadelphia Yard.

Because of the modest building program begun in 1813 the small construction organization was adequate, and the only weakness was the lack of supervision of the contract builders by trained naval inspectors. As before, the building supervisors were usually commissioned officers. The general administration of the Navy was, however, remarkably inefficient; the incompetent secretary and staff were still attempting to manage naval affairs on a political level without regard to the necessities of war. There was no change of importance in the naval administration, and matters proceeded in the same haphazard fashion as before the war. Once again most of the shipbuilding contracts were placed in a relatively confined area, with two vessels building at Washington, three at Baltimore, and one each at Philadelphia, New York, Newburyport, and Boston. Thus five of the vessels could have been kept from getting to sea by merely blockading the mouth of the Chesapeake Bay; the others, with one exception, were in ports of such importance that their blockade was assured when the war began. The placing of the contracts seems to have been hurried, without any regard to the problems of getting the finished vessels to sea. There was still some idea that the government could build ships faster and more cheaply than private contractors. This is indicated by the choice of the Washington Navy Yard to build a frigate and a sloop, though the experience of building the earlier *Wasp* and *Hornet* had shown that the Navy Yard was slower and more costly than the private shipyards. The old tendency to concentrate shipbuilding contracts near the national capital is worthy of notice. There were always "practical" reasons for this. However, the records show that, in view of the huge number of privateers built in 1813, most of which were set up in small towns and villages from Georgia to Maine, there could have been no practical difficulty in spreading out the naval building program, away from the large ports or from those areas whose importance assured an immediate blockade. By the end of 1813 the Chesapeake and the ports of New York, Philadelphia, and Boston were under such strict blockade that even the very fast privateers were having great difficulty in escaping to sea.

The coasting trade was now at a halt, and the privateers and a few fast letters of marque were the only sources of employment; the Navy was still too small to require a large part of the available seamen. The shipyards were busy, however, turning out privateers and letters of marque. By the middle of 1813 the day of the small privateer was practically over. The new type included large schooners, brigantines, and brigs, 90 to 115 feet in length, heavily armed, and worthy antagonists for the smaller British cruisers, and large armed merchant ships.

Of the Navy vessels building under the new program, only the *Frolic* and *Peacock* were launched in 1813, September 11 and September 27 respectively. But neither got to sea until 1814, by which time the *Wasp* was also ready. These three cost almost a third more to build, curiously enough, than each of the two Baltimore-built sloops whose building was much delayed by the shortages of shipwrights caused by the demand for such men to build privateers at Baltimore and on the shores of the Chesapeake. The estimates also indicated that the Navy Yard sloop was going to cost more than any of the others.

At the end of 1813, the need of ships of the line to break the British blockade was fully apparent, and pressure was now being placed on the government to build such ships. It appears that work on the designs for two or three liners was started as early as November of this year. Humphreys probably began designing one to be built at Philadelphia, and Doughty may have made a design for two sisters to be built at Boston and Portsmouth, New Hampshire, but the records are not clear as to either the date the designs were ordered or as to the responsibility for the design of the New England–built 74's.

Early in 1814 the American frigate *Essex* was captured by the British frigate *Phoebe*, 36, and the ship sloop *Cherub*, 18, at Valparaiso, which ended the destructive career of the American cruiser in the Pacific. The first of the new ship sloops to sail was the *Frolic*, in early February. She met a South American "privateer" or pirate and sank her with a single broadside. On April 20, she met H.B.M. frigate *Orpheus*, 36, and an ex-American privateer schooner, now H.B.M. schooner *Shelburne*, 12 guns, and a thirteen-hour chase ensued. The American beat to windward in an effort to escape, but after having thrown overboard her guns, boats, and stores, the sloop was forced to surrender and was taken into the Royal Navy under the name *Florida*. She was finally broken up at Chatham Dockyard in 1819.

The *Peacock* was the next to get to sea, sailing from New York March 12. On the 28th of April she fell in with a small convoy of British merchantmen bound for the Bermudas under the protection of the 18-gun brig *Epervier*, a new brig (or properly "brigantine," since she did not have the spencer mast on her main as in a naval "brig") laid down in 1812 at Rochester, England, by Mrs. Mary Ross, who seems to have been the owner of a well-known yard there. *Epervier* was ordered to carry 16 guns and was on the lines of the 18-gun brig *Cruizer*. The *Peacock* captured the *Epervier* in a short action. The prize, being new and still in serviceable state, was sent home and was purchased into the United States Navy under the same name as an 18-gun brig, armed with 32-pdr. carronades. The brig was considered a fine vessel of her class. Her plan as redrawn from her design draught is shown in Figure 64. In the past, historians have speculated as to the relative size of the British 18-gun brigs and their American opponents, *Argus, Hornet, Wasp,* and *Peacock*. The plan of the *Epervier* will settle the question. This brig was exactly the dimensions of the standard *Cruizer* and on her exact hull lines except for a slightly modified sheer and alterations in her cutwater and above-water appearance. The *Epervier* was one of the *Bacchus* class built in 1811–12.

With the fall of Napoleon, the British were able to give more attention to the American war. The destruction caused by the big American privateers added to the startling defeats of British frigates and man-of-war brigs were matters too important to be left unattended. Not only did the blockade become more strict, but shore attacks were made in an effort to liquidate both American privateers and naval vessels before they could get to sea. The Chesapeake was the scene of many British raids, and as the year drew to a close the Bay was almost completely sealed against the escape of American raiders. In the process, land expeditions were made against the cities of Washington and Baltimore. In the Washington adventure the British were eminently successful, and not only captured the national capital and destroyed many of the public buildings, but they also forced the Americans to burn the navy yard with the two new ships on the stocks, the sloop *Argus* and the frigate *Columbia*. The old frigates *New York* and *Boston* were also destroyed. In the preliminary actions on the Bay, before the capture of Washington, the American gunboats were in combat but had little success. The reports of the American officers indicate the basic trouble with the American boats. With few exceptions they were too small to carry their guns and to withstand the recoil, and owing to their small size they could not carry men enough to resist British boat attacks, to which gunboats were particularly susceptible.

The Medford-built brig *Rattlesnake* was also lost to the American service in this year. She was taken in June, off Cape Sable, by H.B.M. frigate *Leander*, 50, after a long chase in which the brig threw overboard all but two of her guns. The small, fast American cruisers were usually captured in blowing weather by British frigates or liners, when the greater size of the pursuer gave her the advantage.

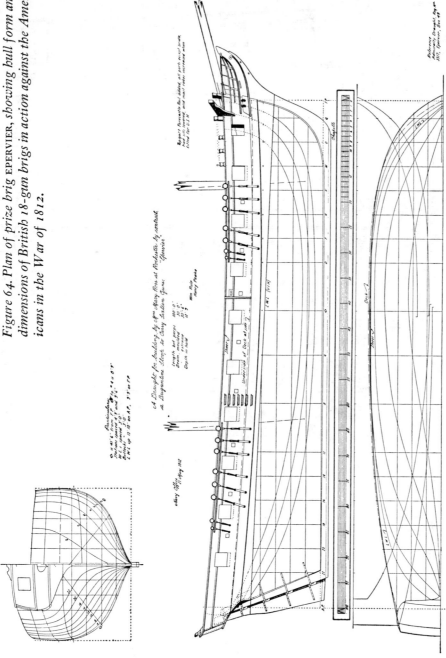

Figure 64. Plan of prize brig EPERVIER, *showing hull form and dimensions of British 18-gun brigs in action against the Americans in the War of 1812.*

281

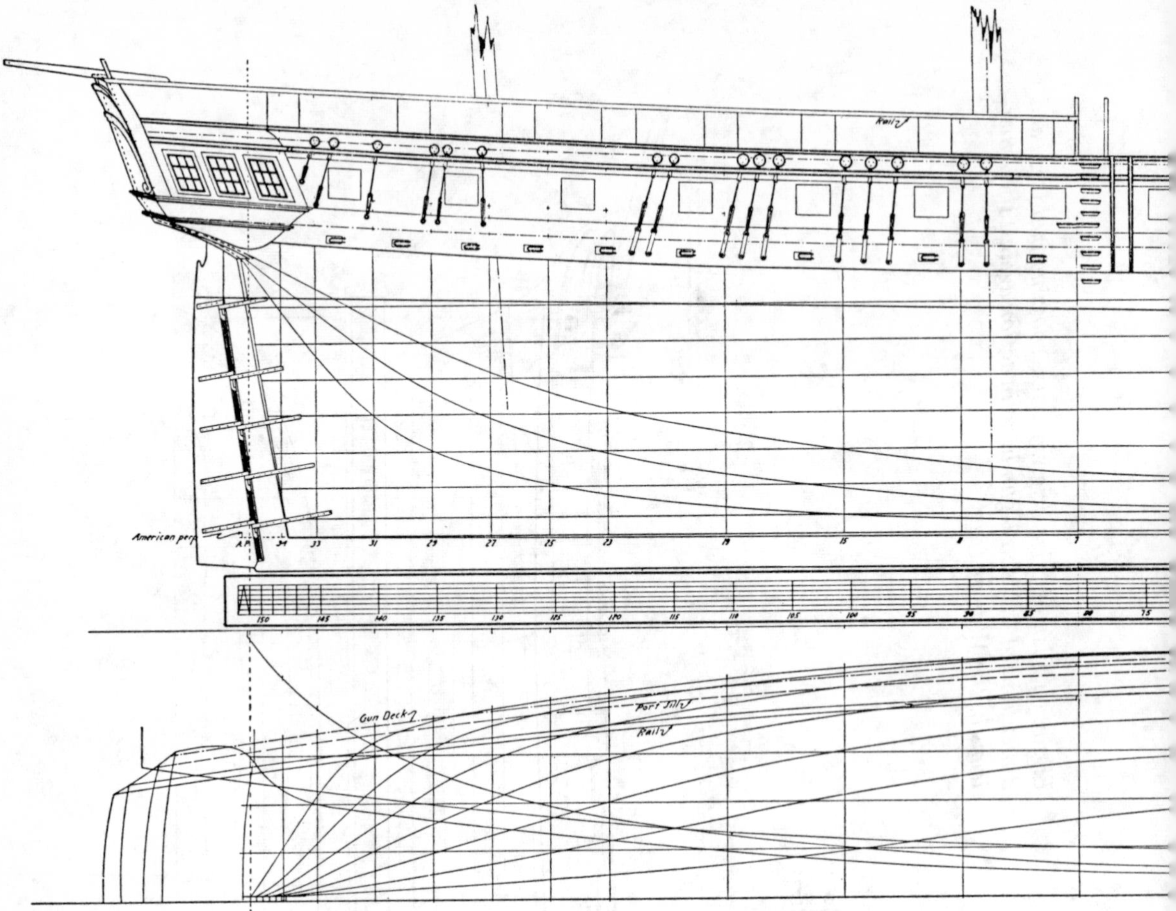

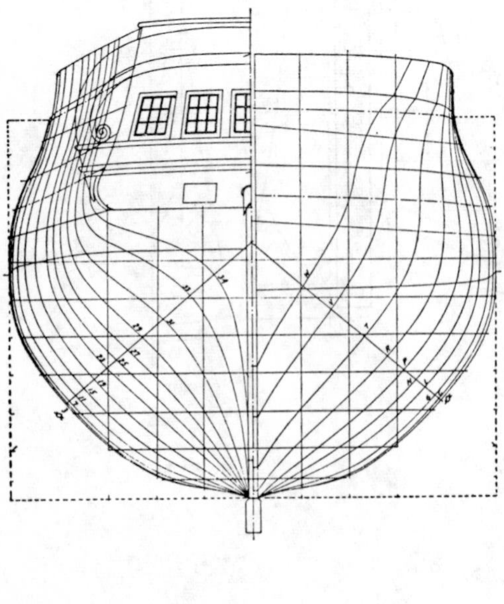

Spars

	Masts Length Yds	Masts Length In	Masts Dia. In	Yards Length Yds	Yards Length In	Yards Dia. In	
Main	30	0	30	27	26	19⅛	
Top	18	9	17¾	20	9	12⅝	
Galt	9	7	9⅛	12	13	7⅛	
Fore	27	22	26½	24	7	16¾	
Top	16	30	16¾	18	2	11½	
Galt	8	3	8	11	0	6½	
Mizzen	23	20	22½	14	6	10⅛	Gaff
Top	17	27	16¾	13	26	8½	
Galt	6	32	6⅛	9	24	5½	
Bowsprit	20	3	28¾	18	2	11½	
Jibboom	13	12	12	11	0	6½	
Crossjack				20	9	12⅝	

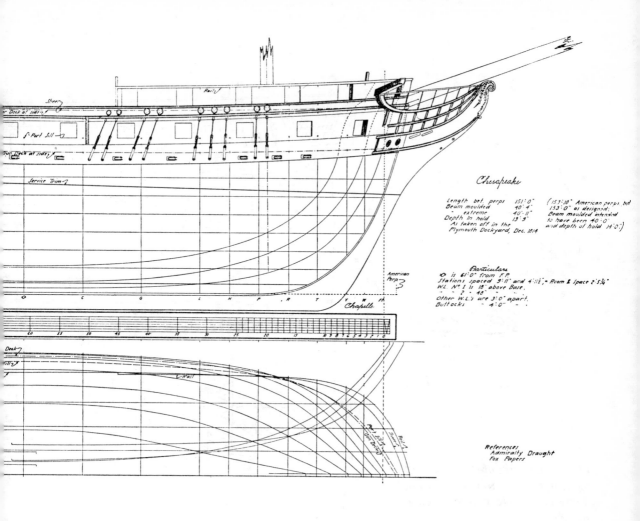

Chesapeake

Length bet. perps   151'.0"   (153'.10" American perps. but
Beam moulded   40'.4"   153'.0" as designed;
     extreme   40'.11"   Beam moulded intended
Depth in hold   13'.5"   to have been 40'.0"
As taken off in the   and depth of hold 14'.0".)
Plymouth Dockyard, Dec. 1814

Particulars

O is 61'.0" from F.P.
Stations spaced 9'.11" and 4'.11½" = Room & Space 2'.5¾"
WL N° 1 is 16" above Base.
   "   2 " 48 "
Other W.L.'s are 3'.0" apart.
Buttocks   " 4'.0" " .

References
Admiralty Draught
Fox Papers

Plan 17. *Draught of the frigate* CHESAPEAKE *as she appeared in the War of 1812, after
the Admiralty drawings of the ship.*

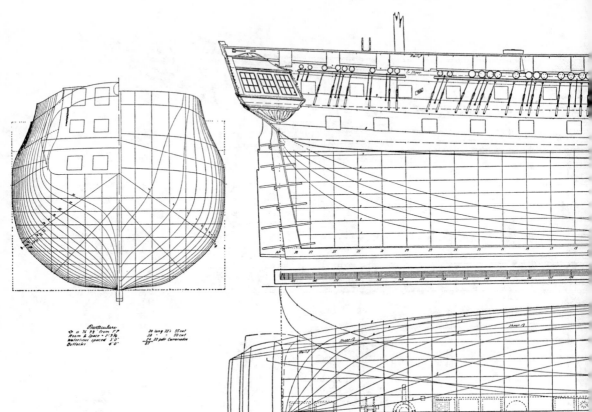

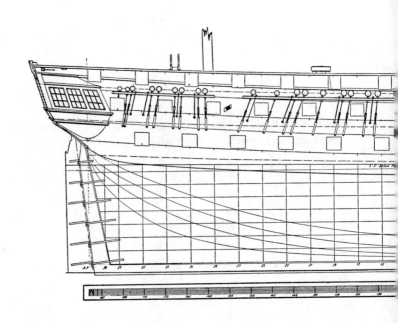

Plan 18. Draught of the American 74-gun ship FRANKLIN, *showing alterations made in the original design.*

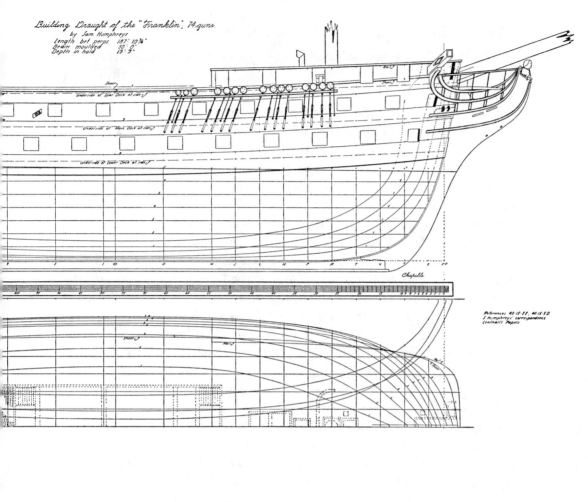

Building Draught of the "Franklin", 74 guns.
by Sam. Humphreys
Length bet. perps.   187: 10¾"
Beam moulded   50: 0"
Depth in hold   13: 9"

Chapelle

References 40-15-55, 40-15-50
S. Humphreys' correspondence
Lenthall's Papers

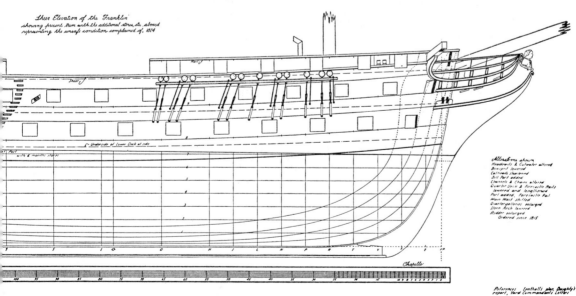

Sheer Elevation of the "Franklin"
showing present trim with the additional stores, etc. aboard
representing the unsafe condition complained of, 1824

Chapelle

Alterations shown
Headrails & Cutwater altered
Bowsprit lowered
Catheads shortened
Sill Port added
Channels & Chains altered
Quarter Deck & Forecastle Rails
lowered and lengthened
Port waved, Forecastle Rail
Main Mast shifted
Quarter galleries enlarged
Stern Arch lowered
Rudder enlarged
Ordered since 1818

References Lenthall's plan, Doughty's
report, Yard Commandant's Letters

The *Wasp,* of the new ship-sloop class, got to sea this year, leaving Portsmouth, New Hampshire, on May 1. She fought and captured the British brigs *Reindeer* and *Avon.* The first of these was burned, and the second sank after the *Wasp* had been driven off by other British cruisers. The *Wasp* disappeared in the fall of the year, and it is assumed she foundered with all hands.

The brig *Syren* was captured in strong winds off the West African coast on July 12 by the British 74 *Medway.* As usual, the American brig tried to escape to windward and threw overboard boats, guns, and gear in an effort to get away. The *Syren* was retained in the British service but does not appear to have been employed as a cruiser. In 1815 she was stripped and housed over to be used as a "lazaretto," or hospital ship for contagious diseases.

The *Adams,* now a large flush-deck corvette carrying 26 18-pdr. columbiads and 1 long 12-pdr., had gone to sea, out of the Chesapeake, in January. Her cruise was not very successful so far as captures were concerned, though the numerous times she was chased show that she was as fast as a sloop as she had been as a 28-gun frigate. As a vessel of the latter class she had been considered too sharp; it is a pity that her design cannot be found. The *Adams* finally ran into the Penobscot, in Maine, and in September she was attacked by British boats and her crew destroyed her to prevent capture.

In December the British began operations against New Orleans. Five American gunboats and two tenders were taken in a boat attack on Lake Borgne—*Nos. 5, 23, 156, 162,* and *163,* and the *Alligator* and *Seahorse.* The schooner *Carolina* was subsequently burned, on December 27, during the military operations before New Orleans, while in action against the British.

In addition to the three brigs, *Epervier, Reindeer,* and *Avon,* the British schooners *Pictou* (a former American privateer), *Ballahou,* and *Landrail* were captured and the 22-gun ship sloop *Hermes* was sunk while attacking an American fort. The *Ballahou* and *Landrail* were not impressive captures; they were no more effective vessels than the small American gunboats, being tiny schooners 55' to 56' long on deck and about 18' beam, on a Bermuda design. So far as naval ships were concerned, it can be seen that the British suffered no important losses at sea in this year.

By the end of 1814 it was apparent that the privateers were not effective weapons in a naval war. Though destructive to British commerce and, in combination with the letter of marques, able to bring into the United States many cargoes of great value, they were substitutes neither for naval vessels nor for merchant traders. The privateers could rarely whip any but the smallest and weakest of the British naval cruisers, and indeed, with few exceptions, were not inclined to attack regular naval ships. Thus, they were of no benefit in breaking the strangling blockade. Neither privateer nor letter of marque was effective in cargo carrying; too much capacity had to be sacrificed for speed and gun carrying. Though the privateers often captured very valuable and useful cargoes, too often they did not bring home the items most needed. Of course, a privateer could hardly go about shopping for, say, boots: she had to take what fell in her way. This made prize cargoes of relatively little value in a war economy. The belated realization of this, combined with the effect of naval successes on public opinion, now induced the administration to try to establish an effective navy capable not only of breaking the blockade but also of being far more destructive to the British merchant marine than anything before.

The new plans called for three 74-gun ships to be built, and in addition two squadrons of fast brigs and schooners were to be sent out under Commodores Porter and Perry. The vessels of these two squadrons were to be equal to the best privateers in speed and power but, in the hands of regular naval officers, would be ready to attack British convoy guards or light cruisers and to burn and destroy merchantmen without the necessity of taking prizes for a profit, as was required in privateers. In addition, a number of small craft were to be obtained for use as dispatch vessels, service craft at navy yards, and supply and transport craft, and for other purposes.

The small craft taken into the Navy in this year were schooners and sloops. *Buffalo*, sloop, was bought at Philadelphia for a transport and armed with 4 short 18-pdrs. and 1 long 6. The *Bulldog* was a felucca of 2 guns bought at New Orleans. *Camel* was a sloop tender bought at Philadelphia and armed with 2 long 18's and a long 4 as well as 2 carronades, 24-pdrs. The *Corporation* and *Dispatch* were two schooners of about 50 tons, each armed with two small guns, bought on the coast as packets. Another schooner was the *Ranger*, one gun, bought at Baltimore as a lookout vessel on the Chesapeake. A store ship, the schooner *Tom Bowline*, of 260 tons, was bought at Portsmouth, New Hampshire, in this year and rerigged as a brig or brigantine. This vessel was intended to cruise with one of the two squadrons of light cruisers. Another purchase was a schooner named *Torpedo*, for which no description or intended service has yet been found. A 7-gun schooner, the *Roanoke*, was transferred from the State Department to the Navy.

It was expected that the three 74's could not be completed within a year and that they would not be at sea for at least 18 months after their keels were laid. The 74 *Franklin* was designed by Samuel Humphreys and was built at Philadelphia, apparently under contract, by Humphreys and Penrose; Samuel Humphreys was thus both designer and one of the builders. As originally designed (Plan 18), her appearance was somewhat like the 1799 design of the 74's, except for the round bow and some variations in sheer plan. She was altered both during construction and after launch. Her service appearance is also shown in Plan 18. Her appearance was much admired; she measured 187' 10¾"

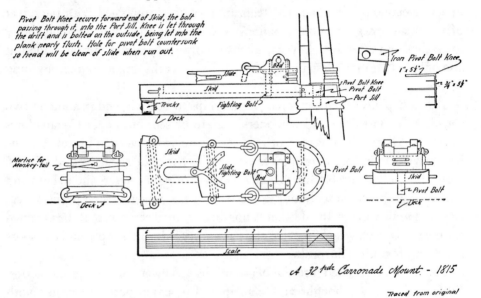

32-pdr. carronade mounting, FRANKLIN, *1815.*

between perpendiculars, 50' moulded beam, and 19' 9" depth of hold. Armed with 30 long 32-pdrs., 55 cwt. each, 33 long 32's of 50 cwt. each, and 24 carronades, 32-pdrs., she was found to be overloaded and below her lines to an undesirable degree. She was launched in August, 1815, too late to see action in the war.

The other two 74's were the *Washington*, built at Portsmouth, New Hampshire, by contract with Hartt and Badger, and launched in October, 1814, and the *Independence*, built by Hartt and Barker at Charlestown, Massachusetts, and launched in July, 1814. No design for these two 74's has been found, but both were close to 190' 0" between perpendiculars, 50' moulded beam, and 20' depth of hold; the *Washington* appears to have been 10" longer and 7"

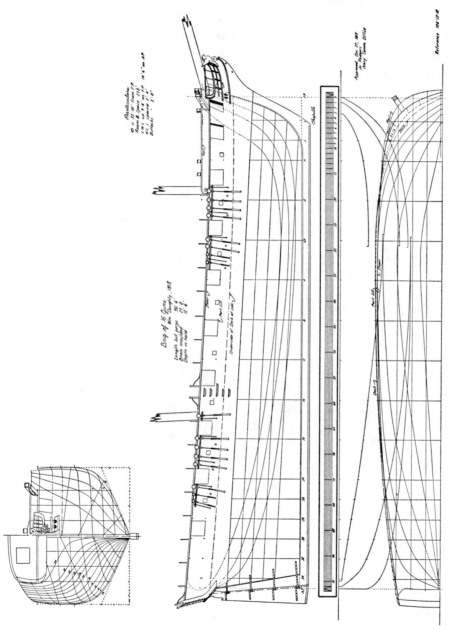

Figure 65. Draught of an American 16-gun brig, 1815.

wider than *Independence*. It is therefore probable that they were on the same plan. Whether Doughty was the designer or whether the vessels were designed by one of the Hartts is uncertain. Apparently no plan for either was ever sent to the Navy Department, for some years later, when the *Independence* was cut down into a huge frigate or "razee," her lines were taken off.

In addition to the 74's, there was to be some building to make up the two raiding squadrons. Three fast brigs were to be built: the *Boxer*, 14 guns, by

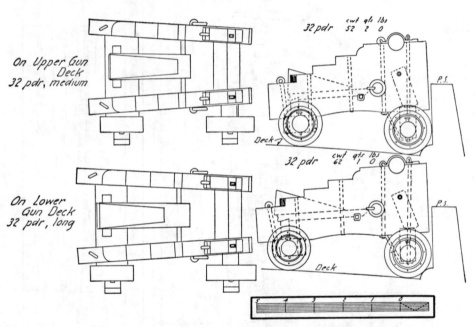

Medium and long 32-pdr. gun carriages, FRANKLIN, *1815.*

Beldin and Churchill at Middletown, Connecticut; the *Saranac*, 16 guns, by the same builders; and the *Chippewa* or *Chippeway*, 16, at Warren, Rhode Island. These brigs were to be designed by Doughty, who, it appears, had re-established himself at Washington after the British evacuation. Though the plans of each of the three brigs cannot be identified with certainty, the two brigs shown in Figures 65 and 66 may well represent the two plans used for the three brigs. Figure 65 shows a brig pierced to show 16 guns exclusive of the bridle ports. The design was for a clipper brig 96' 6" between perpen-

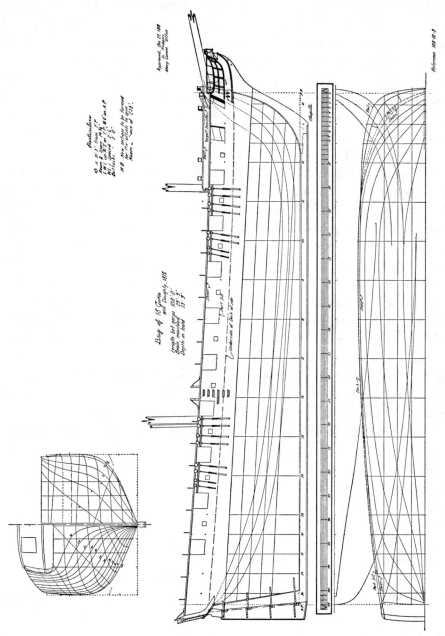

Figure 66. Draught of an American 18-gun brig, 1815.

diculars, 27′ 0″ moulded beam, and 12′ 6″ depth of hold. The plan was approved by the Navy Commissioners late in 1815, though it was made early in the year, as there is a reference to the plans of brigs in January. The second design was for a clipper 18-gun brig, 108′ 0″ between perpendiculars, 29′ 9″ moulded beam, and 13′ 9″ depth of hold. The three brigs were said to have been hurriedly built of green timber, for though they sailed well they were soon rotten. The records of the three brigs are unsatisfactory, as there was apparently some confusion about their tonnage and armament in the official correspondence. They were to carry 2 long 18's and 2 long 12's, and the balance of their armaments was to be made up of 32-pdr. carronades. Each brig was to carry two more guns than her rating, "as this can be done without filling the bridle-ports," according to one officer's letter. From this it would appear that the designs had been prepared for larger vessels than the official ratings. The three brigs were to be part of one squadron of four under Perry, the fourth being the purchased hermaphrodite schooner *Prometheus*, which had been bought in this year at Philadelphia. The *Prometheus* had been built for a privateer under the name *Escape* by William Sequin at Philadelphia and was bought there from her owners, Savage and Dryan. She was a typical vessel of her class, judging by the only drawing of the schooner that has been found, a carefully detailed sail plan, about 100′ on deck, 82′ keel, 27′ beam and 11′ 4″ depth of hold, with raking ends, gammon knee head, and plain, unadorned stern. She was pierced to carry 14 guns excluding bridle ports, but was now armed with 2 long 32's, 4 long 9's, and 6 carronades, 32-pdrs.

The second squadron was to be comprised of five vessels under Porter: the brigs *Spark*, 14, and *Firefly*, 14, and the schooners *Torch*, 12, *Spitfire*, 10, and *Eagle*, 12. A reserve squadron, in effect, was established by the existence of the *Epervier*, to which were added by purchase the brig *Flambeau*, 14, and by building, the 6-gun schooner *Lynx*. All of these vessels, except the *Epervier* and *Lynx*, were built as privateers and then purchased by the government. The *Spark* was a particularly fine brig built at Sag Harbor, Long Island, New York, in 1814; she was launched 40 days from the time her keel was laid. She had been built for Baltimore owners, who had placed the contract at Sag Harbor because the Chesapeake was so tightly corked by the British that it was now too risky to attempt to run out, and was probably built to a Maryland design. Both her model and numerous plans have survived. Her lines are shown in Figure 67, drawn from a plan owned by Constructor Lenthall, and checked against her builder's half-model and offsets. Her sail plan has also survived

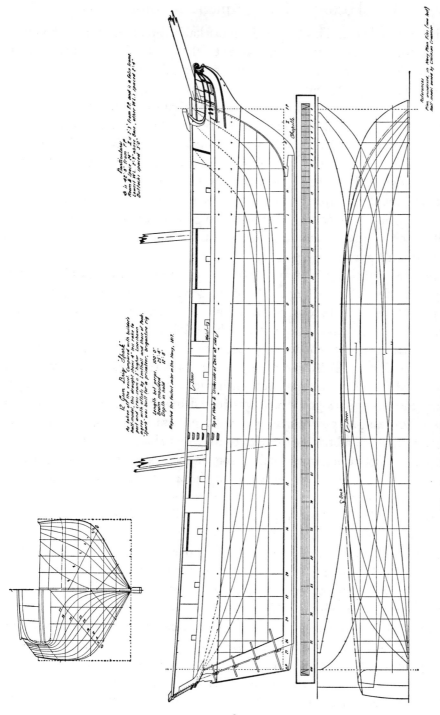

Figure 67. Draught of brig SPARK, *1815, clipper model.*

and is presented here. This brig had a remarkable reputation for sailing qualities and for this reason was recorded, even though she had not been Navy-
designed. She was 100′ between perpendiculars, 26′ moulded beam, and 12′
depth of hold. Some accounts state that she was built in 1813. This brig should
be compared with the two Doughty designs, Figures 65 and 66, to show the
characteristics of the design of clipper brigs in this period. It will be seen
that an almost standard hull model was now in use. Comparison of the sail plans
of the *Chippewa* and *Spark* will also be interesting, in that the two contemporary drawings show the rig of a naval brig in one case and a clipper brig in
the other; the latter (for the *Spark*) shows a lighter rig than the naval brig.
These sail plans show better than words the great spread of sail carried by the
small vessels of this period. The *Spark* was armed with 2 long 18's and 10
carronades, 18-pdrs.

Comparison of the lines of the *Spark* with those of the 16- and 18-gun brigs
shows the effect of naval requirements on vessels of approximately the same
size as the *Spark*. The latter, a successful man-of-war, was much lighter in displacement than her naval sisters because her original privateer owners and her
designer had created no unnecessary requirements. Though the *Spark* could not
carry the rating originally given, 14 guns, and was reduced to 12, she was for
long considered the fastest and finest small cruiser in the Navy. Doughty, in designing the 16- and 18-gun brigs, was forced by naval opinion to allow for
more stores and gun power than was really necessary, judging by the *Spark*.

The *Firefly* was a brig very similar to the *Spark*, but somewhat larger. This
brig was 109′ between perpendiculars, 100′ on the straight of keel, 29′ 4″ beam,
and 11′ 0″ depth of hold. She was armed with 4 long 18's and 10 carronades,
18-pdrs. The *Torch* was another privateer schooner bought at Baltimore, 106′
on deck, 26′ 0″ beam, and 11′ 9″ depth of hold. The *Torch* was rigged like
Prometheus, and her model was somewhat like *Spark*, but with slightly more
rake in the ends and more deadrise, according to one of her officers. The *Spitfire*
had been the Baltimore letter of marque *Grampus*, built at or near Baltimore
in 1812. Her dimensions, according to her register, were 106′ length, 25′ 6″
beam, and 11′ 8″ depth of hold; her naval register said she was 108′ on the
gun deck, 25′ 8″ beam, and 12′ in the hold. She carried two long 9's, one long
18, and 8 carronades, 18-pdrs. The *Eagle* was a 12-gun schooner bought at New
Orleans, said to have been built on the Chesapeake and of 270 tons measurement. The dimensions of this schooner have not been found.

The 6-gun schooner *Lynx* was also of the Baltimore Clipper type, about 80′

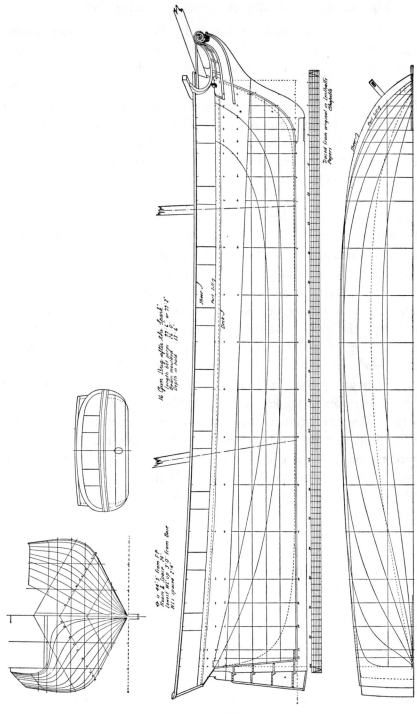

16 Gun Brig after the Spark
Length bet perps   92 c. or 93 2"
Beam moulded   25 0
Depth in hold   13 6

Ø is 44 3' from F.P
Room & Space 24"
Lowest W.L up 3 0 from Base
W.L spaced 2 4

Traced from original in Smithsonii Chapelle Papers

Figure 68. Draught of a 16-gun brig based on the design of the SPARK.

on deck and pierced for 14 guns, but was armed with but 6. She was an extreme clipper schooner without enough displacement to carry the guns she was pierced for; only her sail plan has been found. The details of the rigging of these clipper schooners can be seen in the *Lynx* sail plan. She was built at Washington or Georgetown, District of Columbia, by James Owner. It is not known whether she was built by contract or purchased on the stocks. It is possible that this schooner had been originally intended as one of the reserve vessels to support the two raiding squadrons. However, none of these vessels accomplished anything, as the war ended early in 1815, too soon for the squadrons to be completed.

It is worthy of comment that 1814 saw a complete reversal in the Navy's attitude toward the so-called Baltimore Clipper schooners. Where, in 1804–6, the Navy had eliminated all the very sharp schooners from the Navy List (either by sale or by rebuilding and changing the rig of such vessels as the *Enterprise, Vixen, Nautilus,* and *Ferret*) through the influence of the "practical" officers, such as Tingey, now the trend was toward the clipper schooner, as evidenced by the number of such craft placed on the Navy List in this year. In times of peace the command of a small, sharp schooner was less impressive than the command, say, of a brig, even though the former was by far the more effective ship. In war, however, the most effective vessel was the choice of any competent commander, and under the existing conditions in 1814 the fast-sailing and weatherly schooner was good insurance of both prizes and escape. Pompous dignity was of little value in wartime and impressed few. It had been argued, with some logic, that schooners were unsuitable for naval action, since they were not as easily maneuvered under short sail as a square-rigger; the schooner, unlike the brig, could not be stopped and backed by working her sails alone. This seemed a very sound argument in 1806, but in 1814 it would have been laughed at, for experience had taught that intricate maneuvering of small cruisers was wholly unnecessary, since speed and gun power, properly used, limited the advantages of maneuver, to a very great extent, to the fastest and most weatherly vessel. Speed, the always debatable factor of naval warfare, was now the prime requirement, and particularly so in the small cruisers that had to expose themselves to an overpowering fleet at sea. The hit-and-run privateer schooners had at least taught the Navy that speed in sailing meant survival when the odds were against them, or victory and the choice of position when the odds were favorable or even.

The problem of defending the Mississippi, particularly New Orleans, had been considered as far back as Jefferson's administration and had been "solved" by stationing a few gunboats there. Now there was a strong possibility that the British might attack in this area, and the old "solution" was re-examined. Obviously, the gunboats and tenders were hardly sufficient in the light of experience. It was decided to depend upon the naval ships based at New Orleans and upon the local militia and the few regulars stationed there. The ship sloop *Louisiana* and the schooner *Carolina* were effective vessels, though hardly powerful enough for the purpose. The ketches were of doubtful value. The War Department under Secretary Monroe made no preparations whatever, as was usual with this incompetent politician, but the Navy Department decided to strengthen the naval force there by the construction of a large block ship suitable for the defense of the river and the port of New Orleans.

The vessel was to be a large and powerful corvette, much like the shoal lake vessels built at Presque Isle, capable of sailing and also of entering shoal waters. A contract was let late in 1813 or at the beginning of 1814 to M. Pechon, of New Orleans, to build the vessel, to be rated as a 22-gun ship. It cannot be determined now who was the designer, though the plan of the ship, shown in Figure 69, has survived. The design called for a large vessel that was a cross between a frigate and a ship sloop, in that the vessel had her main armament on a flush deck, like a sloop, but with additional armament on quarter-deck and forecastle, like a frigate. However, unlike a frigate of the period, the ship had a very short quarterdeck and forecastle and no gangways; she was a reversion to the practices in frigate building of an earlier period. Though with some of the structural qualities of a frigate, the new vessel was referred to as a corvette in most official references.

The design in Figure 69 is of the only block ship whose keel was ever laid down for the United States Navy, though there had been numerous proposals for such craft ever since Bergh and Captain Stewart had made their proposal some years before the war. The new ship was named *Tchifonta* while on the stocks and was to measure 152′ 9″ on deck and 43′ moulded beam. She was to draw about 8′ 6″ ready for service. The ship was to be very plain, without adornment of any kind, and was to be rigged to topgallants only, but very lofty nevertheless. She was to carry a battery of 32-pdr. long guns with 42-pdr. carronades on the quarterdeck and forecastle. Work proceeded rather rapidly on the ship for a few months, but in the spring of the year, or early summer, construction was suspended on orders from Washington, the administration having decided there was no danger of attack in this quarter. As a result the big ship was still on the stocks when the British did attack New Orleans in December and January of 1814–15; thus the Navy Department finally did no more than the War Department to defend the place.

The lakes were the scene of much building activity in 1814. At Sackett's Harbor on Lake Ontario the Americans launched two large brigs, the *Jefferson* on April 7 and *Jones* on April 10. These brigs were to carry 16 carronades, 42-pdrs., and 4 long 24's, rating as 18-gun brigs. Eckford also launched the 44-gun frigate *Superior* on May 2, after she had been on the ways only eighty days. During this time her design had been altered. Originally laid down as a 44, she was lengthened when the Americans heard that the British were building a frigate of greater size. The *Superior* was armed with 30 long 32's, 26 carronades, 42-pdrs., and 2 long 24's—58 guns in all. Eckford also launched the 32-gun frigate *Mohawk* this season. She was on the ways only thirty-four days and was a large ship of her class, to carry 26 long 24's and 16 carronades, 32-pdrs. A small brig was also bought on the lake sometime during the year and named *Ranger*. She appears to have been either a transport or a supply vessel rather than a cruiser. It was Eckford's extraordinary ability to design, lay down, and build ships, ranging in size from a very small schooner to the largest frigates, working in a wilderness and in severe winter weather with sick or dissatisfied labor, and to do all this in extremely short periods of time, that maintained American superiority on Lake Ontario. Certainly Chauncey accomplished little with the fleet Eckford produced for him. The appreciation of Eckford's accomplishments can be judged by the fact that, whereas Chauncey's name has been carried on the American Navy List, no vessel was ever named for Eckford, though Fulton and Ericsson have been honored, as have other civilians—Bancroft, for example. Without Eckford and the Browns, none of the naval officers, Chauncey, Perry, or Macdonough, could have defended the Lakes or prevented the invasion of the northern states.

The British had no Eckford, but their commander Yeo was so crafty that he fooled not only Chauncey but also many naval historians since. Yeo launched two new frigates and, by false rumor, convinced the Americans that they were fully as powerful as the two the Americans were building. So well was this aim accomplished that the *Superior*, laid down as a 44, about 175′ between perpendiculars, was lengthened nearly 20′ on the stocks to permit her to carry 62 guns by filling all her ports. It was found, however, that this overloaded her, so she was reduced to 58. Now, the plan of the *Prince Regent*, the largest of the British frigates, shows her to have been a small double-banked frigate

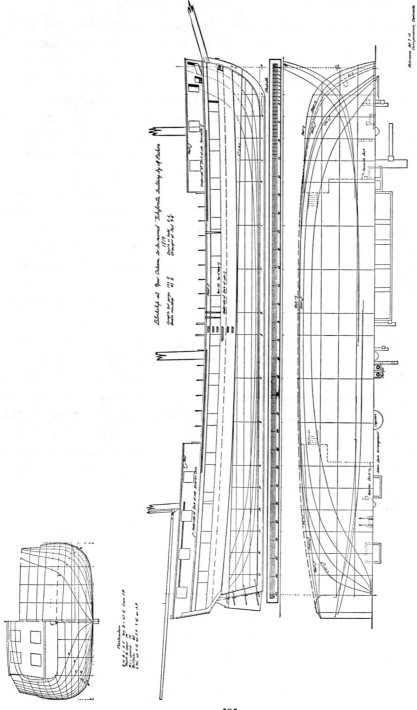

Figure 69. Draught of the New Orleans block ship, TCHIFONTA, 1815.

about 158′ 0″ between perpendiculars, American measurement, and 42′ 6″ moulded beam, pierced for 56 guns exclusive of bridle ports. By filling all of her ports she could have carried 60 guns. She was smaller than the 36-gun *Constellation*. The other frigate, the *Princess Charlotte*, was of the conventional type—only about 128′ 0″ between perpendiculars, American measurement, and 37′ 2″ moulded beam. This ship was pierced for 40 guns exclusive of the bridle ports. These small frigates could carry their armament only because they did not have to carry large quantities of provisions and, of course, did not carry any water. Hence their displacement was much less than that required for a seagoing frigate of the same length. The lake frigates had their capacity much reduced by means of great deadrise, intended to make them fast and weatherly. The *Princess Charlotte* was extreme in this respect.

The *General Pike*, the American 24-gun corvette, was 145′ between perpendiculars and 37′ beam; she was thus actually a larger ship than the smaller of the British frigates. The *Superior* was nearly 35′ longer than the *Prince Regent* and more heavily armed, yet Yeo's release of "information" convinced Chauncey that the British frigates were equal to his. Actually, Yeo was so well aware of his real inferiority that he began another small frigate and two more liners. The frigate was another double-banked ship, the *Psyche*, whose frame had been built in England and erected at Kingston—about 130′ between perpendiculars, American measurement, and 35′ 11″ moulded beam. She was launched in December, 1814. The two new liners were the *Wolfe* and *Canada*, 191′ 3″ between perpendiculars and 58′ moulded beam. They were slightly larger than the 112-gun *St. Lawrence*, which was 191′ 2″ between perpendiculars and 52′ moulded beam, but the two new vessels were to have a quarterdeck so as to carry 120 guns.

To confuse the Americans, Yeo also changed the names of the ships in the old squadron. All of his schooners had been converted into brigs. The *Wolfe* was now the *Montreal*, the *Royal George* was changed to *Niagara*, the *Melville* to the *Star*, the *Moira* to the *Charwell*, the *Beresford* to the *Netley*, and the *Sydney Smith* to the *Magnet*. The schooner *Prince Regent* had become first the *General Beresford* and now the *Netley*, all in two years.

When the Americans heard about the new British liners, they made plans to build two 130-gun ships and one or two huge frigates during the coming winter. The Browns were now to join with Eckford as soon as they were done at Vergennes, and construction was to begin early in 1815. The Americans made two captures on Ontario in this year, the 1-gun *Blacksnake*, a gunboat, and

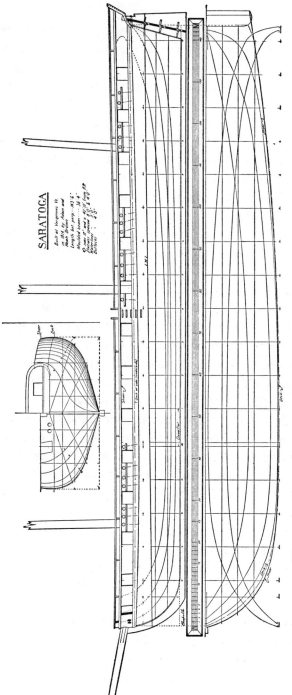

SARATOGA

Built at Vergennes Vt.
in 1814 by Adam and
Noah Brown
Length bet perp.- 143' 6'.
Moulded beam - 36' 4'.
Q cons. 2' and 3' 45';10' from C.B.
Draught, armed 31'0" & 40' 0"
Waterline - - 3' 6"
Ballast - - - 4' 0"

Figure 70. Draught of sloop of war SARATOGA, built for Lake Champlain.

297

the brig *Magnet*, ex *Sydney Smith*. Tension was mounting, as it appeared that the British might have control of the lake as soon as their three liners were ready, one of which, the *St. Lawrence*, was afloat, but not fitted.

Lake Champlain now became an important theater of action. The British had begun construction of a frigate on the lake and had built a large number of gunboats. They also had ready a new brig, the *Niagara*, which they re-named *Linnet*. In March of 1814 Noah Brown was ordered to Vergennes to build a ship and nine gunboats. He designed and built the big corvette *Saratoga*, 26 guns, a flush-decked ship 143' 0" between perpendiculars and 36' 6" moulded beam. She was without adornment, even without a head, and was very loftily sparred. Her lines, in Figure 70, were much like those of the *Niagara* brig, Figure 60, except that the ship had much less rake at the bow. Timber for the vessel began to be cut March 2, and the ship was launched April 11.

The Browns also built the gunboats *Allen, Borer, Burrows, Centipede, Nettle*, and *Viper*, all 75' long, 15' wide, and armed with an 18-pdr. columbiad and a long 24. These were built on the lines shown in Figure 62. It also appears that the Browns either built or repaired the 1-gun *Ballard*. There were at least two old gunboats remaining on the lake when Brown arrived, probably the *Alwyn* and *Ludlow*, and these were repaired. In lieu of the remaining gunboats ordered, it was decided to convert a steamboat hull into an armed schooner. It is not clear whether this steamboat had ever been afloat or was on the stocks when the Browns arrived. At any rate, the vessel was made into a 17-gun schooner and named *Ticonderoga*. She was a long vessel, carrying 8 long 12's, 4 long 18's, and 5 carronades, 32-pdrs., and was nearly flat-bottomed and quite narrow. By early May, the Browns and their gangs were back in New York, but late in June they received word that they were to go back to Vergennes and build a 24-gun brig in all haste. Adam left the day after the order was received, with two hundred men, while Noah stayed in New York to forward material. Fifty-five days after the letter ordering them to build the brig had been written in Washington, Macdonough fought the battle of Plattsburg, with the new brig in his line of battle, for Brown launched the *Surprise* exactly nineteen days after he arrived at Vergennes. The vessel was a large one much like the *Niagara*, to carry 24 long 24-pdrs. She was renamed *Eagle* soon after her launch, and was delivered to the fleet just five days before the battle.

The British squadron came down the lake to aid a British army invading New York along the route Burgoyne had attempted in the Revolution. This squadron was defeated at Plattsburg, New York, September 11, 1814, and the ships were all captured except for some gunboats. By this action, the Americans obtained the *Confiance,* a shallow frigate carrying 36 guns, 147' 5" on the main deck, 37' 2" beam, and 7' 0" depth of hold. She had been launched August 25 and had a furnace for heating shot, 27 long 24's, 2 long 18's, and 6 carronades, 24-pdrs. No plan of the ship has yet been found. They also took the brig *Linnet* and retook the two sloops captured earlier, now the *Chubb* and

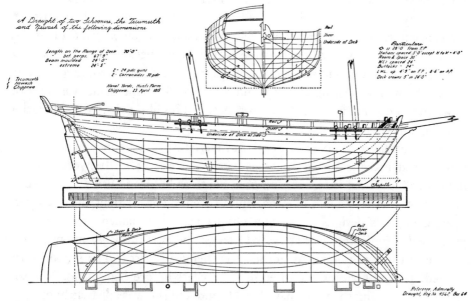

Figure 71. Draught of British lake schooners built at the end of the War of 1812, probably typical of the smaller lake vessels.

Finch. The American squadron consisted of the *Saratoga, Eagle, Ticonderoga,* the sloop *Preble,* and ten gunboats. The sloop *President* was not present, as she had been captured by the British sometime during the year and was taken into their service as the *Icicle.* With the defeat of the British squadron, the invaders retired and the danger on Lake Champlain ended.

By Perry's victory on Lake Erie, the Americans had full control of Erie and the western lakes. However, in September the schooners *Tigress* and *Scorpion* were captured by a British boat attack, as earlier the schooners *Ohio* and *Somers* had been taken in the same manner. These small schooners were liable to capture by boat attacks, as they were low-sided and were so small that their crews were often less numerous than a launch crew. In the fall of the year the British began building some small schooners for use on the western lakes; Figure 71 shows a typical lake schooner, of the type built on Lake Erie.

The treaty of peace between Great Britain and the United States was signed at Ghent December 24, 1814, but was not ratified at Washington until February 17, 1815. It was still later before privateers and naval vessels were informed of the end of the war, so operations continued through the first two months of the year. In January the frigate *President* was captured by a British squadron off New York while attempting to get to sea. The *President* had gone ashore on her way out and was badly strained and leaky when she met the British. As a result her sailing was far below normal and she was taken after a half-day chase. The frigate was taken into the Royal Navy because she had been so widely admired, but she was too much damaged by her grounding to be of value. She was broken up in 1817, and a ship of the same name was built on somewhat the same lines for the British Navy. This also gained the reputation of being a fast ship.

The additions to the Navy List in 1815 were few. A schooner named *Ghent* was built at Presque Isle by Thomas Eyre. She was 55′ 0″ between perpendiculars, 16′ 0″ moulded beam, and 6′ 0″ depth of hold, and had a long 12-pdr. on a pivot. She was much like the 1-gun revenue cutters built the same year from Doughty's designs. A 12-gun clipper schooner named *Firebrand* was purchased early in the year at New Orleans, and was probably intended as a reserve to the two raiding squadrons then being prepared. The schooner remained at New Orleans for three or four years before being sold. No particulars concerning the vessel have been found, but she was apparently of some size. Another purchase here was the 12-gun ketch *Surprise*. This vessel was purchased as late as March and fitted to carry 12 guns, though finally reduced to 6. She seems to have been intended as a guard ship.

One of the more important ships added to the Navy List this year was the British ship sloop *Cyane*. With a consort, the flush-decked sloop *Levant*, she was taken by the frigate *Constitution* on the night of February 20. The frigate and her prizes anchored in the Cape Verde Islands but soon afterward were driven out by three heavy British frigates. The Americans separated, and the *Levant* was chased back to the Portuguese port, where she was retaken by the British. The *Cyane* was carried to the United States and transferred to the Navy. The ship had been built as far back as 1795 as a member of a class of four quarterdecked ship sloops; in 1798 a fifth sister was built with slight alterations. The *Cyane* was built by a Mr. Wilson by contract. She was a miniature

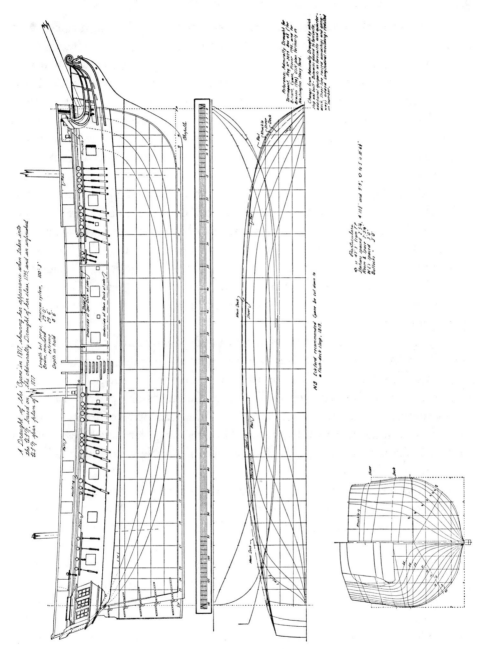

Figure 72. Draught of CYANE *from her Admiralty plan and from drawings of the ship made after her capture by the Americans.*

frigate with detached quarterdeck and a short forecastle, intended to carry 16 medium guns, 6-pdrs., on her main deck, 6 carronades, 12-pdrs., on her quarter-deck, and 2 carronades, 12-pdrs., on her forecastle. Figure 72 shows the design of this ship. She had been captured by the French and recaptured and had gone through many alterations. When she was captured by the Americans she had a spar deck and her waist had been raised, the forecastle had been given bulwarks, and she was, in appearance, a frigate-built ship. However, she was a small vessel for the period of her capture, being only 110′ 0″ between perpendiculars and 29′ 0″ moulded beam. She had a frigate's midsection but, like many British ship sloops, had very fine ends and had been a good sailer when built. Her sailing qualities had been effectively destroyed, however, by over-gunning. The ship appears to have been in rather poor condition when captured and received rather extensive repairs when taken into the Navy. She was now rated officially as a 24-gun ship and was laid up at the Philadelphia Navy Yard. The *Cyane* was rather more of a trophy than a serviceable cruiser, for she certainly was inferior in all respects to the new American sloops built during the war.

An 18-gun brig, the *Penguin*, was taken and destroyed by the *Hornet*, and the East India Company's cruiser *Nautilus*, a small 14-gun brig, was taken by the *Peacock* in this period, but the latter was returned, as she had been seized after the date established by the Treaty of Ghent as the end of hostilities. One schooner, the *St. Lawrence*, a former American privateer, was captured by the American privateer *Chasseur*. Though a regular naval vessel when captured, she was not purchased for the American Navy, of course, having been a privateer's prize.

During the winter of 1814–15 the building race on Lake Ontario reached its climax. The Americans laid down two 130-gun ships and one large frigate. The Browns went to Sackett's Harbor in February, with twelve hundred carpenters, and joined Eckford. The gangs had been at work six weeks when peace put a stop to the work. Had the Browns and Eckford been allowed to proceed, another six weeks would have seen the completion of two of the large ships and probably the one frigate. One of the 130-gun ships was the *New Orleans*, reported to have been 212′ 0″ on her upper deck, 56′ 0″ moulded beam. The other may have been the *Chippewa*. The frigate was the *Plattsburg*, 58 guns. One or two additional frigates had been intended to be started as soon as these ships were launched. The ships were left on the stocks, the *New Or-*

leans being the most advanced. The British liners on the stocks were housed over, and the unfinished ships afloat were laid up.

On the western lakes the British completed three small schooners of the *Tecumseth* class, shown in Figure 71, and built two classes of lugger-rigged gunboats on Lake Champlain, two of which are shown in Figures 73 and 74. They also began work on the brig shown in Figure 61 for use on this lake, but it does not appear that the vessel was completed. Both sides laid up their vessels, except for a few schooners, and the surplus crews were sent home or discharged.

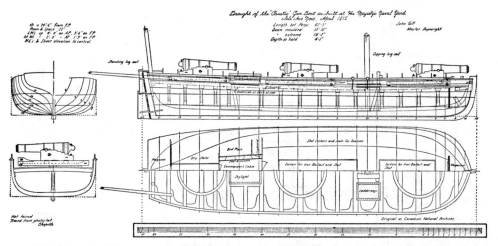

Figure 73. British lake gunboat, CAUSTIC, *designed for use on Lake Champlain.*

The war ended with the Navy larger and more effective than when it started. Of greater importance, the American public was now convinced of the necessity of a navy and, on the whole, was very proud of what it had accomplished in the war. In spite of an inadequate organization, the Navy Department had become somewhat more effective and the weakness of the establishment had been observed by Congress.

One of the wartime 74's authorized had not yet been laid down. It was intended to build her at Washington, but the Navy Yard there was not yet sufficiently restored to begin work. The navy yards at Norfolk, Philadelphia, New York, Boston, and Portsmouth were manned and in operating condition. Two constructors, Doughty and Samuel Humphreys, were employed. The 74 *Franklin* was nearly ready to launch at Philadelphia, and the other two,

Washington and *Independence*, were fitting out. Though many of the ships of the Navy were hurriedly built of green timber, the bulk of the ships were in good condition. The normal reduction in force that followed the war would permit the disposal of most of the unsatisfactory ships and small vessels.

So far as the construction policy of the Navy was concerned, some progress had been made in the last months of the war. It will be recalled that the senior naval officers had practically dictated the construction policies of the Navy since 1794, with only the veto power of the Secretary of the Navy to check them. The theory supporting the practice was that "practical" men knew what

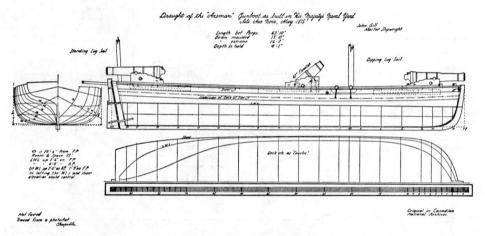

Figure 74. British lake gunboat, AXEMAN, *designed for Lake Champlain.*

was required better than the technical men, shipwrights and constructors, and were also better fitted to judge such matters than the political head of the Navy. However, the latter could control the officers when they ran contrary to the policy of the administration, particularly in matters of economy. Gradually, the power of the Secretary of the Navy over the commissioned officers in all matters became fully recognized and the Secretary had become the acknowledged commander of the service.

So far as the design of new ships was concerned, there were many advantages in having the officers dictate requirements, since the system insured practical design and construction, with emphasis on combat ability. On the other hand, the conservatism of elderly naval officers often led to the retention of obsolete ship types, or to too much emphasis on a single class of man-of-war. Also, the insistence upon heavy armament, without due regard for the ability of existing ships to carry it, led to grave difficulties. Jealousy in rank led to a pompous disregard of small light cruisers and contempt for sea raiders.

The naval constructors, Joshua Humphreys, Josiah Fox, and William Doughty, had in fact been no more than master shipwrights, primarily concerned with construction and repair and fitting out in the navy yards, with the designing of new vessels requiring but little of their time. The Master Shipwright of the Washington Navy Yard, between 1803 and 1815, really acted as chief constructor to a limited degree; he acted as technical adviser to the Secretary and usually prepared plans of new vessels. However, his recommendations were rarely binding on senior naval officers, who often rigged and altered their commands without regard to his technical opinions. This led to a complete lack of standardization and to expensive confusion, in spite of a stream of directives from the Secretary.

Because of the lack of a central design authority, the shipwrights and officers in the navy yards and contract shipyards felt quite free to depart from the authorized designs and specifications, going so far as to change lines and dimensions. As a result each new ship became a special problem in arming, rigging, and sparring. Sails, spars, rigging, and gun mounts could not be transferred from ship to ship, and it was practically impossible to have a reserve supply of this material made up in advance of needs.

The system of centralized power in the Secretary's hands not only made him carry the burden of attempting to control construction and fitting out; it also made him the strategist, who directed the ship movements and the assignment of officers and commanders. In times of peace, with a very small navy, this had not been a difficult problem, but in war it became a great burden for which a political appointee was little fitted. The quasi war with France had shown this to be beyond the capacity of even a competent Secretary, but the lesson had been overlooked in the change of political control of the country that followed the French troubles.

In an act dated February 7, 1815, Congress attempted to correct the basic difficulty in the Navy Department. This act established a Board of Navy Commissioners, consisting of three officers of rank not less than post captain, to be attached to the Secretary's office to discharge certain duties. These were to prepare rules and regulations necessary for securing uniformity of vessels, equipment, and repairs or refitting; they also were charged with "securing responsibility" in subordinate officers and agents.

The language of the act was somewhat vague, which led to a period of dis-

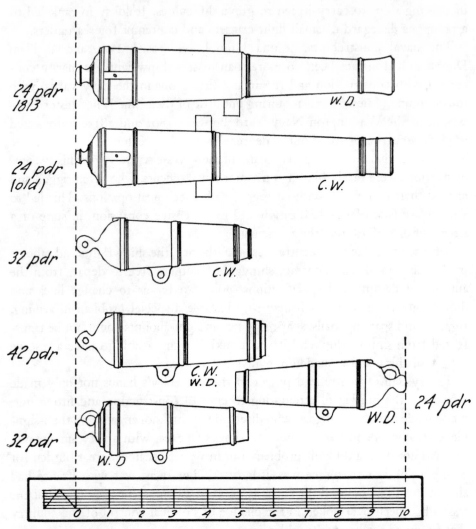

24 pdr
1813

W. D.

24 pdr
(old)

C. W.

32 pdr

C. W.

42 pdr

C. W.
W. D.

24 pdr

W. D.

32 pdr

W. D

0   1   2   3   4   5   6   7   8   9   10

Types of guns and carronades in the American naval service, 1813–15.

agreement between members of the Board and the Secretary, as to the exact division of power and responsibility. Finally, it was established that the Board's powers were confined to the procurement of stores and supplies, materials and armament, and the design and construction of new vessels. The Board had control over all repairs and refitting and over the constructors, agents, and the navy yards in all matters pertaining to these subjects. The Secretary retained control of vessel movements, naval personnel of all descriptions, and all ap-

pointments and assignments. In short, he was still to act as a naval strategist
and nominal head of the Navy in time of war, regardless of fitness.

In addition to the three members of the Board there was a secretary. The
Board members had the honorary title of Commodore, and one of them was
the President of the Board. This office went to the senior officer, of course.
Membership in the Board seems to have been at the Secretary's discretion;
some officers were members for long periods, while others sat only for a short
time. Some officers were assigned to the Board for two tours of duty (one had
three) at different periods. The membership of the Board was never changed
completely, and there was a fairly constant rotation of members. The first
Board consisted of John Rodgers, President, Isaac Hull, and David Porter. Stephen Decatur replaced Hull in the first year. The first secretary appointed was
a civilian, James Paulding.

The character of the Board, as a whole, was highly conservative. Since no
vessel could be built for the Navy until her plan had been approved and her
construction allocated by the Board, it is apparent that the Board's control
over the constructors was absolute. Later some constructors were favored by
the Board, and as membership in the Board changed, so did the favored constructors. The effect of the Board on the design of naval ships will be seen.

The establishment of the Board resulted in the reorganization of the construction branch. A chief constructor and resident constructors in each navy
yard were allowed for, the chief constructor to have authority over the constructors in the yards. All of their reports were to be rendered through the
chief constructor, who was to report directly to the Board. The Board
quickly brought order into construction, repair, arming, and fitting of vessels
of the Navy. It established a working organization of the navy yards and a
system in controlling alterations in new ships. It gave an opportunity for more
than one constructor to design new ships. A definite responsibility for inspection of new construction and all procurement was assigned. Nevertheless, the
control of technical matters remained in the hands of the "practical seaman."

From a naval shipbuilding point of view, the outstanding men of the War
of 1812 were Eckford and the Browns, Adam and Noah. Through the efforts
of these three the Navy held control of the lakes and prevented the British from
invading the North and Northwest, which would have led to their reaching the
American shipbuilding centers on the coast through the back door, so to speak.
No officer or constructor of the Navy accomplished more. There were no
competitors to the Browns and Eckford among the navy yards, or in the con-

tract shipyards on the coasts. A few of the privateer building yards built rapidly, but the vessels they turned out were smaller than those built on the lakes, where building was made infinitely more difficult than on the coast because of climate and geographical conditions, to say nothing of scarcities of labor and some materials. Perhaps the lake builders had one important advantage—no government inspection or red tape to delay them. The moment was too critical to suffer the fumbling delay occasioned on the coast, where government agents lost time trying to make decisions for which they were wholly unequipped in training and knowledge.

The building of the lake vessels required more than setting up a ship, as we have seen in the activities of the Browns at Presque Isle. Eckford not only had to set up a shipyard at Sackett's Harbor; he had to build quarters for his gangs, mess and kitchen buildings, hospital, offices, and blockhouses. Between trips to the lakes, the Browns had found time to build a blockhouse 40′ square at Hell Gate and another at Williamsburg, Long Island. A third was built at Rockaway Beach. The Browns built a steam frigate in their yard, the Fulton-designed *Demologos*, which they launched in the fall of 1814, four months after the keel was laid. She was a vessel 156′ in length, 56′ beam, and 20′ moulded depth, and she had a paddle wheel 16′ in diameter and 14′ wide set in a tunnel between the hulls. This tunnel does not appear to have run the full length of the hull but to have been about 60′ long with sloping ends. The Browns also built another vessel under Fulton's supervision. She was called the *Mute*, according to Noah Brown's statement after the war, and seems to have been a submersible. The Browns also built the noted brig *Warrior*, fitted as a privateer to carry 20 guns. It was sworn that this brig sailed fifteen and a half knots on the return from a cruise.

With the ending of the war Eckford came back to New York and opened a yard. Shortly, however, he was again engaged in naval work. Neither Eckford nor the Browns were asked to deliver the plans of the ships they built until about four years after the war, and the correspondence does not show their answers to the requests. It appears that there was some delay in these builders getting the pay due them under their various contracts. The Browns did no more naval work but became noted builders of packet and other large merchant ships.

The war years had seen some changes in the hull form of fast-sailing craft in America, particularly of naval vessels. The slack, rounded bilges of earlier years had disappeared, and now fast armed small vessels had almost straight rising floors, hard bilges, and almost wall sides, following a trend that seems to have begun in England as early as 1803 in the designs of the British constructor Peake. The American vessels apparently were not copies of the British designs, however; the Americans gave more attention to the ends of their ships than was common in the Admiralty designs. The change in midsection of the American brigs and schooners, and ship sloops too, was undoubtedly due to the need of increased stability to carry heavy guns and more and more sail. The need of rapid construction in the war years had spelled the doom of intricate headrails and carvings of earlier naval craft; the reverse curved topsides also went out of fashion, as they required too much curved timber and narrowed the decks too much. Ships had grown longer, and much experience had now been gained in building long hulls that would not hog excessively.

With the war with England over, the Americans turned their attention to the Barbary pirates again. This time Algiers was the object of American anger. Decatur was sent out in the new 44 *Guerriere*, with the sloop *Ontario*, the *Constellation*, and the ex-British *Macedonian* and *Epervier*. He also had five of the small cruisers intended for raiding squadrons. The *Epervier* and the *Guerriere* captured the *Mashuda*, 46 (she was eventually returned to the Algerines), and the small cruisers ran the *Estedio*, 22, ashore and destroyed her. Decatur had hoped to attack Algiers and the other Barbary piratical powers, but none of them desired more trouble. The British finally destroyed the power of the Barbary principalities shortly afterward. The *Epervier* was lost at sea with all hands late in 1815, on the way home from the Mediterranean.

With the ending of the War of 1812, the disposal of the war-worn small craft began. All but a few of the old gunboats were sold, and the greater part of the schooners that had been purchased on the lakes were also disposed of in 1815–16. The preservation of some of the larger lake vessels was intended; they were stripped and sunk in water sufficiently deep to avoid damage from ice. Beginning in 1816, the small purchased seagoing cruisers were surveyed, and those deemed poorly built or expensive to maintain were ordered to be sold.

The only addition to the Navy was the ship of the line *Columbus*, authorized during the war. This vessel was laid down in the reconstructed Washington Navy Yard in June, 1816, on a design by Doughty, who was also her master builder. The *Columbus* was 193' 3" between perpendiculars, 52' 0" moulded beam, and 21' 10" depth in the hold. She had been designed 193' between perpendiculars and 21' 6" in the hold, but in construction she was raised a few inches, which made her length increase slightly. Her design, as built, is shown in Plan 19. She proved to be the most successful of the 74's authorized during the war, though she cannot be said to have been as good as those ships that followed her. The fault of all of the 74's built for the Navy in these years was that they did not have sufficient displacement to carry the armament placed on board.

In April, 1816, Congress set up a plan for the gradual improvement of the Navy. The intent of the new act was to gradually build up the Navy in all classes, as funds could be made available. This permitted a definite plan of expansion which, owing to the lack of money, did not become effective for a couple of years. The official Navy List as of January 2, 1816, was as follows:

Independence	74	at Boston	Ready for service
Washington	74	at Boston	For the Mediterranean
Franklin	74	at Philadelphia	Will be ready in the spring
Guerriere	44	at New York	Ready for service
Java	44	at New York	For the Mediterranean
United States	44	at sea	Mediterranean
Constitution	44	at Boston	Repairing
Constellation	36	at sea	Mediterranean
Congress	36	at Boston	Requires repairs
Macedonian	36	at Boston	Ready for service
John Adams	24	at sea	Mediterranean, as storeship
Cyane	24	at Boston	In ordinary
Block Ship	24	at New Orleans	On stocks, Tchifonta Lake
Alert	20	at sea	Mediterranean, storeship
Louisiana	20	at New Orleans	To be sold, unfit for service
Hornet	18	at New York	In ordinary
Wasp	18	missing since 1814	
Peacock	18	at New York	In ordinary
Ontario	18	at sea	Mediterranean
Erie	18	at sea	Mediterranean
Epervier	18	missing since July 14, 1815	
Enterprise	14	at New York	In ordinary
Etna	14	at New York	In ordinary, bomb
Flambeau	14	at New York	Recently returned from Mediterranean
Spark	14	at New York	"　　"　　"　　"
Firefly	14	at New York	"　　"　　"　　"
Chippewa	14	at New York	"　　"　　"　　"
Saranac	14	at sea	Cruising
Boxer	14	at New York	Recently returned from the Mediterranean
Prometheus	14	at sea	Cruising in revenue service
Spitfire	ketch	at Norfolk	In ordinary
Vesuvius	ketch	at New York	Receiving vessel
Vengeance	ketch	at New York	Sheer hulk
Nonsuch	14	at Norfolk	In ordinary
Spitfire	sch. 12	at New York	In ordinary
Torch	12	at New York	In ordinary
Tom Bowline	12	at sea	Cruising, storeship
Surprise	12	at New Orleans	In ordinary
Firebrand	12	at New Orleans	In ordinary
Roanoke	sch.	at Wilmington, N.C.	Fitting
Hornet	sch.	at sea	Mediterranean
Lynx		at Boston	Fitting

Dispatch	sch.	at Portsmouth	Ready for service
Asp		at Baltimore	Receiving vessel
Corporation		at Philadelphia	Receiving vessel
Ranger		at Philadelphia	Receiving vessel
Buffalo		at Philadelphia	Transport
Camel		at Philadelphia	Transport
Tickler		at New Orleans	Dispatch boat
New Orleans	74	on Lake Ontario	On stocks at Sacketts Harbor
Chippewa	74	" " "	" " " " "
Plattsburg	44	" " "	Frames, not set up
Superior	44	" " "	In state of preservation
Mohawk	32	" " "	" " " "
General Pike	24	" " "	" " " "
Madison	20	" " "	" " " "
Jefferson	18	" " "	" " " "
Jones	18	" " "	" " " "
Sylph	16	" " "	" " " "
Oneida	14	" " "	" " " "
Lady of the Lake		" " "	In service
Niagara	18	On Lake Erie	Ready for service
Lawrence	18	" " "	Laid up
Detroit	18	" " "	Laid up
Queen Charlotte	18	" " "	Laid up
Porcupine		" " "	Ready for service
Ghent		" " "	Ready for service
Confiance	36	on Lake Champlain	Laid up
Saratoga	24	" " "	Laid up
Eagle	18	" " "	Laid up
Linnet	14	" " "	Laid up
Ticonderoga	14	" " "	Laid up
15 barges		at Sackett's Harbor	
6 galleys		at Whitehall, Champlain	
14 barges		at Baltimore	
A few gunboats in addition			
Steam Frigate		at New York	Ready for service
Steam Frigate		at Baltimore	Suspended

★ ★ ★ ★ ★ ★ ★ ★ ★ ★

CHAPTER SIX

The Postwar Navy
1816-1830

THE INTENDED expansion of the Navy could not begin at once, after the war, as funds became available only slowly and there were many problems concerning a new program that had to be settled. Within two years after the war, a program was established that was based on the lessons of the late war, in which the need of ships of the line was recognized. Six improved 74-gun ships and nine new 44-gun frigates were proposed. In addition, consideration was given to the sloop class, which the war had shown to be particularly useful as commerce raiders, and the program was to include ten of this class, larger and more powerful than the 1813 classes. England, and other naval powers, had been impressed with the sloops of 1813 and now had ships that were their equal, so, to keep ahead, the Americans would have to have vessels superior to the early ships of the *Erie* and *Wasp* designs. The question of a very powerful ship of the line was also raised, and there was some agitation for the construction of one or more vessels of 120–130 guns.

The groundwork for the new program was the responsibility of the newly formed Board of Navy Commissioners, and as soon as the immediate problems of standardizing equipment, armament, manning allowances, control of repair, and the other matters relating to the existing Navy were settled, they prepared for the proposed construction. One of the first steps in organization was in the navy yards, which had to be manned and equipped for building the new ships. It was decided to build in the government yards because of the uncertain factor of funds; it was possible that the slow appropriation of funds might keep a ship on the stocks for years, and no private builder would be willing to do this except on a heavy rental basis.

William Doughty remained constructor at the Washington Navy Yard, and Samuel Humphreys was at Philadelphia; the other yards had no resident constructors. Doughty was put to work on the designs of the new 74's and the frigates. The Board then gradually filled the vacant positions of constructor in some of the other yards. Francis Grice, one of the builders of the frigate *Guerriere* at Philadelphia, was appointed to the Norfolk Navy Yard May 7, 1817, and so became third in seniority. In the same year, July 13, Henry Eckford was assigned to the New York Yard. Josiah Barker was placed at the Boston Yard about the same time. Two years later, two more constructors were appointed.

In 1817 the new program got under way with two new 74's being laid down. One was on the design Doughty had been working on; the other was to be designed by and built under the supervision of Henry Eckford. On May 30, 1816, the latter had been requested by John Rodgers, the President of the Board, to make a model and draught of a ship of the line 193' between perpendiculars and 53' moulded beam. In making his request of Eckford, Rodgers had indicated that the members were "desirous of availing themselves of the most approved professional skill of our country." There has been a tradition that the Board imposed conditions on Eckford and opposed his building the new ship. Griffiths seems to have been one of the authorities for this, but both the official correspondence and the plans of the ship indicate that the Board not only approved the original design, but made no alterations and certainly had no objections to Eckford. Furthermore, the fact that after he had begun work on the *Ohio* he was asked to submit designs for other vessels is sufficient evidence of the esteem in which the Board held him and answers Griffith's claim that he was objectionable to the Board. In view of Eckford's excellent commercial prospects, even in the years of depressed business after the war, it seems probable that he looked upon his appointment as a naval constructor as merely temporary employment and an interesting opportunity to design another large man-of-war.

Eckford, having completed his model and draught and obtained the approval of his design by the Board, laid down the new ship of the line in November, 1817, within the New York Navy Yard. Eckford had designed the ship larger than the Board had requested, for the plans called for a length of 197' 2"

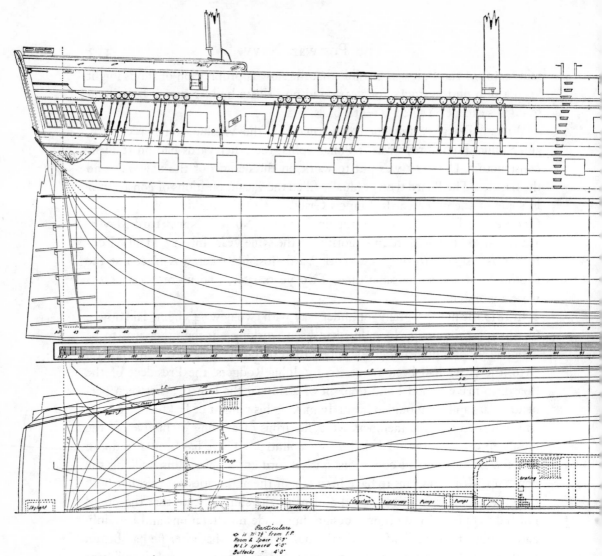

Particulars
O is 71·7⅞' from F.P.
Room & Space 2'·9"
W.L's spaced 4'·0"
Buttocks " 4'·0"

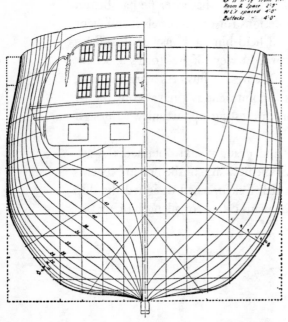

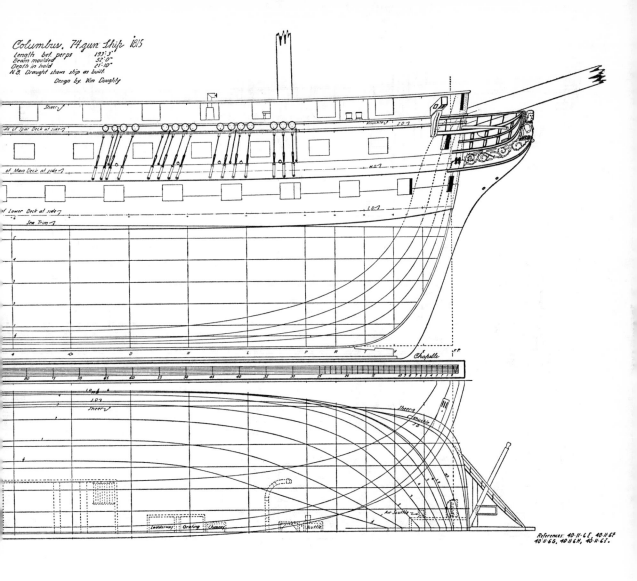

Plan 19. Draught of the 74-gun ship COLUMBUS, 1815, showing full lines often employed in this class.

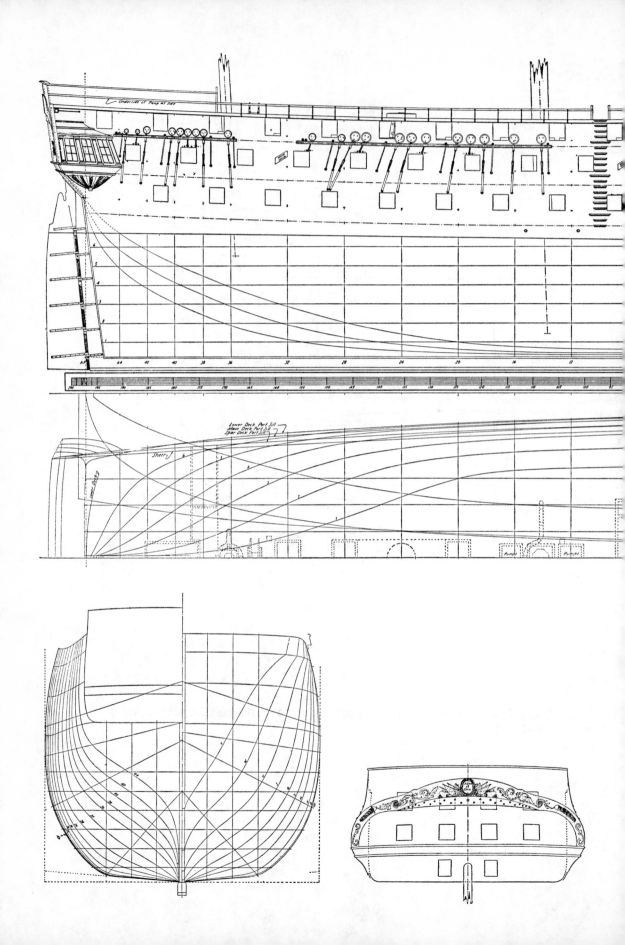

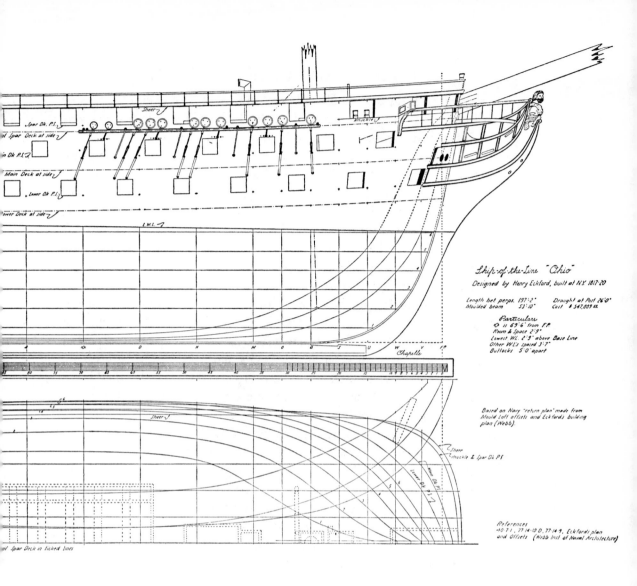

Ship-of-the-Line "Ohio"
Designed by Henry Eckford, built at N.Y. 1817-20

Length bet. perps. 197'·2"   Draught at Post 26'·0"
Moulded beam   53'·10"   Cost $ 547,009 ℔

Particulars
O. 11 69'·6" from F.P.
Room & Space 2'·9"
Lowest W.L. 2'·9" above Base Line
Other W.L's spaced 3'·7"
Buttocks 5'·0" apart

Based on Navy "return plan" made from
Mould Loft offsets and Eckford's building
plan (Webb).

References
40·7·1 , 77·14·10·D , 77·14·9 , Eckford's plan
and offsets   (Webb Inst. of Naval Architecture)

Plan 20. Draught of 74-gun ship OHIO, as built.

on the lower deck, 53′ 10″ moulded beam, and about 208′ over-all length on the spar deck. A good deal of material on the design of this ship has survived; the original working plan by Eckford has been found among the plans of his apprentice, Isaac Webb, and a complete set of plans made after the ship was built, from offsets picked up off the mould-loft floor and measurements from the ship, have been found in the Navy plan files. From these plans it appears that the only important alterations made in building the ship were in raising her 6″ more than called for in the working draught; the frames were also differently spaced in lofting. None of these alterations were of any technical importance, and it is impossible that they would have caused disagreement between the designer and the Board.

Plan 20 shows the design of this fine ship, the *Ohio*, long considered one of the finest vessels of her rate in the world, if not the finest, and by far the best liner in the American Navy. Not only was she a handsome ship of her type, but she was a remarkably good sailer and a good seaboat, carried her guns high, and stowed her allowances with ease. It was often said that she handled like a frigate. During much of her active career she was employed as a flag vessel, and she was long one of the favorite commands in the Navy.

The armament of the *Ohio* varied from time to time. When she was first built, the liner was armed in what was then considered an effective way: all guns and carronades were of the same caliber, 32-pdrs., but the long guns on the lower deck were somewhat heavier than those on the main. Later, the lower deck was armed with long 42's, the carronades also being 42-pdrs. The total number of guns seems to have varied with each commander—ranging from 86 to 102— yet the ship was always classed as a 74. The *Ohio* was not sold out of the service until 1883, after running for at least forty years of active service— showing how well Eckford built her.

Doughty's design for a 74, laid down in 1817, was the *Delaware*, built at the Norfolk Navy Yard. Soon afterward the other ships ordered built on this design were laid down: the *North Carolina* at the Philadelphia Navy Yard, the *Alabama* at Portsmouth Navy Yard, the *Vermont* and the *Virginia* at the Boston Yard, and the *New York* at the same yard as the *Delaware*. The duplication of ships at Boston and Norfolk represented less of a work load than is suggested by a mere listing of the ships, for only the *Delaware*, *North Carolina*, and *Vermont* were completed as ships of the line. By the end of 1818 all six of the new 74's were on the stocks officially, though actually work was going on in only three or four ships.

Doughty's design for the six 74's is shown in Plan 21, which represents *North Carolina* and *Delaware* as built. These two ships were launched in the fall of 1820, and the third ship, the *Vermont*, did not get overboard until 1848. As originally designed, the ships were to have the curved upper headrails popular at the beginning of the War of 1812, but the straight rails, introduced into the Royal Navy much earlier as a matter of wartime economy, were ordered for all the new ships in 1820. Great care was taken to insure that all the new liners were built to their lines, without the slightest departure. However, the effect of the old custom of changing designs could not be overcome in a few years, and so there were slight variations in the appearance of the *Delaware* and *North Carolina*, particularly in the head and in the position of the foremost ports, which were not brought to uniformity until some five to ten years after their launch. The Doughty design was for ships 196′ 3″ between perpendiculars, and 53′ 0″ moulded beam—slightly smaller than the *Ohio*, as may be seen by a comparison of the two designs. The *Ohio* was a larger ship than even the dimensions indicated, however, as she was quite a lot deeper than the Doughty-designed 74's and carried her guns a good deal higher as a result.

The designs of the *Ohio* and the sisters *Delaware* and *North Carolina* were to be improvements over the four earlier liners, *Franklin*, *Columbus*, *Washington*, and *Independence*. The failure of the older ships was in that they were unable to carry their lower deck guns high enough above the water, in service condition, compared to ships of similar rates abroad. Of the older ships, the *Columbus* was the best, next the *Franklin*, then the *Washington*, and last the *Independence*. The last, in fact, was utterly useless as a liner, since she could show but 3′ 10″ of freeboard between the water line and the sill of her lower-deck gun ports amidships, when loaded with war complement and six months' provisions. Even the best of the lot, the *Columbus*, could show only as much as the smaller British 74's, in spite of being a larger and much more powerful ship.

The *Ohio* fully met expectations, but the two Doughty liners were only slight improvements on the *Columbus*. However, the new ships were faster and stronger in construction, so the design was not altered. The *Independence* was now the cause of some recrimination, and a number of surveys were held on the ship in 1816–17. In April of 1817 Doughty recommended that the ship be razeed into a two-decked frigate, or 60-gun ship, by removing her spar deck entirely. However, nothing was done about the proposal for another eighteen years.

As Doughty once pointed out, the unusually heavy armament of the American liners made comparisons with foreign ships of the same nominal rating highly misleading. It was to be accepted that the American ships could either show less freeboard than foreign liners, with the official complement of guns aboard, or could show more by reducing their armament—which even then would leave the American ships superior in force to their European classmates. Actually, the new 74's of 1817–18 were as powerful, in weight of broadside, as many British liners rating 120 guns when the latter were carrying 126 guns and the American liners 102. In justice, it must be said that the new American ships should have been rated as at least 84's, and even then were unusually large for their class when built, and for ten or fifteen years afterward, in fact.

In considering the qualities of the American liners, the policy of arming them should be noted. The War of 1812 had confirmed, it was thought, the early proposition of giving all ships the heaviest armament possible in a given rate. Single-ship actions in the war had shown pretty clearly the advantages of ships so built and armed, and it was decided that all American naval vessels should be superior in size and armament to their European counterparts; hence any American ship not capable of greatly exceeding her rate in gun power was deemed a failure. In the case of the earlier 74's it had been felt that a reduced armament, even though still superior in weight of fire to any European 74, or even 84, was not desirable, because the American ships were of such large dimensions in comparison to the European ships. Though the *Columbus* and *Franklin* had met the requirements within reason, they were not considered good enough to be repeated; hence the decision to have new designs.

The three American liners laid down in 1817 were all considered quite fast sailers, particularly the *Ohio*. As far as the sailing-vessel commander was concerned, 12 knots was 12 knots and there was no particular regard for any relation of length, or size, to speed. Obviously, if a frigate of 165' length could run up to 12 knots under certain conditions and a liner of 190' could go 12½, the latter was fast enough to catch the frigate and so was a good ship, even though the latter's speed in relation to her length was much inferior to the frigate's. Practically, then, there was no real need to become involved in fine-spun argument concerning the efficient design of liners, so far as speed was concerned. Rather, the problem in the design of the liner was to meet the need for carrying the huge weights of armament, stores, and crew, in a strong seaworthy vessel capable of withstanding abuse in combat, rather than in getting the last fraction of a knot out of the model. The liner had to be as manageable as possible, of course, and if she could reach 12 knots or better in strong winds and the accompanying sea conditions, she would meet all practical requirements. Naval designers were perfectly aware that a large ship, of great length and displacement and rigged in proportion, could outsail a smaller ship, of less length and displacement and suitably rigged, under some conditions of wind and sea, while under other conditions the smaller ship might have the advantage in sailing because of her sharper model. Size, particularly length, has always been a factor in actual speed under sail, large vessels having the advantage over smaller vessels under most conditions. By overlooking this, many have become convinced that only the large clipper ships were correctly modeled for high speed, since they often held records for the longer runs under sail. Actually, their greater length would be more of a factor than their model in runs in very strong winds. Furthermore, such is the state of the "science" of sailing-vessel design that throughout the period of the sharp-lined clippers many full-ended vessels competed successfully for the crown of speed. In long runs, where there was likelihood of strong winds over a great period of time, the large ships with full ends usually made better time than smaller ships of sharper models.

The liner, then, really held about the same relation to sharper models of sailing men-of-war that the battleships or large cruisers hold to the fast, small fighting ships of today, so far as speed is concerned. Just as the modern heavy cruiser could overtake a destroyer (of far greater potential speed) in rough water, yet fail to catch her in smooth seas, so the sailing ship of the line might have the advantage in sailing in strong winds over frigate, ship sloop, brig, or schooner, but be inferior to any of them in light or moderate weather, and still be considered an excellent vessel of her class. The competition in design, in liners, was not with the sharp, smaller vessels used in naval warfare, but in the narrower field of her own class. Here again length and size counted, for only by increasing length could the necessary displacement be retained when the ends of the ship were made sharper for speed. Hence, the development of the hull lines of liners was rather slow, and mere possession of sharp lines did not guarantee a successful ship of the line in any respect. There were always limitations on length, for too much length might make the ship unhandy in action, or make her too weak to carry her guns. It took a long time to reach the structural knowledge necessary to build very long wooden ships successfully. The capture of fast frigates, ship sloops, brigs, schooners, and cutters by ships of the line, in the naval wars in the period of sail, is of course the practical answer to any discussion of their relative excellence of design.

There were no sailing vessels that were extremely fast under all the conditions that might be met at sea. It is interesting to note that it was improved armament that finally doomed the ship of the line, rather than her model of hull, for the day of the liner reached into the steamship period.

There is some reason to suspect that Eckford not only employed his own ideas in the design of the *Ohio;* he may also have been acquainted with Doughty's design for the *Delaware* and *North Carolina,* for the latter design seems to have been in existence when Eckford started to design the *Ohio.* It is also probable that Eckford's experience on Lake Ontario had convinced him of the importance of large dimensions for a given rate. The plan of the *Delaware* was among the drawings of Eckford's apprentice, Isaac Webb, and it is possible, at least, that this was a drawing that had been in Eckford's hands. However, the *Ohio* was no mere improvement in lines over the Doughty design; she was a complete departure.

The new liners introduced the practice in the American Navy of naming first-class combat ships after states. A new system of naming naval ships was developing, but it was long before a standard practice evolved for the whole Navy register. In 1817–18 it was intended that liners be named for states, frigates for rivers, and ship sloops for cities or towns. No system for naming small craft seems to have been considered; there was no reason for doing so, of course, since nothing smaller than ship sloops was under consideration at the time.

At the end of the War of 1812, the arming of naval ships with guns of a single weight of shot was popular, since the use of one size of ball simplified supplying the ships, with no danger of part of the ships' batteries being made useless for want of shot. In compliance with the American policy of employing the heaviest broadside fire possible, American ships armed in this manner usually carried 32-pdrs. Liners had long guns on the lower deck, medium guns on the gun deck, and carronades on the spar deck. Frigates carried 32-pdrs. in the same manner unless they were too small; in that case 24's were used. Sloops, it was thought, ought to be able to carry 24-pdrs. when large, and 18's when small. The 42-pdr. was a very large gun, and the drawback to the system was that ships could not carry a full battery of such guns; as a result some liners were shortly rearmed with 42's on their lower deck and also 42-pdr. carronades on the spar deck, retaining medium 32-pdrs. on the gun deck. This of course caused them to revert to the old system of a mixed armament. With the strong desire for guns of great range and power, the uniform armament system was gradually discarded to permit the use of at least a few very heavy guns.

The long, medium, and carronade styles were practically standard in American gun manufacture for naval use. A few short guns were made for special purposes, particularly in sizes under 24-pdrs., but such guns were not used in vessels above a brig. The weight of ball ranged from 6, through 12, 18, 24, 32, and 42 pounds. All naval guns were iron; a few of the smaller guns and carronades, 6- and 12-pdrs., were brass and were used as boat guns or for the revenue cutters.

One shell gun was used to a limited degree in the latter part of the War of 1812—the "columbiad." Little is known about the gun except that it was a short, rather light gun designed as an alternate to the carronade and usually designated as an 18-pdr. It is probable that this gun, like the 8″ shell gun that followed it, was a rebored cannon. It was mounted on slides in gunboats and on broadside carriages on ships. The columbiad was apparently a poorly designed gun that had been developed as a result of reports of guns firing "bombshells" being used in Europe.

The war had also produced an improved mount for pivot guns, which would allow this type of gun to be used in vessels having high bulwarks. The improved mount appears to have originated in privateers; it raised the gun and mount to any required height above the deck and made it unnecessary to employ a raised deck of any kind. With the new mount, the pivot bolt was placed on top of an upright wooden post, or column, and the skids were built so that the bolt was at their after ends. At the forward end there were trucks, mounted on brackets, that permitted the skids to be level with the pivot. The gun was mounted on the usual carriage employed in the earlier pivot guns. The height of the pivot post and of the truck brackets was decided by the height required to permit the gun to fire over the bulwarks. This mount was not particularly strong, and for some years it was confined to the use of pivoted carronades. Later it was considered practical to mount long guns up to 18-pdrs., at least, in this manner. This type of pivot mount became popular in all armed schooners, even merchant vessels, and particularly in slavers. The pivot at the after end of the slide, or skids, was advantageous in such craft, as it brought the gun muzzle well outboard in broadside fire, where the gun blast was not likely to cause damage, even when carronades were used. With the latter, slightly higher mounts were required to avoid damaging the bulwarks by the blast. The pivot was now commonly placed about amidships; this limited its fore-and-aft arcs of fire, but this was not considered to outweigh the many advantages of the mount.

The 44-gun frigates were also designed in 1817. The original plans were very similar to the *Guerriere* and *Java* design of 1813, the lines being practically the same, except that the new design was given 6″ more beam and had a fully armed spar deck. The sheer was unbroken, and the spar-deck bulwark had gun ports in the waist. The new design was a double-banked frigate and, in this respect, a return to the earlier 44's of 1794–96. Originally the design showed the square stern seen in *Guerriere* and *Java*, and the frigates were to have the upper headrails curved upward at the after ends. The design also showed about the same amount of sheer as the 1813 frigates.

Doughty completed his plans in 1817, but the lack of funds and the commitment already made for building the new 74's prevented any frigates being laid down immediately. However, contracts were made for the cutting of frame timber for two frigates at the same time that the timbers for the 74's were ordered. Eckford had a contract, dated January 10, 1817, for getting out the frames of two 74's and one frigate. Doughty's son also had a timber contract, but whether for the two remaining ships or for only one is not shown in the correspondence.

At the end of the War of 1812, the Americans not only had to settle with the Barbary regencies but also had to attend to piracy in the West Indies. The long Napoleonic Wars and the American war had allowed this area to go unpoliced, except by the war craft of the contending powers. Each of these powers had encouraged privateering, which had gradually descended to outright piracy. The power of Spain in America was declining, and her venial governors were benefiting by closing their eyes to the use of their harbors and coasts by freebooters of all descriptions. Small piratical settlements in Cuba and in many other Spanish colonies were formed, peopled with the riffraff not only of the Caribbean, but also of Europe. Whites, Negroes, mulattoes, and even Indians manned the piratical vessels from these settlements. In these rendezvous all kinds of craft were fitted out for preying on unprotected merchantmen—rowboats, barges, sloops, schooners, and larger vessels when possible. Many of the schooners were vessels captured by the pirates, but a great many were purchased craft. The greater part of the schooners used by the West Indian pirates were American-built of the pilot-boat model; many were on the shoal-draft Norfolk design. The small size and light draft of the freebooters' craft enabled them to hide, and to retire when chased, in shoal water out of reach of larger deep-draft naval brigs, sloops, and frigates.

While many of the schooners and brigs bought for the raiding squadrons in the War of 1812 were still available, it was felt that the size of these made them rather expensive to operate; furthermore, some of them were in a doubtful state of repair, owing to the haste with which they had been constructed. In lieu of assigning one of these vessels to the West Indian squadron, a new small schooner was bought at Baltimore in 1817, the 130-ton *Fox*, armed with four guns. However, the government did very little, beyond eradicating some of the pirate settlements on the Gulf Coast, until 1820.

During the War of 1812, the need for service craft in some of the navy yards became very apparent. The only way the demand could be met was by the purchase of some local small craft, though this procedure had already been found to be not wholly satisfactory. Service boats were particularly required at the Boston and Norfolk yards, which were engaged in maintenance of naval vessels to a far greater extent than the others. In both ports there were extensive anchorages used by naval shipping. With the coming of peace, the construction of well-designed service craft for these yards began, Boston receiving most of the attention. In 1816 Josiah Barker was ordered to design and build a navy yard lighter, and he produced a schooner 62′ 9⅜″ between perpendiculars, 18′ 0″ moulded beam, only 4′ 6″ depth of hold, and drawing about 6′ loaded. Her design is shown in Figure 75. Her model is that of a new England river schooner of the period, which was suitable for a yard lighter that did not have to go to sea.

Doughty was busy with his frigate design, but was also ordered to design an anchor hoy for Boston. The anchor hoy was a boat used to lay down and pick up moorings, and to recover anchors lost when moorings parted. These hoys also were commonly fitted with tanks and supplied water to naval shipping. They were harbor craft and were a standard naval type, used by nearly all the European sailing navies. One had been built at Norfolk in 1804, probably designed by Fox, but no others had been constructed since. Doughty's design, Figure 76, was a sloop-rigged double-ender 40′ long and 17′ 8″ moulded beam. She was capable of sailing either end foremost, so that she was handy in restricted waters and among shipping. The plan was forwarded to Boston October 21, 1818, and the boat was immediately laid down.

The building of these service craft marked the beginning of a slow improvement of the navy yards. Until the end of the War of 1812 the yards had been poorly equipped; now the new building program made it necessary to correct this condition. The probable length of time some of the new ships might be on the ways made it necessary that they have cover, so huge ship houses were built in many of the yards. These were wooden buildings with high arched roofs, covering the entire building slip. The yards were also furnished with mould lofts, offices, masting sheers, and other necessary construction. New heaving-down piers were also built, but no dry dock was constructed in any navy yard until about 1830, though private marine railways

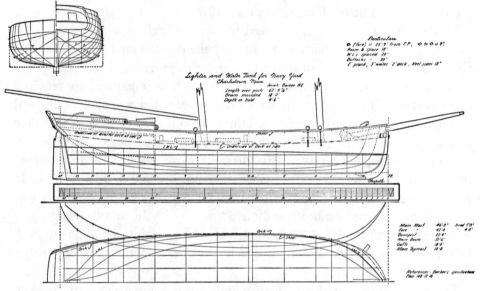

Figure 75. Lighter and water tank schooner.

came into existence in some American ports as early as 1825. The yards were now fenced in, and their waterfronts were improved, so that additional space could be obtained.

The war had taught the importance of the squadron in sea warfare and the accompanying need of suitable maintenance facilities and supply vessels. With the construction of new ships that would make it possible to create squadrons, the facilities and service craft were now being made available. The Board, composed of veterans of the late war, were ready to apply the lessons they had learned and were establishing the foundation for a powerful navy. For the first time in American naval history an effective organization, administrative and service, was coming into existence.

After the War of 1812, no new construction was considered on the lakes, as it was felt that the need was not sufficiently great to warrant the expenditures. The British, however, were disturbed by some American activities and political talk, so they reinforced their lake establishment in 1816–17. On Champlain they built a 32-gun frigate, the *Champlain*, and completed some of the unfin-

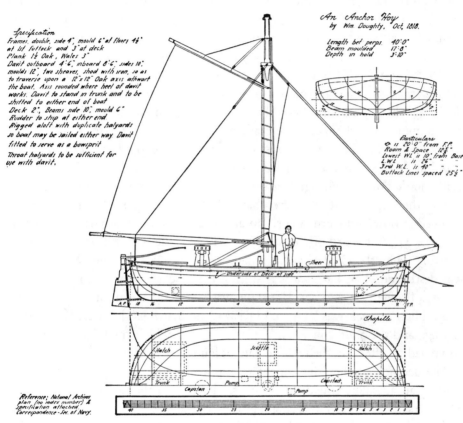

Figure 76. Anchor hoy, 1818.

ished small vessels on Lake Ontario, but the big liners were never completed. Some new names appear on the British naval lists for Lake Ontario in these years, but it is probable that these were the wartime vessels renamed, rather than new ships. It is apparent that most of the British lake ships were never in commission, but were laid up as soon as completed. When relations deteriorated on the Canadian border, as happened from time to time, the ships were given overhauls and repaired, but matters of controversy never reached a stage where the manning of the lake squadrons was required. This would have been a breach of agreement that would have been considered a hostile act and would therefore have been done only as a last resort.

In 1819 the only important change in the construction program was the laying down of the first of the new 44's, the *Potomac*, in the Washington Navy Yard under Doughty's supervision. No new vessel was purchased, and the only changes in the Navy Register were the striking off of some of the condemned small vessels taken into service during the late war. The next year, however, was one of great activity: the 74 *North Carolina* was launched at the Philadelphia Yard, and three more 44's were started—the *Raritan* at Philadelphia, the *Santee* at Portsmouth, and the *Savannah* at New York. The design of the 44's had apparently been the subject of much consideration, for in this year a number of changes were made and applied to all the ships under construction. During the year progress was being made on the *Potomac* and *Savannah*, but these ships were delayed a good deal by the alterations. During the year the design was changed in the following respects: the stern was made round, the upper headrails were changed to straight rails, and the sheer was reduced at bow and stern. Work on all the ships did not progress rapidly; in fact, the 74 *New York* proceeded so slowly that she was still on the stocks at Norfolk when the Civil War began and was burned when the Norfolk Yard was destroyed. The *Virginia* was still on the stocks at Boston in 1874, when she was broken up, and the *Vermont* was not launched until September 15, 1845. The *Potomac* was launched in 1822, the *Savannah* in 1842, the *Raritan* in 1843, and the *Santee* in 1855. The sequence in which the frigates were laid down had no effect on the relative date of launch, as will be seen.

The decision of the government to suppress piracy in the West Indies by sending an adequate squadron to this station led to the construction of new schooners in 1820–21. The disposal of the brigs and schooners intended for the raiding squadrons during the late war had now left the Navy without suitable small craft, except the recently purchased *Fox* and one of the clipper brigs that had not been sold, the *Spark*. It was decided to build five small schooners suitable for the service, of a size that would be adequate, yet not so large as to be expensive to maintain or man. The Navy Board decided to have one designed by Eckford and the others by Doughty. The latter prepared a design of a Baltimore Clipper, 86′ 0″ between perpendiculars, 24′ 9″ moulded beam, and 10′ 3″ depth of hold. His design is shown in Figure 77. From these lines the *Alligator* was built at Boston Navy Yard, the *Dolphin* at the Philadelphia Yard, the

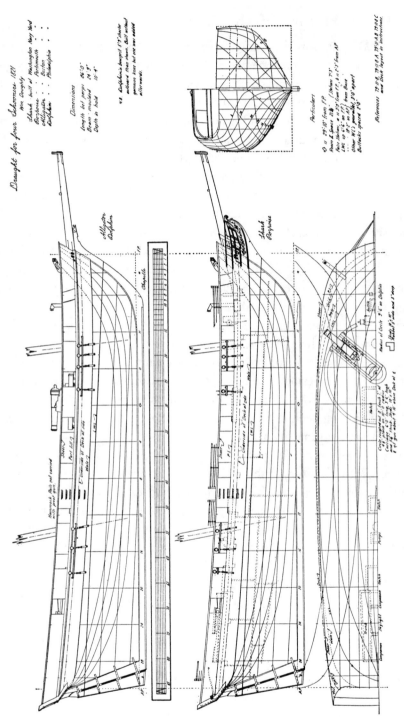

Figure 77. Schooners ALLIGATOR, SHARK, DOLPHIN, *and* PORPOISE, *1821.*

325

Shark at the Washington Yard, and the *Porpoise* at the Portsmouth Yard. There was some difference in the appearance of the four schooners when they were completed, as the manner in which the vessels were to be finished was left to the yards building them. The *Porpoise* and *Shark* were given the regulation head of a man-of-war—billet and headrails. The *Alligator* was given a simple gammon knee with an alligator's head carved on it. The stem of the *Dolphin* is not described and may have been a mere curved cutwater, but it is very possible that she came out with a gammon knee also, as this was a common finish in schooners in this period. There were also differences in mouldings and in the position of channels and deadeyes; the *Dolphin* had her channels below the port sill, the *Alligator* had hers just below the rail cap, and *Shark* and *Porpoise* had theirs about halfway up the gun ports. The *Alligator* and *Dolphin* had mouldings the length of the hull just below the port sills, but this was omitted in the other schooners. The correspondence indicates that the schooner program was in part rather hastily set up, with little time to prepare all the necessary copies of plans and specifications, which may explain the variation in the appearance of these vessels. A great deal of information on the details of these schooners has survived, and the plans were unusually complete for small men-of-war in this period, where lines and possibly a sail plan are usually the most that can be found. In this case the plans included not only lines, but also inboard arrangement, detail of gun mounting, spar plan, and a completely detailed sail and rigging drawing.

In view of the important part the topsail clipper schooner has played in American maritime history, the details of her rig are worth description. The sail plan (Figure 78) shows the sails and rigging in unusual detail and indicates the method used to set the square sails. The fore-and-aft portion of the rig is readily understood and is the standard schooner sail plan of the period. The mainsail, it will be seen, is fitted with what might be termed a "studding sail" boomed out with a boom fitted to the main boom and set to a head yard supported by the gaff, which is longer than the head of the mainsail for this purpose. This is a light-weather sail known as a "ringtail." The mainsail is not laced to its boom but is "loose-footed" and has four lines of reef-points—three parallel to the foot and another diagonally across the upper portion of the sail, the "balance reef." When this last reef was made, the mainsail became in effect a stormsail, or "trysail." The gaff topsail is very lofty, and its head is extended above the topmast by a gunter pole laced to the sail. The gunter pole extends about an equal amount above and below the topmast head. The

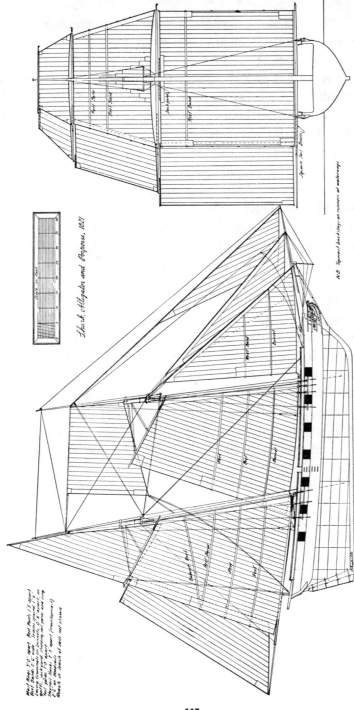

Brit. Alligator and Porpoise, 1821

Figure 78. Sail plan of 1821 schooners showing arrangement of square sails employed in topsail man-of-war schooners.

foresail has no boom and overlaps the mainsail; this is called a "lug foresail" and was the standard arrangement in American clipper schooners throughout the last quarter of the eighteenth century and the first half of the nineteenth. The foresail has what appear to be four reefs in it, but the lower is really a lacing, which allows the portion of the sail beneath it to be removed. This portion was known as the "bonnet." The purpose of this was to reduce the weight of the sail when it was reefed and, as it often would be in such a case, wet. The foresail was usually carried with one or more reefs in it in gales, when all other sail might be off the vessel. It was therefore desirable to make it as easy to handle as possible. Above the foresail is a main-topmast staysail—a sail very much like the modern schooner's "fisherman staysail," but somewhat smaller in proportion. The headsails are much like those of the more recent fishing schooners, except that the innermost sail, the fore staysail, has no boom and is fitted with a bonnet as well as reef points.

The square sails were all on the foremast and consisted of a large forecourse, a fore topsail and a fore-topgallant sail—all with studding sails. Many modern yachts have been fitted with square sails approximately like those shown in this sail plan, but without the rigging details that made the clipper schooner's rig so practical. It had been found that furling the huge forecourse of a schooner on the foreyard not only made an ungainly bundle of sail, but its weight, particularly when wet, hurt the vessel's stability, and its windage effectively destroyed a schooner's ability in sailing to windward. Also, experience had shown that the yards, if left aloft in strong gales, made the vessel unstable and often unmanageable. The problem was therefore, first, to avoid furling the course on the foreyard and, secondly, to rig all yards so that they could be quickly brought to deck. Safety, in the early days, also required that a schooner be able to make sail rapidly and that she carry a lot of it to obtain the greatest speed the weather conditions permitted.

In order to meet the problems raised, the topsail and topgallant yards were fitted with halyards and held to the topmast with running parrels. By lowering the yards and removing the parrels, halyards, and, of course, the lifts and braces, the spars could be stowed on deck. The foreyard was commonly rigged in the same manner, though some schooners had a heavy jackstay running up the fore side of the foremast, with an eye over the masthead and resting on the fore crosstree, thence to deck and set up with deadeyes and lanyards. A thimble was made fast to the yard to travel on this jackstay, which gave better control when the yard was being lowered in rough weather. As schooners grew larger, their spars became long and rather heavy, so it became the practice to stow the yards across the ship a short distance above the rail, without removing them from the mast entirely. In this position they were lashed to the fore shrouds and were usually high enough above the water to prevent their being dipped when the vessel rolled.

With the yards slung in the manner described, they could be braced up very sharply, since the parrel or truss could be slacked off so that the yards were actually a foot or more from the mast and resting against the lee shrouds. This made the squaresail rig more effective to windward than was the case in later years, when the yards were rigidly secured to the masts with ironwork. Of course, the flexible rig of the clipper schooners had the disadvantage of chafing considerably, and this required watching at sea.

The topsail and the topgallant were bent to their yards in the conventional manner and were furled on their respective yards; being relatively small, they could be neatly furled. The course was a different matter; its great hoist made it a huge sail having more area than even the mainsail. The course was hoisted to the yard by means of a halyard bent to the middle of its head and by outhauls to the yardarms. To make it stand, there was a jackyard laced to the head of the sail which made the sail stand neatly; the length of the jackyard was about half the head of the forecourse. By this means, the sail was lowered and furled on deck when desired, or it could be furled to the yard.

The foot of the forecourse was made as wide as the head, to make the sail as effective as possible. To make this stand properly, a "squaresail boom" was employed. This was a spar of the same length, approximately, as the foreyard, to which the foot of the course was secured by the sheets and fore tacks. The boom was rarely secured to the mast by a truss; it was commonly allowed to rest on the bulwarks, or rail, where it was lashed to convenient ringbolts or cleats. The squaresail boom made the forecourse stand better on all points of sailing and simplified the fitting of the studding-sail booms. A large studding sail was fitted to the course in the usual manner; its boom was on the squaresail boom.

Most of the sail area was on the foremast, and for this reason the mast was usually slightly larger in diameter than the main and had more shrouds. The mainstay was double and ran forward, set up by tackles in the waterways close to the rails at the bow, one stay passing on each side of the foremast. It was necessary to slack off the lee one when the foresail was in use. The clipper schooners did not use the modern springstay between the mastheads;

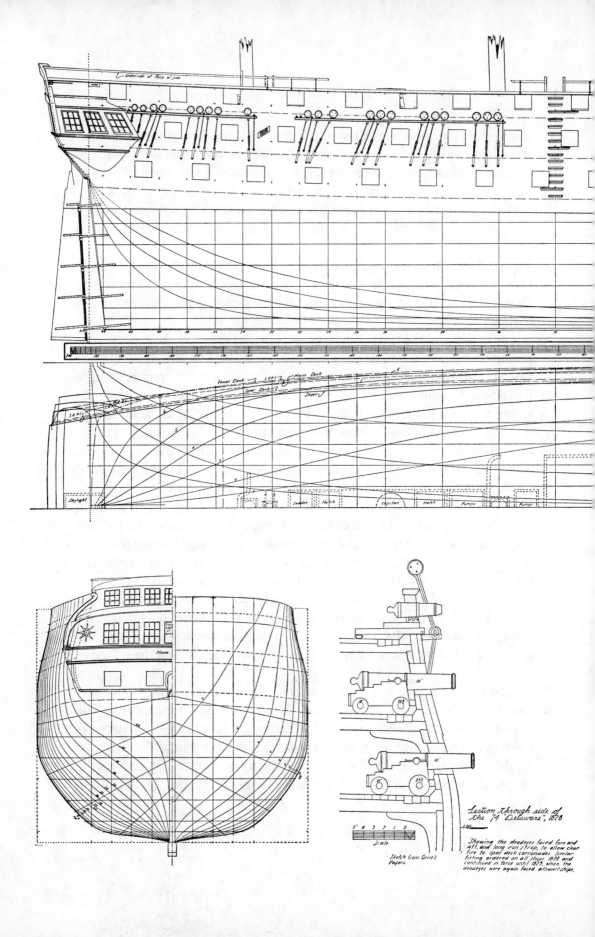

Underside of Poop at side

Lower Deck
Main Deck
Spar Deck
Sheer

Skylight

Skylight   Ladder   Hatch   Capstan   Hatch   Pumps   Pumps

Name

Scale

Sketch from Grice's
Papers.

Section through side of
the 74 "Delaware", 1828

Showing the deadeyes faced fore and
aft, and long iron strop, to allow clear
fire to spar deck carronades. Similar
fitting ordered on all ships 1822 and
continued in force until 1829, when the
deadeyes were again faced athwartships.

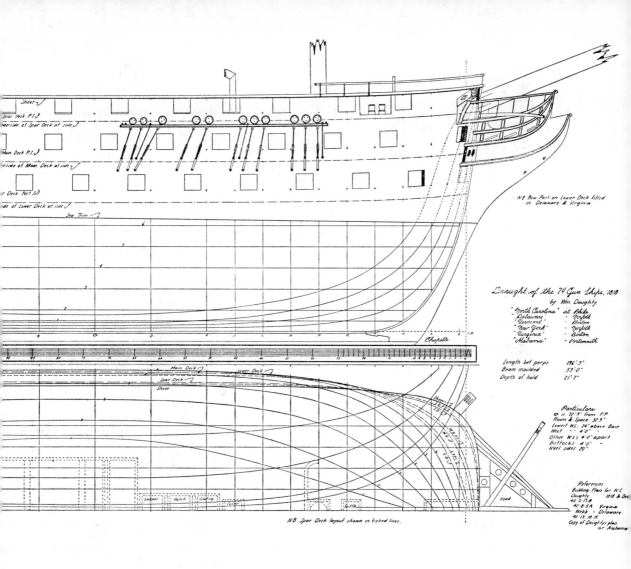

Sheer
Spar Deck P.S
Underside of Spar Deck at side
Main Deck P.S
Underside of Main Deck at side
Lower Deck Port Sill
Underside of Lower Deck at side

Sea Trim

N⁰ Bow Port on Lower Deck fitted
in Delaware & Virginia

Draught of the 74 Gun Ships, 1818.
by Wm. Doughty.

"North Carolina"   at Phila.
"Delaware"   Norfolk
"Vermont"   Boston
"New York"   Norfolk
"Virginia"   Boston
"Alabama"   Portsmouth

Length bet perps   196' 3"
Beam moulded   53' 0"
Depth of hold   21' 7"

Main Deck
Spar Deck
Sheer
Sheer
Lower Deck

Chapelle

Particulars
O. is 72·9" from F.P.
Room & Space 30.9"
Lowest WL. 24" above Base
Next   - 4' 0"
Other WL's 4' 0" apart
Buttocks 4' 0"
Keel sides   20"

Head

References
Building Plan for N.C.
Doughty   1818 & Dec
40·5·15·B
40·8·5·A   Virginia
Webb - Delaware
40·13·18·N
Copy of Doughty's plan
for Alabama

Ladder   Hatch   Grating

Scuttle

N⁰ Spar Deck layout shown in ticked lines.

Plan 21. Draught of class of 74-gun ships, 1818, NORTH CAROLINA *and* DELAWARE.

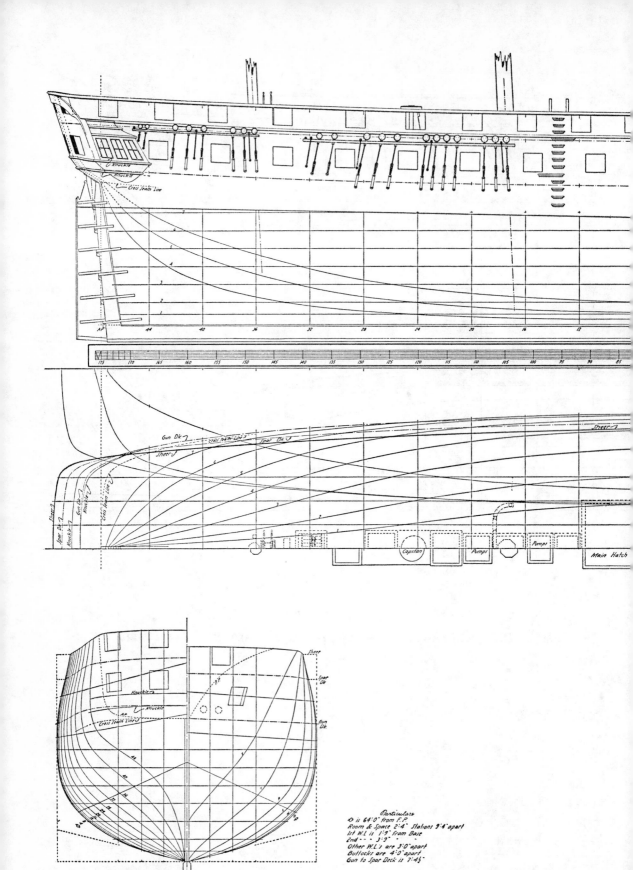

Capstan   Pumps   Pumps   Main Hatch

Particulars

O is 64:0" from F.P.
Room & Space 2:4" Stations 9:4" apart
1st W.L is 1:9" from Base
2nd - " 3:9"
Other W.L's are 4:0" apart
Buttocks are 4:0" apart
Gun to Spar Deck is 7:4½"

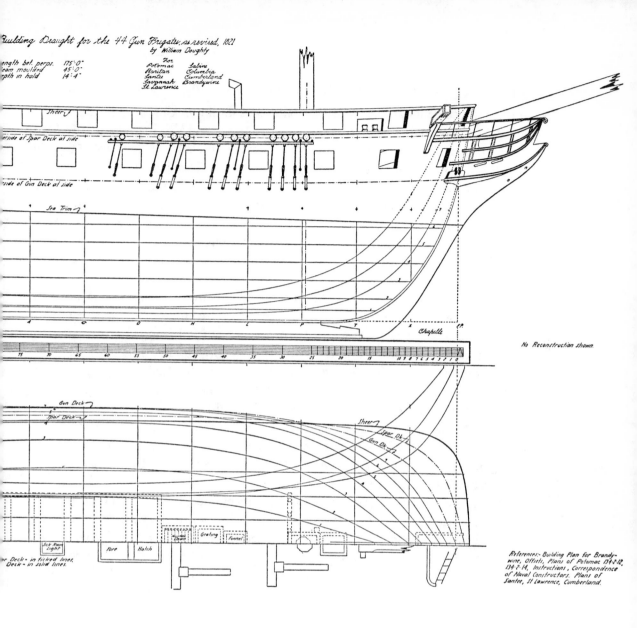

Building Draught for the 44 Gun Frigate, as revised, 1821
by William Doughty

Length bet. perps.   175'0"
Beam moulded   45'0"
Depth in hold   14'4"

For
Potomac   Sabine
Raritan   Columbia
Santee   Cumberland
Savannah   Brandywine
St. Lawrence

Sheer

Inside of Spar Deck at side

Inside of Gun Deck at side

Sea Trim

Chapelle

No Reconstruction shown.

75 70 65 60 55 50 45 40 35 30 25 20 15 10 9 8 7 6 5 4 3 2 1 0

Gun Deck
Spar Deck

Sheer
Spar Dk.
Gun Dk.

Sick Room
Light

Fore Hatch

Down Grating Funnel

Spar Deck - in ticked lines.
Gun Deck - in solid lines.

References:- Building Plan for Brandywine, Offsets, Plans of Potomac 134-7-12.
134-7-14. Instructions, Correspondence
of Naval Constructors. Plans of
Santee, St Lawrence, Cumberland.

Plan 22. Revised building draught for class of 44-gun frigates, 1821, BRANDYWINE, POTOMAC, *and class.*

this did not come into use in American schooners until sometime around 1840, and it first appeared in coasters.

The clipper-schooner rig, with the overlapping foresail and huge area of square sails, was a highly effective rig on all points of sailing. The seamen of the period believed, very properly, that power makes speed and so, when fast sailing was required, they depended on large areas of sail combined with sharp-model hulls. There can be no doubt that the clipper schooners were faster than even the best of the modern seagoing yachts over a long course, but the clipper rig required a big crew to handle it, which was the reason why this rig was eventually replaced.

The new schooners proved to be fast, but like many of Doughty's small vessels they were a little too full aft to be extraordinarily speedy. Their big rigs and full bows made them somewhat dangerous when driven hard, as they then depressed their bows and had a tendency to dive under. The *Dolphin* was the first laid down. She spent much of her career in the Pacific rather than on the station for which she had been built. She lasted until 1835, when she was found to be rotten and was broken up. The *Alligator* was wrecked on the Florida coast, near what is now Miami, in the fall of 1823. The *Shark* had a long and successful career; she was finally wrecked at the mouth of the Columbia River, on the northwest coast, in September, 1846. The *Porpoise* was wrecked in the West Indies in 1833.

The fifth schooner was designed, as has been mentioned, by Eckford. Late in 1819 the Board of Navy Commissioners had asked him to design a corvette and a "light-draft schooner." Eckford designed the corvette first, and it was not until early 1820 that he finally got to work on the schooner design, which was now the design most wanted. When the schooner design was submitted to the Board, the relatively great size of the intended vessel was the subject of some discussion, particularly in the light of the expressed desire of the Board that the vessel be inexpensive to maintain and fit out. However, Eckford appears to have taken his stand on the stated requirements for armament, combined with light draft, and the matter was finally settled by ordering the schooner built at the Washington Navy Yard. There is no evidence in the discussion over this design of any personal feelings on the part of the Board members or Eckford; it appears merely that the Board raised the question and Eckford made a polite reply.

In 1819 an English shipwright named Henry Steer applied for work in the Washington Navy Yard. Steer was born at, or near, Dartmouth, England, in

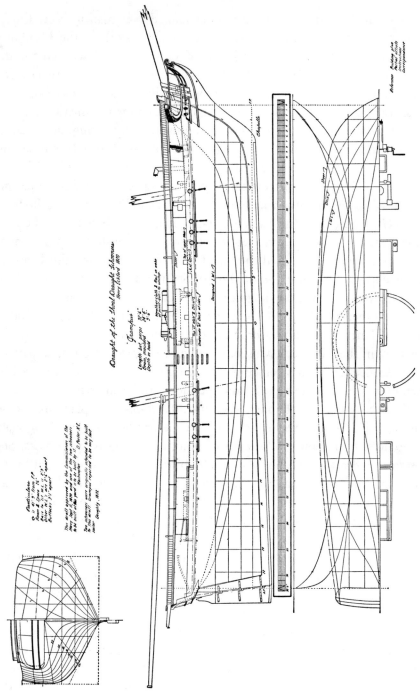

Figure 79. Schooner GRAMPUS, *1821, a noted sailer.*

1780. He learned his trade under a builder named Newman in New Quay, and after completing his apprenticeship he went to work in the Plymouth Dockyard. In 1815 he went to the island of Guernsey and worked for the French government. He was not only a shipbuilder, but also a competent drafts-man and designer. A fellow shipwright in the Plymouth Dockyard, John Thomas, also a competent builder and designer, had gone to America and was working in the Washington Yard. Thomas wrote Steer suggesting that he come to America and, a depression occurring in the trade in Great Britain at this time, Steer and his family—wife and two sons, James R. and Henry T.—ar-rived in New York and went from there to Washington. A third son, George, was born in Washington in 1820. Henry Steer was employed on the schooners *Shark* and *Grampus*, apparently acting as charge man, and remained in the yard until 1822. His sons Henry and George became distinguished ship designers. The younger, George, designed the yacht *America* and many pilot boats, as well as the clipper ship *Sunny South*. Henry Steers (an "s" having been added to the name by usage) was the designer of the famous Collins steamer *Adriatic* and of many other noted vessels. Doughty had been impressed with the drafts-manship of Henry Steer, and a drawing of a clipper schooner made by the latter is now in the Mariner's Museum, Newport News, Virginia, as part of the Steers Collection. It has sometimes been claimed that Steer designed the *Shark* and *Grampus*, but this can readily be shown to be an error.

The Eckford-designed schooner was named *Grampus;* her plans are shown in Figures 79 and 80. She was 92′ 6″ between perpendiculars, 97′ 0″ over all, 24′ 6″ moulded beam, and 9′ 6″ depth of hold, according to her offsets. She was designed to draw 11′ 0″, but was usually ballasted to draw between 11′ 6″ and 11′ 9″ in service. She had the characteristic headrails and cutwater of an Eckford design, and her long clean run was an improvement over Doughty's design for her classmates. The Board approved the design September 11, 1820, with the express direction that she be one of the two schooners built in the Washington Yard. Her spar and sail plans have also survived. The *Grampus* was launched in 1821 and proved to be a fast sailer. She was lost with all hands through capsizing in a gale while off Charleston, South Carolina, in 1843. She was considered one of the fastest schooners of her day.

So far as can be discovered, these five were the first seagoing naval schooners to be fitted with the high pivot gun. The Doughty design made no particular provision for the pivot; ports were placed amidships to permit the usual broad-side armament. They were to carry 10 6-pdr. short guns and a long 18 on the

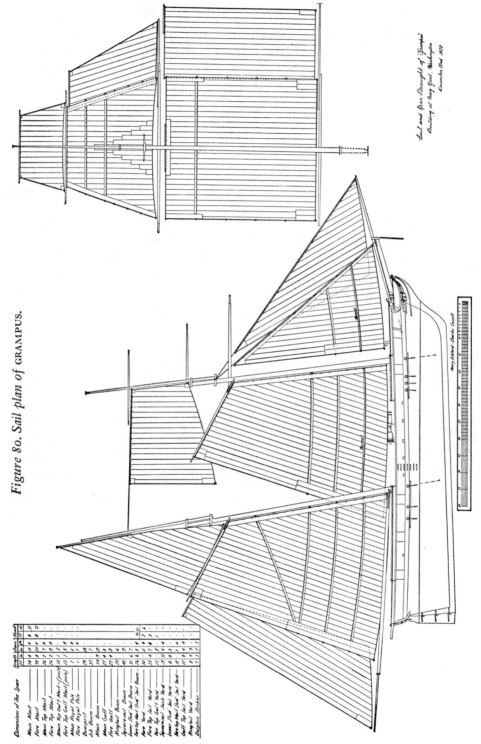

Figure 80. Sail plan of GRAMPUS.

333

pivot. Later the pivot was removed, and two long 18's on carriages were placed aboard. The 6-pdr. guns were soon replaced with 12-pdr. carronades. The *Grampus*, however, was not designed with ports amidships, and so was deliberately drawn for the use of the pivot gun. Her armament seems to have been changed a number of times while she was a new vessel; she had the long 18 pivot gun throughout her career, apparently, and carried 8 to 10 carronades, 12-pdrs.; at one time she had two or more 18-pdr. carronades in place of some of the 12's. The design of the *Grampus* might well have been developed out of the schooner designs that Eckford had produced on Lake Ontario, and it is possible that there were strong similarities.

The launch of the *Ohio* on May 31, 1820, marked the end of Eckford's service as a naval constructor, as he resigned on June 1. His resignation was accepted on the 6th, and he was asked to recommend his successor. He strongly recommended his ex-apprentice, Isaac Webb, who would not accept the appointment. Eckford then recommended his assistant, John Floyd, who was appointed resident naval constructor in the New York Yard. Floyd had been with Eckford for some years and, according to one account, had been with him on Lake Ontario and had helped build the vessels there. Floyd seems to have been a very capable man, but relatively little has yet been found on his career.

Samuel Hartt was appointed naval constructor a year before Eckford resigned, receiving an appointment June 1, 1819. Barker was afterward transferred to Portsmouth. Hartt was then placed at Boston, Floyd was stationed at New York, Humphreys at Philadelphia, Doughty at Washington, and Grice at Norfolk. Hartt belonged to the noted Boston family of shipbuilders, members of which had built the *Constitution, Boston,* and *Argus.* Samuel Humphreys recommended William Easby as a boatbuilder, and Easby was assigned to Washington, becoming master boatbuilder there. Doughty was now acting as chief constructor, for all practical purposes, though he did not have the title, as he was still the senior constructor.

Before resigning, Eckford had made the recommendation that the prize ship sloop *Cyane* be cut down into a flush-decked ship, but as funds were not available, no action was taken on his advice. Eckford now turned to private practice, designing and building merchant ships, as well as men-of-war for foreign governments. By this time the Americans had achieved widespread fame as ship designers and builders and were competing with British and French constructors on equal terms for foreign naval business. In the ten years that immediately followed his resignation from the New York Yard, Eckford built

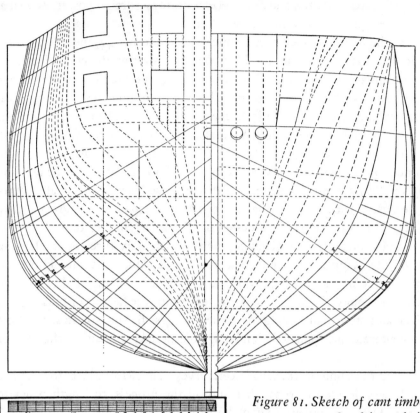

Figure 81. Sketch of cant timber arrangement in 1821 frigate design to show framing of round stern.

U. S. Frigate Brandywine
copied from Wm Doughty's original draught.

Principal dimensions.

	feet - in
Length between perpendiculars	175.
Keel for tonnage	145. 6
Beam moulded	45.
Depth of hold	14. 4
From upper side birth deck beam to upper side gun deck beam at middle line	6. 10
From upper side gun deck beam to upper side of Spar deck beam	7. 4½
Carpenters tons	1550. 69/95ths

Frames spaced 2′ 4″ apart.

335

two huge frigates, *Amazon* and *South America*, for a foreign power, as well as a few packets, merchant ships, and small craft.

In 1821 the new schooners were launched and another 44, the *Brandywine*, was laid down at the Washington Navy Yard. In starting the new frigate, the design was finally settled, and all the changes incorporated in the others then building were worked into the plans. The new ship, built without any great delays, was launched in 1825 and became a noted sailer and a favorite ship. She was burned at the Norfolk Navy Yard at the outbreak of the Civil War. All the alterations in the original design and in the ships building having been accounted for, the design finally used can be established. Plan 22 is the building plan of the *Brandywine* and of the 44's that followed her. The plan also represents, because of the changes made, the frigates that had been laid down in 1819 and 1820. This was the standard design of the American frigates of this class to the end of the usefulness of sailing men-of-war; only three of the frigates placed on the Navy List afterward were on independent designs. However, the appearance of the sister ships of the *Brandywine*, completed at a much later date, was quite different, since in the meantime the fashion of finishing the cutwater and stern had undergone some changes. In spite of this, the lines were not altered, the original design being considered excellent for this class of vessel.

The sloop *Erie*, built in 1813, had been surveyed in 1820 and was found to be rotten. It was decided to repair her and, in the process, to lengthen her to about 122'. Doughty prepared a new drawing for the ship, making her 121' 11" between perpendiculars, 32' 6" moulded beam, and 14' 9" depth in the hold. While it appears that some of the original ship was saved in the rebuilding, nevertheless the *Erie* was practically a new ship when again launched. The practice of "rebuilding" ships on a new design may be said to have begun with this incident; in this case the redesigning was partial, but it was an easy step to the use of a completely new design, producing an entirely different model and even class of ship in the guise of "rebuilding." The *Erie* as rebuilt is shown in Figure 82. The work was done at the New York Navy Yard, and she was launched late in 1821. She ran for twenty years, first as a cruiser and toward the last as a storeship. She was broken up at Boston in 1841. A storeship of the same name, but smaller, was built to replace her.

The year 1822 was one of activity in the West Indies, and the need of more small vessels on that station became apparent. Consequently eight schooners of about 42 to 65 tons were purchased at Baltimore, and all but one were

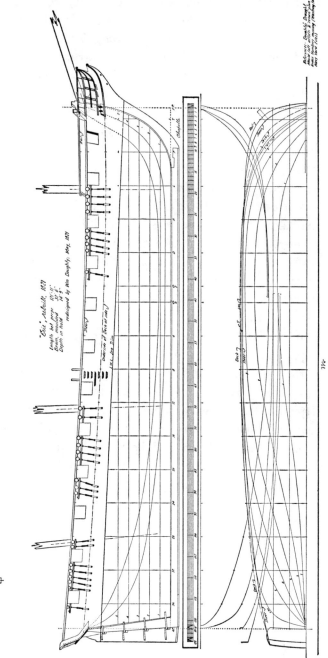

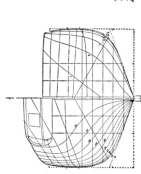

Figure 82. Draught of ERIE *as rebuilt, 1821.*

337

armed with 3 small guns. These schooners were the *Ferret, Beagle, Fox* (the older *Fox* was found too deep for the intended use and so had been sold late in 1821 or early in 1822), *Greyhound, Terrier, Weasel, Jackall,* all 3 guns, and the *Wildcat,* 2 guns. The *Ferret* was lost in the West Indies in 1825, and the others were sold—*Greyhound, Wildcat,* and *Jackall* in 1824, *Beagle, Terrier* and *Weasel* in 1825, and *Fox* in 1838. Little is known about these schooners, except that some of them were on the Norfolk pilot-boat model, while others were of the standard clipper type. The *Beagle* had bulwarks at least; some of the smaller schooners had none. A schooner, the *Revenge,* was also employed in the West Indies with these small vessels; the *Revenge* was formerly the Jeffersonian gunboat *No. 158.*

A storeship, the *Decoy,* was purchased this year at New York. She was a merchant schooner and was intended for the support of the West Indian squadron. The *Decoy* was armed with 6 small guns; she was sold at Norfolk in 1826. The *Sabine,* another 44, was ordered laid down this year at New York; however, work on the ship did not actually begin until February, 1823, and she was not launched until 1855. She was employed in the Civil War and was finally sold out in 1883.

In this year, 1822, the largest sailing man-of-war ever built for the United States Navy was laid down. This was the 120-gun *Pennsylvania,* designed to be the most powerful ship of her class in the world. The design of the ship was prepared by Samuel Humphreys, and the first draught of her lines was completed in 1822. She was intended to be a four-decked ship without a poop, and she showed ports to carry 132 guns exclusive of bow chasers and stern guns. In the early plans she had a small beakhead bulkhead, but as the design developed this was dropped and replaced with a round bow. The whole stern was also changed, and the hull design of this ship developed over a period of at least eight years, if not somewhat longer; she was not launched until 1837. For that reason she will be discussed later, when the design finally employed can be shown in proper sequence. The ship was to be 210′ 0″ between perpendiculars, 56′ 9″ moulded beam, and 24′ 3″ depth of hold; keel to sheer was about 54′ 0″. The ship as completed will be discussed in Chapter Seven. This huge man-of-war occupied the Philadelphia Navy Yard's force of ship carpenters to such an extent that little other work was done there while she was building. This was probably the reason for the delay in building the frigate *Raritan,* even though the Philadelphia Yard was heavily manned, and was then considered next to the Washington Yard in importance, the two yards being capable of handling the construction of a number of large ships.

The proposal to build such a ship as the *Pennsylvania* indicates how much the British blockade of the American coast had hurt; now it was fully realized that the Navy must have vessels of sufficient power to break a blockade, at some of the important ports, at least, in the event of war. This the huge *Pennsylvania*, accompanied by the smaller but very powerful liners built or building, would be able to accomplish. The combination would be so powerful that an enemy would not be able to maintain a blockade unless these liners were captured or destroyed—and no foreign navy had enough huge liners to set up a blockade that would be certain to overpower such a force. It might therefore be said, with some truth, that the *Pennsylvania* was not built to serve as an ocean cruiser, but was rather a coast-defense ship designed solely to overcome or drive off a blockader.

The design of this huge vessel seems to have been based on plans obtained from Europe. Samuel Humphreys had the plans of the big *Santisima Trinidad*, which had been in the Spanish fleet at Trafalgar, and of the British 100-gun ship *Royal Sovereign*, which had also been in that famous battle. The plans of these ships do not appear to have been copied in the design of the *Pennsylvania*, but they were used, apparently, as a guide in establishing the general proportions of the huge American vessel. It is probable that the existence of these plans in Humphreys' hands explains the appearance of a beakhead bulkhead in the original design of the *Pennsylvania*. This type of bow had gone out of fashion in the British Navy long before the American ship was laid down but was employed in the *Royal Sovereign* and in the even older *Santisima Trinidad*. Eckford was probably the only designer in America that could have dared the design of such a large ship as the *Pennsylvania* without the aid of foreign information, as he alone had ever designed a ship of such size—if the tradition that he designed the *New Orleans* on Lake Ontario is accepted. Eckford, however, was no longer available to the Navy Board.

The requirements of the West Indian station placed four small craft on the Navy List in 1822–23; these were the "barges" *Galinipper*, *Midge*, *Mosquito*, and *Sandfly*, commemorating the worst insect pests on the station. These "barges" appear to have been large open boats fitted to row and sail and may have been some of the old gunboat barges of the War of 1812 fitted up and renamed. They carried large crews and one or two guns, and were particularly useful in attacking pirate craft of similar characteristics among the islands and in shoal water. It is also possible that large ship's launches were utilized; the records are unfortunately insufficient to establish the type of hull and rig employed in these particular boats. They were not carried on the Navy Register after 1824.

For some years the design of a class of ship sloops had been a matter of study and discussion among the members of the Navy Board. Commodore Rodgers, who was President of the Board from 1815 to 1824, had been much interested in this class, and the War of 1812 had shown what the type could accomplish. In 1819, it will be recalled, the Board had requested Eckford to submit a plan of a corvette, and in compliance with this request Eckford prepared the design presented in Figure 83—a 22-gun ship 124' 0" between perpendiculars, 32' 0" moulded beam, and 15' depth of hold. The ship sloop *Madison*, which Eckford had built on Lake Ontario in 1812, had measured about 593 tons; the new design was $510^3\%_{95}$ tons. While the matter is one of pure speculation, it is at least probable that the new design Eckford had prepared followed very closely the design of the earlier ship, for, as we have seen, the Lake Ontario vessels employed much deadrise, judging by what is known about the British ships and by the statements of officers, and others, that certain American vessels were on the sharp model. It is notable that Eckford had become the leading exponent of sharp vessels, with respect to deadrise, sometime between his arrival at New York as a young ship carpenter and the end of the War of 1812. It might be suggested that he became converted to this form of hull through his experience with the lakes but, of course, there is no proof. The Board, having Eckford's design in hand, laid it aside for study.

By 1824, the need for ship sloops, particularly in the Pacific, where American interests in the Oregon Territory and on the South American West Coast needed protection, again occupied the attention of the Board. They now had additional designs prepared. Grice presented a proposal for a ship sloop 119' 0" between perpendiculars, 32' 6" moulded beam, and on a sharp model (Figure 84). Floyd also was ordered to prepare a plan, and his design (Figure 85) was the largest ship of all—136' 0" between perpendiculars, 42' 0" moulded beam, and 19' 0" depth of hold, to carry 24 guns. This design showed much Eckford influence, as was to be expected from a man trained under this ship designer. It is evident that Eckford, Grice, and Floyd were not in agreement as to the proper size or armament for the sloops, but in the main they were agreed in much deadrise and a rather high bilge.

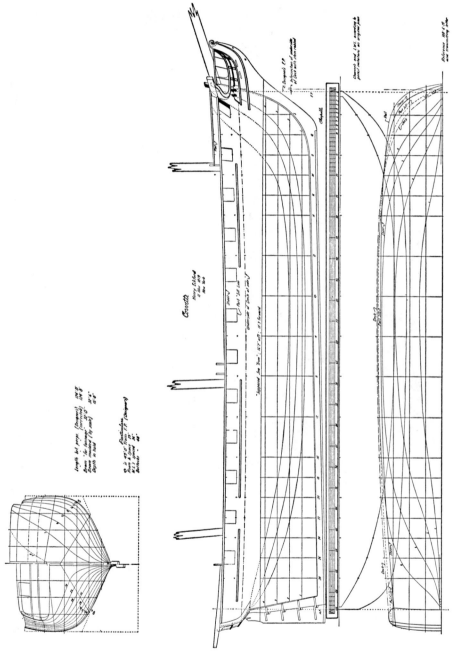

Figure 83. Draught of corvette proposed by Eckford.

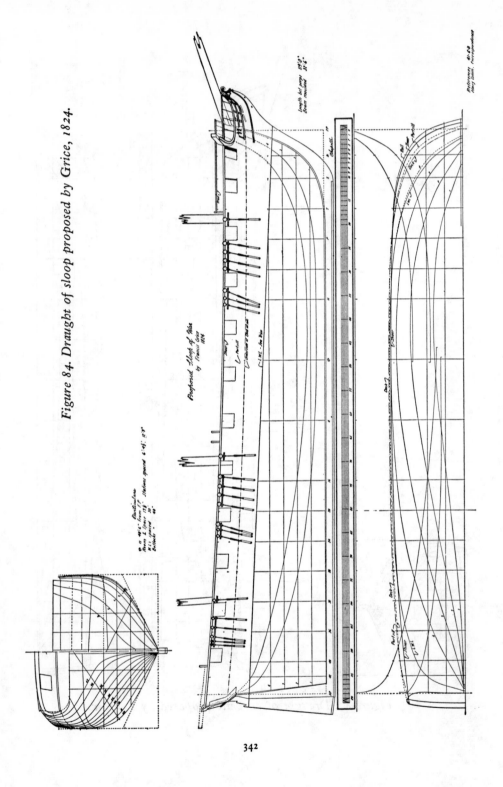

Figure 84. Draught of sloop proposed by Grice, 1824.

342

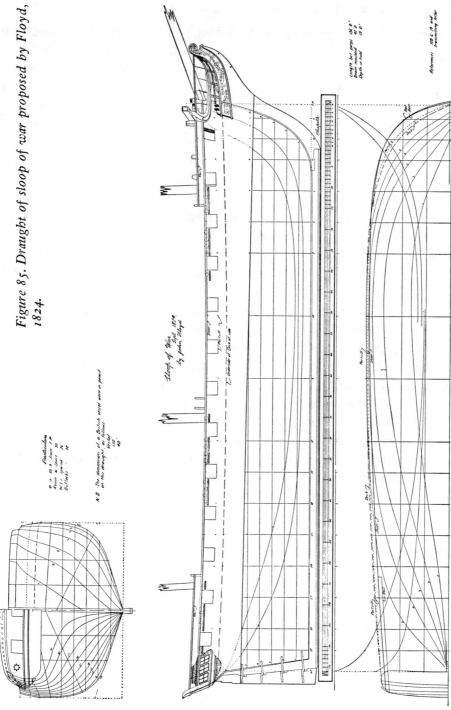

Figure 85. Draught of sloop of war proposed by Floyd, 1824.

343

Samuel Humphreys also prepared a design 126′ 6″ between perpendiculars, 33′ 9″ moulded beam, and 15′ 3″ depth of hold. This design appealed to the Board, and after a few modifications, including the substitution of a round stern for the transom stern first proposed, it was accepted. Figure 86 is the final building plan for the vessels constructed from Humphreys' design; as modified it called for 127′ 0″ between perpendiculars and 34′ 0″ moulded beam. The plan called for 24 gun ports exclusive of the bridle ports and quarter galleries added to the round stern. It was decided to build the ten sloops from this design, the first to be started at the Boston Navy Yard, to be named the *Boston*. It was eventually decided that the ten ships were to be built in the various navy yards, as follows: three at Boston, three at New York, and one each at Portsmouth, Washington, Philadelphia, and Norfolk.

When the preliminary design reached each of the yards, the resident constructors prepared copies, as was the custom. Doughty decided to alter the design, and his plan called for a sloop very like Humphreys' design in model but with 3″ less beam and very full-ended. Barker, who was still at Boston at this time, also made his copy, with variations, calling for a ship 127′ 6″ between perpendiculars but otherwise retaining the original dimensions. Barker's plan omitted the quarter galleries called for by the Board in their modification of Humphreys' original design. The upshot of this situation was that, instead of all the vessels being built to a uniform design, three vessels were built to Doughty's plan and at least one to Barker's, while the remaining sloops were apparently built to Humphreys' plan. This seems to have been done with the consent of the Board, for in Doughty's case at least the official correspondence shows that the Board approved three sloops being built to his plan. Figure 88 is Doughty's design, and Figure 89 Barker's. Thus, the Navy Board had failed to establish uniformity in the design of this class.

It may be said here that the new class of sloops did not add much to the reputation of the constructors involved, for only a few of them proved very fast. They were not particularly handsome ships, and this did not help the designers either. The real source of dissatisfaction with the new class of corvettes can be traced to the Board's insistence upon 24 guns being carried in vessels whose dimensions were better suited to a 20- or 22-gun ship. Eckford had proposed a 22-gun ship slightly smaller than the approved design; Floyd recommended a very large corvette to carry 24. Humphreys' vessel appears to have been a compromise, slightly larger than Eckford's proposal and carrying Floyd's proposal as to armament, 24 medium 24-pdrs. on a flush deck. It was

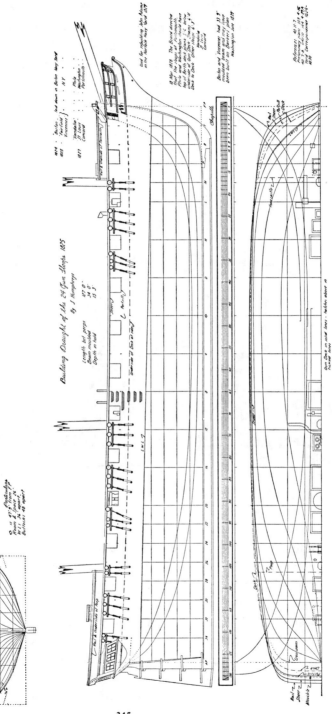

Figure 86. Draught used for building some of the 24-gun sloops, 1824–29, Humphreys' design.

345

eventually discovered that the new sloops would not carry their armament, and they were therefore reduced to 20 guns—2 medium 32's and 18 carronades, 32-pdrs.—and were rated as 18-gun ship sloops. Humphreys was well aware of the difficulty in using a relatively small ship to carry a very heavy armament, as is evidenced by the increase in displacement given his design over that proposed by Eckford. As a result the new corvettes were given rather barrel-

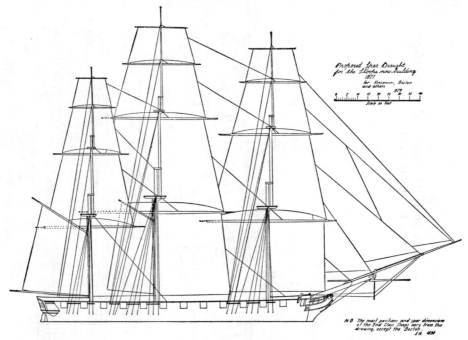

Figure 87. Proposed spar plan for 24-gun sloops, 1827.

shaped midsections and full ends. None of these features were helpful to speed under sail. One of the many lessons taught by the War of 1812 was that a corvette should be a fast sailer and ought to carry a battery of long guns, as these were far more effective in her work than carronades, particularly when acting as commerce destroyers, the employment for which sloops and corvettes were primarily designed. Hence the production of a new class of corvette which was not particularly fast and which had to have gun batteries replaced by carronades was bound to invite criticism both in the service and out of it. The class was not a complete failure, but it was not a complete success either, in spite of being larger and more heavily armed than the successful 1813 sloops.

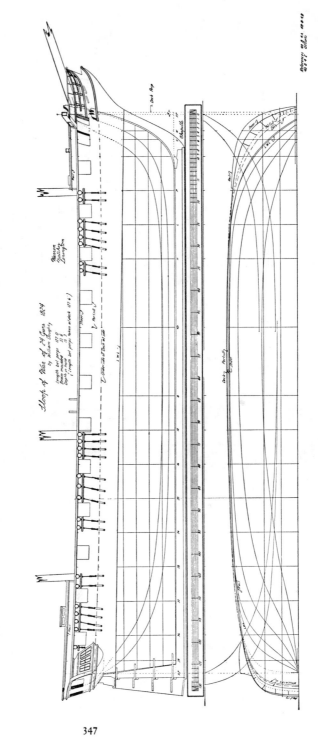

Figure 88. Doughty's draught for 24-gun sloops, 1824.

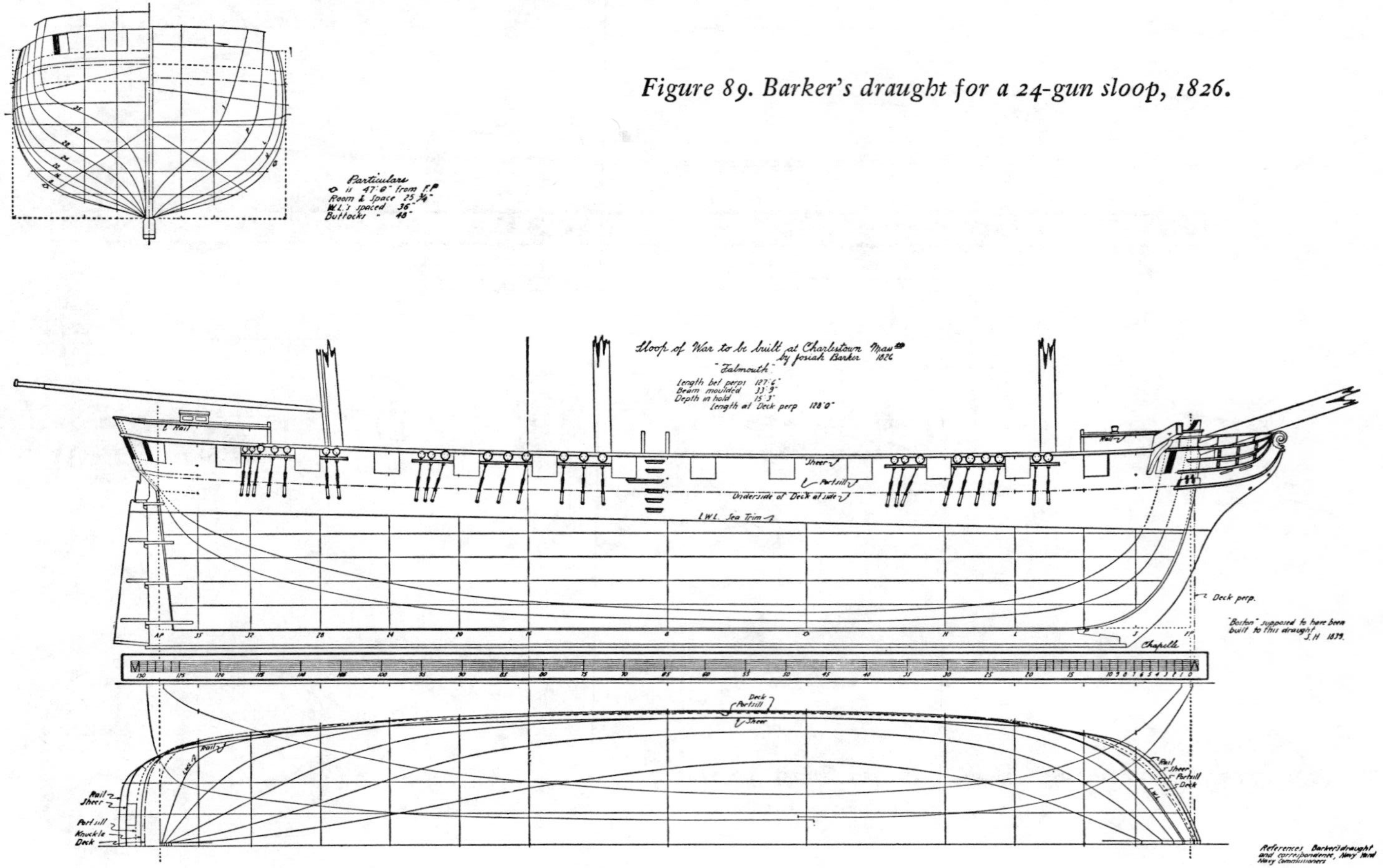

Figure 89. Barker's draught for a 24-gun sloop, 1826.

348

The membership of the Board had been changed a little during the first ten years of its existence. Rodgers was replaced as president by Bainbridge in 1824; Isaac Hull was a member only one year, 1818, David Porter from 1815 to 1822, Stephen Decatur from 1815 to 1820, and Isaac Chauncey from 1822 to 1824. Charles Morris replaced Porter in 1823, and Jacob Jones replaced Chauncey in 1824. Charles W. Goldsborough replaced Paulding as secretary in 1823. Goldsborough was former chief clerk in the Navy Department and a typical bureaucrat of the period. The control of naval shipbuilding and equipment was now firmly placed in the hands of a "service board" comprised of commissioned officers who were "users" or "practical seamen," supported and aided by the constructors, the "technical" advisers. In theory this should have been an ideal arrangement. However, the constructors were completely subordinate to the service board and were also insulated, to a great extent, from civilian developments in ship design and building, since they were no longer forced to compete with outsiders, and their ships were seldom placed in a position where odious comparisons could be made. Since both the Board and the constructors were now jointly responsible for the design of new ships, it can well be imagined how criticism could be suppressed in either the sea service or the navy yards. The long-standing difficulty of the supreme power in design of vessels resting in the hands of non-technical "users" rather than in men trained in shipbuilding and design became apparent. The weakness of the relationship of the constructors to the Board was in the lack of a continuous control of new ship construction, from design to commissioning, on the part of the constructors. The Board could, and did, change its mind after a design was approved and ships built; they might increase the armament, allowances of stores, crew, or the number of boats above the original requirements set forth when the designs were prepared. It will be seen that there was no real improvement in the position of the constructors over the condition that had existed before the Navy Board came into existence; the skilled constructor was still entirely subordinate in the field of his profession to the commissioned officers.

In 1825 the shipbuilding program took a spurt, for five additional 24-gun corvettes were laid down, and two more 44's. The sloops were the *Fairfield*, at New York, launched in 1828; the *Lexington* in the same navy yard, launched the same year she was laid down; the *Vandalia* at the Philadelphia Navy Yard, launched in 1828; the *Vincennes* at New York, launched in 1826; and the *Warren*, built at Boston and launched in 1826. Strangely enough, the *Lexington* and *Warren* are noted as having been built to Doughty's plan, rather than to the resident constructors' drawings. The 44's were the *Columbia*, laid down in the Washington Navy Yard and launched in 1836, and the *Cumberland*, laid down in the Boston Yard and launched in 1842. No new designs were prepared in the year 1825, and all of the constructors were busy with ships building in their yards. The Board was now dealing directly with each of the constructors when any question arose, and this was a burdensome administrative function. The appointment of a chief constructor would relieve the Board members of much of this detail, and so the matter began to receive consideration. In the meantime, the Board was forced to refer technical matters to the constructors located in the vicinity of Washington, Doughty and Humphreys, when the matters were beyond the comprehension of the sea officers.

In the next year, 1826, another 44 and a corvette were laid down—the frigate *St. Lawrence* in the Norfolk Navy Yard, launched in 1847, and the sloop *Falmouth* at Boston, built to Barker's drawing, launched in 1827. The new sloops were being built as rapidly as the yards could turn them out. The older sloops built during the War of 1812, except the rebuilt *Erie*, were in need of extensive repairs, and new vessels were required to take their place. The old *Hornet* had been nearly worn out during the War of 1812 and had received extensive repairs after the war, which changed her appearance a good deal and brought her to look much like the 1813 sloops. The old frigates, *Congress*, *Macedonian*, *United States*, *Constitution*, *Constellation*, and *John Adams*, were either rapidly becoming unserviceable, or were requiring expensive repairs. The problem of retaining old ships in service was becoming acute, for a great deal of the naval appropriations was being spent on them which might better have been applied to new construction, if some way could be found to manage it.

From 1820 to 1826 the New York shipbuilders had been actively engaged in building men-of-war for foreign governments. Eckford, as has been mentioned, had taken the lead in this, but other builders had taken similar contracts, and ships were built for Russia and other European powers as well as for Central and South American governments. Many of these vessels were ordered by revolutionary governments, and there was often a strong element of risk in these contracts for a builder. Among the contracts let in New York were some vessels for the Greek revolutionists. Smith and Dimon had built a huge frigate named *Liberator* for them, but the Greeks were unable to pay for her. By means of political influence the builders were able to dispose of the ship to the American government, and the *Liberator* came into the Navy as the 44-gun frigate *Hudson*, the last privately built sailing frigate in the United States Navy. She was, of course, designed by her builders.

The *Hudson* made but one cruise, on the Brazilian station, and was laid up. In 1844 she was rotten and was broken up at New York. The ship was the subject of much controversy, and it was claimed that she was poorly built. It is now impossible to pass on the truth of this, for it is apparent that there was much prejudice against the frigate in the Navy, chiefly because of the manner in which she was fobbed off on the service, and there is strong evidence that the reports on the ship were sometimes very unjust. Her design was not criticized, for she was actually considered a very good model, but rather her construction and the quality of the timber in her were made the issues.

Plan 23 is a drawing of this frigate. She was 177' 10" between perpendiculars, 45' 0" moulded beam, and 13' 8" depth of hold to berth deck. Her builders had built packets, and the design of the *Hudson* followed these rather than the standard frigate model. The *Hudson* was really a much larger ship than the American 44's and was pierced to carry 66 guns exclusive of her bridle ports. She was a double-banked frigate with an unbroken sheer. Her size and design really made her more like the earlier 64-gun ships than a frigate, but with the coming of the double-banked vessel the true frigate went out of fashion in ships from 36 guns upward. The *Hudson* was plainly finished, but she was a handsome frigate in a strikingly bold manner.

Plan 23 is a redrawing of the original, which was made from the builder's half-model and from measurements made from the ship in 1828, according to a note on the original drawing. It is apparent from this that Smith and Dimon built their ships from half-models rather than from drawings. It cannot be said with any degree of accuracy when the fashion of employing half-models in merchant-ship construction replaced drawings in New York or in the leading yards at other shipbuilding centers. Of course, it is probable that this was a gradual development and not a sudden innovation, but it would be interesting to know the approximate time that models were used by a large majority of the builders. There is reason to suppose that all the shipbuilding centers did not adopt the half-model method of design at the same time. Without going into details of no particular moment to naval design, it can be said that there is evidence that the New York builders did much to introduce the use of the half-model elsewhere.

There are a number of plans of merchant vessels built in New York, Philadelphia, and elsewhere before the War of 1812, and both Christian Bergh and Noah Brown are known to have made drawings of their ships. In 1819, on September 6, the Navy Board wrote Brown for "draughts and plans" of all government vessels he had built; they received one at least, the corvette *Saratoga*. Eckford also made drawings, for much of his work has survived. On the other hand, the half-model was used by Eckford's apprentice, Isaac Webb; Brown's foreman, Sydney Wright; Smith and Dimon; and Noah Brown's adopted son, David Brown, of Brown and Bell. On this scanty evidence it might be assumed that the change from draught to model, as a method of design, took place soon after the War of 1812 in the New York area. From here the practice was spread by the apprentices from the leading New York yards, who went to New England, to the lakes, and southward, as independent builders.

By 1825 the practice had spread throughout New England, at any rate, and was slowly spreading southward. In 1820 it was still not universal on the Chesapeake, however, as the French naval architect Marestier found drawings of schooners in this section and made copies of them for his report on American steam vessels and schooners. At this time the builders at Philadelphia and Baltimore were using half-models to a limited degree, at least, but appear to have depended upon drawings much more than was the case in New York. Conclusions of this nature should be accepted with caution, however, for the evidence is as yet scant and some of it may be misleading. In considering the matter it must be remembered that the use of the half-model did not bar making drawings; the Webbs, for example, made a model first and from this made, in most cases, a drawing of the lines and of some details—deck arrangement and sail or spar plans. Other builders made no drawings whatsoever and took all their measurements directly from the half-models, as is evidenced by offsets that are found recorded on the "lifts" when the models are taken apart. It appears quite certain that the majority of the New York merchant-ship builders had dispensed with all but sail plans and a few deck sketches by 1825 and designed wholly by means of the half-model.

The half-model had the advantage over lines, or a "draught," in that it readily conveyed the shape of the intended hull to anyone, such as a merchant or a captain, who had not been trained in drawing plans of ships. The Navy Board, in fact, usually required a half-model, as well as a draught, of any new design. However, naval practice in designing did not recognize the use of the half-model as a primary design method; the drawing of the lines was first prepared and the calculations made, the important details of arrangement and finish were worked out in plans and, finally, a half-model was usually made to check the plans and to show the non-technical Board just what the ship would look like. The Navy half-model was a cheap substitute for the expensive and handsome built-up model once employed in the British Admiralty, and was not the official design of the ship. However, when the Navy obtained a ship from private builders, they were often forced to accept a half-model in lieu of plans for record, and from the half-model they made a file drawing, as in the case of the *Hudson*. Possibly the reason why the constructors preferred to work with plans is that the weight calculations could be most conveniently made from plans; and weight calculations had now become important in naval ship design. However, all of the constructors had been trained in the use of plans, rather than half-models, and this certainly had much effect on their practices. The merchant builders, however, were not required to make weight calculations, and usually made none of any kind whatsoever, even in large, important vessels such as the North Atlantic packets.

The growing organization needed for the construction of the new ships now required a technical supervisor. Doughty, as senior constructor, would naturally be the person to receive the appointment as chief constructor. However, he had become a man of some wealth, and his son had become active in the lumber business, supplying timber to the Navy. He felt that he did not desire the burden and responsibilities of the appointment, which therefore was tendered to the constructor next in seniority, Samuel Humphreys. Doughty remained as naval constructor in the Washington Yard, but ceased to be active in naval design. In 1837 he resigned and joined his son in the lumber trade. Humphreys was appointed chief constructor November 25, 1826, and accepted December 4, 1826.

With a chief constructor appointed, the resident constructors now made their reports to him rather than directly to the Navy Board as before. If the surviving correspondence of the chief constructor is any indication, the yard constructors made very few written reports, and there was very little technical correspondence of any kind, except where new designs were being allotted for construction. The routine yard reports were made by the commandants, who reported on progress and the state of the yards at regular intervals. It is apparent, however, that the various constructors carried on correspondence among themselves, apart from official letters, and that a good deal of the business was done on an informal basis.

The chief naval constructor was, of course, responsible for all new ship designs; he could either prepare these personally or assign a design to one of his subordinates, as he wished. His attendance on the Board of Navy Commissioners was only occasionally necessary, so he remained for a while at his post in the Philadelphia Navy Yard. Hence no additional constructor was considered necessary to replace him. At this time Humphreys had as his apprentice John Lenthall, who acted as his draftsman and assistant. Lenthall was recommended by Humphreys for appointment as assistant naval constructor at the Philadelphia Yard in 1828. Assistants had been assigned to many of the constructors, who prepared plans and specifications under the supervision of the resident and also helped in supervisory work of construction. Such men as Henry Allen, C. F. Waldo, Richard Powell, and Foster Rhodes were very competent draftsmen, and even designed small vessels in their own right.

In most cases, the characters and personalities of the constructors cannot be accurately estimated by the relatively scant official correspondence that now exists. Much of the official correspondence was formal and of a professional nature, or consisted merely of letters transmitting plans and specifications. In a few cases there is personal correspondence outside the official files, and from this source some opinions might be drawn. Samuel Humphreys appears as an executive of much ability, but somewhat vain and pompous. He was quick to resent slights and stood on his dignity. His relations with the constructors seem to have been very friendly and pleasant, however, though there is little evidence of any close personal relationship, except with those who had been his apprentices. Of the resident constructors, Grice was by far the most progressive and active-minded. He was strongly opinionated and did not agree with Humphreys' ideas on hull design. Floyd was a nonentity as far as design was concerned, and he was interested only in construction problems. Barker seems to have had ability but was not particularly interested in designing. Hartt was as yet untried; he was later to become a noted constructor. Doughty, highly competent and experienced, wished to retire from designing, and in addition there was the delicate question of seniority in his case. As a result of the character of the constructors, it is not surprising to find Humphreys assuming all design work, with the aid of his assistant, Lenthall, and having once done this with the Board's approval, retaining the function as long as the Board existed.

As a result, there was no design work for the resident constructors, who either pottered with the slow-moving construction program, if indolent and unambitious, or branched out into design for commercial interests, as did Grice and, eventually, Hartt and Lenthall. The constructors who maintained outside interests were able to keep abreast of the new developments in merchant-ship design and construction and of the new methods employed in shipbuilding outside of the navy yards. These men came into contact with those interested in steamers and other new types of vessels. The result was that these constructors remained highly progressive and steadily became better informed while the others vegetated. Unfortunately, the outside activities of the more progressive constructors brought them into conflict with the yard commandants on occasion, and this in turn led both the Board and the chief constructor to regard them with doubt and suspicion. Hence, when advice or consultation was desired, the constructors who had applied their whole energies to the naval construction program were usually the most influential. Some of the constructors were growing old with minds shaped in the bureaucratic mould.

In 1827, two more 24-gun corvettes were laid down—the *St. Louis* in the Washington Yard and the *Natchez* in the Norfolk Yard. Both were built rapidly and were launched in 1828. The *Natchez* was the third sloop built to the Doughty modifications, in spite of the fact that it would have seemed rational to employ the Doughty drawings in a single yard, Washington. However, the official designation indicates that *Lexington, Warren,* and *Natchez* were built to the Washington constructor's plans.

The light cruisers of the War of 1812 had gradually disappeared from the Navy Register. Members of the proposed raiding squadrons had been sold or wrecked; the *Boxer* was lost off Honduras in 1817, the *Chippewa* was lost off Caicos, West Indies, in 1816, the *Firefly* and *Flambeau* were sold in 1816. The *Saranac* was sold in 1818, and the fine *Spark* was finally worn out and sold in 1826. The schooners were all sold between 1818 and 1820, except *Lynx*, which was lost at sea in the West Indies in 1820, and the *Nonsuch*, broken up in 1826. The old *Enterprise* was wrecked in the West Indies in 1823. Except for the surviving members of the class of schooners built in 1821, the sharp clipper was rapidly disappearing from the Navy, and no replacements were being made or planned for in the construction program. The old story of neglect of the light, fast cruiser by American naval authorities in time of peace was being repeated—so readily were the lessons of the War of 1812 being forgotten. Again, the small schooner or brig was not a sufficiently dignified command for officers gradually becoming pompous with age and the inactivity of mind developed by peaceful years. Though the ineffectiveness of the privateering system as a substitute for a navy was now recognized, the old habit of expecting to be able to obtain fast raiders from this source had not been conquered.

The old sloop *Peacock* was now worn out with hard service. She had been surveyed a number of times, and it was agreed that she was not worth repair. Still another sloop was urgently needed, so it was decided to "rebuild" her; officially a new ship was not possible, since the congressional appropriation made no provisions for any new ships outside of the existing program of new construction. However, the funds for repair of the old ships were available, and it was decided by the Board that the *Peacock* should be officially "rebuilt." In doing this it was realized that funds budgeted for other old ships would have to be used and that these ships must be allowed to decay still further. However, these vessels too might eventually have the same treatment, in turn, that the *Peacock* was to receive. There was no question in the minds of the Navy Board of preserving the old *Peacock* either in form or in dimensions; the only concern of the Board was to build a satisfactory replacement. By retaining the ship on the register as "rebuilt," the legal question of building a new vessel without proper authorization was avoided. The morality of this method of avoiding compliance with the intent of Congress is of relatively small moment; the Board had the practical problem of maintaining an effective navy with insufficient funds rather than of the examination of moral questions of government administration. However, the "rebuilding" system was eventually to reach extraordinary heights and misled not only Congress but also the public as to the true age of some of the ships of the Navy.

Humphreys prepared a new design for "rebuilding" the *Peacock* in 1827, and the old ship was hauled up in the New York Navy Yard and broken up. In 1828 the "rebuilt" ship was laid down. Her design is shown in Figure 90; she was 118′ 0″ between perpendiculars, 31′ 6″ moulded beam, and 14′ 10″ depth of hold, and had the now fashionable round stern. It will be seen by comparing the "rebuilt" ship with the original that the dimensions had changed but little; however, the lines were much altered. The new sloop was very sharp, with an unusual amount of hollow in her ends for her time. She was too small to carry her armament, however, and both her speed and her stability were adversely affected. It was not until she was reduced for an exploration ship that she showed the speed her model promised. There is no mention in her specifications or in the scanty correspondence relating to the incident, of the retention of any portion of the old ship in the new one; it is possible that some of the

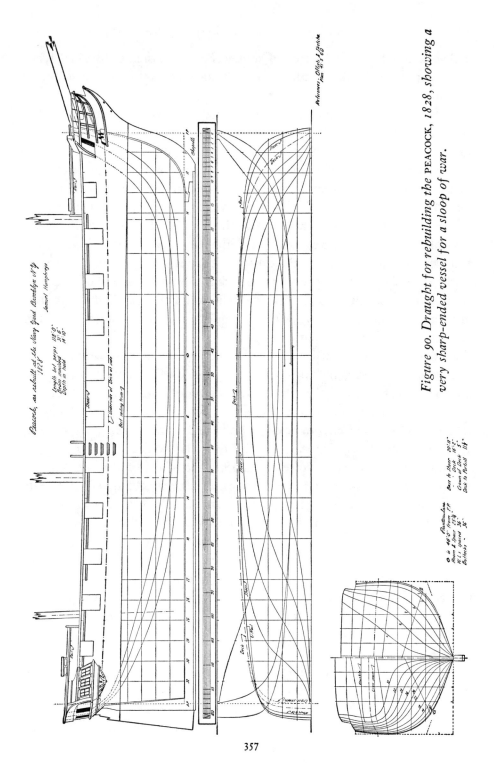

Figure 90. Draught for rebuilding the PEACOCK, *1828, showing a very sharp-ended vessel for a sloop of war.*

metalwork could have been used. The new *Peacock* lasted until 1841, when she was part of the Wilkes Exploring Expedition and was lost off the mouth of the Columbia River, Oregon, in July.

The last of the ten 24-gun corvettes, the *Concord*, was laid down in 1827. This ship was built at the Portsmouth Navy Yard, was launched late in 1828, and went into commission in 1830. It should be noted here that the dates officially given for the date of a ship's build are not consistent; sometimes the date of launch was used, sometimes the date the keel was laid, and sometimes the date of first commission. In addition, there was often a lag of time between the date the keel was ordered laid and the day the work on the ship actually began. This makes it very difficult to fix the time the navy yards actually required to build these ships; in the case of the *Concord* it appears to have taken seventeen months to build her hull, ready for launching. It took the same yard four months and seventeen days to build the schooner *Porpoise*. The Portsmouth Yard was much more consistent in time required to build sailing men-of-war than were most of the other navy yards.

The ten sloops authorized were now accounted for; as has been said, they were the subject of much criticism in later years. Their inability to carry the heavy armament assigned them hurt their sailing qualities in most cases, and two were eventually converted to storeships. The *Boston* was wrecked in the Bahamas in 1846, the *Concord* was lost on the African coast in 1843, the *Falmouth* was sold at Panama in 1863, the *Fairfield* was sold in 1852, the *Lexington* was raised and made into a storeship in 1840 and sold in 1860, the *Natchez* was broken up at New York in 1840, the *St. Louis* was sold in 1860, the *Vandalia* was broken up in 1870–72, the *Vincennes* was sold in 1867, and the *Warren* was made a storeship in 1840 and sold in 1863. It will be seen that most of the vessels were carefully built, for they had long lives. Some of them saw many adventures and a great deal of active service; they were, on the whole, a useful class of ship. One or two were noted as being good sailers, at certain times at least, the *Falmouth* and *Vincennes* in particular. This was undoubtedly due to the lighter armament placed aboard these vessels in later years, when they carried but 16 carronades, 32's, and 2 to 4 8″ shell guns. The *Natchez*, *Warren*, and *Lexington* were poor sailers throughout their career. In spite of their lack of grace, the remaining sloops were undoubtedly improvements on the 1813 designs in many respects and should have been equally fast had their runs been sharper. The fact that they did not make equal reputations as fast sailers was due to their full afterbody and to the overloading that always marked the peacetime sailing navy, either in the United States or abroad. Not only were the sloops of the 1820's overgunned, they were also overequipped and carried too many boats and too much spare gear and other unnecessary weights. Had they been treated as were the 1813 sloops in the War of 1812, carrying a normal gun load for their size and stripped of the extra boats and unnecessary gear, it is highly probable that they would have been found better vessels, though rather small for their ratings. Their fault was in the increase of displacement over the 1813 sloops without sufficient increase in length.

The slow rate of construction in building the 74's led to the consideration of changes in design of some of the ships. Humphreys prepared a revised design of this class in 1827 which called for ships 196′ 6″ between perpendiculars, 53′ 0″ moulded beam, and 22′ 0″ depth of hold and fitted with the round stern now popular in the American as well as the British service. The design, Plan 24, shows the improved vessel proposed, but there is no evidence that it was used in any of the ships already laid down. In 1838 it was submitted to the constructors Barker, Hartt, and Lenthall, who approved it, but, again, there is no evidence of its use in construction. It is of value, however, in showing what was, in 1827–30, the American idea of an effective 74, and also the very moderate changes that had taken place in the hull form of the type since 1817.

In 1829 there began an intensive period of "rebuilding." The state of the old ships has been noted previously, and the diversion of funds from the maintenance of all of these ships to rebuild the *Erie* and *Peacock* had hastened the deterioration of the worst ships into an unserviceable state. These were the old *John Adams*, *Macedonian*, and *Congress*. Orders were now issued for rebuilding the *John Adams*. Survey showed the ship to be so badly decayed that it was no longer worth while to attempt to cobble her up into usable condition as a frigate. Humphreys reported that the funds available made it wholly impossible to "rebuild" her, as was done in the *Peacock*, as a vessel of her original class. The Board, faced with this dilemma, now decided she should be "rebuilt" as a sloop. Humphreys prepared a new design based on his estimate of the probable cost compared to the funds available. The result was a ship sloop only about 100′ between perpendiculars; the Board would have none of it. After more study and thought, and a few glances at the budget, it was decided that the frigate *John Adams* should be "rebuilt," or "cut down" into a 24-gun corvette exactly like Humphreys' *Vandalia*. This was ordered done. The old ship was broken up in the Norfolk Navy Yard, and the new sloop of the same

name was laid down there and launched in the fall of 1830. Again, there is
no evidence that any part of the old ship was used in the new one, though
it may have been done. At any rate, "rebuilding" had now reached the state
where a ship was not only "rebuilt" on a new design or to new dimensions,
but was even in a different class! That such administrative fiction as carrying
this sloop on the register as a "rebuilt" frigate could exist is sufficient evidence
of the attention Congress was then giving to naval affairs, and also of the
bureaucratic evasion of budget requirements that has not been entirely unknown in recent times.

With the *John Adams* taken care of, the old *Macedonian* was now to be
taken in hand. The ship had been entirely unserviceable for years but had been
carried on the naval registers as a convenient method of obtaining maintenance
funds from Congress. By her existence in the register her alleged cost of maintenance could be budgeted and so obtained from Congress; then it was found
that the funds could be diverted either to other ships, as in the case of those already "rebuilt," or to the needs of the steadily growing shore establishments
and administrative organization. Little or nothing need actually be spent on
the ship in question.

Eventually, of course, something would have to be done about this ship, at the
expense of some other old crock. Otherwise embarrassing questions might be
asked in Congress. The Board felt that the *Macedonian* would have to be rebuilt
as a frigate; there were enough sloops, but commands suitable for the senior
officers were none too numerous. The old ship, though built of the much-
praised English oak, had now become entirely rotten, just as many American-
built ships of the equally praised live oak had decayed in a relatively short
time when neglected. Humphreys prepared a new design for the ship, a
nicely modeled frigate, double-banked, 164′ 0″ between perpendiculars, 41′ 0″
moulded beam, and 13′ 6½″ depth of hold. She was pierced for 58 guns, excluding bridle ports, and was much sharper, both in water lines and in deadrise, than previous American frigates. She was, in fact, a clipper model with
a long and well-formed run and was a very fast sailer throughout her career.
She was classed as a 36, to rate with the old *Constellation* and *Congress*, and
carried 32-pdr. medium guns and a few 8″ shell guns in her first commission.
She had been intended to carry 32 medium 32-pdrs. and 24 carronades, 32's,
but she was unable to carry these armaments, and early in her life most of her
spar-deck guns were removed. Her relatively small dimensions and sharp model
really made her unsuitable for a full-fledged frigate, and eventually she was

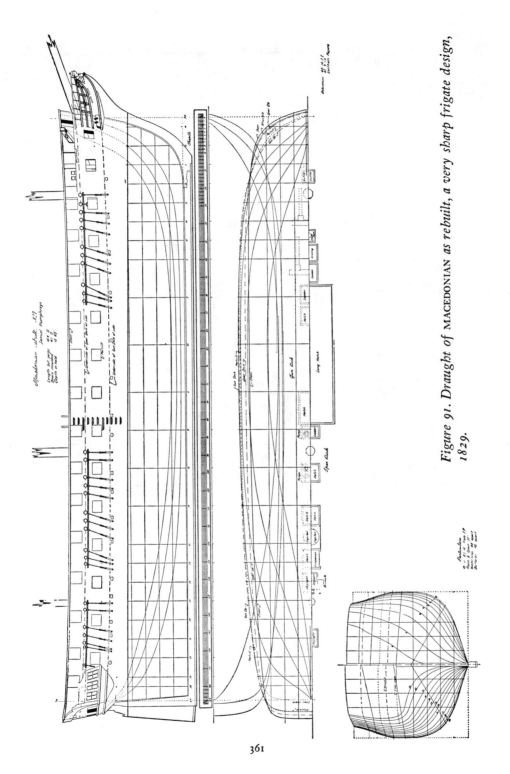

Figure 91. Draught of MACEDONIAN *as rebuilt, a very sharp frigate design,*
1829.

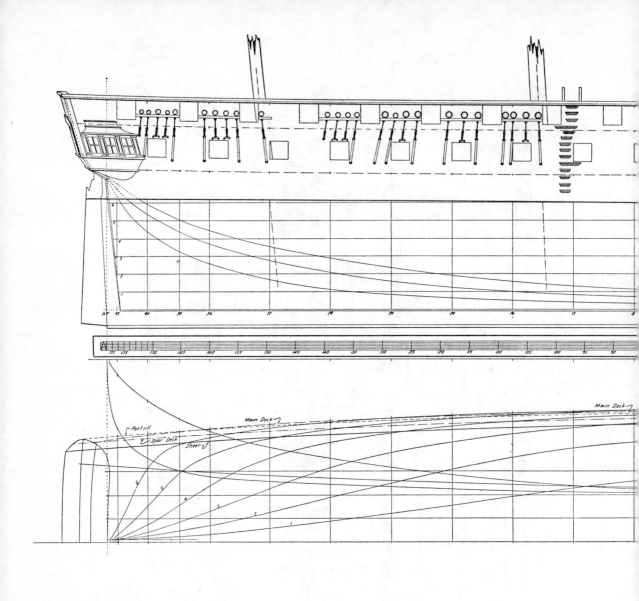

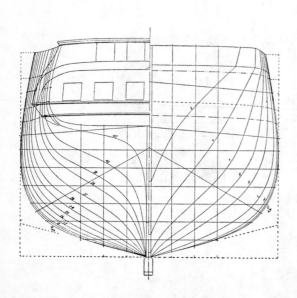

Particulars

O is 65' 6" from F.P.
Room & Space 31½"
W.L's spaced 30"
Buttocks 48"
Height of Main Deck at O, from Base 22' 9"
  "   "   Spar   "   "   "   30' 3"
  "   "   Sheer   "   "   "   31' 4¼"
  Depth of Rail 8¾"
  Knuckle, 11" above Spar Deck

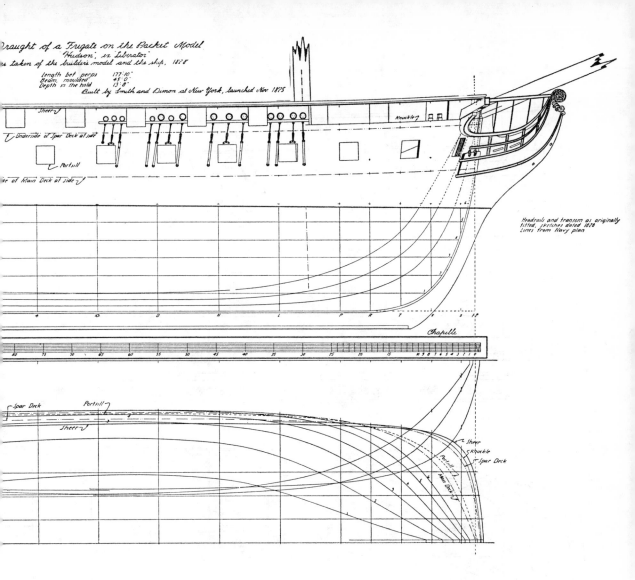

Draught of a Frigate on the Packet Model
'Hudson', ex 'Liberator'
as taken of the builders model and the ship. 1828

length bet perps   177·10'
Beam. moulded   45·0'
Depth in the hold   13·8'
Built by Smith and Dimon at New York, launched Nov 1875

Sheer

Underside of Spar Deck at side

Portsill

side of Main Deck at side

Knuckle

Headrails and transom as originally
fitted, sketches dated 1828
Lines from Navy plan

Chapelle

Spar Deck   Portsill

Sheer

Sheer
S. Knuckle
Spar Deck

Portsill

Main Deck

Plan 23. Draught of the frigate HUDSON, *modeled on packet-ship lines.*

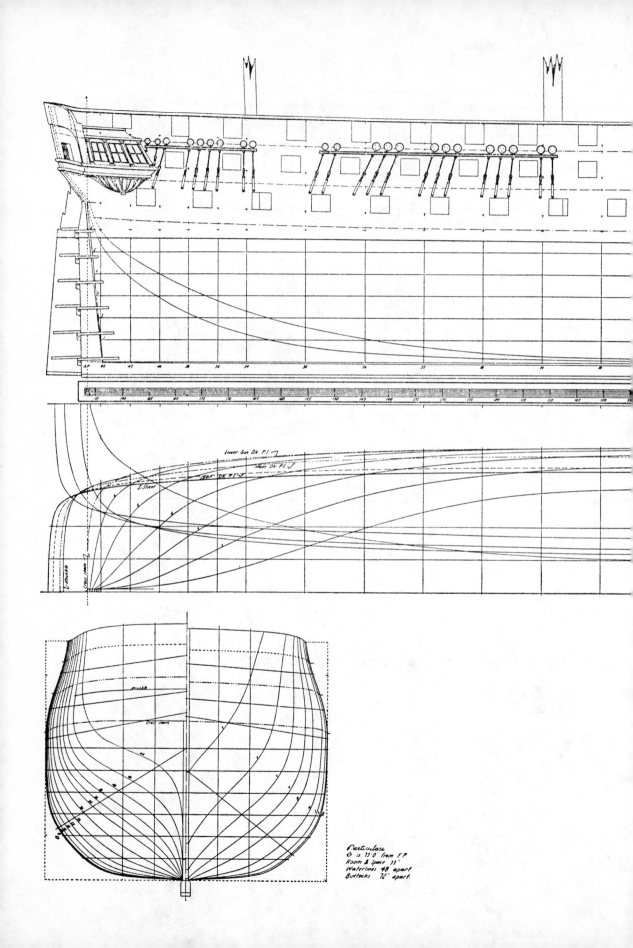

Lower Gun Dk P.S

Main Dk P.S

Dk P.S

L.Sheer

Particulars
O is 75'0" from F.P
Room & Space 33"
Waterlines 48" apart
Buttocks 72" apart.

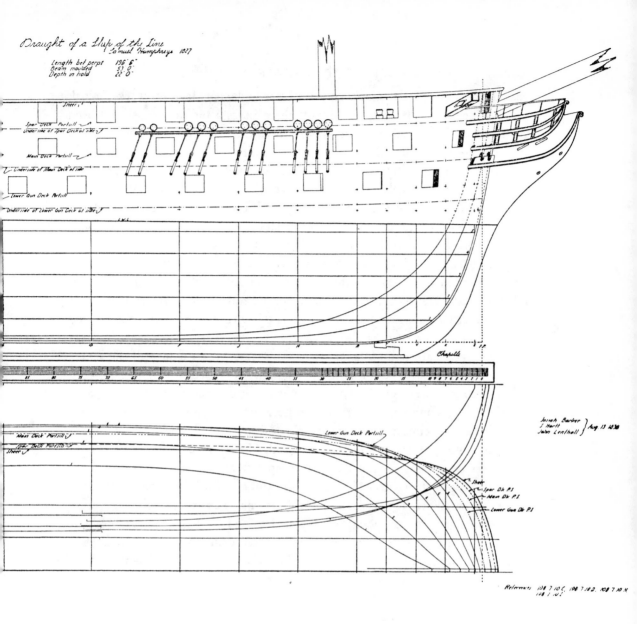

Plan 24. Humphreys' draught for an improved 74-gun ship, 1827.

reduced to a corvette by the removal of her high spar-deck bulwarks. Work was not begun on this ship for nearly three years after the design had been prepared, as funds had to be accumulated and a yard cleared. The Norfolk Navy Yard was finally selected to build the ship, and work actually began in 1832. The old prize frigate, thus "rebuilt," was not broken up until 1835–36.

The Board personnel had rotated between 1827 and 1830. Bainbridge was relieved as President of the Board in 1827, and Rodgers returned to the assignment, where he was to remain for the next ten years, until 1837. Lewis Warrington was assigned to the Board vice Charles Morris, and Thomas Tingey was assigned for a portion of one year in 1827; then Daniel T. Patterson was placed on the Board in 1828. At times there were vacancies on the Board that were not filled immediately, as the officer having the required seniority might be at sea or otherwise unavailable. However, the length of time vacancies existed was rarely over two months.

Fifteen years after the War of 1812 the war captains were still the senior officers of the Navy. There was no provision for the retirement of aged officers, and promotions were gradually ceasing as the vacancies in the higher grades vanished. The young and progressive officers of the war were now becoming the old and ultra-conservative officers of a peacetime navy. No longer was there the competition of a war to keep the naval officers, responsible for the state of the service, striving for excellence in equipment or tactics. Now the emphasis was on a perfect drill, the "spit and polish" and tasteful deck arrangement, the rendering of the correct ceremonies, the establishment of privileges of rank, and routine peacetime operations. New ideas and new material or methods might make it necessary to change time-honored drills or deck arrangements, or might require study and work; such things were beneath the dignity of the tried veterans of the war. It is not surprising, then, to find the members of the Board increasingly adamant in their opposition to the introduction of anything new, whether a new method or a new type of ship. Instead of the ruthless efficiency of the war Navy, there was a sentimental attachment to traditional things, ships, ceremonies, and drill, that has so often marked the peace navies.

The training of new personnel for naval requirements was now almost wholly a function of the service. No longer were men to be taken from civilian professions or trades and utilized in the Navy. This applied not only to officers but to the construction organization of the Navy as well. Instead of civilian-trained shipwrights or designers, such as Eckford, being accepted, all the construction personnel were now being trained in the navy yards. There the ship carpenters, riggers, caulkers, smiths, and joiners of the Navy were trained in a system of apprenticeship in which they were educated in the naval way of doing things. The constructors had apprentices, who were trained in the naval ship design methods that were in vogue. At last the American Navy was, so far as its constructors and foremen shipwrights were concerned, independent of the merchant yards and was developing a specialized field of shipbuilding from which private ship designers and builders were barred. The naval constructor was no longer exposed to the competition of some talented naval architect outside of the tight little circle of government servants. With a comfortable position assured them by maintaining this state of affairs, it was natural for many of the constructors to look with contempt on the work of the merchant builders and to disregard any improvements in shipbuilding that they might make. When, by some misfortune of politics, the Navy was forced to accept a privately built and designed vessel, it was natural for the constructors to view her with prejudice and to report adversely on her qualities at every opportunity. In this they were given the support of the hierarchy of the navy yards, whose work might suffer by comparison with the privately built man-of-war. In war it is always necessary eventually to come to building men-of-war merchant-ship fashion in one respect at least—that is, "just good enough and no better than needed." In peaceful times, however, naval construction becomes luxurious in the use of costly materials and workmanship—"the best is none too good"—even when the vessel building is nothing more than a garbage scow. By this means the constructors deluded themselves on the excellence of their designs and construction. The system also permitted an easy dismissal of any good features a privately built sailing man-of-war might have, by dwelling on her shortcomings in material and finish.

The matter went beyond mere specifications; the amount of design work that had been done since 1816 had been small, and there had been ample time to dawdle over many of the plans that had been used. This led to the setting up of some imaginary requirements for expensive construction or fittings. It also led to the establishment of a system of design that required unnecessary drawings or calculations in all vessels, whether or not the importance of the ship warranted the care and time expended. Had war come in the late 1820's, the cumbersome designing systems so carefully established would have had to be discarded and a new method hurriedly developed, which by its emergency nature might have been much more faulty than the practices of the civilian profession. This condition has not been unknown in the armed services in recent times and is a characteristic of governmental efforts in the design of naval and military shipping. Instead of the design practices and specification writing being based on a "war view," they are too often founded on "perfection" and on the assumption that labor and materials will be as available when war comes as in peacetime. This was the reason for the frigates and sloops built in navy yards usually costing so much more, and taking so much longer to build, than contract-built ships in time of war.

The same condition existed in the other departments of the navy yards that existed in the drafting room. There was an unnecessary degree of finish given all work, regardless of use, and everything was of the finest, regardless of actual requirements. Cost was high and waste was great in both labor and materials. One apparent advantage was the argument for the system: ships built by navy yard methods usually lasted a long time and were not always requiring repairs. The argument assumed, of course, that the good qualities of the ships in these respects were inherent in a system requiring the "best and most." The fact that some merchant craft had equally long lives, and this with more neglect and harder usage, was conveniently overlooked.

American naval ships had changed their appearance but little in the fifteen years since the end of the War of 1812. They had grown longer in some classes, and now the ornate carvings of earlier years had almost disappeared. The ships were plainer and without the multitude of mouldings and beadings that had decorated the earlier ships. All the external longitudinal mouldings and projections that had been traditional in ships were now gradually being suppressed.

The ends of the ships were changed in more ways than by the omission of florid carvings, however. The stern underwent a change in fashion in the American Navy in 1825 with the building of the first of the 24-gun corvettes. In 1824, when Humphreys made his first drawings for the class, he prepared a number of preliminary designs. His first plan for the new class, like those of Eckford, Floyd, and Grice, called for a square stern in the traditional style, with raking transoms and round tuck below. The final building plans, however, show the round stern that was to be fashionable in American frigates and sloops for many years.

The advantages of the round stern were supposed to be in greater strength as compared to the older stern, and particularly in the possibility of guns being mounted to fire on the quarters. The new stern was introduced in the Royal Navy in 1819–20 by Sir Robert Seppings, the surveyor, or chief constructor; at about the same time a sub-surveyor, Roberts, proposed an elliptical stern.

The round stern and the elliptical were but variants of the same principle; the quarters were rounded off, and the angular meeting of the sides and transom of the old construction was eliminated. This permitted ports to be placed in the quarters, allowing an angle of fire astern, at around 45 degrees to the center line of the ship, long a blind spot in the broadside method of arming naval vessels. By framing up the stern with cant timbers radiating somewhat like the spokes of a wooden wheel, and then bending the planking around these, the stern was made very strong compared to the old transom and round tuck, with its complicated system of framing and many angles and long seams.

However, the practical advantages of the round stern were soon largely imaginary, for the traditional quarter galleries were demanded. In both the Royal Navy and the American service, the old sea officer was dominant; he demanded the retention of the traditional quarter galleries and other conveniences of the older stern. Almost immediately the round stern and the elliptical stern that replaced it were masked by quarter galleries and an arched sternboard, which not only made the quarter gun ports impractical, but also made the stern look very much as it did before the change. The omission of the stern galleries in the first designs of the 24-gun corvettes and their appearance in the building plans illustrate the same influences in the peacetime American Navy that existed in the peacetime British Navy. Perhaps the greatest objection to the early round-stern men-of-war was the very full runs given most of them by the designers, who had not solved the fairing of the new stern sufficiently well to obtain easy buttocks combined with powerful quarters in this style of stern. Of the designers of the 24-gun sloops, only Barker had produced a good afterbody with the new stern.

The years between 1800 and 1830 were marked by a steady improvement in the methods of constructing long ships in the navies of the world. The British had adopted a system, projected by Seppings and others, of using internal bracing. This was a series of diagonally fitted timbers, or "riders," placed on the inside of the frames to stiffen the structure longitudinally. In the American ships, this was accomplished by a complicated system of diagonally set knees and riders and by a trusswork of timber on top of the keelson. This took up much room, and metal knees and diagonal strapping soon took the place of the older timber trusses and bracing. A good deal of attention had been given to the framing of the long wooden hulls that were now becoming common in sailing ships, and in addition to the improved bracing and trussing which gave greater longitudinal strength, transverse strength was also attended to by the introduction of new reinforcing of the knees, used at the ends of the deck beams. These improvements made the ships more rigid and strong, and better able to carry either armament or cargo, for the use of improved bracing was not confined to naval craft alone. The merchant builders were also in need of these improvements, for the merchant ships were rapidly growing in size and length as the needs of expanding sea trades made them desirable.

The bows had changed little except for the surrender of the curved upper headrail. In the Royal Navy, the curved upper rails were gradually replaced with straight rails (seen in the American corvettes and frigates launched in the 1820's) as early as 1812, when the requirements of the long war then engaging her energies caused Great Britain to do everything possible to speed up the construction of her men-of-war and to lower their cost. The American Navy had followed this lead for reasons of economy, and now few ships retained the older curved upper rail and faired-in cathead knees, except for small craft, schooners, and brigs. The cutwaters of American naval ships now became shorter and deeper, giving them a somewhat massive appearance. This, with the straightened sheer and the short, round stern, caused the vessels to look heavy and "blocklike," particularly the 24-gun corvettes. Figureheads were becoming rare except in the liners and in a few frigates; the simple billet was now popular.

There were also many minor improvements or changes. The hammock rails were now projected forward and aft by raising the freeboard at bow and stern by a low monkey rail, which would continue unbroken the line of the top of the hammock rail fore and aft, as in the 24-gun corvettes. Ironwork became more common, and chain was used increasingly on shipboard. The ships were becoming more cluttered with boats and were still overloaded with guns.

The rigs had changed little; the American men-of-war retained their distinctive short lower masts and long topmasts and were, on the whole, grossly overcanvased. Many of the men-of-war could not carry their courses, with topsails and topgallant sails, in winds in which merchant vessels worked under full sail. In strong winds, the huge topsails of the men-of-war often overpressed the ship, particularly in the sloop classes. In the small vessels of the Navy overmasting was extreme and was reaching exceedingly dangerous proportions. The steeve of the bowsprit was slowly decreasing, and the rake of the masts showed less difference between fore, main, and mizzen.

Merchant shipping, which had been limited during the War of 1812 to fast-sailing small craft, was now improving rapidly. American builders were not only building fine merchant ships; they were turning out vessels that were the equal of any in the world in speed, size, and strength. The great packets, looking much like huge frigates, were now appearing and were teaching the lessons of obtaining speed through ability to carry sail in strong winds. Merchant builders were taking great pains to learn all they could about foreign ships and to better them. There was great scientific curiosity in the merchant shipyards, and the term "mechanic" was deemed an honorable one. New York and the New England ports were replacing Philadelphia as the center of advanced shipbuilding ideas and practice. The Chesapeake area was still producing the fast clipper schooners and brigs, for which it was famous, but the model of these was slowly changing to give more capacity without appreciable loss of speed. Already merchant-ship designers were beginning to notice the backwardness of Navy designs and to offer well-meant but, to the majority of the constructors, highly objectionable suggestions for improvements.

The building of war vessels for foreign powers had been common in American yards through the 1820's. Twelve schooners, designed by Humphreys, had been built in Philadelphia for the Colombian government in 1824. A ship sloop named *Kensington*, designed by Eckford, was also built here in 1830; intended for Russia, she was finally sold to Mexico. In addition to frigates built by Eckford for Brazil and for the Greeks, a number of corvettes, brigs, and schooners were built in New York for various foreign powers, and a large number of schooners and brigs, as well as two corvettes, were built on the Chesapeake and southward for South American revolutionists and Central American patriots. Many slavers were built, and the illegal trades were still attractive. For these the builders turned out small, fast armed craft in large numbers. So, in spite of the effort to restrict naval ship design to government employees, the private ship builders and designers were still showing themselves competent in turning out men-of-war and fast armed vessels, and were still being given an opportunity to do so.

Steam made little impression on the American Navy in the 1820's. Fulton's steam battery was employed only as a receiving ship. A small steamer, or "galiot," named the *Sea Gull* was purchased at Philadelphia and employed in the West Indies in 1822–23, but she was laid up at the end of this period. None of the Navy, and least of all the Navy Board, considered that there was any possibility of steam men-of-war; steamers might be useful as tugs and service craft, or a few might even be armed as coast-defense floating batteries, but obviously a steamer would not do as a seagoing man-of-war.

The two fields of specialization open to young American naval officers were seamanship and gunnery, in the now American tradition. The first had been well explored, and by 1820 any advances were mere refinements of the art of handling ships and rigging them. Gunnery was a more appealing subject to a curious mind; there were many mysteries of which the practical gunner was well aware but which he could not explain. In this field, too, an officer might expect some slight support from his seniors in view of the American policy of employing the largest and most powerful batteries in their ships. In addition, an interest in the improvement of cannon had appeared in France during the last years of the Napoleonic Wars and had gradually spread over Europe. The English, mortified by their defeats in the naval actions of the War of 1812, had decided that these were due to inferior guns and gunnery and were now seriously trying to improve their position. The study of the science of gunnery now became fashionable, and this finally led to the rapid improvement in naval guns that marked the last days of sailing men-of-war.

The speed of American men-of-war had become an accepted fact both at home and abroad. Where the British were concerned, an exaggerated sense of inferiority in this matter had grown up, both among naval officers and in the Admiralty itself. In fact, it had now become traditional that British-designed ships were slower than those of the United States or France. The fact of the matter was that the tradition was an excellent excuse for an incompetent and bungling captain, or for the popular naval historian explaining why the British were not successful in some particular action or maneuver. It has been pointed out earlier that the British constructors had been experimenting, with great success, in fast-sailing craft as early as 1796, and were doing this in the face of opposition from the conservative sea officers and administrators. After 1800 the experimental work continued, Henry Peake, an Admiralty surveyor (or constructor), being particularly prominent. Peake turned out designs of a number of brigs, schooners, and cutters of narrow beam and sharp lines, some of which were successful and some not. Copies of successful foreign vessels were also built, and on the whole a healthy desire for improvement then existed in the Admiralty.

To further improve British Navy ships the Admiralty had established a "School of Naval Architecture" as early as 1811, to educate "superior shipwright apprentices" in the art and science of ship design. The selected apprentices entered the Royal Naval College at the Portsmouth Dockyard, where they received a sound mathematical foundation in ship design calculations and also were given an opportunity to draw plans and practice lofting. The apprentices were also to have practical experience in the Dockyard, in addition to what they had already had in their earlier training. There was very little sympathy or enthusiasm for this plan among the older shipwrights and administrative officials, and this finally led to the liquidation of the school, as well as to neglect of its graduates, for many years. The school, in fact, lasted little more than a decade.

The school was undoubtedly proficient in teaching the mathematical branch of design and did much to explore the then mystery of stability. Its faculty was headed by Professor Inman, a noted mathematician and divine interested in naval architecture, but not a practical naval architect. The weakness of the school seems to have been the lack of understanding of the application of theory to practice.

The popular criticism of the speed of British men-of-war now led to the establishment of "experimental squadrons," composed of ships and small vessels of various models and rigs, in which competitive sailing was to be the objective, with an intent to establish a method of design that would insure fast and otherwise satisfactory men-of-war. Beginning about 1820, the School of Naval Architecture, the surveyor, Seppings, and a few naval officers, including Hayes and Symonds, designed vessels for these squadrons ranging from brigs to small frigates. Lengthy trials were sailed in 1824–25 and again in 1827–28, but the results were not instructive. Some of the experimental vessels sailed very well under certain conditions, but all-around superiority was not established. Changes and "tuning up" were permitted, and it was very difficult to establish whether the advantages of certain vessels were due to their model or to the "tuning up" they received, so lacking in uniformity were the results of sailing trials. The School of Naval Architecture produced good ships, but these did not show the marked superiority expected from "science" applied to the art of sailing-ship design.

The British experimental squadrons did, however, produce many good designs and gradually raised the level of speed in the various classes of British men-of-war. There was no equivalent squadron in the American service, though the British activities were watched with interest. At every opportunity, American commanders tried out their commands with foreign men-of-war and sent in reports. These had some effect on the Navy Board and the constructors; the criticism implied when an American ship was reported to be outsailed was far more effective than any objections which might be filed on technical grounds by civilian builders and sailors. The effect of foreign designs was thus felt somewhat, and the American constructors took pains that there should be no more slow sailers, such as some of the 24-gun corvettes had shown themselves to be. However, no organized effort was made to insure superior designs, and, in fact, the Americans were now competing with the British rather than leading them in the models of men-of-war.

Since the end of the War of 1812, the old idea of a navy organized as a purely defensive arm had been thoroughly suppressed. Now it was realized that the best defense was attack and that the ships of the Navy had to be designed for sea service, and not for mere coast defense. The only exception to the policy—and that is open to argument—was in the building of the *Pennsylvania*, a fully seagoing liner of great power, whose basic function appears to have been to break a blockade rather than to lead a cruising squadron. Nevertheless, she could have performed either service had it been necessary, so there was actually no real divergence from the naval policy in her construction. In the powerful 74's built or building, the Navy would have had a battle squadron dangerous to any foreign power in the event of war; and these were to be supported by a large number of commerce destroyers, represented by corvettes intended to overmatch similar ships in foreign navies. In addition, the battle squadron had the support of the light or heavy cruisers of the frigate classes, which were capable of also acting as raiders. The American frigates being built were superior to any under construction for European navies, except for a few individual ships at most. Support for the seagoing ships was being established in the existence of navy yards and some service craft. There were still weaknesses—small light craft were lacking, and there was a need for faster corvettes—but on the whole the sailing Navy had at last become an effective instrument of war.

★ ★ ★ ★ ★ ★ ★ ★ ★ ★

CHAPTER SEVEN

The Bureaucratic Navy
1830-1840

THE 1820's had been years of peace, so far as the American Navy was concerned, with no warlike activities beyond the suppression of piracy in the West Indies and rather abortive attempts to put down the slave trade. Stagnation set in, and by 1830 the United States Navy was thoroughly bureaucratic in organization, controlled, so far as naval construction and design were concerned, by the Board of Navy Commissioners. The Board members were still the aging veterans of the War of 1812, and extreme conservatism was now the rule.

The evolution of the design of the ship of the line *Pennsylvania* reached the final stages in 1830, and the plans now showed the ship about as she was completed. Minor changes, however, were made after this year, the most important being a slight alteration in her after cant frames just forward of the sternpost to ease her run. Her headrails and stern were also altered slightly. Plan 25 is the final design and represents the ship as she was built. It will be seen that the *Pennsylvania* had no pretensions to grace; she was merely a very powerful gun carrier, of enormous displacement for her length. The designer had apparently recognized her shortcomings and, at the last moment, had revised her run in an effort to improve her sailing qualities. The *Pennsylvania* was not an unqualified success after her launch; some officers thought her cumbersome, leewardly, and crank. To commanders trained in the smart frigates and the handy 74's—*Columbus, Franklin, Ohio,* and the popular *North Carolina*—the

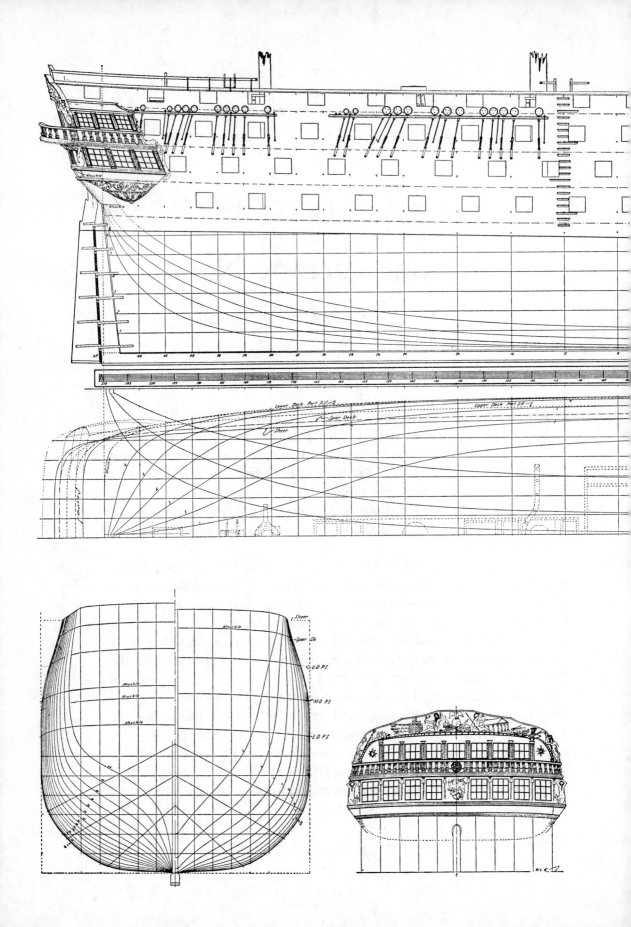

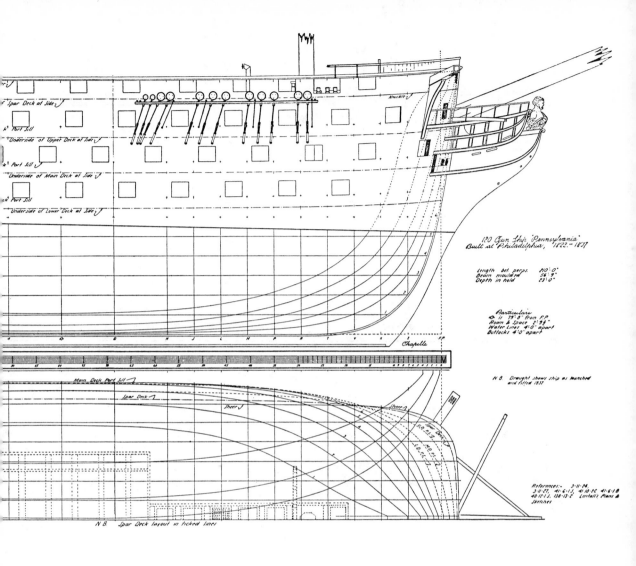

Plan 25. Building draught for the 120-gun ship PENNSYLVANIA, *showing ship as launched and fitted.*

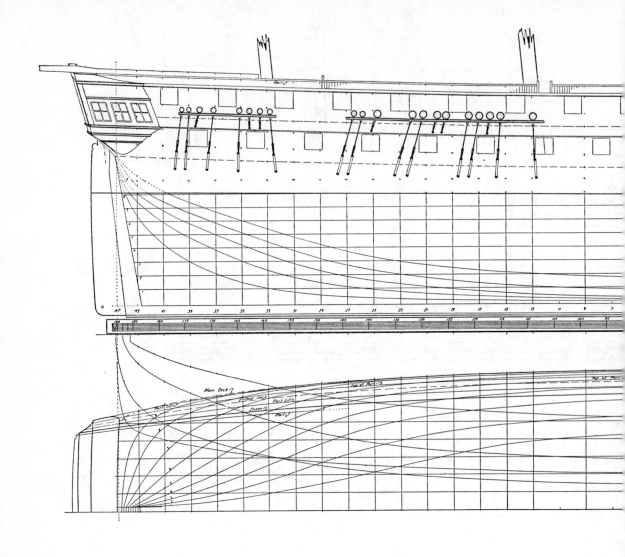

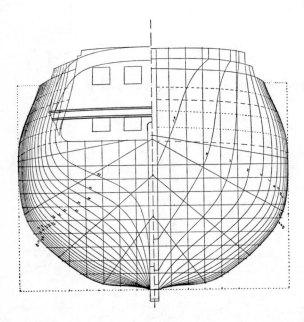

Particulars
O ̈ 75·4' from F.P.
1 ̈ 79·0' from F.P.   a ̈ 54' from F.P.
Stations spaced 5·0'.
1st W.L. 3·0' above Base, others spaced 2·6'.
Buttocks 3·3' apart.

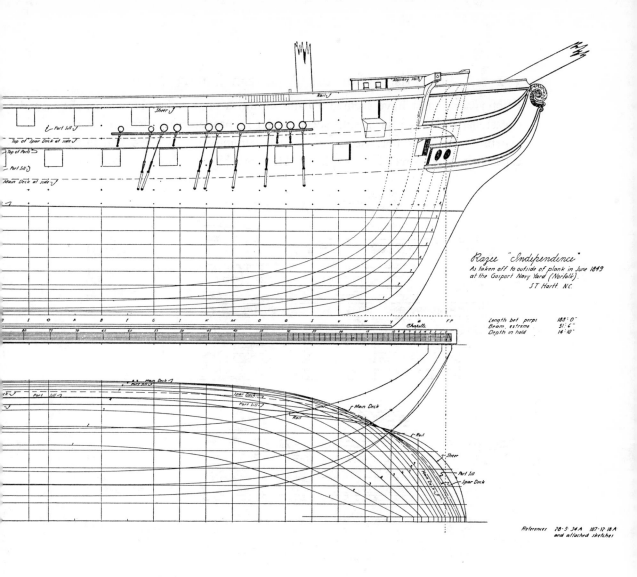

Razee "Independence"
As taken off to outside of plank in June 1849
at the Gosport Navy Yard (Norfolk).
J.T. Hartt. N.C.

Length bet perps   188' 0"
Beam, extreme   51' 6"
Depth in hold   14' 10"

References   28-S 34 A   107-12 18 A
and attached sketches

Plan 26. Plan of INDEPENDENCE *as a razee, made from measurements taken from the ship after her alteration.*

Pennsylvania must have seemed a handful and a poor sailer. However, she occasionally showed surprising speed when in proper trim. Because of the expense of manning her, she saw very little commissioned service, and so her capabilities were never fully explored. Her very high freeboard undoubtedly

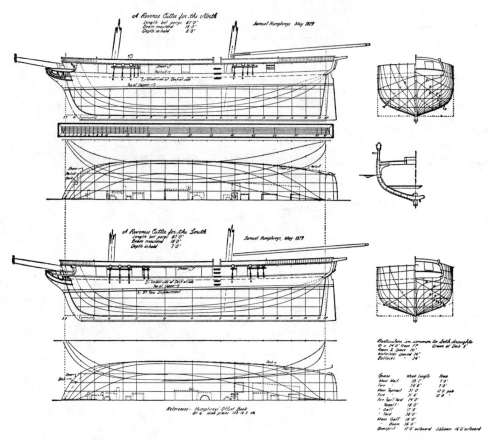

Figure 92. Draught of revenue cutters for a northern and a southern station, 1829.

made her less weatherly than the 74's, and her full lines would have prevented her from sailing as fast as the *Ohio*. However, she was no more awkward than most of the foreign liners and was as fast as most ships of her rate. The cost of maintaining this ship was the greatest objection to keeping her in service, and the vessel was, indeed, somewhat of a white elephant to a navy required to be strictly economical. In fact, the whole liner class was very expensive to operate in peacetime, as experience had shown. Hence the slow progress on the liners

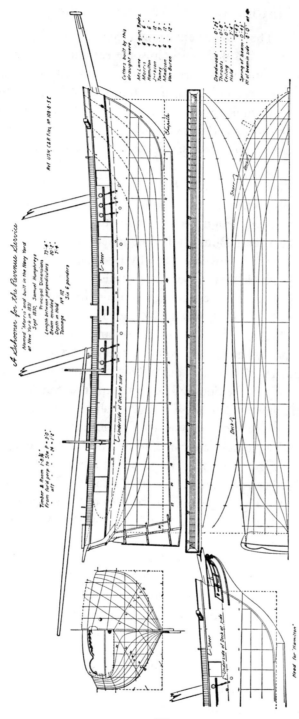

A Schooner for the Revenue Service

Named "Morris" and built in the Navy Yard
at New York in 1831.   Samuel Humphreys
Sept 1830.   Principal Dimensions
Length between perpendiculars   73'-4"
Beam moulded   20'-2"
Depth in Hold   7'-4"
Tonnage   No 112   Six 6 pounders

Ref. U.S.N. C & R File, No 108-9-5 E

Timber & Room 1'-8¾"
From ford perp to Sta 9 = 3'-0";
aft " = 2'-1½"

Cutters built by this
draught were:
Mc Lane   1 gun, 3 pdrs
Morris   6   "   6
Hamilton   2   "   6
Jackson   2   "   12
Toney   2   "   9
Madison   6   "   12
Van Buren   6   "   12

Deadwood .... 0'-6"
Throats .... 0'-8"
Ceiling .... 0'-7"
Hold .... 7'-4"
Spring of beam 0'-4½"
Ht of beam at side 8'-0" at ℄

Figure 93. Draught of revenue cutter MORRIS and class.

373

then on the stocks. They were kept "under construction" as an economical mode of maintaining ships of the class in some readiness for war, if it should come. From time to time in the early '30's the desirability of creating an improved class of liners was considered, and Humphreys' 1827 design appears to have been extensively studied with this aim in view. However, economy and the experience with the giant *Pennsylvania* prevented anything being done to produce a new class of large liners: frigates and sloops were more useful in a peacetime navy.

Beginning in 1830 the Revenue Service received a number of useful additions to their cruising cutters. As many of the new vessels were to be used later by the Navy, their design becomes a matter of consideration now. As early as 1815, Constructor Doughty had designed three classes of small one-gun cutters. These were followed in 1825 by two classes of more burdensome schooners, one of which was given "drop keels." The relatively small size (60′ 0″) and force of these cutters, however, made them of little value as naval units. As in the earlier period, when Fox had designed revenue cutters, the function of design for this class was now in the hands of the naval constructors, and in 1829 Humphreys designed two improved cutters, each 62′ 0″ between perpendiculars and 18′ 0″ moulded beam. One was for a northern station and the other for a station in the South. The cutter for the North was 10″ deeper than the southern schooner, and she was slightly sharper. Figure 92 shows both designs; they were vessels of very heavy displacement. These designs were followed, in 1830, by a much faster one, to be used to build the *Morris* in the New York Navy Yard. The new design was for a very handsome clipper schooner 73′ 4″ between perpendiculars, 20′ 2″ moulded beam, and 7′ 4″ depth of hold. The *Morris* (Figure 94) was pierced to carry 14 guns, brass 6-pdrs. of medium length, or, as an alternate, 12-pdr. carronades. As a cutter, the *Morris* carried but 6 guns.

It was originally intended to build ten cutters in the navy yards, but this was found impractical because of the building program already in effect, so only the *Morris* and three others were built in government yards—the *Alexander Hamilton* and *Albert Gallatin* at the New York Navy Yard, and the *Andrew Jackson* at the Washington Yard. All were built to the *Morris* plan, but with the addition of a naval head; only the *Morris* came out with the simple curved stem and the moulding underneath the gun ports. The rest of the vessels were built by private contract using the *Morris* plan as the "contract design." The builders were not required to hold to the plan, however, and the contrac-

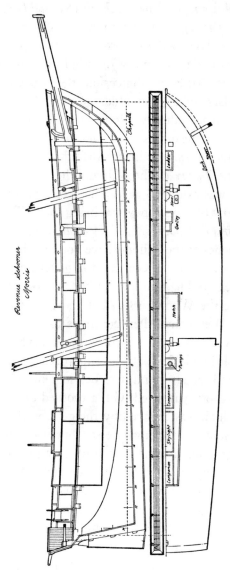

Figure 94. Inboard arrangement of MORRIS *and class.*

tors prepared new designs. Webb and Allen, of New York, contracted for six cutters—the *Louis McLane*, *Richard Rush*, and *Samuel D. Ingham*, all launched in 1832, and the *Thomas Jefferson* (later renamed *Crawford*), *James Madison*, and *Roger B. Taney*, launched the next year. Isaac Webb, Eckford's able apprentice, made the design for some of these at least, shown in Figure 95. This design called for somewhat larger dimensions than the contract design, 74′ 6″ between perpendiculars, 20′ 8½″ moulded beam, and 7′ 6″ depth of hold. No record has been found to indicate whether all the Webb-built cutters were on this design or whether the others were built to individual plans. The sail plan of the *Jefferson* made in 1843 indicates that this cutter was about ten feet longer than either the *Taney* or the *Morris*. The *McLane* was noted for her beautiful finish and was exhibited at Washington to show Congressmen and influential citizens how the tax money was being spent. The remaining cutters, *Oliver Wolcott*, *Campbell*, *Dexter*, and *Washington*, were all built in New York also, but the names of the builders have not been found.

These cutters appear to have been the first government vessels fitted with geared steering wheels. Joshua Humphreys had proposed this method of steering sometime before the War of 1812, but there is no record of its having been used until the Webb and Allen contracts for the revenue cutters. The steering gear employed in the cutters consisted of a wheel and gear mounted on a shaft, the forward end of which was supported by an A-frame just abaft the steering wheel and the after end by a bearing, swivel-mounted, on top of the rudderpost. The post was fitted with a toothed quadrant, extending forward of the post, which was engaged by the gear on the shaft. This type of gear was found satisfactory for small vessels but was not strong enough for large ships, as the gear teeth sometimes broke, or jumped on the quadrant, when exposed to a heavy strain. The cutters seem to have used this style of gear until about 1850. Humphreys had proposed many other improvements, such as an improved bilge pump, a fire engine, and rudder ironwork, but he was apparently unable to get the government to adopt his ideas when they were presented. Later most of them were employed, but he was not given the credit he deserved, though he had been very active in the support of improved ship fittings and hardware.

Three more revenue cutters were built at Baltimore which were much larger vessels than the *Morris* and the Webb cutters. The *Levi Woodbury* was built by L. H. Duncan, and a second *Washington* and the *Martin Van Buren* by builders whose names are not on record. The *Woodbury* was launched in

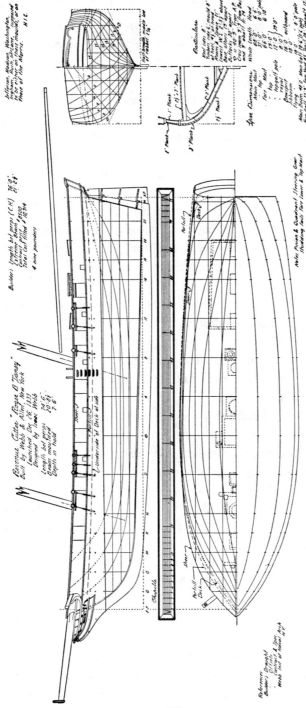

Figure 95. Draught of revenue cutter ROGER B. TANEY, *a vessel showing some features employed later in the design of the yacht* AMERICA, *1851.*

1836, the *Washington* in '37, and the *Van Buren* in '39. The repetition of the name *Washington* was brought about by replacing the earlier cutter of this name, which was found in 1837 to be infected with dry rot, and so was sold. Of these Baltimore-built cutters, the plans of the *Washington* exist (Figures 96, 97, and 98). This vessel was built as a schooner but was rerigged as a brig in 1838, as she was large for a schooner cutter, 91′ 2″ between perpendiculars and 22′ 1″ moulded beam. She was a noted sailer, and her lines show the ideas of the Cheseapeake Bay builders for a fast seagoing vessel at the date of her build. Her deck arrangement was a common one at this period in Chesapeake-built schooners and brigs, the afterhouse extending clear across the ship to form a raised deck, with a sunk poop abaft it. This deck arrangement had been introduced in pilot schooners and remained a characteristic of them as late as 1850. The *Washington* was transferred to the Navy in 1838 and was finally returned to the Revenue Service in 1848. Most of her naval career was spent as a survey vessel.

The lines of another brigantine or schooner are shown in Figure 99. This is an undated plan made by Samuel Humphreys, probably about 1835. The design calls for a vessel on the same general model and dimensions as the *Dolphin* but with an improved run. This plan appears to have been one submitted to the Treasury Department about this time, but there is no indication that it was actually used to build a cutter. The sail plan of the *Jefferson* will serve to show the appearance of cutters of this size and type.

The large cutters formed a useful reserve to the Navy, since they could have been employed either as light cruisers or as dispatch boats in the event of war. Some of them, in fact, were utilized for these purposes in the Seminole War and later in the Mexican War. There was apparently one drawback to the plan of building revenue cutters for the dual purpose (of cutter and naval vessel) that has caused difficulties in more recent times: the cutters grew steadily larger to meet naval requirements, until eventually the point was reached where the vessels were too big and too expensive to operate as revenue cutters. Then the large cutters were surrendered to the Navy and the Revenue Service was forced to build smaller replacements. Proposals for 100′ cutters, brigantine- or brig-rigged, were made in the late '30's, but none were built, though two or three designs appear to have been made.

The government held large tracts of timber land in southern states, particularly on the Georgia and Gulf coasts, containing the much-prized live oak. It was found that illegal timber cutting was denuding the government pre-

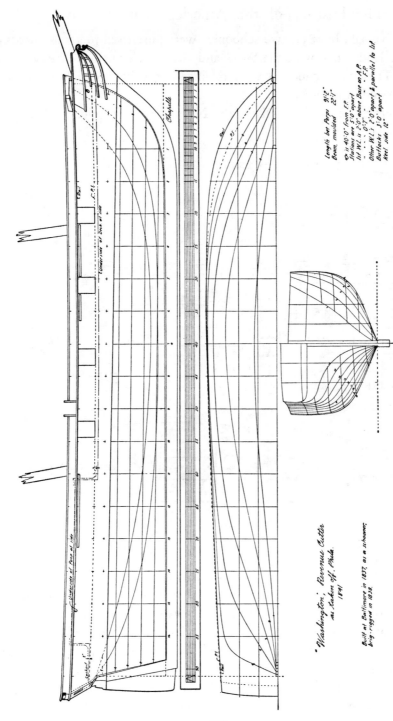

Figure 96. Draught of the revenue cutter WASHINGTON.

serves of live oak. In 1831, two schooners were purchased to act as guards of
the timber lands; they were the *Spark* and *Ariel*, each small and carrying but
one gun. These two schooners were retained but a short time, however, and
both were sold in 1832–33.

The shortage of small vessels in the Navy was now quite marked. This

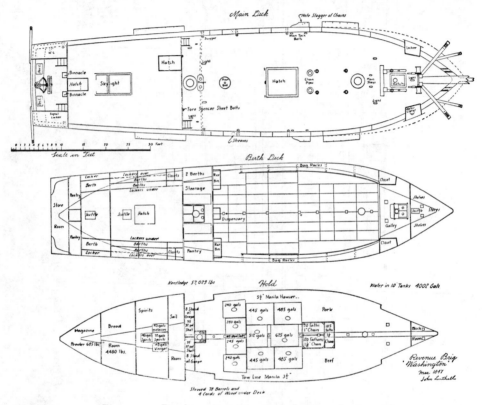

Figure 97. Deck arrangements of the WASHINGTON.

necessitated the use of large vessels, of the sloop class, in work for which they
were unsuited either because of their size, or because of the expense required
to maintain them on distant stations. It was finally decided to build three 10-gun
schooners, and plans were prepared for the class. Humphreys made a number
of preliminary studies of sharp schooners from 100′ downward to 88′ between
perpendiculars; the Board, however, decided on the smallest dimensions. The
approved design (Figure 100) called for schooners 88′ 0″ between perpendiculars, 23′ 6″ moulded beam, and 10′ 0″ depth of hold. On this plan, the

Boxer was laid down in the Boston Navy Yard, the *Experiment* in the Washington Yard, and the *Enterprise* in the New York establishment. The *Experiment* lived up to her name, as she was to be built on a new construction apparently employing some light frames and longitudinal stiffeners, which suggests that she may have been diagonally planked with two or more layers

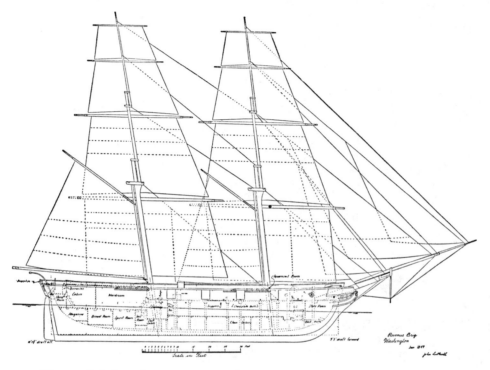

Figure 98. Inboard arrangement and spar and sail plan of the WASHINGTON.

of thin stuff. The intent was, obviously, to develop a way to build vessels with timber of small scantling. No drawings of the construction, however, have yet come to light. The schooners were designed to draw but 12′, to fit them for the West Indian station, and were to carry 8 to 10 carronades, 24-pdrs., and 2 long 9's. These craft were all launched in 1831. They were very useful and lasted quite well. The *Enterprise* was sold in 1845, and the *Boxer* and *Experiment* in 1848. They were fast sailers for naval schooners, overloaded as they were with guns and boats. Not only was the *Experiment* different in construction, but there were also minor differences in the appearance of the *Boxer* and *Enterprise*. The *Boxer* had the old curved upper rail at her head and had deeper ports with a moulding underneath. She also had slightly greater rake to her upper transom, and her knightheads were narrower than those in *Enterprise*. The model was that of a clipper schooner of the period, but somewhat more full in the bow, perhaps, when compared to the best of the revenue cutters or private-owned clipper schooners and brigs. The *Boxer* was rerigged as a brig in the early '40's. The unpopularity of the schooner in the Navy remained unchanged until the end of the usefulness of the sailing man-of-war,

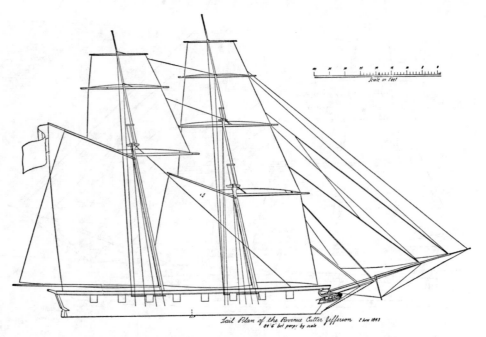

Figure 99. Sailmaker's sketch of the revenue cutter JEFFERSON.

in spite of the extraordinary popularity of the rig in the merchant marine in the same period and the record of the earlier privateers and naval schooners. The *Enterprise* and her sisters were heavily rigged as schooners and, with their load of guns and boats, were considered tender; the *Boxer* as a brig was by far the worst in this respect.

The exact uses to which the various congressional appropriations were put are now difficult to follow. The authorized construction appears to have exceeded the actual, in some classes of ships, so there should have been some surplus funds to be applied to "rebuilt" vessels. Beginning in 1813, the Act of January 2 had authorized the construction of the last of the wartime-built

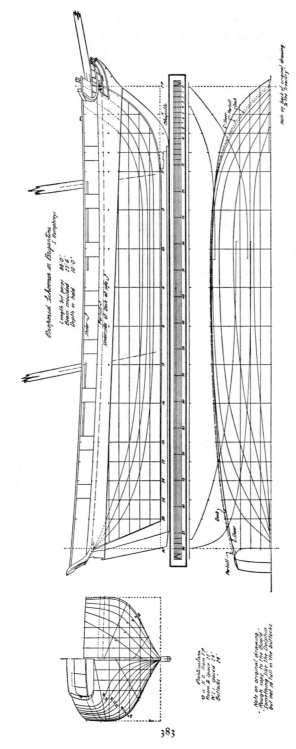

Figure 100. Proposed schooner or brigantine by Samuel Humphreys.

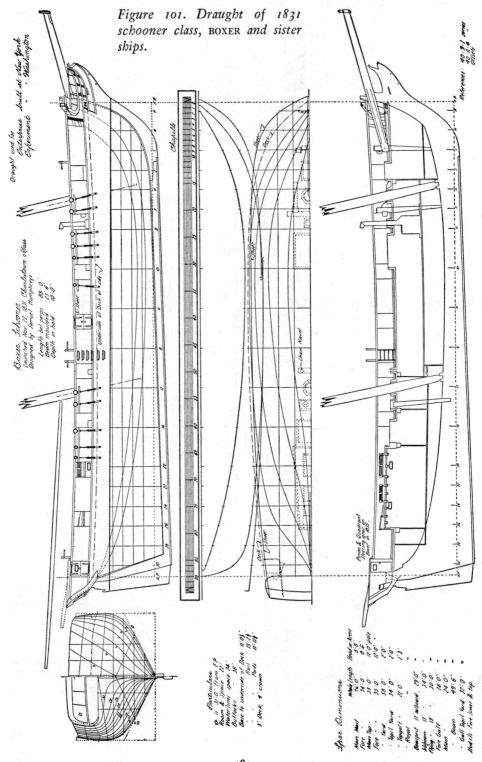

Figure 101. Draught of 1831 schooner class, BOXER *and sister ships.*

384

74's and three frigates. One of the latter was burned before she was completed, so there should have been unallotted funds from this source. The Act of April 27, 1816, authorized an additional eight 74's and nine 44's, and also three steam batteries, which were to have frames and engines contracted for, but which were not required to be completed. There is no evidence that the instructions in regard to the three batteries were actually put in force in full, and therefore authorized funds were apparently left from this act. The 1824–25 corvettes appear to have used funds from this source, and it is highly probable that the little remaining went into the "rebuilt" ships and the building of shore stations. It is to be noted that, in 1831, Congress granted some money to permit the rebuilding of the *Macedonian* and *Cyane* and, in 1834, additional sums were granted for the rebuilding of the last-named ship. The art of juggling appropriations in a government agency was then well understood, as was also the exceeding of estimates.

In 1832, the new *Macedonian* was laid down at Norfolk, Virginia. She was launched in 1836 and had as her figurehead the bust of Alexander the Great taken from the old ship. As has been noted earlier, the old British ship was not broken up for some years after the new ship was laid down, and she finally disappeared just before the "rebuilt" ship was launched. It is not possible to explore in full the methods by which this ship and others were accounted for to Congress, and the matter is of relatively little importance now. With the "rebuilt" *John Adams* launched, the *Macedonian* started, the *Cyane* with funds already earmarked for her, there remained the *Congress* to be similarly "rebuilt" and the old *Independence* to be attended to in some manner to make her a useful ship.

In 1833–34 Congress added to the funds available for new construction under the Act of 1816, and it was decided to divert a small portion of these from the ships now on the stocks and to use the money to build a good storeship for the fleet. The various old storeships, purchased from private owners, had become worn out and had been disposed of, and there had been nothing available as a replacement. In peacetime a storeship was used to carry supplies to distant stations and also to act as a packet or dispatch vessel. Humphreys prepared a design of a small ship, on merchant-vessel lines, which was allotted to the Philadelphia yard for construction. The design (Figure 102) was for a ship measuring 109′ 0″ between perpendiculars, 30′ 0″ moulded beam, and 12′ 0″ depth of hold, named *Relief*. The design was nothing unusual; she was pierced to carry 16 small guns, and her usual armament was 4 18-pdrs. and 2 12's,

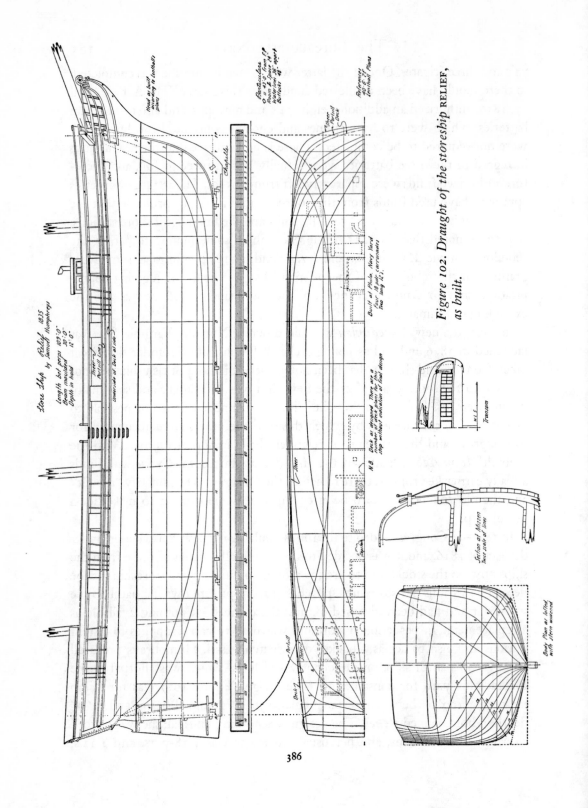

Figure 102. Draught of the storeship RELIEF, *as built.*

386

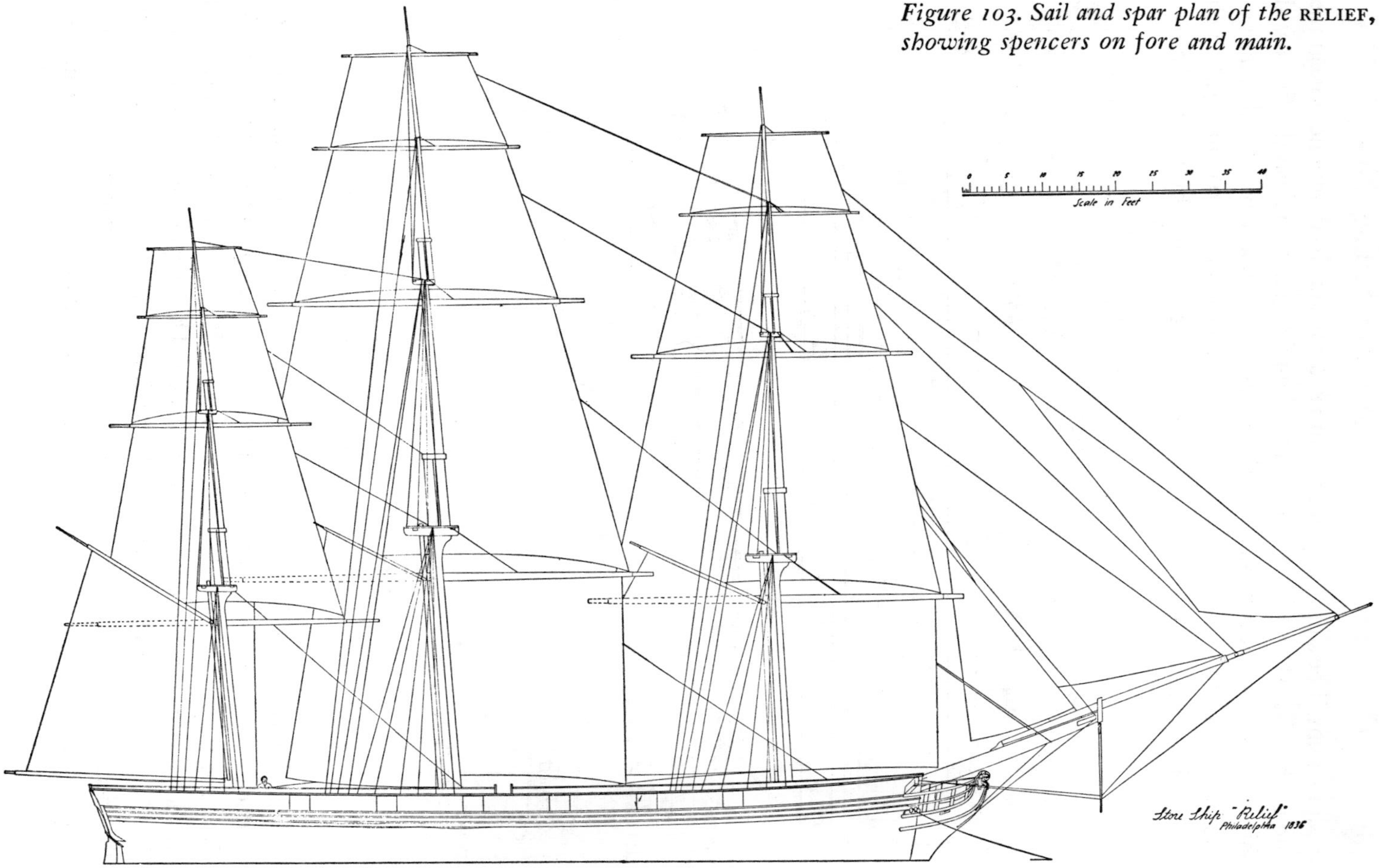

Figure 103. Sail and spar plan of the RELIEF, showing spencers on fore and main.

Scale in Feet

Store Ship "Relief"
Philadelphia 1836

medium guns. The ship was launched in 1836 and survived until her sale at the
end of the Civil War. Her rig, shown in Figure 103, is notable as the first naval
ship to employ spencer masts on both fore and main in any of the sail plans yet
found. The spencer mast was nothing more than the snow's trysail mast which
was set just abaft the mainmast, and supported at the head by the main cross-

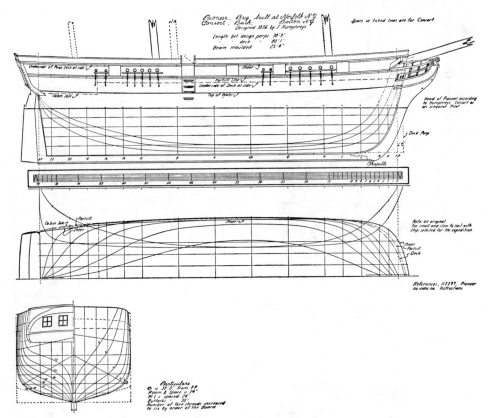

Figure 104. Draught of exploring vessels PIONEER *and* CONSORT.

trees and bolsters. At the foot it either rested on deck or, more commonly, on
a table or chock secured to the after side of the main, a little above the deck. On
this mast the spanker was hoisted, with its gaff jaws riding on the stick, and
the boom either on the stick or on the chock. The purpose of this was to permit the main yard to be lowered to deck without interfering with the spanker.
Practically all man-of-war brigs in the American Navy had been actually snow-
rigged since about 1806, but the term "snow" had gone out of use. The method

of setting the spanker, or trysail, of the snow had also been used for the spanker
of frigates and sloops a few years before 1832, but the exact date when this
rig was introduced has not yet been determined. The 24-gun corvettes of
1825–26 had spencers on the mainmast but none on the foremast. The innovation in the *Relief* was in the use of the trysail mast, and its attendant gaffsail, on

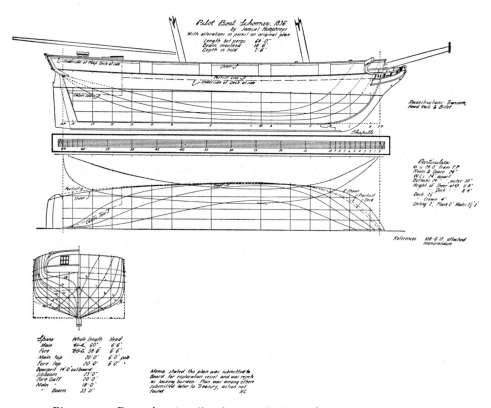

Figure 105. Draught of a pilot-boat exploring schooner, proposed 1836.

all three masts, instead of employing main and mizzen staysails. In strong winds,
a vessel rigged with spencers could be worked to windward under them and
would be, in effect, a three-masted schooner. The advantages of this were
obvious and the later American sloops and corvettes followed suit. It must not
be supposed, however, that the *Relief* or the earlier corvettes introduced the
innovation, for merchant ships and some packets were certainly carrying this
rig in 1825, if not much earlier; it now seems probable that the rig employed
in the *Relief* was first introduced in the packet ships.

In 1829, Edmund Fanning of Stonington, Connecticut, was instrumental in fitting out an expedition to the South Seas. This attracted much public attention. In 1836 the government organized a similar expedition of exploration, known as the Wilkes Expedition. The question of suitable craft for exploration being thus raised, it was decided to build three vessels for the purpose and to purchase one tender. It was considered that these, with a war vessel as flagship, would constitute a useful squadron. Humphreys was ordered to prepare plans to very rigid requirements; the results were far from happy for all concerned. He supplied a design that could be rigged as both a brig and a bark. This design (Figure 104) was used to build the bark *Consort* at the Boston Navy Yard and the brig *Pioneer* at the Norfolk Yard. Measuring 78′ 9″ between perpendiculars and 25′ 4″ moulded beam, they were, in short, very deep and tubby craft. The third vessel to be built was a schooner tender. Humphreys, working under the instructions of the Board and Wilkes, prepared a design for a schooner 64′ 0″ between perpendiculars and 18′ 4″ moulded beam—a heavy-displacement pilot boat somewhat like the sealing schooners sailing out of New London, Connecticut, at the time. She had a rather good model, as can be seen by Figure 105, but the Navy Board wanted a vessel of greater capacity. Another design was then made by Humphreys, for a schooner 65′ between perpendiculars and 21′ 6″ moulded beam. The model was somewhat similar to that of the first design but much fuller (Figure 106). The schooner was pierced for eight guns and had a large stern cabin about 12′ long. The Board accepted this design, and the schooner was built at the New York Navy Yard, as the *Pilot*, in 1836.

The three exploring ships were rigged and tested in 1837; it was found that all three were very slow, the two larger ones particularly so. This was a blow to the planners of the expedition, and after some effort they arranged for the Navy to furnish another man-of-war and, in addition, to buy two New York pilot schooners, the *Independence* and *Seagull*, in 1838, before the expedition was ready to leave. The *Independence*, renamed *Flying Fish*, was 86′ 5″ long over all and 22′ 6″ moulded beam; the *Seagull* was slightly larger. The latter went missing off Cape Horn in 1839 while acting as a survey vessel for the expedition, and the *Flying Fish* was condemned at Singapore in 1842 and was sold. She afterward became a notorious opium smuggler, under the name of *Spec*. The substitution of the sharp, light displacement pilot schooners for the Board's schooner and brig illustrates how much the Board of Navy Commissioners really erred in estimating the requirements of the vessels for the expedition. The three useless exploring ships were employed for a time in salvage work and were sold as soon as the matter quieted down. The reputation of the three vessels did not add to the Board's prestige, nor was the "official" designer benefited; in fact the vessels were the laughing stock of the civilian builders and seamen who learned of the fiasco.

In 1834–35 it was decided to build two more small vessels, an "improved"

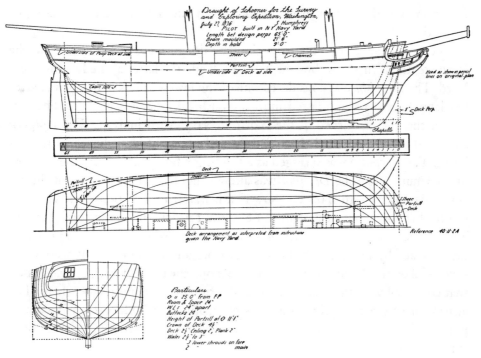

Figure 106. Draught of PILOT, *for survey and exploring service.*

edition of the schooners built in 1831. The new vessels were to be brigantines of the same length as the older vessels, 88′ 0″ between perpendiculars, but the moulded beam was increased to 25′ 0″ and the depth in the hold to 11′ 0″. The revised dimensions were intended to create brigantines of greater stability and capacity than the earlier schooners. The lines were very good for a full-ended clipper, as can be seen by Figure 107. The sail plan (Figure 108) will give an idea of the rig of the new vessels. While Humphreys was preparing the new design, Samuel Pook made a proposal for a somewhat larger schooner, 90′ 0″ between perpendiculars, 26′ 6″ moulded beam, and 11′ 0″ depth of hold (Figure 109), but the greater draft caused the Humphreys design to be preferred. About this time Humphreys prepared a design for a sharp, deep brig 88′ 0″ between perpendiculars and 27′ 0″ moulded beam, shown in Figure 109a. This design and Pook's schooner were apparently submitted both to the Navy and to the Treasury, so it may have been intended for cutters and naval service jointly. The idea of large cutters suitable for naval service occupied a good deal of attention throughout the 1830's, and the scanty records make it difficult to determine whether a plan was intended for a cutter or for a naval vessel, or for both.

The two brigantines built from the new design were the *Dolphin* and the *Porpoise;* the former was built at New York and the latter at the Boston Navy Yard. The *Dolphin* was considered one of the fastest sailers in the Navy, after her launch in 1836, and lasted until the outbreak of the Civil War. She was one of the vessels burned in the Norfolk Navy Yard in 1861. The *Dolphin* and the *Porpoise* retained the old upturned upper headrail beneath the cat-heads. The *Porpoise* was rerigged as a full brig a few years before she was lost in the China Seas. The *Dolphin* was altered slightly from her draught during construction; her return offsets show that her aftermost sections were changed to give her easier buttocks than those in the *Porpoise* or in the class draught. The correct body plan of *Dolphin* is shown in Figure 114, showing a proposed design made by lengthening this very fast brigantine. Both vessels were quite successful on the African coast and were among the few American naval vessels that could sail with the best of the British brigs and brigantines met there. The armament of the two brigantines was originally 10 24-pdr. carronades and 2 long 9's. These were the last two-masters under 100′ in length that were built for the Navy.

A schooner yacht, named *Wave*, was purchased for naval service in 1836. The *Wave* had been designed on pilot-boat lines by John C. Stevens and built for him in 1832. She was armed with two small guns and employed as a surveying vessel until 1846. Her model is now in the New York Yacht Club's model room. The revenue brig *Washington*, described earlier, was transferred to the Navy in this year.

Another important undertaking this year was the cutting down of the 74-gun ship *Independence* into a frigate, officially rated at 54 guns. This made her a "razee"—a term applied to liners that had been cut down into frigates or two-decked ships. The practice had been an old one; the British had cut down a number of liners into frigates during the Napoleonic Wars, and the French had

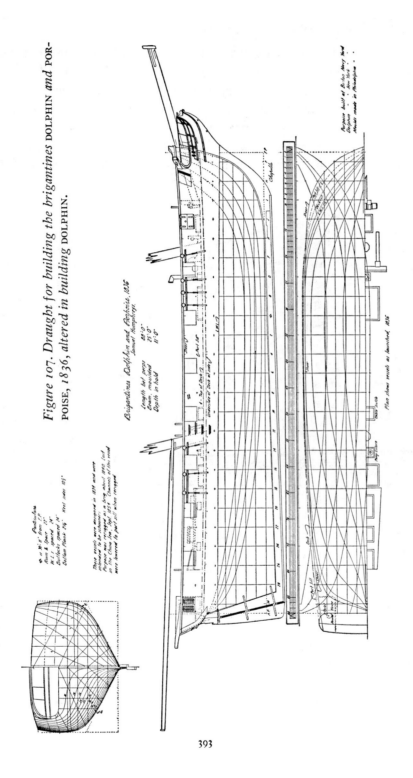

Figure 107. Draught for building the brigantines DOLPHIN *and* POR-
POISE, *1836, altered in building* DOLPHIN.

393

also cut down a few of their ships. The practice had been confined to either old ships of the line whose upper works were weakened by rot and age, or to 74's that had shown a lack of stability or which did not have sufficient displacement to carry their lower deck guns high enough above the load water line to be satisfactory. The cutting down consisted of the removal of the spar, or uppermost, decks, leaving the two lower armed decks intact in most ships, though occasionally the waist guns on the newly formed spar deck might also be re-

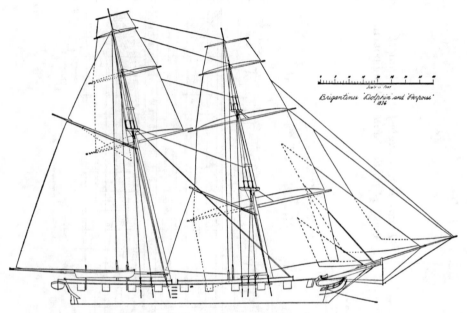

Figure 108. Sail plan for DOLPHIN *and* PORPOISE.

moved. The vessel was thus lightened a great deal, and this, with the huge rig of a liner, often made the razee a very fast ship. The *Independence* was the only American liner ever cut down, though it was intended to razee the *Franklin* at one time.

The *Independence*, as a razee, was a very satisfactory ship and proved to be a very smart sailer. No plans were made when the ship was cut down, but later the lines of the ship were taken off in dry dock, and these (Plan 26) show the ship as she appeared after the alteration. The lines were taken off to the outside of her planking, and her measurements were found to be 188′ 0″ between the corrected perpendiculars (which would be somewhat less than when a 74), 51′ 6″ extreme beam (about 49′ 8″ moulded beam), and 14′ 10″

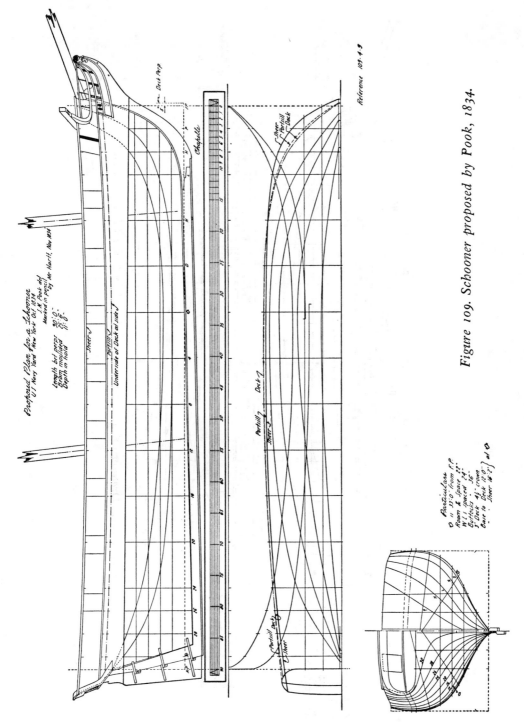

Figure 109. Schooner proposed by Pook, 1834.

395

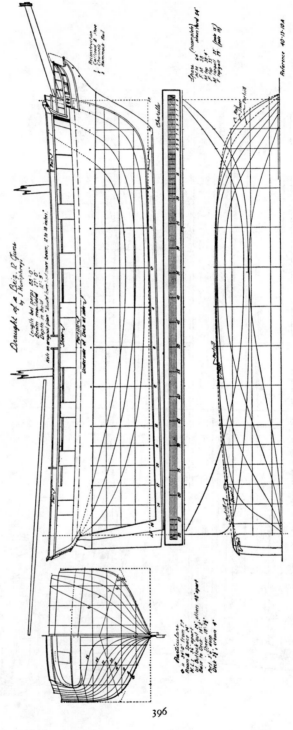

Figure 109a. Draught for a 12-gun brig proposed by Samuel Humphreys.

depth of hold. The alterations made the ship the largest frigate in the Navy and, after extensive repairs to her hull, she became a very noted ship. She spent much of her career in the Pacific and was a receiving ship at the Mare Island Navy Yard, California, from 1857 to 1900; she was sold and broken up in 1914. Thus a ship considered a failure and useless for almost twenty-two years became one of the best ships in the Navy.

In 1837 another schooner was purchased, the *Active*, 122 tons, 2 guns, which was intended for a tender for the Wilkes Expedition. Like the *Pilot*, she was found too slow to keep up with the men-of-war in the squadron and so joined the *Pilot* in salvage work, and was sold in 1838. These salvage vessels were really engaged in rescue work. They were sent to sea in the winter months to be on the lookout for vessels in distress. The Navy schooners worked with the revenue cutters for a few years, carrying out this duty. Finally the responsibility for this work was assigned to the Revenue Service alone.

In this year, 1837, two more ship sloops were laid down—the *Cyane*, an administratively "rebuilt" vessel, and the *Levant*, an admittedly new ship. The vessels were sister ships, officially being built from the same design; the *Cyane* was constructed at the Boston Navy Yard and the *Levant* at the New York Yard. The plans for these ships were started in 1836 but underwent some alteration, and when they were issued to the navy yards in the next year they called for a corvette 132′ 3″ between perpendiculars and 34′ 3″ moulded beam. In design the corvettes were improved and enlarged copies of the earlier 24-gun ships of 1825. They had much the same appearance, but they were somewhat easier in the bilges, the run was slightly sharper, and the proportions of length to displacement better suited to speed. Figure 110 represents the building plan of the two ships and contains all of the alterations made in the preliminary design. The extensive changes in the first plans of the ships were obviously an attempt to insure better sailing qualities; Humphreys was probably alarmed by the criticisms leveled at the 1825 corvettes and the exploration vessels and now was insistent that the new ships have a good turn of speed. His improvements and changes were undoubtedly successful; the new corvettes were good sailers and very satisfactory cruisers, though not handsome, carrying their armament and allowances with ease. For a short time the corvettes carried 18 carronades, 32-pdrs., and 4 long 24-pdrs.; the long guns were then replaced with 4 shell guns, 8″. A proposal was made to arm these vessels with an entire battery of long 24-pdrs., but nothing seems to have come of it; perhaps it was decided that this powerful battery was too heavy for the

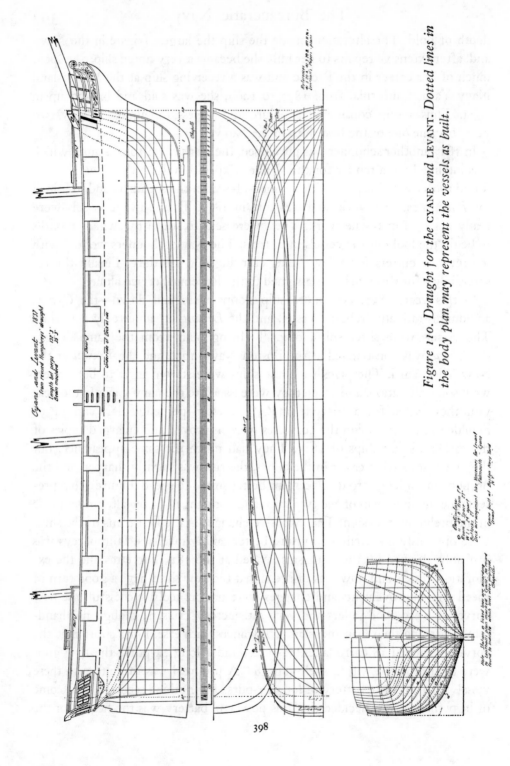

Figure 110. Draught for the CYANE *and* LEVANT. *Dotted lines in the body plan may represent the vessels as built.*

sloops. The final design of these two vessels showed Humphreys' progress in achieving better hull forms in the sloop class. Beginning with the 24-gun corvettes, he had improved on them in the rebuilt *Peacock*, by fining the ends, but the small dimensions of that ship had made the experiment unsatisfactory. In the new class he had first resorted to rather full ends to obtain all the displacement the Board apparently required, but on later consideration he again sharpened the ends and in particular greatly improved the run, at the expense

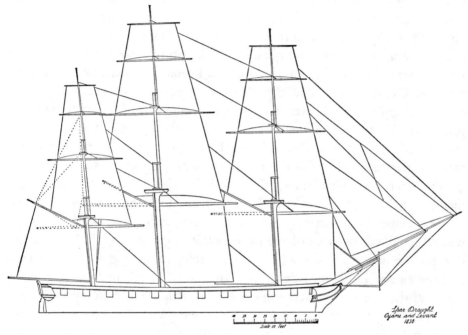

Figure 111. Spar and sail plan for CYANE *and* LEVANT.

of displacement. Even after this reduction in displacement the ships were amply burdensome, as is shown not only by the reports on their sailing and working as cruisers but also by the fact that spar decks were added to the *Cyane* late in her career.

The *Cyane* and *Levant* were the first American corvettes fitted with fore and main spencer masts when launched. The two vessels spent much of their lives on the Pacific stations. The *Cyane* was sold in California in 1887, and the *Levant* went missing with all hands in the Pacific in the fall of 1860. The ships were usually rated as 22-gun corvettes, though sometimes as 18's, and when the fashion of numerical classification came into existence, in the late '30's, these corvettes, with the earlier 1825 sloops, were placed in the "2nd Class" of ship sloops. Their lack of grace and beauty drew the same unfavorable comment that had characterized the earlier sloops.

The next year, 1838, saw the construction of a new class of ship sloops, which were intended to be economical cruisers particularly suited for distant stations, and were to rate as 16-gun sloops, "3rd Class." They were intended to carry a battery of 16 carronades, 32-pdrs., in time of peace, with the addition of two long guns to complete their war armament. The fashion had now become general, both in the United States Navy and in foreign services, of giving ships a light battery in time of peace, and establishing a larger or more effective war armament. The question of the proper size for the new class was a matter of some difference in opinion. Proposals for the new class were made by Grice, who submitted a plan for a sloop 111′ 0″ between perpendiculars (Figure 112), Barker, who sent in a design for a much heavier displacement ship 114′ 6″ in length, and Lenthall, who proposed a sloop of the same length but lighter in displacement. It was pointed out to the Board that these small ships would be unable to carry a heavy armament and still be fast, as suited their class. Grudgingly, the Board considered an increase in size and finally seized upon the idea that the new class should be the same length as the 1813 classes, approximately 117′ between perpendiculars. Lenthall's design was accepted, but he was ordered to redraw it to greater length. His final design for the new class of sloops called for ships measuring 117′ 7″ between perpendiculars, 32′ 0″ moulded beam, and 15′ 0″ depth of hold. It will be seen that the new sloops were slightly shorter than the old Doughty designs, but were 6″ wider and deeper, which increased their official tonnage to 566. The round stern, or rather elliptical stern (since the latter was the type used in the American Navy), was now discarded, and the approved design (Figure 113) reverted to the old transom stern. The new sloops, so far as dimensions and rig were concerned, were practically reproductions of the *Wasp-Peacock-Frolic* class of 1813; only the displacement and model of the new sloops differed from the old. In the new design, the deadrise amidships was straight, rather than slightly hollow, and the greater beam and depth permitted the slight increase in displacement. The design allowed for 18 guns, excluding the bridle ports.

Lenthall produced a handsome class of sloops. It is not known how much of a part the chief constructor had in this design, but in view of the close personal relationship between the two, it seems probable that Lenthall consulted with

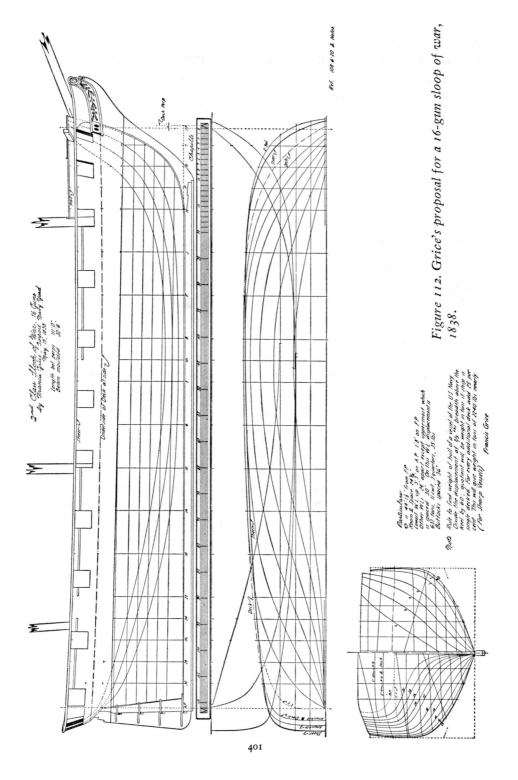

Figure 112. Grice's proposal for a 16-gun sloop of war, 1838.

Humphreys while preparing the drawings. There is no evidence, however, to indicate that the chief constructor prepared a preliminary design for Lenthall's guidance. Five ships from this design were ordered—the *Decatur*, to be built at the New York Navy Yard, *Dale* at Philadelphia, *Marion* at Boston, *Preble* at Portsmouth, and *Yorktown* at the Norfolk yard. These small ships, all launched in 1839, were rather popular; they sailed very well and were stiff. The *Dale* lasted until 1906, and was a school ship for many years; the *Decatur* was sold in 1865; the *Marion* was broken up in 1871–72; the *Preble* was accidentally burned in 1863 while acting as a guard ship; and the *Yorktown* was wrecked in the Cape Verde Islands in 1850.

The minutes of the Board meetings are too incomplete to enable an accurate analysis to be made now of the reasons why the "3rd-Class Sloops" were made so small, at a time when the trend in the American Navy was toward greater and greater size in all classes. In Europe, the ship sloops and corvettes were also rapidly increasing in size with each new ship. Had the "3rd-Class Sloops" ever been required to carry out the functions of their type, it is doubtful that they would have had much success, desirable though they might be as station ships in time of peace. In war they would certainly have been no match for large and powerful merchant vessels, suitably armed, such as the North Atlantic packets and the British East Indiamen. The American sloops of the *Dale* class were little more effective, in fact, than many of the large brigs then in the British Navy.

The only vessels purchased in 1838 were the schooners for the Wilkes Expedition, which have been mentioned earlier. When there was a need for small, fast sailing craft, the New York, Boston, Norfolk, Charleston, and New Orleans pilot schooners could be purchased. These swift vessels would meet all needs, whether to carry dispatches or to serve as a tender to a flagship. The pilot boats had become larger and faster with the passing years. Where, in 1812, this type was usually from 50 to 65 feet long, in 1838 many were from 85 to 100 feet in length. In the event of a naval war, these schooners would have been very useful naval auxiliaries.

The frigate *Congress* was the only naval vessel built in 1839. This frigate, as has been mentioned, was another of the administratively "rebuilt" ships. The old frigate, which had been authorized in 1794, was broken up in 1836. She had been unserviceable for years; even during the War of 1812 she was in such poor state that she could be used only for a short period. The *Congress* had been soaking up maintenance funds until it had been discovered that she might

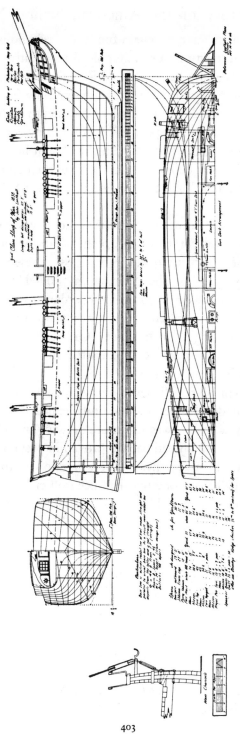

Figure 113. Building draught for the 16-gun ship sloops, 1838.

be used as a budget justification to obtain funds for "rebuilding" old ships into wholly new and useful men-of-war. There need be no attempt to reproduce the old ship in any way; only her official register need be kept intact.

In 1826 Samuel Humphreys had prepared a design for a frigate 179′ between perpendiculars, 45′ 0″ moulded beam, and 14′ 10″ depth of hold. This design had never been used to build a ship. In 1837 Humphreys prepared a plan for the intended rebuilding of the *Congress;* in this design he followed his 1826 plans, but increased the moulded beam to 46′ 6″ and the depth to 15′ 5″. From this revised plan the "rebuilt" frigate was laid down in the Portsmouth Navy Yard that same year.

For reasons which will be dealt with later, there was convened early in 1838 a committee of naval constructors which set up the proper dimensions and characteristics for a "Frigate of the First Class"; these were contained in their report dated July 23, 1838. The report was approved by the Board, which then ordered that a draught be prepared in accordance with the committee's requirements. Humphreys prepared a design which was forwarded to each of the constructors of the original committee—Grice, Hartt, and Barker. The plan was signed by each in token of committee approval. The Board then approved the design in January, 1839.

The approved design of the "Frigate of the First Class" was that of the "rebuilt" *Congress* in dimensions, model, and details. However, the actual building plan of the new frigate was a separate drawing, which was completed in November, 1838, and which had been approved in preliminary form a year earlier. It will be seen (Plan 27) that the new frigate was to be an improved design; in fact, it actually was one that had been officially established by the committee of naval constructors. The peculiar circumstances surrounding the various plans cannot but lead to a suspicion that the report of the committee had been adjusted to fit the ideas of the chief constructor, instead of representing the individual opinions of Messrs. Grice, Hartt, and Barker in full.

The *Congress* was built rapidly; her keel was laid early in 1839, and she was launched in 1841. For years she was considered a very fine frigate, and she was also a fast sailer. She was sunk in action in Hampton Roads on March 8, 1862, by the Confederate steam ram *Virginia,* ex *Merrimac.*

The *Congress* was the last sailing frigate designed for the United States Navy. Though some of the frigates on the stocks were launched after 1841, they were on the design of 1820. The *Congress,* therefore, represented the highest development of the frigate type in the United States. The improvement in frigate design between 1820 and 1838 had actually been slight; the angularity seen in the midsection of the earlier design had now been smoothed out, and in the *Congress* the modern faired midsection appears. This alteration in frame was applied to a limited degree in the 1820 designs still building in 1839, but not to the same degree as in the *Congress*. The old longitudinal mouldings and the projecting wales had now disappeared in American ships; the sides were smooth and fair, without ornamentation. However, the beloved quarter galleries still remained, not only in American naval ships but in merchant ships as well.

Compared to many of the earlier American frigates, the *Congress* had much deadrise. The American constructors of the period were sharply divided regarding the desirability of sharp deadrise in large ships, just as American builders had been long before the War of 1812. Generally speaking, the trend among merchant-ship designers from 1815 to 1840 was toward flat-bottomed ships. This was even true to some degree in the sharp Chesapeake Bay built schooners and brigs in this period. There were, of course, a large group of builders and designers who did not agree with the trend, and these maintained the need and desirability of a marked degree of deadrise. The controversy was to continue into the '50's, and at the end of the sailing-ship period the difference of opinion remained violent. The ruling faction in the Navy—the Board and the chief constructor, supported by the majority of the constructors—was in favor of some deadrise, and it was not until it was necessary to design steamers that the flat-floored model was finally accepted.

In 1832 the sailing trials of the British experimental squadrons had apparently established the superiority of ships formed with very sharp deadrise, as recommended by Captain William Symonds of the Royal Navy. There could be much questioning of the accuracy of the conclusions drawn from the sailing trials, for the tests were far from unbiased and scientific. Nevertheless, they indicated that the ships designed by Symonds were generally faster sailers than those having rounded or flat floors, or with S-shaped midsections, as represented by vessels designed by the School of Naval Architecture, Hayes, or Seppings, or the vessels built to earlier models. This conclusion gave great popular support to Symonds' pretensions, and the surveyor, Seppings, being ready for retirement, Symonds was appointed in his place. With great courage and self-reliance, the new surveyor designed all new ships, without regard to rate and size, with a great deal of deadrise. This, combined with easier and sharper lines fore and aft, created many fast sailing ships in the British Navy, particularly in the smaller classes, from frigate downward. Symonds was not a trained or experienced designer before his appointment; he was primarily a sailor and, like his competitor, Captain Hayes, was no more than an amateur with strong opinions on hull form. As a result it was eventually determined that, while speed of the British ships had been markedly increased by Symonds' principles of design, the improvement had been accomplished at the expense of many of the most desirable qualities in sailing men-of-war, particularly in the larger types of ship. A change in policy then took place, and Symonds was replaced by an officer who made no pretense of being a designer, the design functions going to trained constructors under his supervision. This change enabled a review of the qualities of the various ships designed by Symonds to be made and, as a result, new British men-of-war ceased to be distinguished by extreme deadrise, particularly in the larger vessels.

The British experiments had been carefully observed by many Americans, and undoubtedly Symonds' appointment as surveyor and the success of some of his vessels may have influenced some American merchant-ship designers and encouraged others in a belief in the desirability of extreme deadrise. During the late '30's a few plans of Symonds' brigs came into Humphreys' hands. Two of these have survived in the Navy plan files. Just as the sailing trials had not convinced all of the British constructors, so all the Americans were not impressed with the results and conclusions. It is interesting to find, in this period and later, that the American constructors were divided into the same factions as the British: Grice was in favor of extreme deadrise, with straight rise of floors; the chief constructor and Lenthall preferred moderate rise of floor, and Pook at first favored hollow garboards. Doughty had employed hollow garboards in the *Wasp* class of 1813, but had used straight floors in the *Erie* class of the same year and in his later designs of small vessels. Hartt and Pook became supporters of flat-floored models in the '30's. Every variation of opinion that divided British naval constructors was apparent among the Americans. Symonds had not originated a new idea, as far as Americans were concerned, but his success in the British Navy had given support to the partisans of extreme deadrise in America, in their contest with the exponents of the packet hull form.

Eckford and Grice might be presented as the leading American exponents of extreme deadrise in large ships, as well as in small craft. Eckford's design for a 24-gun corvette in 1819 and his schooner design of 1820, the *Grampus*, show his ideas regarding sharp deadrise in 1817–20. The frigates he and his former apprentice, Isaac Webb, built for the South American nations Brazil,

Peru, Chile, and Colombia also had rather marked rise of floor. In 1830–31, Eckford designed and built a 26-gun corvette on speculation, which he named *United States;* the lines of this ship show extraordinary rise of floor for a square-rigged vessel. The midsection of this corvette was more like that of an extreme model for a pilot schooner than a ship. The *United States* was reputed to be very fast and was sold to Turkey for a naval vessel. Eckford went to Turkey in 1831, and that year he became the chief naval constructor for the Turkish Navy. While in Constantinople Eckford designed a very large frigate, the plan of which reached Humphreys' hands in the late '30's and is still in existence. This design indicates that Eckford employed a straight rise of floor as a principle of design of sailing ships, from the smallest schooner to the largest ships. However, he seems to have governed the amount of deadrise to fit the size and type of ship to a far greater extent than his British counterpart, Symonds. Isaac Webb, however, did not have the same high respect for dead-rise that his master had, and so the Webb designs were usually rather flat-floored, in the packet style. Eckford died suddenly November 12, 1832, in Constantinople, and David Porter (of *Essex* fame) settled his affairs. It appears from Porter's letters that Eckford designed a large frigate and an advice boat, as well as a ship of the line, for the Turks and that all of these were finished, the liner and frigate after his death.

The design and construction of men-of-war for foreign powers remained a source of income for American builders in the '30's. One of the nations seeking ships was the newly created Republic of Texas. In 1839 Grice was commissioned to design a corvette for the Texas Navy, and the vessel was built at Baltimore by Schott and Whitney. She was a flush-decked ship 130′ 2″ long, 31′ 9″ beam, and 15′ 10½″ depth, customhouse measurement. When Texas joined the Union the remnants of her Navy were taken over by the United States, and the new ship, named *Austin,* was on the American register for a few years, 1846–49, as a ship sloop. A former revenue cutter, the *Ingham,* was carried in the Texas Navy under the name *Independence.* She was taken by the Mexicans and was afterward in their naval service as a cruiser.

The only commercial vessel purchased for the Navy in 1839 was a New York pilot schooner named *Flirt,* of 150 tons. She was bought at New York as a tender and was sold out sometime in the '50's. The need for more small vessels was now apparent to the Board, which had been considering the desirability of a class of fast schooners or brigantines of 10 guns to supplement the earlier *Enterprise* and *Dolphin* classes. The Board thought the new design ought to be slightly larger than either of the two classes just mentioned, but that the length should not exceed 96′ between perpendiculars.

There had been a possibility that the Revenue Service might build some large cutters to Navy requirements during 1837–39, but nothing came of the matter. The Board, being made aware of the probability that no such cutters would be built, ordered preliminary designs prepared in 1838. Humphreys had suggested the redesign of the *Dolphin* class, which had proved to be fast sailers. It was proposed to lengthen the model to 96′ between perpendiculars, but hold to the same beam and depth as the original design. Lenthall prepared a drawing for Humphreys (Figure 114), which showed that the result would have been a very long, low clipper that would undoubtedly have been very fast but which had insufficient displacement for a naval vessel. Humphreys himself prepared a variant of the same proposal, in which he increased the displacement somewhat. His drawing, while incomplete, shows that the vessels were intended to carry 8 carronades, 24-pdrs., and 2 long 9's on carriages; the vessels were to be schooner-rigged with the foremast 78′ and the main 80′ long.

Grice was asked by the Board, through Humphreys, to prepare a proposal. He disregarded the length preference of the Board and submitted a plan for a handsome brigantine 100′ between perpendiculars, 26′ moulded beam, and drawing about 13′ 9″ (Figure 115), as compared to the lengthened *Dolphin*, which would have drawn about 13′ loaded for sea. The Board seems to have studied the matter in a desultory way in 1839–40, before any action was finally taken.

Perhaps the Board's attention was so involved in a controversy over steam men-of-war in this period that it had little time to consider the brigantines or schooners. The matter of steam vessels for the Navy had almost continuously plagued the members since 1834. In that year, an anchor hoy being wanted for one of the navy yards, Hartt had the temerity to submit a proposal for a steam hoy and water tank (water boat). This is shown, in his drawing, to have been a side paddle wheel steamer, with wide guards running the full length of the hull, the dimensions of which were 80′ between perpendiculars and 17′ 4″ moulded beam inside the guards. Hartt submitted the plan and proposal February 28, 1834, but the Board immediately rejected it and ordered Humphreys to prepare plans for sailing hoys; these are shown in Figure 117. The new boats were to carry 14,000 gallons of water and were to measure 65′ 0″ between perpendiculars, 22′ 0″ moulded beam, and 7′ 0″ depth of hold. A num-

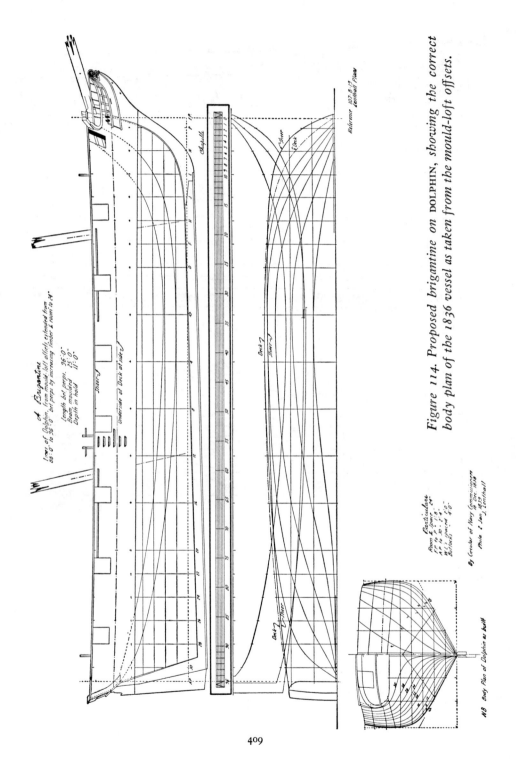

Figure 114. Proposed brigantine on DOLPHIN, showing the correct body plan of the 1836 vessel as taken from the mould-loft offsets.

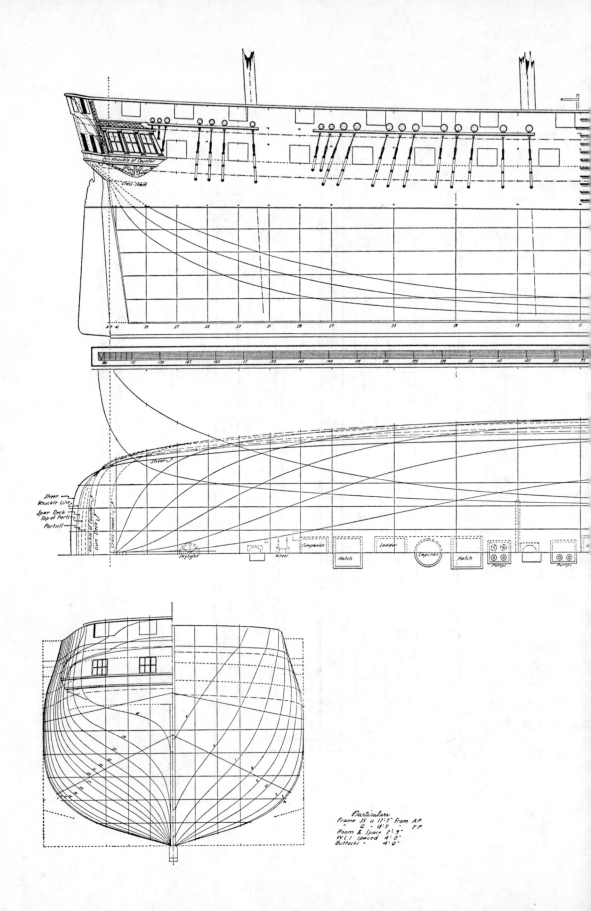

Particulars
Frame 35 is 17'7" from AP
" 0 = 18'5" " FP
Room & Space 2'9"
WLs spaced 4'0"
Buttocks 4'0"

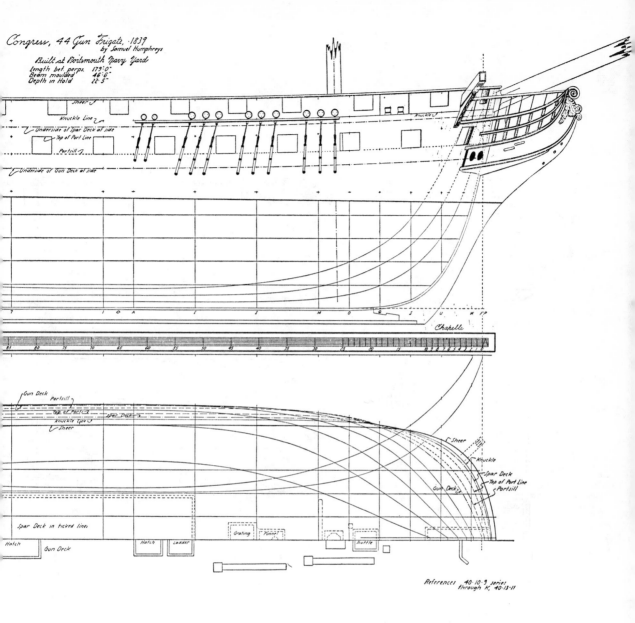

Plan 27. Draught of the 44-gun frigate CONGRESS, 1839, the last design to be prepared
for a vessel of this class under sail alone.

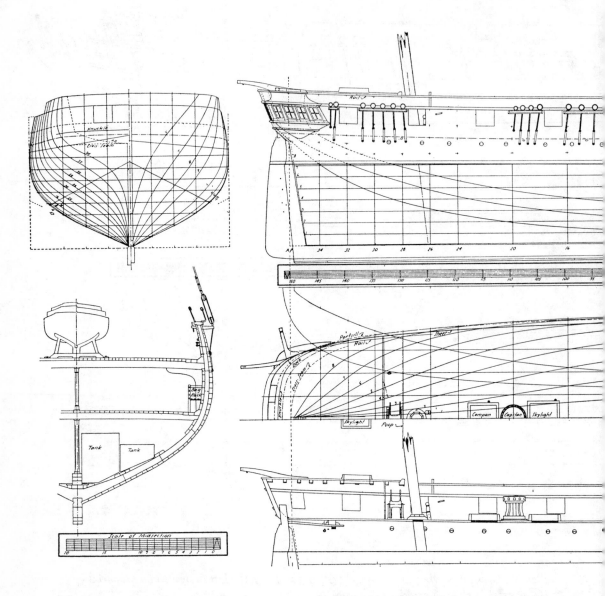

Plan 28. First-class sloop GERMANTOWN, *showing typical deck fittings of the class.*

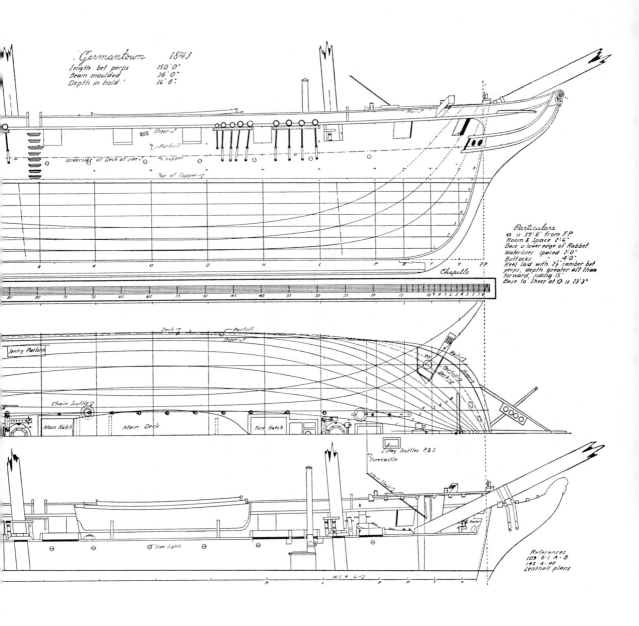

Germantown 1843
Length bet perps   150'0'
Beam moulded   36'0'
Depth in hold   16'8'

Sheer
Portsill
Underside of Deck at side.   Supper
Top of Copper

8   4   0   D   H   L   P   R   T   Y   F.P.

Chapelle

Particulars
O is 59'6' from F.P.
Room & Space 2'6'
Base is lower edge of Rabbet.
Waterlines spaced 2'0'
Buttocks   4'0'
Keel laid with 2½' camber bet
perps, depth greater aft than
forward, siding 15'
Base to Sheer at O is 23'3"

85 80 75 70 65 60 55 50 45 40 35 30 25 20 15 10 9 8 7 6 5 4 3 2 1 O

Sentry Platform
Deck   Portsill
Sheer

Chain Scuttle
Main Hatch   Main Deck   Fore Hatch

Stay Scuttles P.&.S.
Forecastle

Star Lights

WL 67

H   L   P   R   T   Y

References
103·6·1 A·B
142·4·46
Lenthall plans

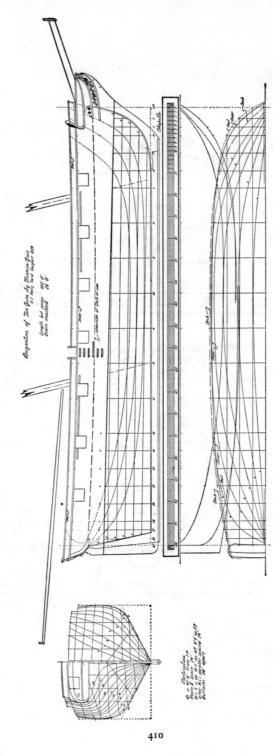

Figure 115. Grice's proposal for a 100-foot brigantine of 10 guns.

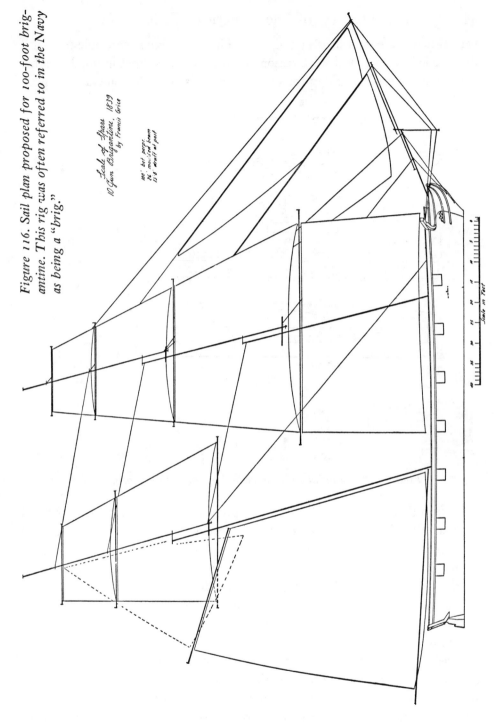

Figure 116. Sail plan proposed for 100-foot brigantine. This rig was often referred to in the Navy
as being a "brig."

Scale of Spars
10 Gun Brigantine, 1839
by Francis Grice

10' bl. perp.
26' mould beam
10.8 draft at port

Scale in Feet

ber of these were built in 1835 and 1836. These new hoys were able to handle the heaviest anchors and were reasonably seaworthy, so that in good weather they could operate outside protected waters to salvage lost anchors or gear.

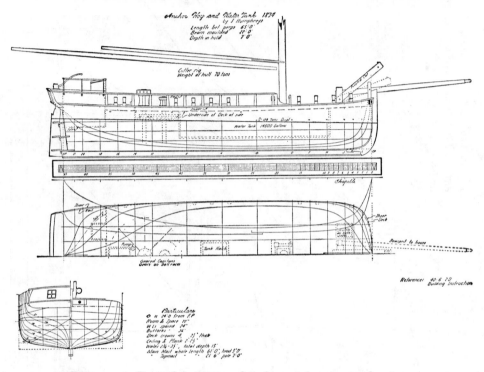

Figure 117. Draught of an anchor hoy and water tank, 1834.

In 1836 there were complaints in Congress about the cost of towing naval ships at New York with privately owned tugs; the result was that a small steamer of about 142 tons, named the *Engineer*, was purchased for the purpose in that year. There were over 700 steamers in existence in the United States by this time and, since the destruction of the first steam battery in 1829 by a magazine explosion, the Navy had but two, the *Sea Gull* of 100 tons, laid up at Philadelphia and unserviceable, and the *Engineer*.

The Secretary of the Navy called attention, in 1835, to the authorization for steam batteries contained in the Congressional Act of April 29, 1816, and ordered the Board to have one of these designed and built. The Board disliked the idea intensely and finally suggested to the Secretary that, since they knew nothing about steamers, a competent steam engineer be obtained to advise them. This was done, and Charles H. Haswell of New York became the first naval engineer. The steam battery was built in 1836–37 and on her trials made nearly twelve knots. She was 180′ between perpendiculars and 34′ 8″ extreme beam—a long ship when compared to the sailing frigates—and was named *Fulton*. Three more war steamers were authorized at the President's discretion by Congress, March 3, 1839. Two boards were set up, one composed of senior officers of the Navy and the other of constructors and the one engineer. In spite of strenuous objections from the older officers, the final word rested with Congress, and the Board made its report on the proper size and power for the steamers. As a result the President directed that two huge war steamers be laid down in 1839. These were launched in 1842—the *Mississippi* and *Missouri*. These ships really marked the beginning of the decline of importance of sailing men-of-war, though it was twenty years more before the last die-hards would recognize the supremacy of the steamship. The surrender of the Board, in 1839, to the construction of war steamers was not brought about by a belated realization on the part of its members of the advantages of steamers, but by the pressure from civilians, who were alarmed at the existence of war steamers abroad while the American Navy lagged. In general, the popular concept of the part that war steamers were to play was that they would be effective in calms and would be employed to bring large sailing men-of-war into action by towing, while using their own batteries to protect themselves. They would also be invaluable for coast defense.

During the decade between 1830 and 1840, the improvement of the navy yards continued. The steady requirements of the large program of new construction placed the yards in a favorable situation when making requests for new equipment, additional men, and floating equipment. Lighters, hoys, tugs, and sheer hulks (derrick boats) were now in use in all the yards requiring them. The standard naval lighter was a small scow, 35′ to 45′ in length, that could be moved with sweeps or towed with ships' boats. One of these lighters is shown in Figure 118; according to an inventory in 1838, a boat of this type at the Portsmouth Yard had one or two leeboards and a spritsail and steered with a rudder. The lighters were also decked, and some of them, like the one in Figure 119, served as anchor hoys in protected harbors or close to the navy yards.

The sheer hulks were old craft, ranging from large sloops to ships of various classes, that were worn out and were stripped of masts and gear. They served to float huge sheers, which were necessary to lift out or replace masts. The hulks were often towed, but usually the ship being repaired was brought alongside the hulk, which was tied to some convenient wharf or on a mooring. Masting sheers were also placed on the heads of some wharves in the navy yards, and many yards had both hulk and wharf sheers in service. Tugs were hired steamers, except where the *Engineer* was available from her post at the New York Navy Yard. Steam was employed in sawing timber in all the navy yards by 1840; though it had been introduced in English dockyards as early as 1798, it only appeared in American yards in the 1820's. The exact date when steam saws were first used in American navy yards has yet to be established; saws operated

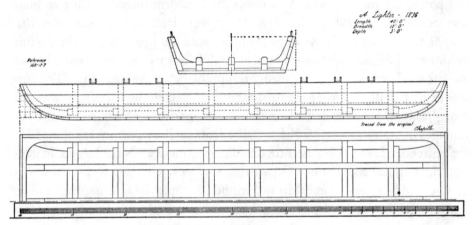

Figure 118. A Navy lighter, 1836.

by water wheels were used in a few American shipyards as early as 1810, but this source of power was unavailable to the locations of most merchant yards and all the navy yards. The British dockyards were equipped with machinery to a marked extent by 1808, but the Americans were slower, owing to war and economic difficulties. All the American navy yards had been fitted with heaving-down wharves, but only the Norfolk Yard had a dry dock; it went into operation June 17, 1833, with the docking of the 74-gun ship *Delaware*. The pumping machinery in this yard was operated by steam. Ironworking equipment was steadily increasing in the yards, and now far exceeded that formerly required by the old shipsmiths, owing to the maintenance requirements of the yard machinery, as well as the few naval steamers.

The rotation of Board membership was somewhat slower in 1830–40 than before. Rodgers was President of the Board to 1837; Chauncey replaced him and held the assignment until 1840. Charles Stewart was a member from 1830 to 1833, vice Warrington. Charles Morris was again a member from 1832 to 1841, and Chauncey had been made a member in 1833, five years before being appointed president. Alexander Wadsworth was appointed to the Board in 1837, vice Rodgers, and remained a member until 1840. It should be noted that the veteran officers of the War of 1812 were still in control. The steadily growing conservatism of the Navy Board was now widely acknowledged, and this was drawing much criticism. The difficulties of the Board over the construction of the new steamers merely emphasized the backwardness of

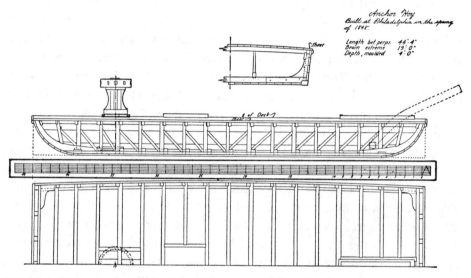

Figure 119. A navy yard hoy, 1848.

senior officers of the Navy, and the matter did not enhance public confidence. The chief constructor was now in an unenviable position; his relations with the Board were strained and his public reputation was damaged. Humphreys had obtained two of Eckford's designs for the Turkish Navy, the frigate and the liner, which he offered to have copied for the Board. This had been accepted, but when the plans were done the Board had refused to honor Humphreys' bill. The chief constructor had made an indignant protest which led the Board to reprimand him for discourtesy. So far as the public was concerned, the success of Humphreys' design for the *Dolphin* had not counterbalanced the woeful failure of the exploration ships. The 24-gun corvettes of 1824–25 and the rebuilt *Macedonian* were rumored to be unsatisfactory, and there were the criticisms of the huge *Pennsylvania*. Unfortunately for Humphreys, he was being held responsible, to a great extent at least, for the mistakes of the Board in setting up the required characteristics of the ships he designed. Humphreys had certainly been forced, over his protest in some cases, to comply with the Board's instructions and specifications. Humphreys and his brother constructors attempted to resist the Board's insistence upon excessive basic design requirements, but rarely with much success. Admittedly his ships were becoming marked by a lack of beauty, but this did not make them less effective as men-of-war. Humphreys was in no way involved in the Board's prejudice toward steamships, for he had designed such craft before 1830. In spite of his personal difficulties with the Navy Board and the criticism of his ships by the public, he had obtained a great reputation abroad as a naval constructor. It is said that he was once offered the appointment of chief naval constructor in the Russian service at a handsome salary, but that he refused it on the grounds that he preferred to employ his talents in his country's behalf.

Lenthall was made a naval constructor July 21, 1838, and Pook was made an assistant somewhat earlier. Floyd retired, and Hartt took over his assignment. A number of very able men were now being trained as constructors: Brodie, Rhodes, Hanscom, and Delano, all of whom were to be highly competent in their profession. The apprentice system in the constructors' offices was remarkably successful in spite of the lack of an established system of teaching or a school of naval architecture such as had been attempted in the British service. The reasons for this are easily found. The American constructors were engaged in design work outside of the Navy. Lenthall was designing merchant ships for Philadelphia merchants, including a packet or two for the famous Cope Line; Grice was designing schooners and an occasional ship at Norfolk, and Hartt was active at New York. While it is true that a few of the constructors had fitted comfortably into the bureaucratic mould, most of them had been too ambitious and active to be satisfied with the little that was required of them in the navy yards and had turned their energies to study and the commercial designing that would enable them to keep abreast of progress in their profession. This is a remarkable exception to the rule in a naval bureaucracy in peacetime— all the more so because of the stultifying influence of the Board of Navy Commissioners, which prevented the constructors from utilizing their knowledge for their service. The active constructors increased their knowledge entirely by their own efforts and without official encouragement. Such men were well fitted to teach, for they had a personal interest in their profession and desired scientific knowledge for its own sake. They were well informed in the existing theories of naval architecture, as is evidenced by their designs. Unfortunately little has survived that expresses the state of their knowledge other than this.

It is difficult to arrive at conclusions concerning the design practices of the leading naval constructors in the 1830's by judgments based entirely on surviving plans and papers. However, it can at least be said that Grice, Pook, Lenthall, and Hartt were able to make extensive calculations and were also well informed on the theories of ship design then in existence. The calculations were not particularly difficult or profound; they included displacement and weight calculations, tons-per-inch immersion, center of buoyancy, center of lateral plane, and center of effort—the most common calculations in the design of sailing craft still in use. Stability was not often calculated, as the methods then known were very laborious, and none have been found for American naval ships in the '30's. Little was known about resistance, and the full bow and fine run were still looked upon as necessary to speed, in theory at least, though the sharp bow was gradually becoming popular, particularly as it was proving so successful in the packets.

Construction methods in the navy yards changed very slowly in the 1830's; the most important innovation was the use of some iron strapping in the last years of the decade. The light construction attempted in the *Experiment* attracted little interest and was not repeated. Ironwork was very slowly increasing in the fitting of hulls and in rigging. In this the Navy was very conservative because of the assertion that iron fitting would be shattered by a shot and form dangerous fragments, and that once damaged, the ironwork could not be repaired on shipboard. Chain cables were permitted, and now some vessels had chain gammonings to secure their bowsprits.

It is rather curious that the painting of the ships of the Navy was left to the commander's taste for a very long period; at least no regulations concerning this have been found prior to the '30's. In the War of 1812, the American frigates were usually black, with a bright yellow streak along the gun ports, British fashion. This streak was usually as wide as the ports were high. The 74's had three such streaks if spar-decked, and two if the spar-deck waist was unarmed. Some vessels also had a narrow band on the mouldings, below the upper deck ports. Some frigates had rather wide yellow bands, reaching from a line about the height of the main deck to a couple of inches above the main-deck gun ports. During the War of 1812, the bands were extended forward on the cutwater. The port covers were often the same color as the band, and not checkerboarded in the Nelson style. The guns and port sills were black, tompions white, black, or red. About 1825, the yellow streaks or bands became very light in color and gradually they became white. Small craft, schooners, and brigs, began to use streaks that were only half the depth of the ports; these had their lower edge at port-sill height and ran the whole length of the hull, out onto the cutwater. The inside of the bulwarks, from waterways to rail, was usually red or brown, until the late '30's, when white became common. Decks were left "bright" and holystoned in the Navy throughout the sailing-ship period. Deck furniture and the sills of deck structures were red, but later, when bulwarks became white, they were painted the same color. Mastheads, bowsprit, and royal masts in small vessels were painted black; the lower masts and topmasts of large ships were black until well into the '30's, when white was used. Billetheads were yellow, or green and white. Finally, about 1840, the billets were often painted white without gilding. By 1836 some of the small men-of-war, schooners and brigantines, began to omit the port band entirely, retaining only a yellow or white moulding line in some; in others the side was wholly black. Since nearly all naval vessels were copper-sheathed with "yellow metal," the bottom was a yellow or light green in color, depending upon age. All standing rigging was black. Gun carriages were brown, black, or natural wood, oiled: black was regulation in 1839. Even as late as 1840, American men-of-war were not limited to black and white paint. Boats were often painted to the fancy of the captain, though white hulls were now predominant; the plank-sheer or gunwale might be black, red, or green. Even after regulations fixed the colors to be used in naval vessels, there were many ships that did not conform, well into the '40's. Frigates and liners, in the '30's, generally had the white bands checkerboarded British fashion; sloops and corvettes were less standardized, but the checkerboard seems to have been most common, disappearing in the middle '40's.

The administration of the Navy, in so far as construction was concerned, changed very little in the '30's. The Board's dominance could not successfully be challenged by the constructors in any technical matter, though the character and professional attainments of the chief constructor and his subordinates had by now won the grudging respect of most of the senior naval officers. Suggestions from the constructors were now received with somewhat more attention than had been the case in Fox's and Doughty's times. The chief constructor sometimes took sharp exception to the comments of the Board, and the constructors occasionally differed with their chief. Independence of professional opinion was slowly being accepted and utilized. It was being realized that overriding the constructors in matters pertaining to design and construction, rigging and fittings, or even armament, was a very risky proceeding, for the results were usually most unfortunate. Nevertheless, there was no official recognition of the changing relations, and the '30's saw little improvement in the establishing of detailed requirements for new vessels.

The navy agents had been retained in the establishment of the Board, but with naval construction confined to the navy yards, they no longer placed building contracts but were concerned only with the purchase of materials and supplies. The commandant of a navy yard reported directly to the Board on matters relating to repair and maintenance of vessels, construction and repair of buildings, storage of materials and supplies, and employment of civilian personnel, as well as the estimates and accounts pertaining to such matters. The resident constructor was his adviser in all technical matters and was under his administrative supervision. The constructor was no longer responsible for routine repairs and confined his activities to the new construction in the yards, unless called upon to give advice by the commandant (who was not officially required to accept it, of course) with regard to repairs or some other technical matter relating to ships. The resident constructor was still the master shipwright, it will be seen, and had a force of loftsmen, draftsmen, foremen and ship carpenters, joiners, caulkers, spar-makers, and other tradesmen under him. The relations of the resident constructor to the commandant and the captain of a new ship fitting out in a yard were rather ill-defined, and as a result there were sometimes differences of opinion as to the manner in which a vessel should be rigged, fitted, trimmed, and ballasted.

In attempting to pass judgment on naval ships and the men who designed them, it is necessary to understand the administrative procedure in force during the 1820's and 1830's. From the time of Humphreys' appointment as chief naval constructor to 1838, he prepared the designs for all naval vessels. The Board, in authorizing a design, set down the requirements, size, rate, rig, and desirable characteristics. Sometimes Humphreys was consulted while these were being prepared, but this was rather unusual. Having prepared a plan, Humphreys submitted it to the Board for approval. When this had been obtained (and to get this he sometimes had to alter his drawings) the design was sent to the navy yards in which the vessels were to be built. The resident constructors then prepared "return" plans incorporating any suggestions they might care to make. These were passed on by the Board, with the chief constructor usually present. If the Board could agree that the changes were valid they were incorporated in some or all of the vessels to be built. This was seen in the case of the 24-gun corvettes of 1824–25. By this time, between the resident constructors and the members of the Board, the original design had often been altered a good deal. Generally, the experienced seamen on the Board were more concerned with practical requirements, characteristics that they believed a vessel ought to have, rather than with the technical problem of fitting such characteristics into a given design—as in the case of the exploration vessels of 1836. In the event of failure the fault was, of course, the chief constructor's.

So, in 1838, the criticism of some of the naval vessels led the Board to require that the constructors sit as a committee to approve of all new designs submitted to the Board and also that they set forth their opinions as to the proper dimensions and models of various classes of men-of-war. The basic idea behind this move was to enable the Board to escape responsibility and to obtain the opinions of all the experts available, by vote of the majority. In short, this was to be "design by committee." Various methods were tried to accomplish this end: a number of constructors were requested to send in competitive designs and then by committee action one was to be chosen. The result can be readily imagined. Next the Board attempted to make the final decision but found that they would have to depend entirely upon the recommendations of the chief constructor or assume responsibilities that the Board had already learned to fear. By the end of 1839 there was still no satisfactory procedure for the control of design, nor for the steps to be required before submission to the Board. It had been found that no matter how well a design was prepared and fitted to the Board's requirements, there was always the possibility of irresponsible changes being made either in the process of approval, or before construction actually started. A procedure under which the chief constructor had prepared designs to minute specifications established by a board of officers had failed, and an attempt to make designs by committee had failed; now a new process would have to be found.

The success of the ship sloops in the War of 1812 and the usefulness of the type in a peacetime navy led some officers to support a theory that this class might be made even more effective than most frigates. As guns grew in power and range and became increasingly accurate, a school of thought developed in the Navy which believed that huge corvettes, armed with a few of the most powerful guns these ships might carry, would be more effective than the usual frigate or liner, armed with a large number of smaller guns. The War of 1812 had shown that ships armed with long-range, heavy-hitting guns were generally victorious over ships less heavily armed; furthermore, it was apparent that the heaviest guns in the American ships, usually chase guns, did the greatest damage. With explosive shells coming into use, it was thought possible that corvettes might be armed with a few shell guns, of great size, and a supporting armament of heavy, long-range guns firing solid shot. To carry the armaments proposed by the adherents of such large guns, naval ships would have to be very large for their classes.

The trend in the direction of great size had marked American designs for naval craft since 1794. The gradual increase in dimensions had been prevented, in frigates and liners in the '30's, only by the long-term construction program. Even then, there was an increase in size in the frigate class through the design of the *Congress*. The schooners and brigantines of 1831 and 1834 were already considered too small by 1838. Only in the small ship sloops of 1838–39 had there been a reduction in size; these, however, must be classed as men-of-war built entirely to economic and peacetime requirements, rather than ships designed for existing tactical requirements. Yet even in these small vessels the weight of broadside fire was much heavier than in similar sloops in 1813–15. It was traditional in the American Navy, before 1839, that its ships should be more heavily and efficiently armed than European classmates. From this precept it was but a short step to the acceptance of the principle of arming large ships with a few very heavy guns and omitting the ineffective but numerous small guns that had long been carried in an effort to crowd the greatest possible number of guns into American ships. However, the massive broadside armament was too firmly entrenched in tradition, custom, and administration to be easily displaced, even on the grounds of fighting efficiency.

The possibility of employing an armament made up of a very few guns, of the greatest power and range that the dimensions of a hull could bear, had attracted the attention of both constructors and naval officers for generations. The old Mediterranean galleys had been armed with from two to four heavy guns fitted for bow fire. The famous Swedish naval constructor Chapman had designed, in 1760, galley-type vessels that were armed with a battery of heavy guns along the center line, pivoted so that they could fire over each broadside. Chapman remained the leading exponent of this type of armament until Captain Schank of the Royal Navy armed a merchant ship named *Rattler*, purchased by the Admiralty in 1798, with guns on somewhat similar plan. This vessel, bark-rigged, was renamed the *Wolverine* in the Royal Navy. She could fight her eight main-deck guns on either side, employing thwartship tracks, or skids, and pivot mounts.

The Americans had arrived at the same conclusion as had Chapman and Schank earlier, for in Jefferson's administration they armed their gunboats with a few heavy pivot guns. Eckford and the Browns had followed suit in some of the lake vessels in the War of 1812; the *Sylph*, with her original battery of pivoted long guns, and *Ariel* were examples. The original pivoted battery of Chapman was taken over bodily by the Americans and was used in small vessels, brigs, and schooners—the Americans employing fewer but much heavier guns than Chapman's vessels. So the principle of arming with a few very heavy guns on effective mounts, instead of a full broadside battery of much smaller guns, was no innovation in 1839 and could be accepted even by the veteran officers of the Board—with some misgivings, however. The well-established and long-standing custom of classing naval ships by the number of guns they carried (which in turn had established the rank required of their commanding officers, and rate of pay as well) made an official acceptance of the Chapman-Schank principle of arming very slow indeed. The relation of a ship's rate to a captain's rank and pay was a very real administrative difficulty in the minds of the senior officers of the Board of Navy Commissioners, and it was not until they were faced with the anomaly of the new steamers—huge ships with few guns—that they accepted the idea that the value of a ship was in the effectiveness of armament and that the rank of her captain need not be related to the number of guns in her battery. This, once applied to the steamers, could equally be applied to the sailing men-of-war.

The change from rating a ship's effectiveness by the number of guns she carried to rating by efficiency of the armament was revolutionary in 1840. Custom and tradition are always strong influences on naval affairs, and this was particularly so in the days of the Board of Navy Commissioners, with its membership of aged veterans of a glorious naval war. Such men found it difficult to accept so basic an alteration in the importance of commands, and for many years there were difficulties over the appointment of senior officers to large ships having fewer guns than others in a squadron that were commanded by juniors.

The controversy over deadrise in large ships was not the only one that aroused the tempers of constructors and shipbuilders in the 1830's. Since colonial times, ships had been designed with raking sternposts and bows made to long sweeps or, later, with a strong rake. In the 1820's some American pilot schooners were designed with almost upright stems. These first appeared at Norfolk and later at Charleston, South Carolina, and New Orleans. The boats proving fast and seaworthy, with no loss in steering qualities, the fashion spread to northern pilot boats. In the early '30's the rake of the sternpost was also decreased. About the same time large ships were built in the United States without rake in the ends, reverting to the fashion that had been followed by the French nearly a century earlier. The packets, now growing longer, were among the leaders in having little rake to bow and sternpost; their steadily increasing length made the use of the overhangs created by raking stem and sternpost a serious structural problem. In spite of the theoretical advantages of the raking ends on steering qualities, the success of many ships without rake raised the question of how much importance the time-honored rake of ends really had. As in the matter of deadrise, there was never unanimity on the question of rake, but the extreme rake that had marked the early clipper schooners went slowly out of fashion in the 1820's and 1830's. In full-ended ships, in particular, it was found that an upright stem allowed sharper entrance lines in the bow and that an equally upright sternpost eased the run. The packets were the exponents of this model, and some of them, particularly a few Philadelphia and New York ships, came out with almost vertical stem and sternpost as early as 1835.

The search for speed in packets, in the '30's, attracted the attention of American ship designers and builders to the possibilities of many changes in the hull form of large ships. Gradually the old frigate model which had so long been accepted as the acme for large, fast merchant ships went completely out of fashion. Instead of the bluff bows above the water being formed with S-shaped timbers, they became bell-shaped—thin below and flaring outward above the water line to the deck. The plan of the bow rail may not have grown appreciably sharper, but the shape of the bows below was far finer than it had been in the sharpest of the earlier frigates. The sterns also changed; a few merchant ships adopted the man-of-war's elliptical stern; most retained the old transom stern, but the width of the bottom of the lowest part of the transom, the "cross seam," was made less by rounding the outer ends, which made planking easier. The hollow profile of the lower transom gradually disappeared, and the athwartship camber of both transoms became much less. In keeping with the upright stem, the rake of the upper transom was much reduced, and the ships now began to look straight and heavy, in the naval fashion.

There were many constructors who disapproved of the fashionable packet model. Some believed in deadrise and rake, others in the old frigate model; still others had theories of much sharper bows and finer sterns than had yet been seen. A number of fast river steamers had been built, the models for which, by a combination of requirements for length, beam, and speed, had become long, narrow, and very sharp-ended. There were, therefore, iconoclasts who wanted to apply the same general model to seagoing sailing ships, with the necessary modifications of proportions to permit sail carrying and weatherliness.

One of the obvious experiments that can be seen in plans of American naval vessels in the '30's and earlier was in the shape of the run. Doughty had gradually developed a hull form that carried the body well fore and aft (but made it relatively shallow by use of great deadrise) with a short and rather full run. This "duck" hull form may be seen in his 1821 schooners and in some of his ship sloop designs. The earlier constructors had obviously preferred to employ long, easy runs and rather sharp bows. These features may be seen in the *Constitution* and *Constellation* classes of frigates and in their contemporaries in the smaller rates. Eckford, Bergh, and many of the Chesapeake country builders utilized this method of forming hulls in fast craft, but there was no unanimity on the desirability of such a form. Samuel Humphreys seems to have wavered in adherence to this hull form, for he occasionally resorted to Doughty's short run and long, shallow body; however, his designs were commonly easier in the buttocks than Doughty's had been. All the designers, from at least the time of the Revolution onward to the '40's, had cautiously experimented with hollow in the bow water lines, but not until the '30's does it become apparent that much emphasis was being placed on this feature. Unfortunately, it is almost impossible to explore the theories of the designers in this period, as no statements by them exist regarding the advantages of short or long runs, or of convex or concave water lines, and all that is available on which to base judgments is an occasional plan. These are of limited value in this single respect, since few designers had learned to employ buttock lines in fairing, as had Fox and Joshua Humphreys in the earlier period and Bergh, Eckford, and Webb later. As a result it is highly probable that few designers realized the exact degree of fullness in the runs of their ships. This may well be an explanation of the rapid rise in popularity of the half-model as a mode of design in the 1820's, 1830's, and 1840's.

The time was one of intense curiosity and activity of mind among ship designers and builders in America. With only a few books on naval architecture

PLATE XIII. (Top) United States corvette ERIE (rebuilt). (Center) United States sloop of war ONTARIO. (Bottom) United States frigate BRANDYWINE and sloop of war CONCORD.

PLATE XIV. (Top) United States naval schooner, 1843. (Center) United States ship of the line NORTH CAROLINA. (Bottom) United States frigate ST. LAWRENCE.

available, and these European, the average American designer depended upon practical observation to arrive at theories of proper hull form and rig. He was less interested, perhaps, in the mathematical explorations that fascinated the European authorities on naval architecture than in the art of forming hulls to sail fast and to carry well. The first American book on practical ship design appeared in 1839—*The Practical Shipbuilder*, by L. M'Kay, "practical shipbuilder and carpenter, of the United States Navy." The book not only gave instructions for "the inexperienced," but also contained plans of various classes of ships as examples referred to in the text. The book had an extensive sale and undoubtedly had much influence on shipbuilders in the United States. M'Kay was not sparing in his criticisms of Navy ships; he refers at some length to their oversparring and mentions the control of the constructors by the Board. His remarks on the latter are worth quoting: "The Navy has suffered from an opposite course [he has said earlier that merchant builders had to depend upon their own judgment for the lack of scientific instruction] and consequently has made no advancement for the last twenty years. I hear of no reason for this other than that the constructors have not been allowed to alter their models according to their own judgment, but have been confined to the improvements of a few individuals who must be united in their plans; whereas, if the constructors had been allowed to put their individual plans into execution, the result would have been the introduction of a course of rapid and advantageous improvements." In short, he had a low opinion of "committee design," even by competent constructors, and he knew that development in design could not be accomplished by a controlling group of any kind, but that it must be left to the individual designer to decide what and how he wants to design. M'Kay had put his finger on the inherent weakness of government control of ship design—the administrative and bureaucratic procedure that invariably leads to attempts to design by majority vote rather than by the knowledge of a single designing authority. The result is always the same; the designs become merely a hash of the opinions of many and the masterpieces of none. The answer to this problem had not been found in 1840—and there is little evidence that it has been found since.

★ ★ ★ ★ ★ ★ ★ ★ ★

CHAPTER EIGHT

The Last Years of Sail
1840-1855

THE '40's were years of great activity in American shipbuilding. Both sailing vessels and steamships were built in great numbers and on new models. These years saw the first attempts to build iron hulls, sharpended packets, and finally the first of the "clipper ships" for the China trade. War steamers were becoming common in Europe and were steadily increasing in size and power. The decade beginning in 1840 was one of the greatest periods of advance in the art and science of marine architecture and engineering that had yet been seen.

The start of this period of progress was a slow one, as far as the Navy was concerned. The weight of the now mentally dormant Board of Navy Commissioners oppressed the progressive younger officers and naval constructors. This, with the lack of public support of naval appropriations, prevented the service from keeping pace with the developments in the merchant marine. No new ships were built by the Navy in 1840; the only addition was the schooner *Otsego*, loaned by the War Department. This small vessel was retained until 1844 and was then returned. The old sloop *Peacock* had been employed on the west coast in exploration and survey work, as part of the Wilkes Expedition, and on July 18, 1841, she was wrecked at the mouth of the Columbia River, Oregon. A small merchant brig was purchased at Vancouver, British Columbia, to bring the officers and men of the sloop home. This brig, under the name of *Oregon,* was carried on the Navy register for a few years; she was placed

426

in ordinary in 1845 and was sold soon afterward. A schooner named *Phoenix*, of 90 tons, was also added to the Navy in 1841; she was a new vessel built at Baltimore, by contract. No plans of the vessel have yet been found, and it is probable that the contractor who built the schooner also made her design. She was retained in the service but a short time and disappeared from the register sometime before 1848. Both the *Phoenix* and the *Oregon* were classed as 2-gun vessels.

The faction among the officers that supported the building of large corvettes with heavy armament had at last convinced Congress and the Board that such ships ought to be built, and Samuel Pook and Humphreys were assigned to the preparation of a sample design. The lines were completed in the summer of 1841 and were for a corvette having a flush deck and a short, heavy, elliptical stern, without quarter galleries. She was a very large vessel for her class and date, measuring 146′ 4″ between perpendiculars, 35′ 3″ moulded beam, and 16′ 3½″ depth of hold, yet she was pierced for only 22 guns, excluding bridle ports. Her armament was to be on the then new battery—18 medium 32-pdrs. and 4 of the 8″ shell guns, 64-pdrs. All guns were mounted on carriages and were of an improved design, with heavy breech and light muzzle. The new style of shell gun was dual-purpose and could fire either shells or solid shot. The new ship, *Saratoga*, was longer than her namesake on Lake Champlain in the War of 1812; she was 13′ 3″ longer than the *Cyane* and *Levant* of 1836–37. Comparing the *Saratoga* with the British 26-gun ship *Alarm*, a Symonds design built in 1843, the American corvette was 15′ 3″ longer between perpendiculars, 4′ 11″ less moulded beam, and 1′ 3″ less depth to the main deck.

The lines of the *Saratoga* (Figure 120) show a moderately sharp ship with a good deal of deadrise, but nowhere as extreme as the Symondite *Alarm*. The model was really an improved *Cyane*, and the *Saratoga* proved to be a very fine vessel in all respects, fast-sailing and very weatherly. In the late '50's she was raised slightly and a grating spar deck was added. The ship was launched in 1842 and lasted until 1907, when she was broken up. For many years she was employed as a cadet school ship. The Portsmouth Navy Yard built the *Saratoga* very rapidly; she was launched eleven months after her keel was laid and went into commission six months later.

The design of the *Saratoga* having been generally approved, the designs of six more large corvettes were authorized, and it was decided to distribute the work among the naval constructors. Each was to be allowed to choose the model and dimensions he thought best without Board or committee consent being first obtained. The requirement to be met in all the new corvettes was that they be superior vessels capable of carrying the same armament as the *Saratoga*. The matter of smaller craft, which had been under consideration by the Board since 1838, was also brought to a head, and four "schooners or brigs" were ordered built. The designs of these were to be prepared by Humphreys and Grice, each to design two.

The new procedure was to allow the designers freedom to shape their vessels as each thought best. However, the change from complete dominance by the Board was difficult to accomplish; thus Humphreys was handicapped by the Board's indecision as to whether the two small vessels he was to design were to be brigs or schooners, and the rig was not actually decided until after he had completed his lines. The schooner was now out of official favor again and so was the brigantine, in spite of *Dolphin*.

The old *Erie*, rebuilt in 1820–21, had now become rotten, so she was hauled out at the Boston Navy Yard and broken up. Some portions of the old ship were then used again to build a new storeship, which was launched in 1842. No plan for this vessel has been found. The explanation may be that the storeship was built to the 1813 lines of the ship; this is indicated by her register dimensions, 117′ 11″ between perpendiculars, 31′ 6″ moulded beam, and 14′ 6″ depth of hold. This storeship carried 4 guns, 9-pdrs., but was considered too small, and so she was sold at New York in 1850; she was afterward run as a bark-rigged merchant vessel and had the reputation of being a fast ship.

The Seminole War had made it desirable to employ some small schooners on the Florida coast to protect settlements and outlying garrisons from Indian raids. The revenue cutters *Jefferson* and *Madison* were obtained by the Navy for this purpose, and another schooner, the *Badger*, was purchased. The two cutters, it will be recalled, were among those built by Webb and Allen in the early '30's; the *Jefferson* was now brigantine-rigged. These vessels were retained only for the duration of the Florida war, and all three were then turned over to the Revenue Service.

Since it had been apparent for some years that the Board of Navy Commissioners was most unprogressive and that it had proved inadequate to administer properly the construction of new ships, public opinion forced Congress to abolish the Board. This was done by an Act of Congress, passed August 31, 1842. In place of the Board, the three officers then members of the defunct group were made the heads of newly formed bureaus; the secretary was made chief of a bureau also. The construction and repair of ships was made

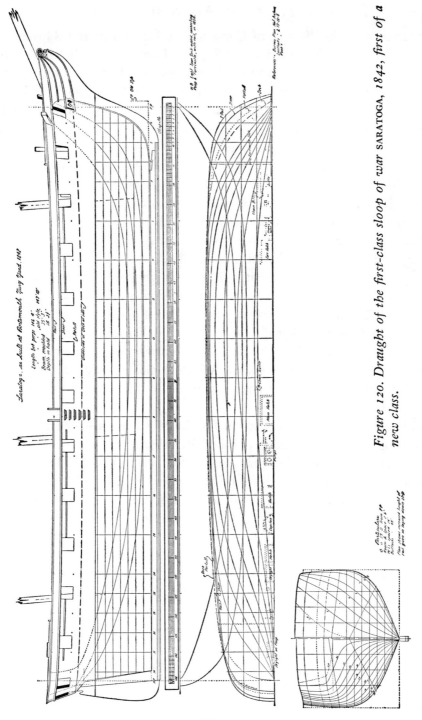

Figure 120. Draught of the first-class sloop of war SARATOGA, *1842, first of a new class.*

the function of the "Bureau of Construction, Equipment and Repairs," later called "Bureau of Construction and Repair." Disrespectful officers soon nicknamed the bureau the "Bureau of Destruction and Despair." The last three officers to hold membership in the old Board were Warrington, William M. Crane, and David Conner; Warrington was President of the Board, and Goldsborough was the secretary. One officer had been appointed in 1840, John B. Nicolson, but his term had ended in 1841.

The new act established five bureaus—Construction, Equipment, and Repairs; Yards and Docks; Ordnance and Hydrography; Provisions and Clothing; and Medicine and Surgery. The act also created the Engineer Corps of the Navy and the office of Engineer in Chief. The Bureau of Construction, Equipment, and Repairs was considered as two organizations under one chief. Construction and Repairs had control of design, building, and repair of ships; Equipment had the responsibility for all gear, rigging, sails, anchors, cables, fuel, water tanks, stoves, furniture, and other similar items usually supplied to ships. In 1845 the ships in ordinary were placed under the control of Construction and Repair; originally they had been under the jurisdiction of Yards and Docks. The records of the Bureau of Construction, Equipment, and Repairs are scanty, and there is relatively little in the surviving correspondence of the constructors that gives information on technical or administrative problems.

Humphreys prepared one design for the two brigs assigned to him. His plans (Figures 121, 122, and 123) called for a sharp hull, 100′ 0″ between perpendiculars, 25′ 0″ moulded beam, and 11′ 0″ depth of hold. The design was obviously based on his successful brigantines of 1834, *Dolphin* and *Porpoise*. The two brigs built from the design were the *Somers*, at the New York Navy Yard, launched in 1842, and *Bainbridge*, in the Boston Yard at the same time. The two brigs were fast and weatherly; they were somewhat oversparred, however, and both were lost at sea. The *Somers* became a notorious vessel; as a cadet school ship she was the scene of an attempted mutiny, and the instigator, Midshipman Spencer, son of the then Secretary of War, was hanged with two alleged accomplices. This led to a storm of criticism and the overhauling of the Navy regulations. The *Somers* capsized and foundered in the Gulf of Mexico, off Vera Cruz, on December 8, 1846, with the loss of forty officers and men. She was commanded by Raphael Semmes, of *Alabama* fame. The *Bainbridge* foundered in the same manner off Hatteras on August 21, 1863, and only one of the crew survived. The brigs were armed with 6 medium

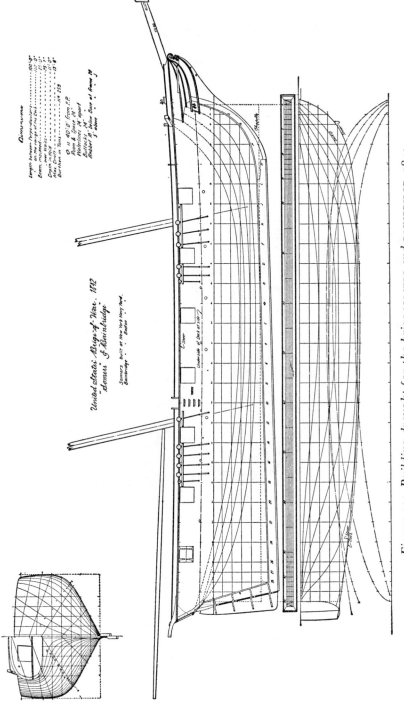

Figure 121. Building draught for the brigs SOMERS *and* BAINBRIDGE, *1842.*

431

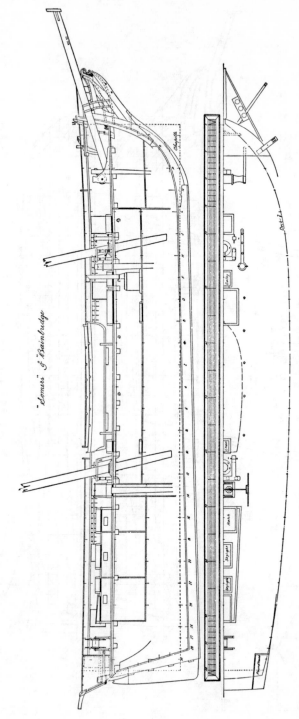

Figure 122. *Inboard profile of* SOMERS *and* BAINBRIDGE.

432

32-pdrs. and 6 short guns of the same caliber. The latter were soon replaced with 32-pdr. carronades, and eventually the armament was 10 carronades and 2 medium 32's, which were all that the brigs could bear properly.

Grice prepared two designs for the two brigs allotted to him; the first was for the brig *Truxton* (Figure 124), which was built under his supervision at the Norfolk Navy Yard in 1842. The dimensions of the brig were 100′ 0″ between perpendiculars, 27′ 4″ moulded beam, and 13′ 0″ depth of hold. She

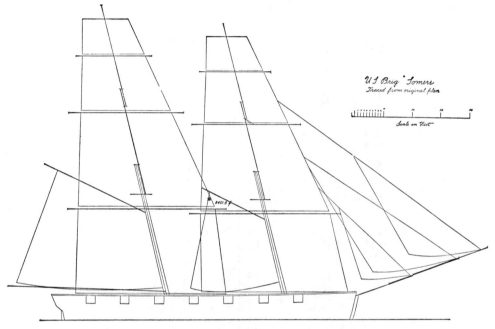

Figure 123. Sketch of spar and sail plan for SOMERS.

was somewhat sharper than Humphreys' brigs and was of deeper draft. Grice gave her much deadrise and somewhat slacker bilges than were used in the *Somers* and *Bainbridge*. The armament of the *Truxton* was specified by the constructor, who preferred to use the old 32-pdr. carronades, in preference to the new short guns, because he decided that the small hulls of these sharp brigs could not bear more weight. As we have seen, his conjecture was found to be correct in Humphreys' brigs. The sail plan of the *Truxton* (Figure 125) was typical of her class, and now the foremast of war brigs was fitted with a spencer. The new brig was very heavily sparred and proved to be a very fast sailer. She beat the *Saratoga*, considered a very fast sailer in 1844, and was particularly

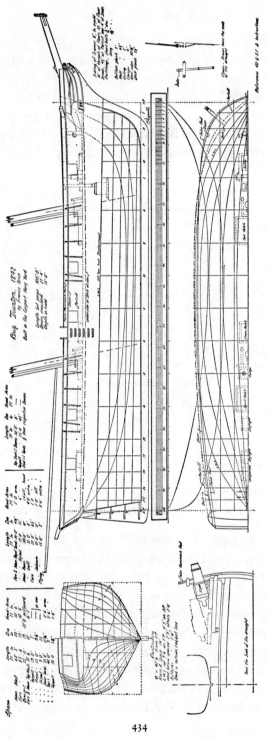

Figure 124. Draught of the brig TRUXTON.

434

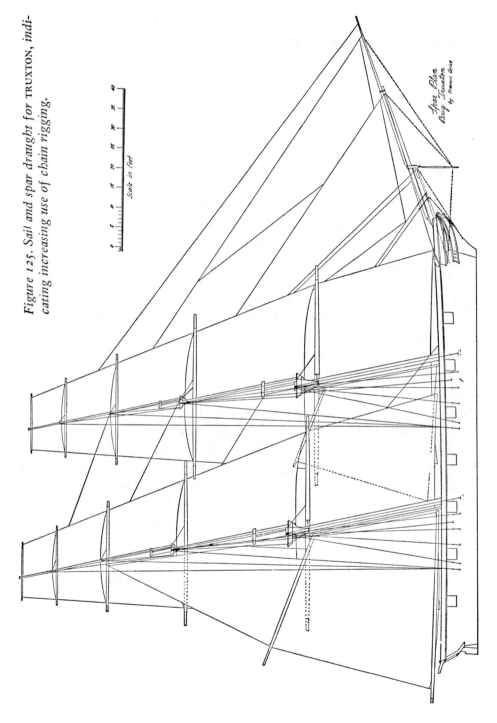

Figure 125. Sail and spar draught for TRUXTON, *indicating increasing use of chain rigging.*

Scale in Feet

Spar Plan
Brig Truxton
by Francis Grice

435

weatherly in rough water. Her deep draft was the cause of her stranding on Tuxpan Bar, on the coast of Mexico, on August 15, 1846. The wreck was afterward burned to prevent it from falling into the hands of the Mexicans. This fine brig carried 9,790 square feet of sail in her working suit, exclusive of royals and skysails; her launching weight was 168 tons, and her loaded displacement was 355 tons on 13′ 0″ draft at the sternpost. Her design was the first American naval vessel that has yet been found in which a calculation was made for stability; her metacenter was calculated as being 6.83′ above her center of buoyancy, or 3.33′ above the load water line.

Another revenue cutter was taken over by the Navy in 1842—the *Van Buren*, mentioned earlier, built in 1839. She was rated as a 4-gun schooner and had apparently been built to the dimensions of the *Morris*, if her registered tonnage is correct. The frigates that had been building slowly since 1820 were gradually being launched; the *Cumberland* and *Savannah* were launched this year. Only one of the frigates had been launched in the '30's; the *Columbia* and five of the nine frigates authorized after the War of 1812 were now completed.

By 1843, the constructors were at work on the designs of the big corvettes. The designs were not all completed at the same time, and so work did not begin on all the vessels in this year in the yards to which they had been assigned. However, it will be easier to describe them together as a class than to take each up in the chronological order of its launch. The first of the designs to be completed were those of the *Portsmouth* and *Plymouth*. The *Portsmouth* was designed by Josiah Barker, and the plans were made by B. F. Delano under the constructors' direction. It was maintained by Barker that this sloop was modeled after a merchant vessel built by him named *Union*, which in turn had been designed on the lines of a French-built privateer. The accuracy of his statement is open to doubt; there is nothing in the design of this handsome ship that indicates an unusual model, as can be seen in Figure 126. Delano once stated that she was drawn as an improvement on the *Saratoga*, built in the same yard a year earlier. The *Portsmouth* had lower bilges and hollow floors, compared to the *Saratoga;* she was also a much larger ship. The *Portsmouth* measured 151′ 10″ between perpendiculars, 37′ 3″ moulded beam, and 16′ 9″ depth of hold; she was armed with 18 medium 32's and 2 Paixhans 8″ shell guns, according to her design. Her plans were sent to Washington in May and were approved, and the ship was laid down at the Portsmouth Navy Yard on the 15th of June and launched on the 23rd of October of the same year. She was not ready to commission, however, until November 10, 1844. This sloop was

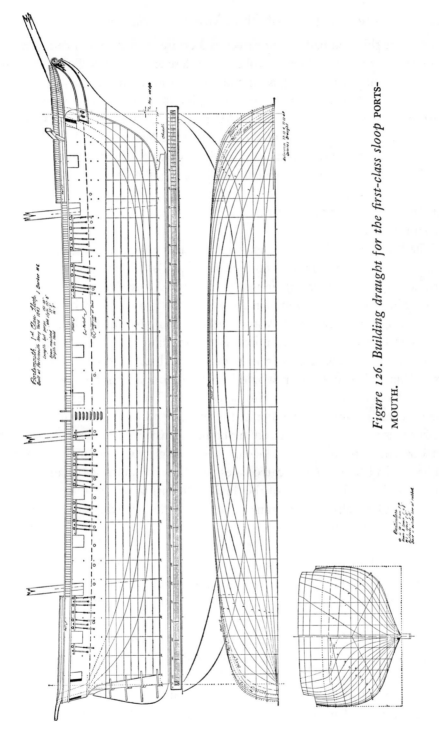

Figure 126. Building draught for the first-class sloop PORTS-
MOUTH.

a very fine ship and had a long career as a cruiser and then as a cadet training ship; she was finally sold and broken up as late as 1915. The *Portsmouth* was a very sleek-appearing vessel, as she had no mouldings and her side was unbroken between the rail cap and the water line. Her stern was almost round, with a very short overhang. After the Civil War she was fitted with a light spar deck, like many of her class; as built she had (like the *Saratoga*) a short, light top-gallant forecastle, and a short poop, made of gratings at the level of the top of the hammock rail, for convenience in handling the anchor and in conning ship. These short decks originally had only light iron stanchions and a life-line, instead of rails or bulwarks, and had first appeared in the 1825 class of 24-gun corvettes.

The Paixhans shell gun, used in these corvettes, was named for Henri Joseph Paixhans, a French general who had developed shell guns and had been in-strumental in introducing them into the French Army and Navy. In 1841 the guns of his design were known as *canons-obusiers* in the French Navy. These were guns of medium length, with a sharp increase in outside diameter begin-ning just forward of the trunnions and extending back toward the breech about two-thirds the length from trunnions to base ring. Here the diameter was reduced sharply to what would have been normal had the taper been con-tinuous from the muzzle end. This design of the breech was permitted by the use of a small-diameter chamber at the breech end of the bore in which the charge was rammed, the shot coming home against the shoulder formed at the forward end of the chamber. The chambering of guns was not new in Paixhans' design; it had been used in carronades for the same purpose, to allow heavy charges to be used by means of the thick walls formed by chambering a large-bore gun. Gradually all shell guns came to be called "Paixhans guns," whether or not they were on the Frenchman's design. The "Paixhans guns" of the *Portsmouth* were actually 64-pdrs. with chambered bore of 8″ and on the bottle-shaped design that had been proposed by Dahlgren of the United States Navy. Later designs of this and larger guns of the same model were known as "Dahlgren guns" and were extensively used in the Federal Navy in the Civil War.

In the design of the *Plymouth* Samuel Pook not only had a second chance to work on a design for a large corvette, but now, unlike the time when the *Saratoga* was designed, he could follow his own ideas in model and in the dimen-sions necessary to carry the required armament. The other constructors de-signing corvettes had the same privileges. As a result, the *Plymouth* was quite

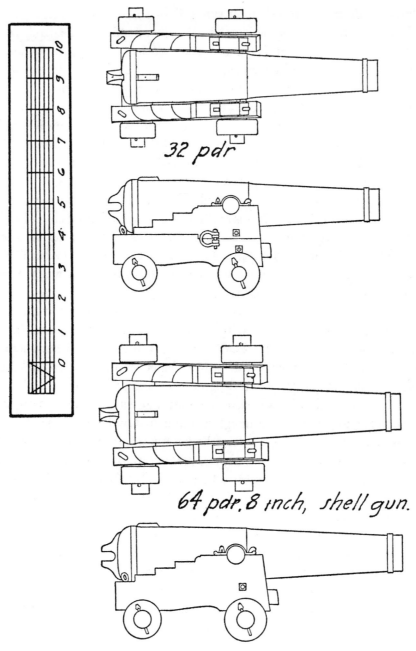

32 pdr

64 pdr. 8 inch, shell gun.

Guns and carriages for the first-class sloops of war, 1840–45.

different in design from the earlier sloop. Pook's new design called for a corvette 147′ 0″ between perpendiculars, 37′ 3″ moulded beam, and 16′ 3½″ depth of hold. She had much less deadrise than had been given the *Saratoga*, so that she had lower and somewhat harder bilges. Unlike the *Portsmouth*, the *Plymouth* had straight-rising floors and had much less rake to the stem. The *Plymouth* was the first of her class to be designed with a full spar deck and, in this respect, was a reversion to the style of 1798–99. This sloop was built in the Boston Navy Yard and was launched shortly after the *Portsmouth*, being finished late in 1844. The new corvette proved to be an exceptional ship, stiff, dry in rough water, and very fast in both light and heavy winds, and also very handy. In appearance she was much like a packet ship, but she was sharper-ended than most of this class. This corvette was much admired abroad and was considered by many officers to have been the finest vessel of her class in any navy. The design of this fine ship is shown in Figure 127. Her sail plan is shown in Figure 128. This ship was like the *Portsmouth* in finish, without quarter galleries or other gingerbread work.

The sloop *Jamestown* was a vessel very like the *Plymouth* in model and arrangement; she was designed with a full spar deck and had a straight rising floor and rather low, hard bilges. She had very little rake in both stem and sternpost and had sharp ends. She was a longer ship than *Plymouth*, as her dimensions show: 157′ 6″ between perpendiculars, 35′ 0″ moulded beam, and 16′ 2″ depth of hold. She was also much more ornate, as can be seen by her building plan, Figure 129. Her design was prepared by Rhodes, one of the least known of the constructors. Foster Rhodes appears to have been assistant to Grice and was a very capable designer, judging by the few plans of his ships that have been found. His sloop was built at the Norfolk Navy Yard and was launched in 1844. She was somewhat more heavily built than the *Plymouth*. Like that ship, she was a very good sailer; however, because of her weight, the *Jamestown* required careful trimming with ballast. With the *Macedonian*, she carried food to Ireland in the great famine in 1847, making a very fast passage under hard driving. The ship lasted until recent years, her last days being spent as a marine hospital in New York Harbor. The model of this corvette, like that of the *Plymouth*, has a very strong suggestion of a packet ship in it, though the corvette was relatively sharp-ended compared to most of the packets built in the early '40's.

The *Germantown* was designed by Lenthall and was built in the Philadelphia Navy Yard from 1843 to 1846. Lenthall's design was for a low-sided

PLATE XV. (Top) First-class sloop of war SARATOGA. *(Bottom) First-class sloop of war* JAMESTOWN.

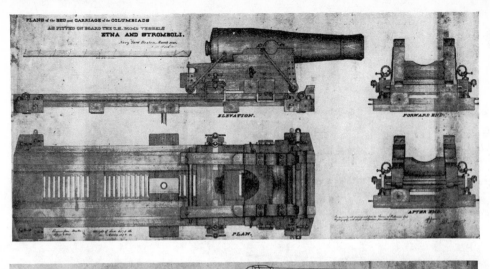

Columbiad, mounted for a howitzer on bomb vessels ETNA and STROMBOLI.

U.S. Navy gun and carronade, 1827–35.

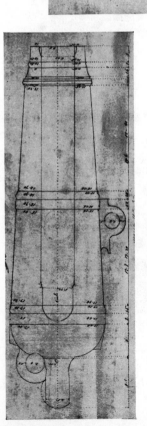

U.S. Navy 32-pdr. carronade, 1827.

U.S. Navy 24-pdr. medium gun, 1827.

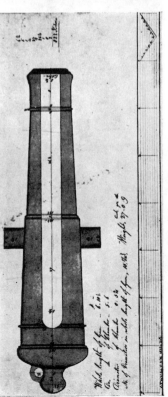

18-pdr. medium gun, War of 1812.

PLATE XVI. Naval guns

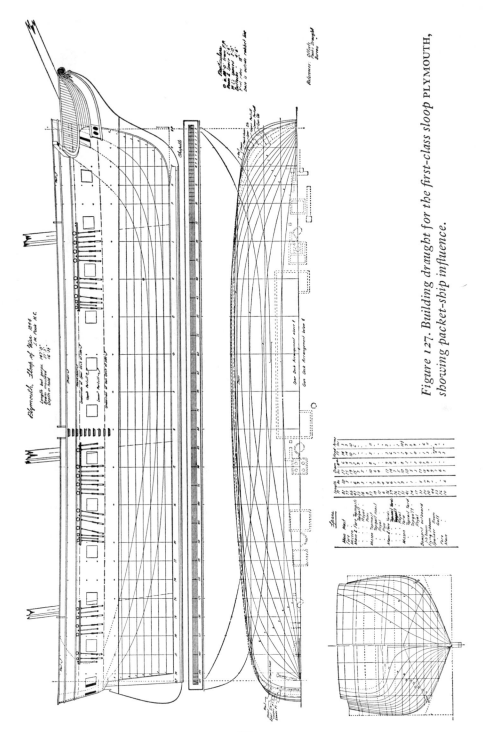

Figure 127. Building draught for the first-class sloop PLYMOUTH, showing packet-ship influence.

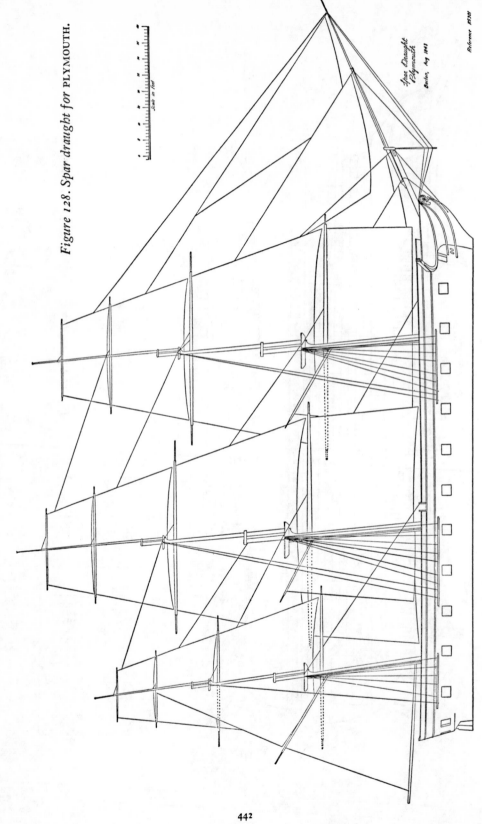

Figure 128. Spar draught for PLYMOUTH.

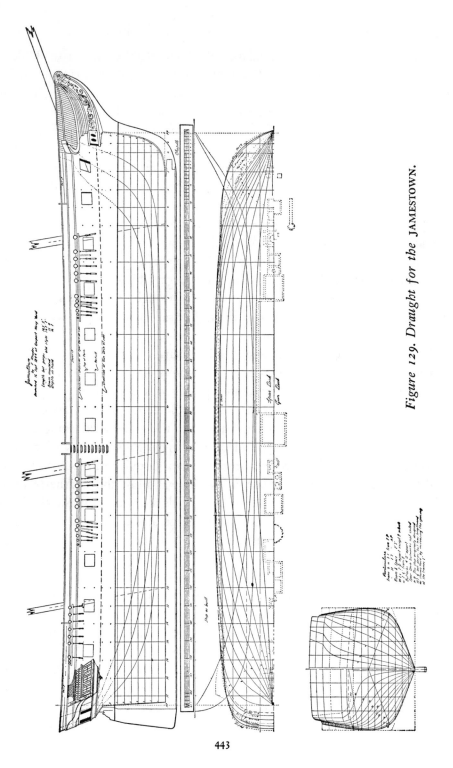

Figure 129. Draught for the JAMESTOWN.

443

ship, 148′ 6″ between perpendiculars, 36′ 0″ moulded beam, and 16′ 8″ depth of hold. She was lengthened 1′ 6″ in building, and her plans (Plan 28 and Figure 130) show the ship as built, 150′ 0″ between perpendiculars. The *Germantown* plans are in far greater detail than most of her class and are therefore of value in showing the deck fittings of the corvettes of her date. She was on a very sharp model and was a handsome ship, as can be seen in her plans. Like her classmates, she was very fast; the *Germantown* was said to have shared a great reputation for speed in light airs with the *Albany*, another of her class. The Lenthall sloop was one of the sailing men-of-war burned in the Norfolk Navy Yard in 1861; her wreckage was raised and sold in 1863.

Plan 28 shows the deck details of this sloop and indicates the gradual increase in ironwork in naval ships that had taken place by 1843. Iron-strap gammonings had replaced chain or rope, the mooring bitts were now fitted for chain cable, and in other details the ship was brought up to the standards of the best of contemporary merchant craft. The sail plan, though lofty, showed no important difference from others of her class.

The corvette *St. Marys* was designed by Charles D. Brodie and built in the Washington Navy Yard in 1843–44. She was a vessel of much deadrise, like the *Germantown*, though very different in appearance as can be seen by Figure 131. Brodie's sloop was 150′ 0″ between perpendiculars, 36′ 6″ moulded beam, and 16′ 6″ depth of hold. This ship had about the same deck arrangement as the *Germantown*. The *St. Marys* had less rake in her ends than any of the other corvettes except the *Jamestown*. Brodie's sloop lasted until 1908 and was a well-known school ship in her last years. She was a fast and weatherly vessel. Like many of her classmates, built as a single-decked corvette, the *St. Marys* had a spar deck added after the Civil War. Some of the sloops first had a light spar deck of gratings added in the late '50's, but this was converted to a laid spar deck in later years in all cases.

The last corvette to be mentioned was a very beautiful vessel, the *Albany*. This ship was the design of Francis Grice and was built in the New York Navy Yard in 1843–44. The *Albany* was the only one of the new corvettes designed with a square stern, and she also was a reversion to the old Baltimore Clipper model, as will be seen in Figure 132. This corvette was 147′ 11″ between perpendiculars, 38′ 6″ moulded beam, and 17′ 9″ depth of hold. She had very sharp deadrise and also was very sharp-ended, compared to her classmates. She sat low in the water and looked more like a clipper than any other naval ship. Grice wished to turn out a corvette that would be very weatherly and fast.

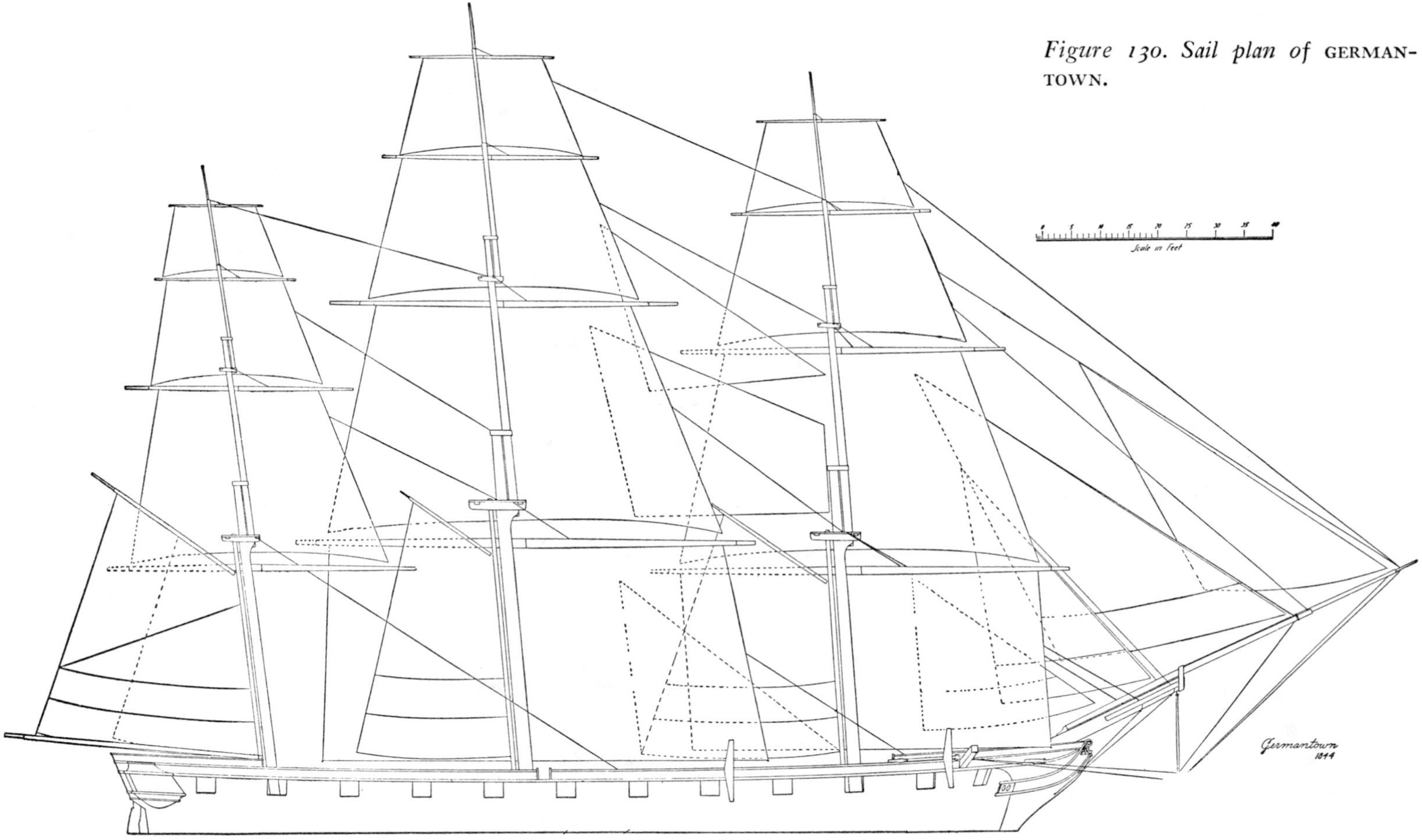

Figure 130. Sail plan of GERMAN-TOWN.

Scale in Feet

Germantown
1844

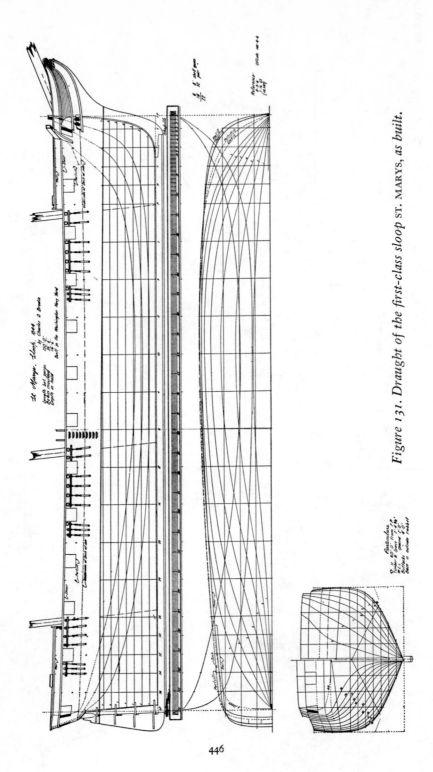

Figure 131. Draught of the first-class sloop ST. MARYS, *as built.*

446

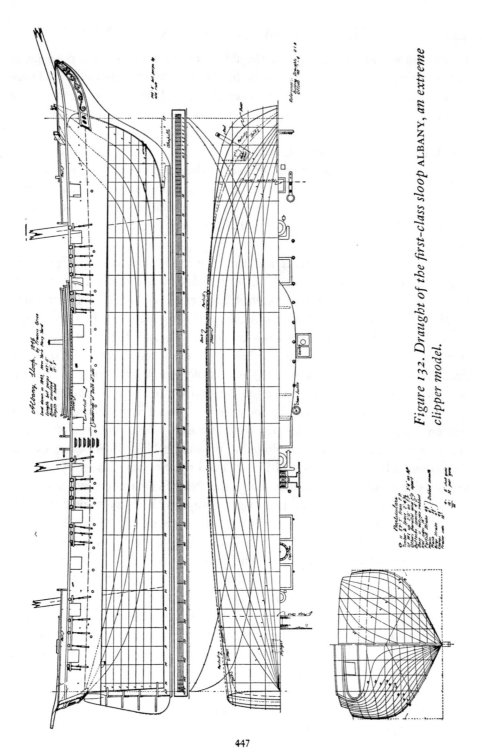

Figure 132. Draught of the first-class sloop ALBANY, *an extreme clipper model.*

447

In this aim he was successful, for the ship gained a remarkable reputation in her short life; she was lost at sea with all hands in the West Indies in 1854. There were some criticisms of the ship, however; she would not stow as much as some of the other corvettes and, like most fast ships, she was very wet when close-hauled in a breeze. Pook wrote that she had far too much deadrise for a large vessel; he was also critical of *Germantown* and *St. Marys*. The difference in opinion regarding the advantages of extreme deadrise had reached a crescendo in the '40's, and, under the literary leadership of John Griffiths, the adherents of the flat-bottomed model were aggressively attacking the sharp-bottomed hull form. Griffiths was an active, if not always accurate, critic of the design of Navy ships.

In the design of the *Albany*, Grice wanted to employ the bark rig; Figure 133 shows the sail plan as recommended by the designer. The bark rig was not common among men-of-war, though it had been used successfully on a few naval ships abroad. In the Napoleonic Wars this rig was used in a few ships, most of which were merchant ships bought and armed for naval service. A few brigs, considered too large for their rig, were fitted as barks. In 1801 the French built a bark-rigged corvette named *Diligente*, which proved very fast, and for years they tried to reproduce the ship without much success. In the 1820's and 1830's the rig became popular in the United States among merchant seamen. This was also true in Britain, and a few British naval vessels were rigged in this fashion. No bark was employed in the sailing Navy in America, except the unsuccessful *Consort*, but Grice believed the rig would be very suitable for his sharp corvette. Unfortunately, the Navy Department thought differently, and she came out as a full-rigged ship, in the conventional manner. The *Albany* could be readily identified by the extreme rake in her masts; this characteristic of the proposed bark rig was employed in her ship rig as well.

There was some similarity between Grice's ideas and those of the British surveyor, Symonds; both believed in sharp deadrise amidships and fine ends. The American, however, usually designed his vessels so that the turn of the bilge, at the intersection of the rising V-bottom and the topsides, was below the load water line. Symonds usually placed the turn of the bilge either at the load water line or slightly above it. Either plan produced a fast hull under sail, particularly in the smaller vessels. The Symonds midsection had been tried out very extensively in America, long before the English constructor appeared on the scene. In the early 1800's a number of pilot-boat schooners were designed and built with exactly the same midsection that Symonds de-

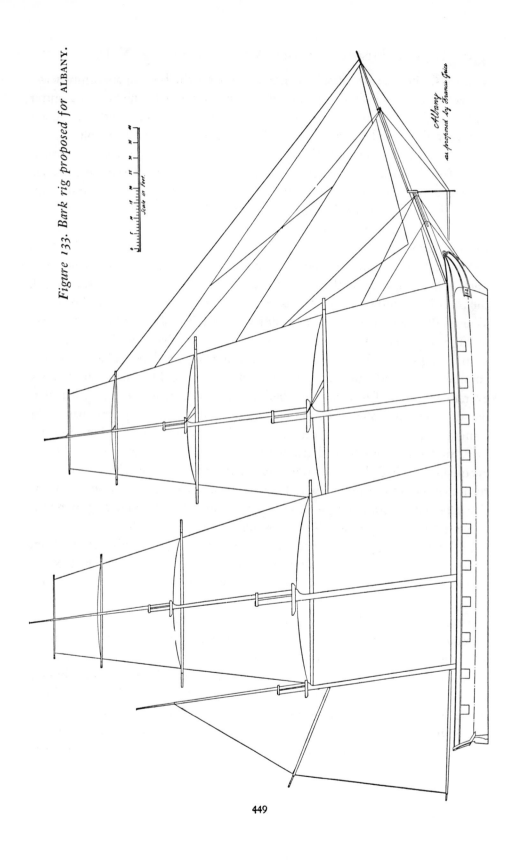

Figure 133. Bark rig proposed for ALBANY.

Scale in feet

Albany
as proposed by Thomas Grice

veloped in the '20's. In these American schooners the bottom amidships was a perfect V with the bilges entirely above the water line; the revenue cutter *James Madison* (Figure 52) is an example of the form. Some of the schooners had very flaring sides instead of the high bilges. Eckford had employed this hull form in *Grampus* while Symonds was as yet unknown as a ship designer. Also, Chief Constructor Humphreys had designed a pilot schooner named *Nimble* about 1806 with the sharp bottom and high bilges that were to mark Symonds' designs in the Royal Navy. These ideas were not new in 1806, of course, for Americans, French, and British had experimented with the hull form as early as 1770. Generally, the very sharp-bottomed hull, with high bilges, had been employed only in small craft—cutters, sloops, schooners, luggers, and brigs; but in the 1790's the French built a ship sloop on this model, the *Bourdelais*, and the English master shipwright on Lake Ontario during the War of 1812, a very able man named Sutherland, had also employed this form in large ships. The Americans had decided that the sharp deadrise combined with flaring sides or bilges above the load water line produced a fast vessel and employed this model in many of their fast schooners. They had found, however, that this same form, when applied to large ships, made a very uneasy roller, one that not only rolled deep but ended each roll with a sharp jerk that might dismast a ship. Hence, when they employed much deadrise in a ship or heavy brig, they usually employed hard bilges below the load water line. The British eventually reached the same conclusion with regard to the "Symondite" hull form that the Americans had with the pilot-boat model. The Americans' extensive experience with this style of model prevented them from taking Symonds very seriously, though the *Albany* was much like a Symondite.

In January, 1843, Grice had completed the design of his second brig, to be named *Perry*. He had intended to employ the round stern in this design, but after making a set of lines he changed his mind, and the final plans were for a brig having a transom stern. The transom in this design had become less angular in shape, for now the cross seam and the lowest part of the transom stern became curved and was developed into the modern counter. The *Perry* (Figure 134) was 105' 0" between perpendiculars, 25' moulded beam, and 11' 6" depth of hold. Her model was that of a Baltimore Clipper, and in many ways it also resembled Humphreys' brigs. The *Perry* was built at the Norfolk Navy Yard during 1843, and upon completion proved to be one of the fastest ships in the Navy. When first tried she was found to be tender, however, and about 1845 her rig was altered slightly, and her boats

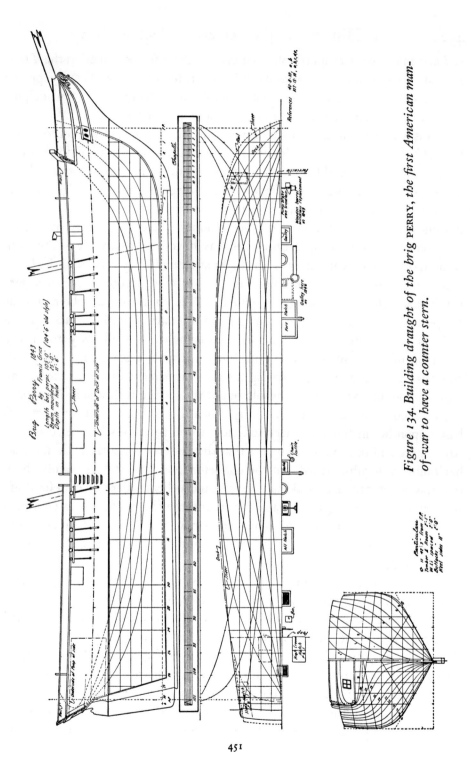

Figure 134. Building draught of the brig PERRY, *the first American man-of-war to have a counter stern.*

and armament were reduced. She first carried the armament used in the *Truxton*, but two of her carronades were removed by 1850. The *Perry* captured a Confederate privateer in the Civil War; she was finally sold at Philadelphia in 1865, after which she was employed as a merchant vessel.

It was decided to obtain a fifth brig in 1843, and a contract was let to Langley B. Culley, of Baltimore, who was to furnish the design and build the vessel. Culley was a noted builder and had turned out many fast schooners and brigs in the '40's; in 1848 he built a very fast clipper ship named the *Architect*. It is not possible to say why this fifth brig was contract-built, and the records dealing with this contract have not been found. The contract may have been a matter of political manipulation, or it may have been the result of the large amount of work now in the navy yards. At any rate Culley produced the *Lawrence*, a brig of the extreme Baltimore Clipper model, 109′ 9″ between perpendiculars, 26′ 2″ moulded beam, and 13′ 3″ depth in the hold. Her draft at the post was 16′ 6″, an extraordinary draft for a naval brig. Her lines (Figure 136) show her interesting model; she was launched at Culley's yard on the south side of the Basin August 1, 1843. She was copper-fastened and -sheathed, and rated as a 10-gun brig carrying the same armament as the *Truxton*. She was an unpopular vessel, and was sold out of the service at Boston in 1846, having been condemned at New York by a board of officers. Their report was based upon her inability to carry sufficient stores for a vessel of her class and size. There had been various rumors that the vessel was poorly built and that her timber was substandard, but the condemnation proceedings plainly show that this was not the case and that she was an excellent sailer as well. Her draft was certainly excessive for a man-of-war, and the fact that she was contract-built and -designed did not add to her popularity. She was employed as a merchant brig for a while, then her rig was altered to a brigantine. Her end has not been discovered.

The *Perry* and *Lawrence* had stern cabins, or "hurricane houses," which were formed by dropping the main deck, close to the stern, low enough to give headroom under a short poop deck built at rail level. This space was closed off by a bulkhead at the break and formed a cabin for the commander. The short, light poop provided a handy place to con the ship and handle the spanker sheets. There were often two hatchways through the forward bulkhead from the main deck into the cabin, but there was no passageway from the cabin below deck, and in the event the cabin was swamped through the hatchways, no water could get below and fill the ship. However, the cabin prevented the

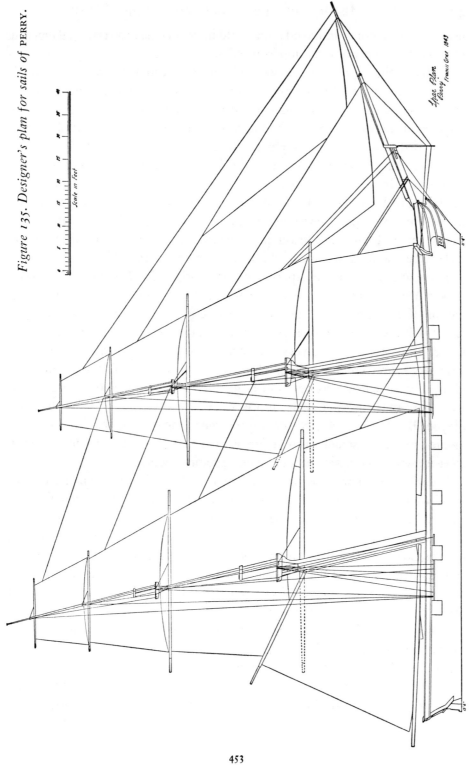

Figure 135. Designer's plan for sails of PERRY.

Spar Plan
PERRY Francis Gree 1843

Scale in Feet

453

use of the stern ports, and so no guns could be trained dead astern—a dangerous blind spot in a naval sailing ship in wartime.

As far as the captain was concerned, the stern cabin was a most desirable feature when the vessel was in the tropics. This style of cabin had been popular in revenue cutters in 1798, and some of the commanders had tried to have it installed in the 1821 class of schooners, but without success. It had, however, been added to some of the 1825 corvettes and to the storeship *Relief*.

The steering wheel was on the main deck just forward of the stern cabin bulkhead. The *Perry* had no capstan but employed an anchor windlass on the bowsprit bitts. These brigs all carried half-ports; these were port covers divided into two parts horizontally, both being hinged. The upper portion swung upward while the lower part opened downward. Port covers of this style were also used in some of the sloops and corvettes.

There were a number of experiments in the brigs. The *Truxton* had no dead-eyes in her chain plates but had her shrouds brought down through rollers at the top of each chain plate and then the shroud set up on itself with seizings. Chain bobstays and bowsprit shrouds were also used in some of these brigs. For their time they were very advanced vessels and were a credit to their designers, who were now taking advantage of the opportunity to try out new ideas in arrangement, fittings, and rigging. The possibilities of improvement were now much greater than before, since ironwork could be lavishly employed. But the real chance for improvement came from the freedom now granted to the constructors to design as each thought best, without having to meet unreasonable basic specifications or requirements.

A curious schooner was purchased for the Navy in 1843, on the recommendation of Commodore Charles Stewart. This was an experimental yacht named the *On-ka-hy-e*, which had been built by William Capes at Williamsburg, New York, in 1839–40. The schooner was designed by her owner, Robert Livingston Stevens, of Hoboken, New Jersey, in 1837–38 as a result of extensive testing with large sailing models. Stevens and two brothers had been owners of the schooner *Wave*, purchased by the Navy in 1836; a model made to the lines of this schooner was one of those tested. The *On-ka-hy-e*— or *On-ca-hy-e*, as it was sometimes spelled—was on a most peculiar design, as can be seen by her plan, Figure 137, for she had an unorthodox midsection and was a centerboard vessel as well. She was 96' 0" over all and about 22' beam; with her centerboard up she drew nearly 10'. On her trials she proved very fast and extraordinarily stiff, but was slow in stays. Her rig was then altered and

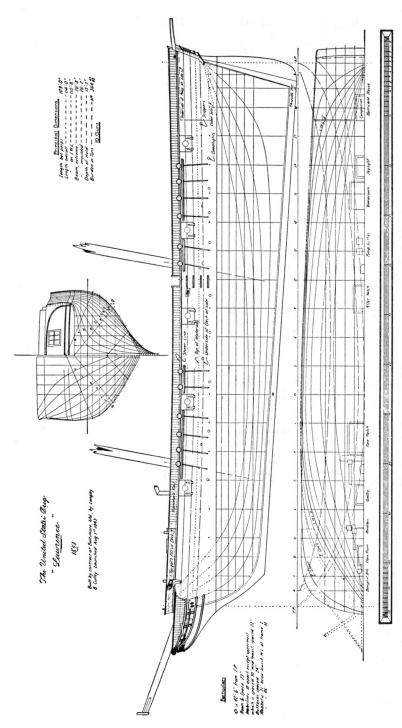

The United States Brig

"Lawrence"

1843

Built by contract at Baltimore, Md., by Langley
B. Culey. Launched Aug 1st 1843

Principal Dimensions

Length bet. perp.	109' 0"
Length overall	116' 0"
on L.W.L.	112' 8"
Beam, extreme	26' 8"
moulded	26' 5"
Depth of Hold	13' 3"
Burden in Tons	~ 364 ⁴⁵⁄₉₅
10 Guns	

Figure 136. Draught of Baltimore Clipper-model brig LAWRENCE.

455

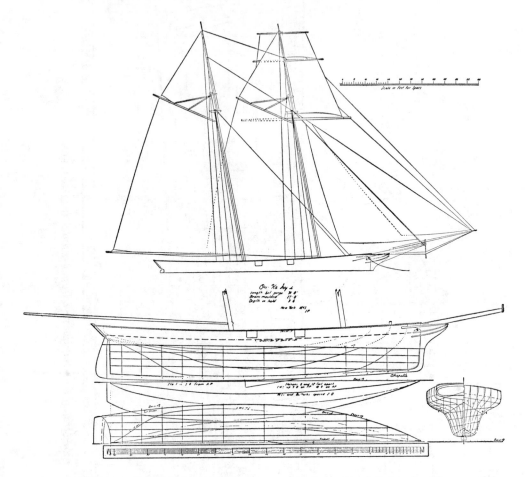

Figure 137. Plans of the schooner ON-KA-HY-E, a radical design based on model tests.

her staying was much improved. She was a good seaboat, but rolled very hard; she once rolled her masts out and had to be towed in. She was sailed against a fast brig named *Exit* and against a pilot boat, the *Jacob Bell*, and beat both. Stevens tried many experiments on this schooner: at one time she had outside ballast and sail tracks; he also put two centerboards in her. The Navy took out her centerboard and added bilge, or sister, keels on either side of her shoe and also gave her square sails on her topmasts. She carried 2 guns. On June 21, 1848, she was wrecked on Caicos Reef in the West Indies, after cruising to Brazil.

The frigate *Raritan* was launched in 1843, which left three of the class still building. The plans of the *Raritan* had been revised by Lenthall from time to time; Plan 29 shows this frigate as she was built. It will be seen that the appearance of the frigates had changed since the plan of the *Brandywine* was drawn, though the dimensions were unaltered. The *Raritan* was found to be a fast-sailing frigate. As built these frigates did vary a few inches in length, owing to minor errors in building; the *Raritan* was actually 174' 10" between perpendiculars when measured by Lenthall for preparing an "as built" plan.

The year 1843 marked the end of the long-drawn-out Seminole War, which had been going on intermittently since 1835. This permitted the disbanding of the mosquito squadron of small schooners that had been operating on the Florida coasts. It was not long, however, before the war with Mexico re-created the need of these small craft.

It is notable that Samuel Hartt is not credited with the design of any sailing vessels in these years. There is no reason for this omission in the records of the Board and of the Bureau that succeeded it, but it seems probable that Hartt was fully occupied in the design of war steamers in the early years of the decade. In 1842 he designed and supervised the construction of the first iron man-of-war in the United States Navy, the steamer *Michigan*. A number of experimental steamers were also built, and constructors Grice, Hartt, Lenthall and Pook were employed in steamship design, but there is evidence to support the assumption that Hartt was the constructor most interested in steamers.

The last spurt in naval sailing-ship construction was over in 1844; though sailing men-of-war were added to the Navy after this year, most of them were small purchased or prize vessels, or were ships placed on the stocks in earlier years and completed after 1844 or 1845. The boom in the years 1842–43 appears to have been at least partly due to the controversy over steamers; the Board and senior naval officers were anxious to utilize any available funds in the construction of sailing vessels at the expense of the steamers, wherever this was possible. However, it was slowly becoming apparent to intelligent and progressive naval officers that the usefulness of sailing men-of-war was being increasingly limited and that steam, as an auxiliary at least, was now highly desirable in naval ships. The constructors appear to have been generally sympathetic to the idea of auxiliary steamers, though many of them disliked to attempt such vessels as long as side paddle wheels were to be used.

In a number of cases steamers had been built both by government agencies

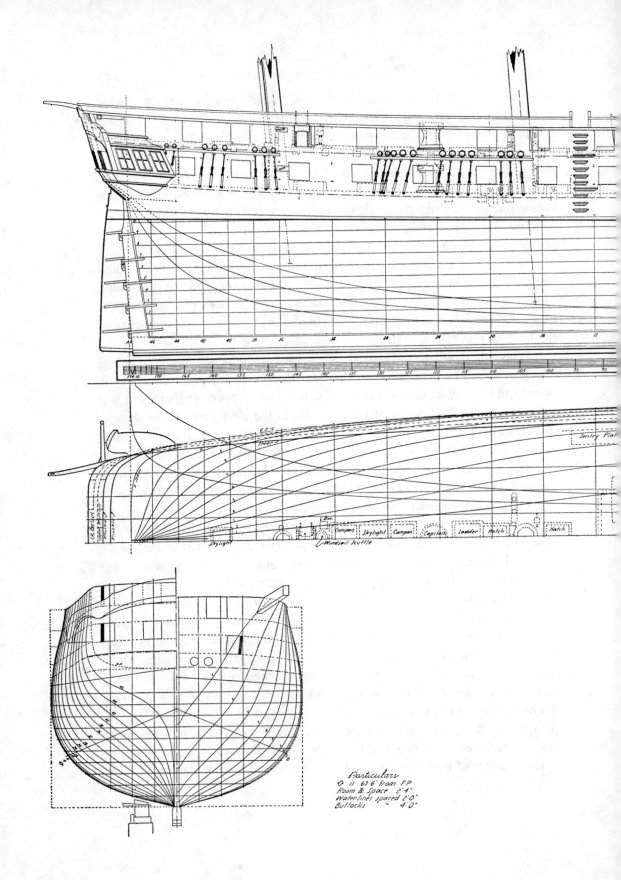

Sentry Plat

Skylight   Bn.

Skylight   Compan   Skylight   Compan   Capstan   Ladder   Hatch   Hatch

Windsail Scuttle

Particulars
O   11   63'6" from F.P.
Room & Space   2'4"
Waterlines spaced 2'0"
Buttocks   "   4'0"

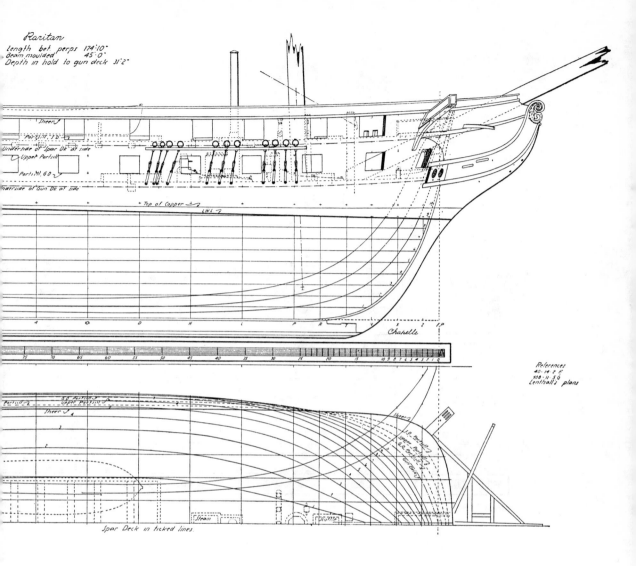

Plan 29. Draught of the 44-gun frigate RARITAN, as built.

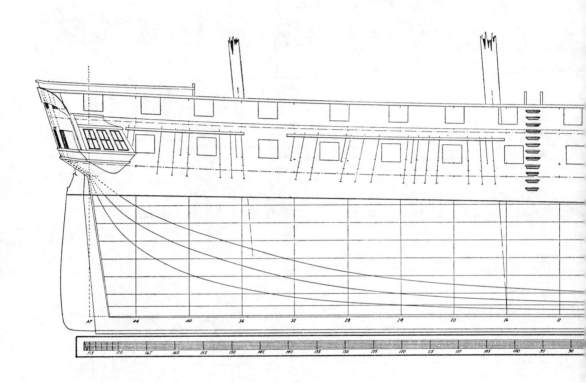

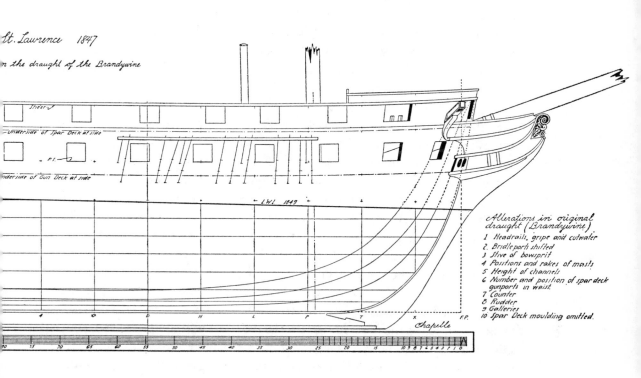

St. Lawrence 1847

on the draught of the Brandywine

Sheer

Underside of Spar Deck at side

P.S.

Underside of Gun Deck at side

LWL 1849

Alterations in original
draught (Brandywine)

1 Headrails, gripe and cutwater
2 Bridleport shifted
3 Stive of bowsprit
4 Positions and rakes of masts
5 Height of channels
6 Number and position of spar deck
  gunports in waist
7 Counter
8 Rudder
9 Galleries
10 Spar Deck moulding omitted.

Chapelle

Plan 30. Profile of the 44-gun frigate ST. LAWRENCE.

and by private industry which, for one reason or another, were unsuccessful. In a few cases the private owners failed and could not complete the ships; in others the machinery proved faulty or of insufficient power. A number of ships that had been designed as steamers were completed as sailing ships, as a result of such failures. Eckford had an experience of this kind in the 1820's, and there was an even earlier case on Lake Champlain, in the War of 1812, the *Ticonderoga*. Such a vessel was the storeship *Southampton*, purchased in 1845. She was built at Norfolk, her keel having been laid in October of 1841, as a paddlewheel vessel. Her machinery was found unsatisfactory, so it was removed and the vessel was rigged as a ship, to carry 2 carronades, 42-pdrs. Her lines (Figure 138) show her to have been a typical seagoing steamer hull of her period, rather narrow for a sailing vessel. She was 152' 6" between perpendiculars, but only 27' 0" moulded beam, while her depth of hold was 16' 0". She was a fast sailer but was considered tender and was sold out of service. The record of this ship is very incomplete; though she is said to have been purchased, there is some indication that she was built for government use. This vessel was used as a merchant ship after her disposal by the Navy. She had the short, heavy cutwater that marked early naval steamers, though her head and bowsprit had been raised when she was converted to a sailing ship.

The 74-gun ship *Vermont* was launched this year, the last ship of the line to be completed as such for the American Navy. Though the *Alabama* was finally launched as the *New Hampshire* in 1864, she was completed as a storeship. The 74's were now nothing more than a suitable vehicle to "show the flag" on foreign stations, and even here they were gradually being replaced by smaller ships and steamers of greater war potential. The liner was too expensive to maintain by 1845, unless as a flagship. Most of the liners were placed in ordinary in the '40's and allowed to deteriorate.

During 1845 a good deal of consideration was given to the possibility of constructing a large clipper brig and a very long corvette. The matter did not progress very far, as the growing demand for steamers made such craft of doubtful value. However, Humphreys had Richard Powell, an assistant of Lenthall's at Philadelphia, design a proposal for each. The brig, shown in Figure 139, was to be named *Burrows*. She was a very large clipper brig, 126' 0" between perpendiculars, 30' 0" moulded beam, and 14' 0" in the hold. The design called for a peacetime armament of 14 guns and a war armament of 16. The vessel was to be round-sterned and would undoubtedly have been a fast and very powerful brig, had she been built. The plan of the corvette was

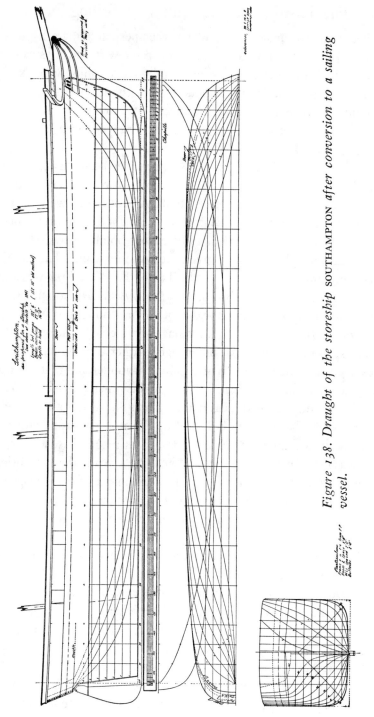

Figure 138. Draught of the storeship SOUTHAMPTON *after conversion to a sailing vessel.*

459

not finished; it called for a ship 205′ 0″ between perpendiculars, 43′ 6″ moulded beam, and 21′ 0″ depth of hold—a size comparable with the big steam sloops of the Civil War. The corvette was to be a single-decked ship, which would have made her much like the later steamers in hull, though the sailing vessel was to have much deadrise; in fact, her lines were very much like those of the proposed brig. This vessel was to be diagonally strapped with iron and was to carry 26 guns.

The Mexican War, which began in 1846, produced some naval activity. The Mexican fleet at that time was made up almost entirely of ex-merchant brigs and schooners, most of them American-built. A few vessels were purchased by the United States Navy for service in this war, the most important being some steamers and three brigs or schooners fitted for bomb vessels, for the attack on Vera Cruz. These bombs were given the volcanic names that the Navy had employed for bomb vessels ever since the Tripolitan War: *Etna* was a schooner or brig of 182 tons bought at Boston; the *Stromboli* was bought in the same port and was a brig; the *Vesuvius* was another brig bought at New York.

Plans of one of these vessels, the *Etna*, have survived. (Some of the references to this ship spell her name *Etna*, but others properly name her *Aetna*.) The drawings show that the vessel was originally a schooner and that she was either bought under the name *Walcott* or was to be renamed that. *Walcott* was then struck out and the vessel was named *Etna*. She was 80′ 0″ between perpendiculars, 22′ 8″ beam, and about 10′ depth of hold—apparently a coasting schooner. It was first intended to fit her as a topsail schooner, but the mainmast was in the way of the gun, so the rig was made that of a brig, which enabled the mainmast to be moved aft. The armament of these brigs is shown to have been a short 10″ shell gun fitted as a howitzer, rather than the traditional mortar. The gun was mounted on a pivoted slide amidships, with the carriage fitted for high-angle fire. Figure 140 shows the appearance of this vessel and probably represents her sisters. All three were sold out in 1848, as soon as the war was over.

Three storeships were also purchased: *Electra* of 248 tons, *Fredonia* of 800 tons, and the *Supply* of 547 tons—all merchant craft. A pilot schooner named *Reefer* was bought as a dispatch boat, and a small schooner named *Petrel* was built at Baltimore. Another schooner was bought at New York, the 76½ ton *Bonita*, probably a pilot boat also. The revenue cutter *Forward* was obtained from the Revenue Service, and six prize vessels, taken from the Mexicans, were placed on the Navy register. These were the schooner *Nonata*,

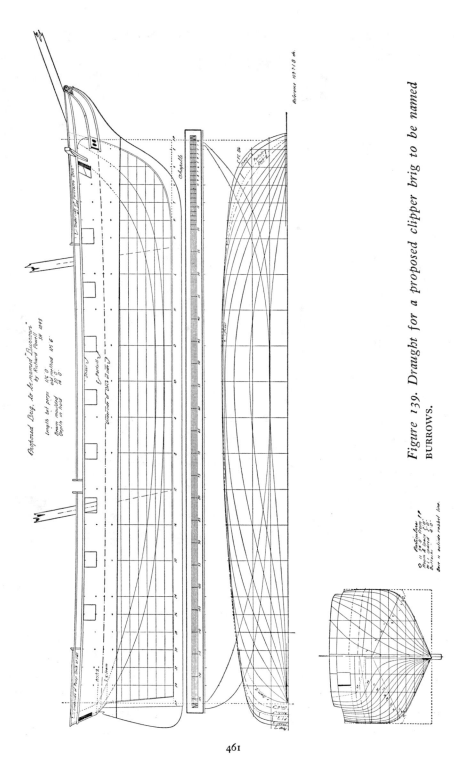

Figure 139. Draught for a proposed clipper brig to be named BURROWS.

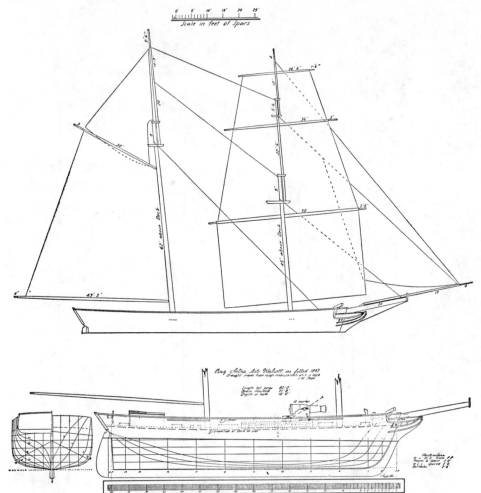

Figure 140. Bomb brig ETNA, *ex* WALCOTT.

taken in August by the steamer *Mississippi;* the *Mahonese,* schooner, 100 tons, taken off Tampico in November; *Morris,* schooner, ex *Laura Virginia,* taken in the Gulf of Mexico in October; and the fine brig *Malek Adhel,* taken by the *Warren* at Mazatlán, Mexico, in September. The *Malek Adhel* was a vessel built by William Webb for the Pacific trade in 1840; she was 80′ 0″ on deck, 20′ 7″ moulded beam, and 7′ 9″ depth in the hold. The lines of this brig are among those in Webb's book of plans, but the drawings show a flush-decked brig, whereas the customhouse description shows her to have had a quarter-deck to the mainmast at rail level, and she probably had a sunk poop like the revenue cutter *Washington* of 1837. The remaining prizes were the *Tampico*, a schooner originally named *Pueplana*, taken at Tampico in November, and the *Union*, a schooner taken at the same time. The latter vessel was wrecked while in the American service, off Vera Cruz, in December, 1846. All the remaining prizes were sold at the end of the war, in 1848.

In 1847 another prize schooner was added to the Navy, the *Liberdad*, which had been taken by the *Cyane* in Lower California in October of 1846; she was employed as a tender and placed on the register in 1847. She carried a single 9-pdr. and was sold at the end of the Mexican War. A schooner named the *Nautilus* was taken over from the Coast Survey, and the ex-revenue cutter *Taney* was bought at Baltimore. Both schooners went to the Coast Survey at the end of the war. The records of the Navy and the Coast Guard are often at variance on the date of transfer of these early cutters, and the confusion seems impossible to straighten out with existing records.

The frigate *St. Lawrence* was launched in 1848, and her plan (Plan 30) shows another variation in appearance of the 1820 class of frigates. In 1848 and 1849 no ships were added to the Navy, but in the '50's one ship sloop was built, five exploration vessels were purchased, and the remaining frigates of the 1820 class were launched.

Meanwhile Samuel Humphreys had died in office, on August 16, 1846, at the age of 68. He had been inactive, however, since he designed the brigs in 1842, as his health had been poor. Humphreys was succeeded in 1847 by Francis Grice, who went on sick leave in 1859 and died at Philadelphia in 1865. Lenthall was the next chief constructor, succeeding Grice. Samuel M. Pook became a constructor January 1, 1841, and retired in 1866; he died in 1878. He was the father of Samuel Hartt Pook, a noted designer of clipper ships and also a naval constructor. The naval constructors, like the veteran captains of the Navy, had very long careers in those days.

In the '40's a number of modifications had taken place in some of the frigates. The decision to build up a sailing navy of large corvettes soon developed a school of thought that recommended that the serviceable frigates be cut down or razeed into large corvettes. Between 1849 and 1852 the "rebuilt" *Macedonian* was converted from a spar-decked frigate to a spar-decked corvette, stripped of quarter galleries and her head extensively altered. Her spars were lengthened, and a very handsome ship resulted, as can be seen by the draught, Plan 31. This converted her to a 24-gun ship. She remained in service until 1875, when she was sold. Some of the frigates were not cut down, but had their spar decks stripped of guns to make them into huge corvettes; *Constitution, Congress,* and some of the 1820 design of frigates were so treated. Part of this was due to the improved armament policy and part to economy; the corvette-armed frigate required smaller crews than a 44-gun frigate of the old classes.

One of the best examples of a cut-down frigate was the *Cumberland.* It will be recalled that this ship was relatively new, having been launched in 1842. She originally carried 40 carriage guns, 32-pdrs., and 10 of the 64-pdr. 8″ shell guns. She was treated in the same manner as the *Macedonian* in 1850–56 and was reduced to a magnificent corvette carrying 26 guns on her main deck, 32-pdrs., and 2 10″ shell guns on pivots, one each at bow and stern, on the spar deck. Plan 32 shows this vessel as altered. The lines of the ship were taken off in 1856; they show the hull drawn to the outside of the planking, as was done in the case of the razee *Independence.* Stripping these ships of the weight of their spar-deck bulwarks and armament, as well as removing the heavy quarter galleries (and the reducing of windage that resulted from the removal of the spar-deck bulwarks and hammock rails) made the ships very fast sailers. Their rig either remained the same as when they were frigates, or their sail area was increased. The *Cumberland* was a corvette when she fought the *Virginia* ex *Merrimac* in the Civil War; she is often referred to mistakenly as a frigate in descriptions of this action.

European navies were somewhat less enthusiastic than the Americans about the razeed frigates, but a few such vessels did appear in the English and French navies. The British had, in fact, cut down a few frigates in the '20's and '30's, but these ships were nowhere as large as the cut-down American frigates. The appearance of these ships, however, indicated how obsolete the improved naval guns, particularly the heavy shell guns, were making the massive broadside armament of the liners and frigates of earlier years. The Americans believed now that shells would be very destructive to large wooden ships and were attempting to maintain supremacy by employing the most powerful guns their ships could float, even though they were forced to cut down their large ships into vessels of lower rates, that would outrange the massed batteries of foreign frigates and ships of the line.

The year 1850 marked the beginning of arctic exploration by American naval

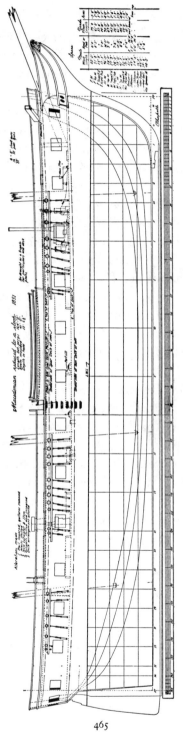

Figure 141. MACEDONIAN as razeed to a corvette.

465

vessels. The Grinnell Expedition in search of Sir John Franklin was organized this year, and special vessels were fitted for the work. These were purchased brigs: the *Rescue*, a 90-ton brig, and the *Advance*, a 140-tonner. The brigs were strengthened and fitted particularly for working in ice. The *Advance* was abandoned in the ice in 1855. Ringgold's expedition to the North Pacific in 1853–56 also required the purchase of vessels. The pilot schooner *Skiddy* of New York was bought in 1852 and renamed *Fenimore Cooper*. She was used as a tender in this expedition and was wrecked on the Pacific coast in 1859. A storeship was also bought, a New York merchant ship named *Sea Nymph*, and named the *John P. Kennedy*, to serve in the same expedition. This vessel was purchased in 1853. The Ringgold Expedition really included two separate squadrons, one commanded by Commander Cadwalader Ringgold and one by Commander John Rodgers. In addition to the purchased ships mentioned, the expedition included *Vincennes*, *Porpoise*, and the steamer *John Hancock*. Another arctic exploring or rescue vessel was purchased and fitted in 1855, the bark *Release*. The work on this vessel was done in the New York Navy Yard under the supervision of constructor B. L. Delano. These exploration vessels were treated as naval vessels though they were not, of course, fighting ships.

The last two of the 1820 frigates, the *Sabine* and *Santee*, were launched in 1855, the *Sabine* at New York, February 12, and the *Santee* at Portsmouth, February 16. Up to the time of their launch there were numerous projects to change them. It was proposed to lengthen them by the bow 20′ on the load water line and also to reduce them to corvettes, to be armed with 24 shell guns, 8″, on the main deck and 2 pivoted 10″ shell guns on the spar deck. However, nothing appears to have been done about these projects, and the ships were completed as lengthened frigates only. In the many years that they had been building their appearance and lines had altered somewhat with the changing fashions. Plan 30 shows the lines of these frigates as reported in 1854. The *Sabine* was sold in 1883, and the *Santee*, after a long stay at the Naval Academy, was finally sold in 1912. These ships were obsolete when launched.

The last sailing man-of-war designed and built for the United States Navy was the first-class corvette *Constellation*, built in the Norfolk Navy Yard in 1853–54. Her design, prepared at Norfolk, called for a large and sharp spar-decked corvette, 176′ 0″ between perpendiculars, 41′ 0″ moulded beam, and 21′ 0″ depth of hold to the gun deck. This ship was, however, administratively "rebuilt," just as the *Macedonian*, *Cyane*, and *John Adams* had been

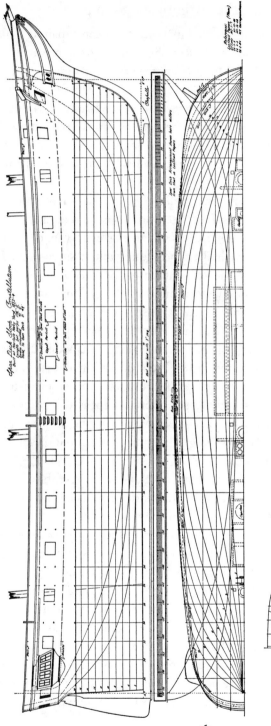
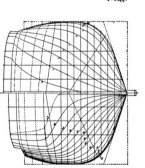

Figure 142. Draught of the spar-decked corvette CONSTELLATION, *now in existence.*

467

earlier. The old *Constellation*, authorized in 1794, had been repaired again and again; in the years between 1805 and 1812 she had a "great repair" that increased her beam by 14″. She had long been in very poor condition and was broken up in 1852 at Norfolk. A new design had been prepared, and this was laid down in 1853 as the "rebuilt" *Constellation*. The new vessel was a corvette, not a frigate, and she differed in model and dimensions from the original frigate of the name. The differences in the two ships may be readily seen by comparing the design of the corvette (Figure 142) with the design of the original frigate, Plan 8.

Unfortunately some of the semi-official lists of American naval ships have listed this ship as though she had, in fact, been preserved and altered. This has led to many believing the corvette, which is still in existence (1949), to be the oldest ship in the Navy and to have had a continuous identity since 1797. This is as untrue as it would be to accept the "rebuilt" frigate *Macedonian* as the original prize, or the "rebuilt" sloop *Cyane* as another British-built ship. A claim has been made that the *Constellation* now in existence contains material taken from the original and therefore retains her identity. The reply to this claim is that the ship lost her identity by the process of having her model, dimensions, appearance, and rate entirely altered in her "rebuilding" in 1853–54. She was constructed as what was then accepted to be a modern and efficient man-of-war. Therefore, accepting this completely altered ship as the original is as unreal as it would be to accept a cap-and-ball revolver as one of Washington's dueling pistols on the grounds that the gun contained a couple of screws salvaged from the original flintlock.

The "rebuilding" of the *Constellation* in 1853–54 represents a different situation from that of the numerous rebuildings of such naval monuments as the *Constitution* and the British *Victory*. In the case of the corvette, she was rebuilt into what was then a modern ship of war without any attempt to preserve the original, and the only reason her register was maintained, by means of an administrative fiction, was to enable the work to be done without the need of applying to Congress for authority and funds to build an entirely new ship. Yet a new ship was produced, as we have seen by the plans. The *Constitution* and *Victory*, however, in their numerous rebuildings have maintained their form, rate, and dimensions, though it is true that their appearance was slightly altered from time to time. Their present forms are, of course, reconstructions of their appearance at the height of their glory, as near as knowledge would permit when the work was done. The sentimental question of whether or not they have portions of the original ship in them is of small moment; the important thing is that, in rebuilding and reconstruction, they have retained their form, rate, and dimensions and thus their identity. Without attempting to discuss the advisability of retaining the corvette as a national monument, it can be said that the ship neither is the original frigate nor looks like her.

The new corvette *Constellation* was somewhat full-bodied, but she was given sharp ends and compared favorably in her lines with the corvettes built in the '40's. She was intended to be equal in size to the cut-down frigate *Cumberland* and had nearly as powerful an armament. The new ship was to carry 20 shell guns, 8″, on her main deck and, in addition, 2 guns of 10″ bore were to be fitted as shifting guns. She does not appear to have been intended to carry pivot guns on her spar deck, as did the *Cumberland*. In the Civil War it was planned to throw two of her midship ports into one port 10′ long and to mount two heavy guns, one on each side, to fire through this, in place of the four broadside guns thus eliminated. One of the big guns was to be a 100-pdr. and the other an 11″ Dahlgren; both were to be pivot-mounted with a shifting pivot bolt. This plan was never carried out. During the '50's the ship usually carried her 20 shell guns, 8″, but her shifting 10″ guns were omitted. The *Constellation* was considered a very satisfactory corvette of her class and was an excellent sailer, particularly in heavy weather. In her later years her rig was reduced and she was employed as a school ship for a long period of time. Until recently she was stationed at Newport, Rhode Island, at the Naval War College.

While the *Constellation* was being built, another "rebuilding" indicated that the sailing corvette was already obsolete as a first-class man-of-war. The old 74 *Franklin* had been included in the ships to be razeed, but when she was surveyed she was found not worth preservation. She was broken up at the Portsmouth Yard and "rebuilt" as a huge screw frigate, 265′ long. As the amount of money available each year from maintenance funds was small, she was not launched for many years after she was laid down. The Act of Congress of April 6, 1854, authorizing the construction of six first-class screw steam frigates, might be accepted as the official recognition that the day of sailing men-of-war as effective ships was completely over.

Though many sailing men-of-war saw service in the Civil War, they were accepted only as mere substitutes for steamers. Sailing frigates, sloops, and brigs, and a number of purchased armed merchant vessels, were employed, but there was rarely an attempt to use them to oppose steamers, except in the gravest emergencies. A few sailing ships were used in hunting Confederate sea raiders; however, most of them were used to fill out squadrons on stations distant from the scene of war. For many years afterward the more serviceable sailing craft were used as training ships for naval and merchant marine cadet officers, and this permitted some of the corvettes built in the '40's to have exceptionally long lives. It was the superior maneuverability of the steamer, without regard to wind, that created the war steamer, though the early steamers were not fast under power. In fact, a smart corvette or frigate could easily outrun the first clumsy side-wheelers, even when the latter had the help of sails in addition to steam—if there was wind. It was the "if" that finally decided the issue.

Just as the sailing man-of-war lacked certainty of movement, so the sailing craft used in her support were inferior to steamers for the same reason. As a result, the service craft of the '40's and '50's were gradually going over to steam. A few sailing craft were built, however; Figure 143 represents a sailing water boat built at Norfolk in the '40's—a centerboard schooner of a type that had become popular on the Chesapeake and elsewhere. The design was made by Rhodes to produce a fast-sailing tank boat; the water boat in use had by her slowness caused delays to ships waiting to go to sea. The service boats were steadily growing in size, and this schooner was no exception to the trend; she was 80' 0" between perpendiculars.

Sailing craft remained popular for carrying powder, and as late as 1858 sailing schooners and sloops were built for the purpose. These carried powder from magazines located outside the ports, away from danger to the large cities, to the navy yards, where ammunition was placed aboard the ships. They also carried ammunition out to anchorages when necessary. The powder vessels were usually coasting vessels in model and were not very large. Figure 144 is the plan of a powder sloop building in 1857 at New York, a typical centerboard river and harbor vessel of her day. She was only 58' long and had a very long mast in her, but no topmast was carried. A schooner was used at Boston and another at Norfolk, while a sloop about the size of the New York vessel was employed at Philadelphia. Portsmouth apparently shared in the use of the Boston powder boat.

Just as there had been a slow recognition of the virtues of the war steamers by commissioned naval officers, so there had been a gradual acceptance of the need of steamship designs by the naval constructors. It was a rather remarkable coincidence that all of the naval constructors had experimented with steamship

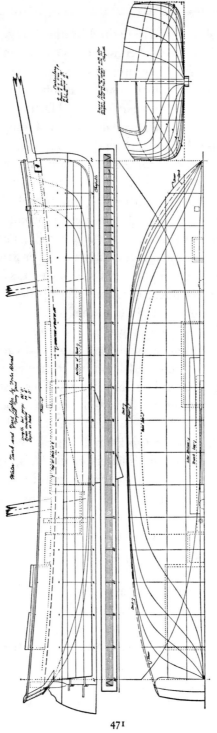

Figure 143. Schooner-rigged water tank and yard lighter.

471

design long before such craft were desired by the Navy. The rather peculiar circumstances that had allowed the constructors to engage in outside work was undoubtedly the reason for their progressiveness, as compared to the naval officers as a class. There can be little doubt that some of the constructors were far more interested in steamers than others: Hartt seems to have had the greatest personal interest, with Lenthall second. Humphreys had designed steamers as early as 1818, but he apparently was not particularly interested in these craft, or had so little time for design work outside the Navy that he did not continue to experiment with steamship design.

Grice, who had been the most advanced and radical of the sailing-ship designers, cared little about steamer design, yet he produced one of the finest of the early war steamers in the big side-wheeler *Powhatan*. It is regrettable that the personal papers of more of the early naval constructors have not been found, for it would be interesting to learn the viewpoints of such men as Grice and Pook on the same technical questions of ship design and steamers that Griffiths, Bates, and others wrote about in the '50's.

In judging the last sailing men-of-war one is tempted to compare them unfavorably with the clipper ships of the late '40's and early '50's, as Griffiths did. It was assumed in the '50's, and again in recent years, that the California Clippers were the acme in sailing-ship design. This assumption is open to question, for much of the speed of the California Clippers was due to their great length and size, rather than to an improved model alone. This contention is supported by the records of the later down-easters, which, though full-ended compared to the California Clippers of the '50's, were able to establish many sailing records that rate very favorably with those of the much-touted "clippers." However, the gradual increase in length and size accounted for this, to a very great extent, just as the "clippers" had obtained the same advantage over the earlier packets. The model of either type was certainly not the sole reason for the trend toward shorter passages that had been made the criterion of "clipper" category.

The rise of the California Clipper as a type can be traced to a combination of circumstances: a demand for speed in the earlier China traders, the changes in economical cargo-carrying capacity, and the experience already obtained by both builders and seamen, as well as ship owners, with the North Atlantic and coastal packets of the '30's and '40's. By 1825, the packet-ship model was accepted as a desirable one for cargo ships requiring speed, and, as has been said before, the packet was then closely related in model to the frigate. Gradually

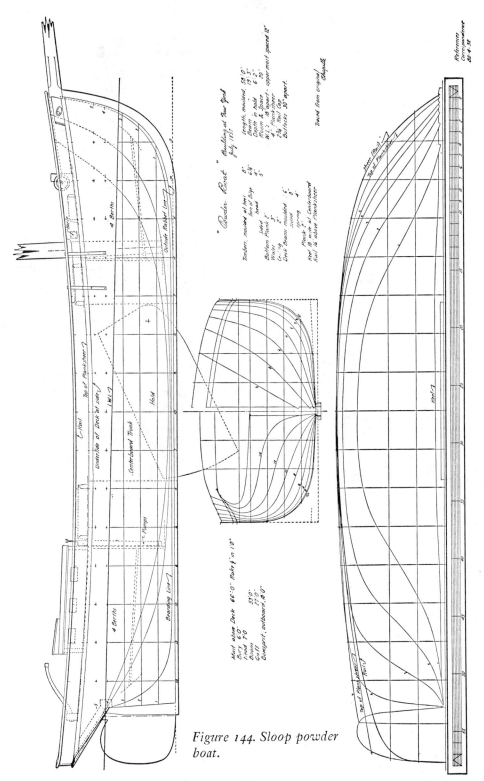

Figure 144. Sloop powder boat.

473

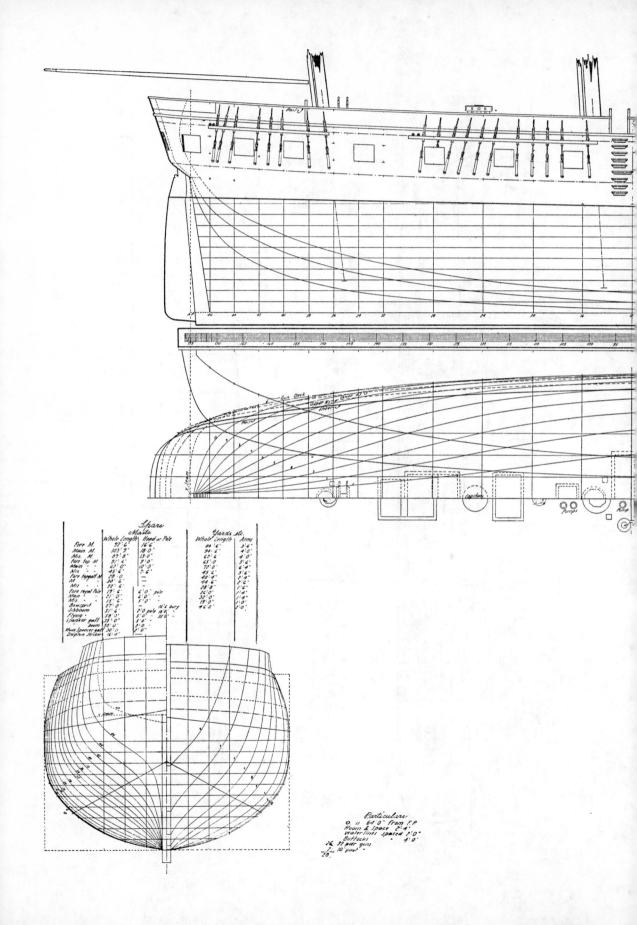

Spars

Masts

	Whole Length	Head or Pole
Fore M.	92' 6"	16' 6"
Main M.	103' 9"	18' 0"
Miz. M.	83' 8"	13' 0"
Fore top M.	55' 6"	9' 0"
Main " "	60' 0"	10' 0"
Miz " "	45' 6"	7' 6"
Fore topgall M	28' 0"	
M " "	30' 6"	
Miz " "	22' 6"	
Fore royal Pole	19' 6"	6' 0" pole
Main "	21' 0"	
Miz "	15' 6"	
Bowsprit	57' 0"	
Jibboom	51' 6"	2' 0" pole 16' 6"
Flying "	38' 0"	32' 0"
Spanker gaff	55' 0"	5' 0"
" boom	50' 0"	5' 0"
Main Spencer gaff	30' 0"	
Dolphin Striker	16' 0"	

Yards etc.

Whole Length	Arms
84' 6"	3' 6"
94' 6"	4' 0"
62' 6"	4' 0"
65' 0"	3' 6"
72' 0"	4' 4"
45' 6"	3' 6"
40' 4"	1' 4"
44' 6"	2' 0"
28' 6"	1' 6"
26' 0"	1' 4"
32' 0"	1' 4"
19' 0"	1' 0"
46' 0"	2' 0"

Particulars

O. 11 64' 0" from F.P
Room & Space 2'4"
Water lines spaced 2'0"
Buttocks " 4'0"
26 32 par guns
2 - 10 pivot "
28

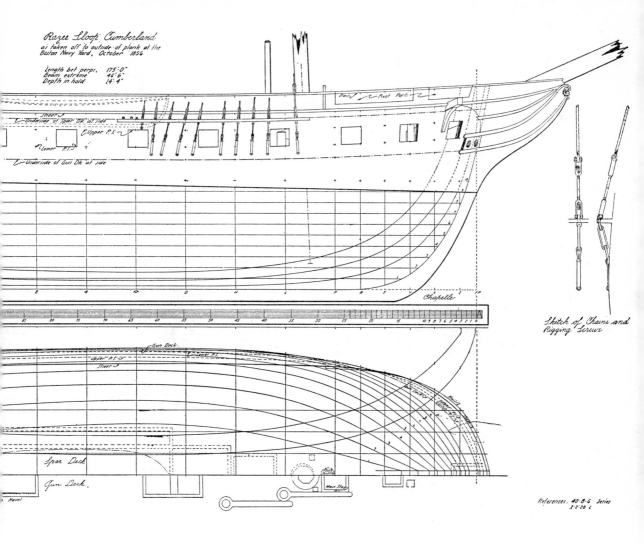

Razee Sloop Cumberland
as taken off to outside of plank at the
Boston Navy Yard, October 1856

Length bet perps.   175'0"
Beam extreme   46'6"
Depth in hold   14'4"

Sketch of Chains and
Rigging Screws

References. 40·8·6 Series
2·8·20 6

Plan 31. Draught of the razeed CUMBERLAND, *made after the reduction of the frigate to a corvette.*

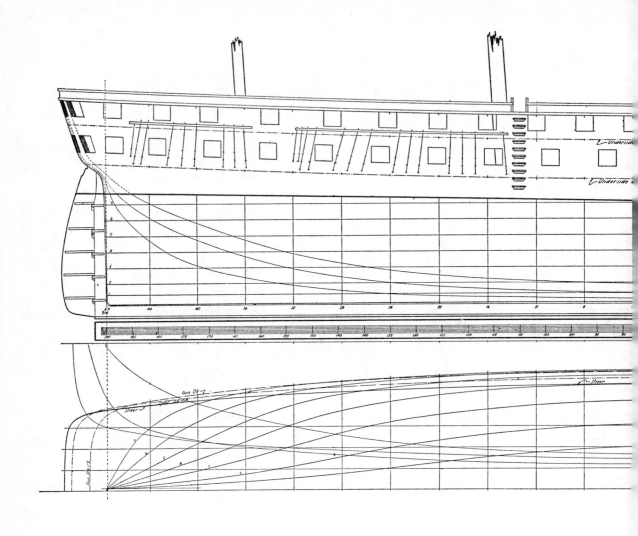

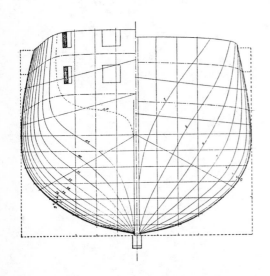

Spars   *Sabine & Santee*

June 1854

Masts	Whole Length	Head or Pole	Yards etc Whole Length	Arms
Fore M	97·4	17	84	4·6
Main M	105·10	18·4	95	4·7
Miz. M	86	13·10	66	7
Fore top M	59·4	9·8	63	4·4
Main " M	63·6	10·2	71·6	4
Miz. " M	47·6	7·9	45	3·6
Fore topgallt M	29·3		41	2·3
Main " M	33·10		46	2·8
Miz. " M	23·10	7	30	1·6
Fore royal Pole	19·9	8	37	1·3
Main "	21·7	6	30	1·6
Miz. "	16·7		19	0·9
Bowsprit	39' out board			
53' Jibboom	29'			
58' Flying Jibboom	23'			
Dolphin Striker	16'			
Fore Spencer gaff			36·6	1·3
Main "			31·6	1·3
Spanker			37	3·6
Boom			52	2·6

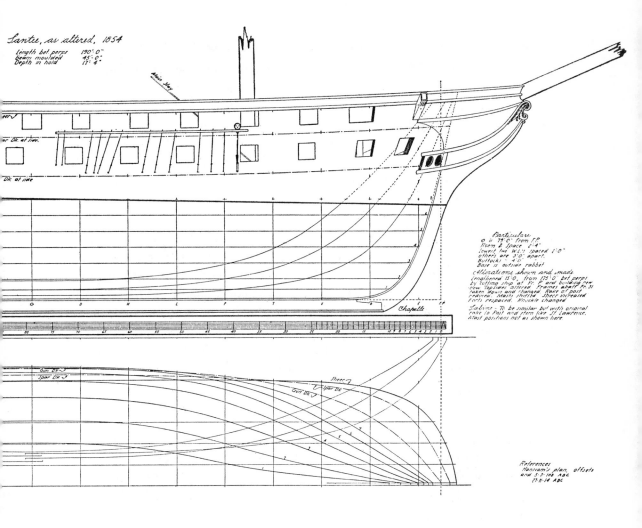

Santee, as altered, 1854
Length bet perps   190' 0"
Beam moulded   45' 0"
Depth in hold   17' 4"

Main Stay

Particulars
O is 75' 0" from F.P.
Room & Space 2' 4"
lowest two W.L.'s spaced 2' 0"
others are 3' 0" apart.
Buttocks " 4' 0"
Base is outside rabbet

Alterations shown and made
lengthened 15' 0" from 175' 0" bet perps
by cutting ship at Fr. P and building new
bow. Topsides altered. Frames abaft Fr. 31
taken down and changed. Rake of post
reduced. Masts shifted. Sheer increased
Ports respaced. Knuckle changed

Sabine - To be similar but with original
rake to Post and stern like St Lawrence.
Mast positions not as shown here.

References
Hanscom's plan, offsets
and S.3-106 N&C
27.11.14 ABC

Chapelle

Gun Dk
Spar Dk
Sheer
Gun Dk
Spar Dk

Plan 32. Plan of the SANTEE and SABINE, *the last sailing frigates launched, bows lengthened 15' and after frames, cants, and stern altered.*

the model was modified, and by 1840 it became flat-bottomed and rather wall-sided, but with increasingly sharp ends. There had been a large number of brigs, brigantines, and ships built during these years on the old Baltimore Clipper model, which had been tested in competition with the new ships of the modified packet design. Popularly the *Ann McKim,* built at Baltimore in 1833 on the Baltimore Clipper model, has been hailed as the "first" clipper ship and the forerunner of the China and California Clippers. While the *McKim* was possibly somewhat more extreme in model than other ship-rigged merchant-men of her time, she was by no means the first Baltimore Clipper built with the ship rig. We have seen that Doughty's ship sloops of the *Erie* class were on this model as early as 1813. As a merchant ship, the Baltimore Clipper was a failure, for it could carry but little cargo in proportion to its size because of its sharp bottom and ends. This same weakness appeared in the naval vessels built on this model—*Lawrence* of 1843, for an example. Neither the *McKim* nor the *Erie* class can be accepted as the first application of the very sharp-bottomed model to square-rigged vessels, for there is ample evidence of earlier attempts in both merchantmen and men-of-war, as has been indicated earlier.

Aware of the disadvantages of the Baltimore Clipper model for a merchant vessel, designers concentrated on improving the nearly flat-floored packet model in order to obtain greater speed. The first outstanding example of the improved packet model was the *Rainbow,* built in 1844–45 by Smith and Dimon of New York, from a design by John W. Griffiths. This vessel has often been claimed as the first "clipper ship"; she could more truthfully be said to have been the acme of the packet model. Her lines, which have been published,[1] show that she was not an extreme departure from previous packet models in any respect, but was merely a refinement. She did not have the "hollow bow" so often accredited to her, nor was she sharper or more extreme than some of the Navy corvettes then building. The *Rainbow* retained a good deal of deadrise and had about the same amount as some of the Navy frigates. Beginning with the *Rainbow,* the sharpening of the ends rapidly increased, but deadrise decreased much more slowly. Some of the clipper ships built for the China trade in the late '40's will serve to show the trend; *Samuel Russell,* built in 1847, and *Sea Witch,* built the year before, retained a good deal of deadrise. The development of the type was paced by rising freights, which were gradually allowing smaller cargoes to be carried with profit. This condition

---

[1] *The History of American Sailing Ships,* New York, 1936.

reached its peak in the early '50's, and then the extreme California Clipper appeared. When the boom in freight rates subsided the California Clipper became uneconomical and disappeared from the building slips, to be replaced by a model that was an almost complete reversion to the flat-bottomed packet of 1840.

Two points can be made in the comparison of the so-called "clipper ships" and the fast naval sailing ships represented by the corvettes. The first is that the corvettes were designed before the *Rainbow* was laid down, with the sole exception of the *Constellation*. The second is that the lines of some of the corvettes show them actually to have been far more extreme than the *Rainbow*. That the *Constellation* was not as sharp as the extreme clipper ships of her time was due to naval requirements rather than to a failure of the responsible constructor to appreciate sharp lines. The *Constellation* was full, to carry her armament and stores, with her length limited by economy. This was exactly what took place in merchant-ship design when the freight boom was over. The truth of the matter is that the corvettes, particularly the *Germantown* and the *Albany*, were far more extreme models than many of the so-called "extreme clippers" of ten years later. There is no longer room for the grandiose claims that the California, and the earlier China, Clippers were startling departures in design or that they represented a sudden change in ideas. The matter can be put to rest by comparing surviving plans of the older ships with the plans and models of the best of the big clippers of the '40's and '50's, which will show that the slow rise of sharper and longer hulls reached back many decades before *Rainbow* and her sisters appeared, and that the extremely sharp hull was nothing new in 1850, 1840, or even 1800, for that matter.

The corvettes built in the 1840's were excellent examples of the high level of ability of the naval constructors who were responsible for their designs. Each designer was given a free hand to choose the model and dimensions he thought best. As has been seen, the result was a variety of hull forms and dimensions; some of the hulls might be classed as extreme in many respects. It would have been normal, under such circumstances, if some of these ships had been utter and complete failures, owing to overenthusiasm for some particular element of design. That this was not the case in any of the corvettes proves beyond a shadow of a doubt that the naval constructors were unusually competent. The steamers that these men designed later bore out the promise they showed in the '40's.

The changes in appearance that took place in American naval ships in the years between 1830 and 1855 were of relatively little practical importance and can be classed as having been due to the slow shift in fashion. Perhaps the one borderline case was the changes in the head and cutwater. As many of the drawings show, the head was gradually closed in by planking up the face of the knees supporting the upper rails of the cutwater with thin plank. The closing in of the "head" began with the use of painted weather cloths above the upper headrail, to give some protection to the men using the head. This was done before the American Revolution. The weather cloths were replaced

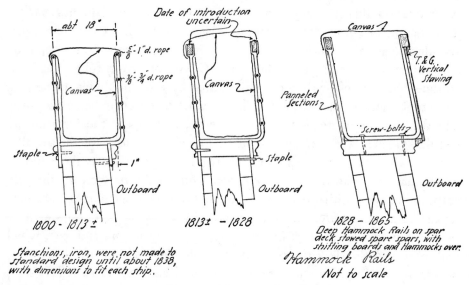

Types of hammock rails.

by wood sheathing, vertically staved, in the early '20's. In the middle '30's the knees supporting the headrails were closed in with plank, and by 1838 the rails themselves began to disappear. In the '40's the rails had disappeared entirely, and the whole head above the cheek knees, or trail knees, was planked in. This was set off by carrying a prominent headrail along the top of the head to the billet—an extension of the rail cap when practical.

In the '30's the hammock nettings had been replaced by wooden hammock rails with vertical staving from rail cap to hammock rail on the outboard side and horizontal panels on the inboard face. In the early '30's the hammock rails were often carried to just abaft the catheads in small vessels, or to the knightheads in large ones; but the fashion of running the hammock rails the full length of the hull by adding monkey rails fore and aft had existed as early as the end of the War of 1812. In the '40's, the hammock rails were extended forward over the head to the bowsprit; the plan of the *Portsmouth* shows this style. This remained the practice in naval ships as long as the wooden vessels were built.

The purpose of the gradual closing in of the head was originally to make this portion of the ship neater and to give added shelter to the men using the toilet facilities there. Privacy was, of course, a factor. These practical considerations were affected by the slowly growing weight of the head, which eventually had to be reduced by removal of the heavy rails and some of the knees. The disadvantages of the closed-in head were that the danger of rot in this portion of the ship was greatly increased and, in action, the head was a dangerous source of splinters and fire when hit by a shell or solid shot. The closing in of the hammock rails and the substitution of staving and wooden rails for netting and rope were peacetime maintenance developments; but wooden hammock rails and staving would also be sources of danger from splinters or fire in action, as was often discovered during the Civil War. The wooden rails, with their staving and panels, were neater than the old nettings, weather cloths, and rope support, but were far less practical. The peacetime urge for neatness and easy maintenance often runs afoul of war requirements.

The alterations in the stern have been described as they appeared, and there were no notable changes in the '50's. The old quarter galleries were going out of fashion very slowly indeed; they were still in existence ten years after the Civil War in American naval steamers of the larger classes, and there were many merchant vessels with these adornments in the '50's. While the cutwaters had grown more pointed in profile, as can be seen in the plans of some of the corvettes, the stern remained short and rather heavy; the rounded finish was retained in the sterns of naval steamers that were built during and after the Civil War, and was one of their ugly features. By 1855 the naval vessels had dropped all adornment except the billet and, occasionally, some carving on the stern and quarter galleries. The channels had become narrower and less prominent, and bar chains to secure the lower deadeyes had come into use.

The stream of investigation into hull form and related problems was now diverted from the sailing ship toward the steamer: as a result of this, and of a steady increase in power that was possible with improving engines and boilers, fast steamers were becoming common in the '50's, and in this the Americans were intensely interested.

The end of the period of the sailing men-of-war was not suddenly apparent, nor was it marked by a dramatic flourish. Slowly but surely steamers replaced the various types of sailing war vessels, until only a few of the latter were in use. Perhaps the sailing warship might have survived longer had she been required to compete only with side-paddle steamers, but the appearance of the screw propeller made the auxiliary steamer practical and hastened the end of the sailing ship. This evolution was completed in the American Navy in the relatively short period of fifteen years; many of the old sailing men-of-war were kept on the register but were laid up in ordinary. As a result, many were wiped out in a single disaster in the first year of the Civil War. The burning of the Norfolk Navy Yard in 1861 created a funeral pyre for the *Pennsylvania*, *Columbus*, *Delaware*, *New York*, *Columbia*, *Germantown*, *Dolphin*, *Plymouth*, *Raritan*, and the old *United States*. The Norfolk Yard was to be the agent of the end of two more fine sailing men-of-war: the Confederate steam ram *Virginia*, rebuilt from the steam frigate *Merrimac*, burned in the Navy Yard with the sailing men-of-war, later sank the *Congress* and *Cumberland*. The helplessness of the two ships sunk by the ram left no possible doubt of the passing of the sailing men-of-war: there was no longer a valid reason for their existence other than the sentimental preservation of an era of naval glory.

Appendix

SPAR DIMENSIONS

THE SPAR dimensions of American naval vessels were never fully standardized in the days of sailing ships, and each vessel usually had an individual rig. While there were many attempts to set up an "establishment" for the spars allowed each class of ship or vessel, none of these were successful, and it was by no means rare to find sister ships with spars of entirely different lengths. Also the spars employed in a vessel varied from time to time as a refit or her commander caused changes to be made. The following is a list of spar dimensions for naval ships and small craft, dated to indicate that they may or may not be her original set. The methods of measuring varied: masts were sometimes measured from heel to hounds (hounded length) and the length of the head was added to give the total stick length; in other cases the stick length is given and also the length of the head; dimensions of yards and booms are commonly the total length, with the length of the arms also given. With the stick length given, the heads or arms are deducted to find the remaining length of the spars or masts. Some spar dimensions are rarely given—the length of the dolphin striker and the length and diameter of the trysail or spencer masts, when present. Where there are no head lengths of the topgallant masts, this indicates that the topgallant, royal, and pole were in one stick. Spar dimensions, where available, are listed only for those vessels whose plans are in existence. In some cases dimensions will be given even though a sail plan is shown elsewhere in this book, either as a matter of useful data for comparison or because there might be some question of the interpretation used in drawing the sail plans. "Length" is commonly the whole length in the following tables.

ALBANY, 1st-class Ship Sloop, 22 guns, 1843 (Ship rig) (Spars of 1844)

	Length	Diameter	Head or Arm		Length	Diameter	Head or Arm
Foremast	81' 1"	29"	13' 6"	Fore topmast	50'	16"	8'
Mainmast	89' 7"	30"	13' 6"	Main topmast	50'	16"	8'
Mizzenmast	70' 3"	21"	11'	Mizzen topmast	38' 9"	12"	6' 3"
Bowsprit outboard	33' 4"	30"	—	Fore topgallant mast	25' 3"	9"	—

	Length	Diameter	Head or Arm		Length	Diameter	Head or Arm
Main topgallant mast	25′ 3″	9″	—	Fore topgalt yard	39′	8½″	2′
Mizzen topgallant mast	19′ 3″	7″	—	Main topgalt yard	39′	8½″	2′
Fore royal mast	16′	6¾″	—	Mizzen topgallant yard	25′	6″	—
Main royal mast	16′	6¾″	—	Fore royal yard	28′ 10″	6″	1′
Mizzen royal mast	13′ 3″	5¼″	—	Main royal yard	28′ 10″	6″	1′
Fore skysail pole	8′	5¼″		Mizzen royal yard	17′	4″	—
Main skysail pole	8′	5¼″		Spanker boom	41′	9½″	1′
Mizzen skysail pole	6′	4″		Jibboom outboard	29′ 6″	16″	2′
Fore yard	77′	18″	4′	Flying jibboom outboard	19′	8½″	4′
Main yard	77′	18″	4′	(total length 48′ 6″)			
Mizzen yard	47′ 6″	11″	1′ 6″				
Fore topsail yard	57′ 6″	13″	5′	Spanker gaff	29′	7½″	5′
Main topsail yard	57′ 6″	13″	5′	Fore gaff	22′	7″	1′
Mizzen topsail yard	39′	9″	2′	Main gaff	22′	6½″	1′

ARGUS, Brig, 18 guns, 1803

Indent for Articles wanted in the Construction and Equipment of the United States Brig *Argus*, to be built in Boston of the following Dimensions

Length of Keel fayable	77 feet
Breadth of Beam	27 feet
Depth of Hold	12½ feet

Cables

3 Bower cable of 13 inches, 120 fathoms
1 Stream   do   13   do   , 120   do
1 Cablet   do   5   do   , 120   do

Spars

Species	Length	Diameter	Length head
Main mast	69	20½	10
top mast	30	11¾	5½
topgt mast	32	6¾	12
Fore mast	60	18½	9¾
top mast	30	11¾	5½
topgt mast	32	6¾	12
Bow sprit	40	18½	

Species	Length	Diameter	Length arm
Jibboom	33	9¼	
Main yard	50	11¼	2⅓
topsail yard	37	8½	2⅔
Top gt yard	26	5½	1½
Royal yard	17	3½	
Fore yard	50	11	
topsail yard	37	8	
topgt yard	26	5¼	
royal yard	17	3¼	
Main boom	53		
gaff	30		
Sprit sail yard	31½	7	2½
4 Top mast stud sail boom	28	5½	
2 Top galt do do do	18½	4	
1 Ring tail boom	20	5½	

Species	Length	Diameter	Length head
2 Lower Stun sail booms	35	5½	
20 Sweeps made of spruce	30	5½	

Rigging

	Inches Circum.	Fathom Long.
Main shrouds	7½	81
Fore shrouds	7½	66
Main stay	9	14
Main spring stay	6	9
Back and topmast stays	6¼	155
Breast back stay and spring stay	5¼	100
Topmast shrouds	4½	120
Top galt back stay	3½	80
Topgalt shrouds	3¼	60
Main and fore lifts	4	60
Topsail sheets	5	66
Topsail lifts	3¼	60
Jack stays and futtock shrouds	3¾	60
Main and fore topgalt sheets	3	60
Main and fore sheets	4	60
Main tacks	5	11
Fore tacks	5	9

Anchors

3 1700 lbs. each Iron stocks
1   640 lbs. do   do   do
1 Kedge 336 lbs. do   do
1 Boat grapnell 60 lbs.
1   do   40 lbs.
1 Creeper   20 lbs.
2 Fire grapnells 30 do each

Boats

1 Cutter with a well and Windlass	25 feet long	1 Pinnace	24 feet long
		1 Jolly boat	18 feet long

Blocks, Hearts, and Dead Eyes, with their Dimensions

N.B. All blocks over 6 inches to be cogged.

Number	Size	Number	Size
40 Deadeyes, 20 iron strapped	9	4 Topsail buntlines	7
16 do , 8 do do	7	4 Reef tackles	7
32 do , 16 do do	6	4 Rolling tackles, 2 double	8
1 Open Heart for the Bowsprit	15	4 Topgallant Halyards	8
1 do	14	4 Fiddle blocks, yard tackles	16
3 Hearts, one Iron Strapped	13	4 do , single	10
1 do , rope do	12	4 Topgallant brace, 2 double	7
4 do , Bobstays	9	4 do Cluelines	7
4 do , Bowsprit shrouds	8	4 Stun sail Halyards	8
4 Hearts for topmast stays	8	4 do do	9
4 do Mⁿ topmast spring stay (main)	7	4 Boom tackles, 2 double	11
		4 Peake and Throat Halyards, 2 double	11
16 do top gallant shrouds	5	1 Throat tye	11
4 Quarter blocks	12	4 Sister blocks	15
4 Fore sheet blocks	11	4 do do	10
4 Fore lifts	10	2 Top leaders	6
1 Main topmast stay block	11	2 Main stay leaders	6
1 do	10	6 Single Blocks	7
1 Fore peake tye, iron strapped	11	12 do	6
2 Top blocks	12	12 do	5
2 For cheeks of the main	11	2 Catt blocks	14
6 main and fore brace	11	7 Snatch blocks from 9-14 inches	
4 Fore sail brace	9	64 Hooks and thimbles	
2 Top sail brace, double	9	70 Thimbles, assorted sizes	
4 For top sail halyard, double	11		
8 Clue garnets	9	1 Messenger, Cablet laid, circum. 7½ inches	
8 Topsail cluelines, 4 double	8	1 Buoy rope do 4½ do	
2 Fore top bowlines	8	1 do do do 2½ do	
2 Sprit sail lifts	7		
2 Fore bowline	9	3 Nun buoys for Bower	
8 Fore lifts, 4 double	7	1 Wood for stream	
8 do trusses, 4 double	7	1 Fish hook	
8 Fore topgallant back stays, 4 double	7	1 Lightning conductor	
6 Fore stun sail brace	7	10 capstan bars	
12 Fore lower buntlines	7	4 Lower stun sail Boom irons	
12 Fore leach lines	6	4 Top mast do do do do	

Note: Channels were first placed below gun ports but were raised to above the ports while the brig was in the Mediterranean.

BOSTON, Frigate, 28 guns, 1799 (Incomplete dimensions, 1804)

Fore Mast 74′ 2″ Dia. 24½″	Mizzen Mast 72′ 0″ Dia. 18″
" Topmast 44′ 7″ " 14¾″	" Topmast 35′ 6″ Dia. 11¾″
" Topgalt Mast 22′ 3½″ Dia. 9″	" Topgalt Mast 19′ 9″ Dia. 8½″
" Royal Mast 16′ 8¾″ Dia. 7½″	" Royal Mast 13′ 4″ Dia. 5″
Main Mast 81′ 8″ Dia. 27¾″	Bowsprit 52′ 6″ Dia. 26¼″
Main Topmast 49′ 0″ Dia. 16½″	Jibboom 44′ 0″
Main Topgalt Mast 24′ 6″ Dia. 9½″	Flying Jibboom 48′ 0″
Main Royal Mast 18′ 4″ Dia. 8¼″	Spanker Boom 56′ 0″

Fore Yard 63' 6"   Main Topsail Yard 56' 0"
  " Topsail Yard 48' 0"   Mizzen Yard 52' 6"
Main Yard 70' 0"   " Topsail Yard 38' 0"

BOXER, Schooner, 10 guns, 1831

	Whole Length	Heads or Arms
Main Mast	76' 0"	8' 6"
Fore Mast	74' 0"	8' 6"
" Topmast	35' 0"	12' 0" pole
Main "	33' 0"	12' 0" "
Fore Yard	58' 0"	2' 0"
" Topsail Yard	34' 0"	2' 0"
" Topgalt "	22' 0"	1' 3"
Bowsprit	29' 0"	outboard 17' 0"
Jib Boom	34' 0"	from cap 17' 0"
Flying "	30' 0"	" " 13' 0"
Fore Gaff	26' 0"	
Main "	24' 0"	
" Boom	49' 6"	
Gaff Topsail Yard	32' 0"	

CHESAPEAKE, Frigate, 36 guns, 1799 (Spars of 1800)

Fore Mast	84' 6"	Head	11' 8"	Fore Yard	75' 9"	Arms	3' 0"
" Topmast	50' 6"	"	6' 9"	" Topsail Yard	54' 0"	"	4' 6"
" Topgalt	24' 3"	Pole	20' 0"	" Topgalt "	36' 0"	"	2' 3"
Main Mast	94' 0"	Head	13' 0"	" Royal "	27' 0"	"	1' 0"
" Topmast	56' 6"	"	7' 7"	Main Yard	84' 6"	"	3' 6"
" Topgalt	27' 3"	Pole	23' 0"	" Topsail Yard	60' 3"	"	5' 0"
Mizzen Mast	80' 6"	Head	9' 0"	" Topgalt "	40' 0"	"	2' 6"
" Topmast	42' 0"	"	5' 9"	" Royal "	30' 0"	"	1' 0"
" Togalt	20' 0"	Pole	16' 0"	Mizzen Yard	60' 3"	"	2' 9"
Bowsprit	60' 0"	outboard	40' 0"	" Topsail Yard	40' 0"	"	2' 8"
Jibboom	45' 0"	"	30' 0"	" Topgalt "	28' 0"	"	1' 11"
Flying Jibboom	50' 0"	"	20' 0"	" Royal Yard	19' 6"	"	8"
Martingale	15' 0"			Spritsail Yard	54' 0"	"	2' 6"
Ensign staff	35' 0"						
Jack staff	15' 6"	Boom	54' 0"	Gaff	38' 0"		

Spars at time of capture by *Shannon* (British report)

	Masts					Yards		
	Length		Dia.			Length		Dia.
	Yds.	In.	In.			Yds.	In.	In.
Main	30	0	30			27	26	19⅛
Top	18	9	17¾			20	9	12⅝
Top Galt	9	7	9⅛			12	13	7⅜
Fore	27	22	26½			24	7	16¾
Top	16	30	16¾			18	2	11½
Top Galt	8	3	8			11	0	6½
Mizzen	23	26	22½	gaff		14	6	10⅛
Top	14	27	13¾			13	26	8¼
Topgalt	6	32	6⅞			9	24	5½
Bowsprit	20	3	28¾			18	2	11½
Jibboom	13	12	12			11	0	6½
Crossjack						20	9	12⅝

CONGRESS, Frigate, 36 guns, 1799 (Dimensions dated 1799)

Fore Mast	84'	Head	12' 6"	Fore Yard	74'	Arms	4' 3"
" Top	52'	"	7'	" top	52' 5"	"	4'
" Topgalt	26' 6"	—		" topgalt	37' 7"	"	2' 2"
" Royal	15' 6"	—		" Royal	28' 3"	"	1' 6"
Bowsprit	60'	Jibboom	45'	Flying Jibboom	18' out		
Main Mast	93' 4"	Head	12' 9"	Main Yard	82' 4"	"	4' 3"
" Top	56'	"	7' 6"	" top	58' 4"	"	4' 9"
" Topgalt	29' 8"	*		" topgalt	41' 4"	"	2' 2"
" Royal	16'			" Royal	31'	"	1' 8"
Mizzen Mast	81' 6"	Head	9' 8"	Mizzen Yard	55' 6"	"	2' 3"
" Top	43' 11"	"	5' 8"	" top	41'	"	3' 2"
" Topgalt	23' 10"			" topgalt	31'	"	1' 8"
" Royal	11' 6"			" Royal	23' 3"	"	1' 3"
				Boom	54'		
				Gaff	41'		

CONGRESS, Frigate, 44 guns, 1839 (Dimensions dated 1839)

		Masts			Yards		
	Length	Dia.	Head	Length	Dia.	Arms	
Main	105'	34"	18'	95'	22.6"	4' 9"	
" top	63'	19⅓"	9' 7"	71' 6"	17.8"	6' 0"	
" topgalt	32'	11"	—	44'	10.2"	2' 0"	
" royal	21' 8"	—	—	30'	6"	1' 6"	
" pole	8' 8"	4"	—	—	—	—	
Fore	95'	30.8"	16'	84'	20.2"	4' 6"	
" top	56'	19⅓"	9' 6"	62' 6"	15½"	5' 3"	
" topgalt	29'	11"	—	41'	9.3"	2' 0"	
" royal	19' 4"	—	—	27'	5.4"	1' 3"	
" pole	7' 9"	4"	—	—	—	—	
Mizzen	87'	24⅓	12' 4"	66'	13.2"	7' 0"	
Mizzen top	46' 4"	13.3"	6' 8"	46'	9½"	4' 0"	
" topgalt	24' 6"	8"	—	30'	6"	1' 6"	
" royal	16' 4"	—	—	19' 6"	3.8"	2' 9"	
" pole	6' 6"	3.6"	—	—	—	—	

Bowsprit 66'; Jib boom 50' x 14.8"; Flying Jib boom 54' x 10⅓"; pole 8' 8"; Main gaff 28' 6" x 7.1"; Fore gaff 33' 6" x 7.8"; Mizzen gaff 32' x 7.8"; Spanker boom 50' x 10½"; Ringtail 25' x 5"; Jackstaff 14' x 4.2"; Dolphin striker 18' x 7½".

CONSTELLATION, Frigate, 36 guns, 1797 (Spars, 1801)

	Masts			Yards	
	Length	Head		Length	Arms
Fore	86' 6"	12' 6"	Fore	76'	4' 6"
" top	53'	7' 6"	" top	54'	5'
" topgalt	43'	pole 15'	" topgalt	38'	2'
Main	96'	13' 6"	" royal	29'	1' 6"
" top	58'	7' 6"	Main	84'	4' 6"
" topgalt	45'	pole 17'	" top	60'	5'
Mizzen	82'	10'	" topgalt	40'	2'
" top	45'	6'	" royal	30'	1' 6"
" topgalt	34'	pole 12'	Mizzen	57'	3' 6"
Bowsprit	60'		" top	42'	3'
Jibboom	43'		" topgalt	31'	2'
Flying Jibboom	44'		" royal	22'	2'
Martingale	15'		Boom	54'	
			Gaff	40'	

CONSTITUTION, Frigate, 44 guns, 1797 (Dimensions dated 1803)

| | Masts | | Yards |
	Length	Head	Length
Fore	96'	14'	84'
" top	52' 6"	7' 9"	60'
" topgalt	32' 9"		40' 6"
" pole	17'		29'
Main	105' 6"	15' 6"	92'
" top	61' 6"	8' 9"	64'
" topgalt	34' 6"		44'
" pole	18' 6"		31'
Mizzen	90'	10'	64'
" top	50' 10"	7'	46'
" topgalt	26'		30'
" pole	12'		20' 6"

Bowsprit	64'	Spritsail Yard	60'
jibboom	51'	Boom	50'
Flying Jibboom	60'	Gaff	40'
Martingale	21'		

(Set of 1815)

| | Masts | | | Yards | | |
	Length	Dia.	Head	Length	Dia.	Arms
Fore	94'	2' 7"	16'	81'	18"	3' 3"
" top	56'	18½"	10'	62' 2"	12½"	5' 3"
" topgalt	31'	11"	—	45'	9"	3' 6"
" royal	20'	—	—	28'	7"	1' 2"
" skysail pole	36'	—	—	—	—	—
Main	104'	2' 8"	19' 6½"	95'	22½"	4' 0"
" top	62' 10"	18½"	10'	70' 6"	15½"	4' 6"
" topgalt	32' 0"	12"	—	46'	9¾"	4' 0"
" royal	21'	—	—	30'	8"	1' 4"
" skysail pole	39'	—	—	—	—	—
Mizzen	81'	21½"	13' 6"	75'	14"	3' 3"
" top	48'	14½"	7'	49'	9½"	4'
" topgalt	23' 6"	9"	—	32'	7½"	2' 6"
" royal	20'	—	—	20'	6"	3' 0"
" skysail pole	30'	—	—	—	—	—
Bowsprit	65' 4"	2' 8½"		60'	14"	
Jibboom	49'	14"				
Flying Jibboom	52'	12"				

Spanker Gaff 40' x 14"
" Boom 55' x 15"

CYANE, Ship Sloop, 18 guns, 1815, prize (Dimensions of 1818)

| | Masts | | Yards |
	Length	Dia.	Length
Fore	66' 6"	22½"	58'
" top	41' 6"	12⅞"	44'
" topgalt	22' hoist	7½"	33' 6"
" pole	16'	—	22' 4"
Main	77' 6"	23"	64'
" top	46' 9"	13⅛"	48'
" topgalt	23' 6" hoist	8⅛"	38'
" pole	18' 6"	—	22' 6"
Mizzen	52' 0"	16½"	48'
" top	34' 3"	9"	35' 8"

	Masts			Yards
	Length	Dia.		Length
Mizzen topgalt	17' hoist	6½"		25'
" pole	11'	—		14' 6"
Bowsprit	41'	—	Spanker Boom 47' 6" x 9¼"
Jibboom	35' 9"	10"	" Gaff * not given
Flying Jibboom	38'	6"	

2 large launches   3 anchors 32 cwt and 29 cwt
                                     2 stream 9 " " 6 "

22	32 pdr carronades on gun deck
6	18 pdr " " quarterdeck
2	12 pdr " " gangways
2	9 pdr long guns on forecastle
32	

"Rig to be retained"

124' 9" on spar deck   Height of Berth deck 5' 9"
123' 3" On gun deck   Depth of hold to gundeck 18' 11"
30' 6" beam at spar deck
31' 6" extreme at gun deck
breadth of transom 17' 6"
Height of gundeck 6' 2½"

DELAWARE, Ship of the Line, 74 guns, 1817 (Dimensions dated 1822)

	Masts	Yards		Masts	Yards
Fore	115'	96'	Mizzen	97'	80'
" top	63'	71'	" top	55'	52'
" topgalt	32'	46'	" topgalt	29'	33'
" royal	22'	33'	" royal	20'	23'
" pole	11'	—	" pole	10'	
Main	124' 6"	107' 6"	Bowsprit outboard	56'	
" top	70'	78'	Jibboom from cap	40'	
" topgalt	41'	52'	Flying Jibboom from cap 20' total 60'
" royal	24'	36'	Spanker Gaff 38'	
" pole	12'	—	Spanker Boom * not given	

FRANKLIN, Ship of the Line, 74 guns, 1815 (Dimensions dated 1817)

	Masts	Yards		Masts	Yards
Fore	106'	90'	Mizzen	98'	80'
" top	63'	67'	" top	53'	49'
" topgalt	37'	45'	" topgalt	29'	33'
" royal	22'	30'	" royal	20'	21' 9"
" pole	6'	—	" pole	5'	—
Main	117'	105'	Bowsprit outboard 48'	
" top	70'	77'	Jibboom from cap 36'	
" topgalt	41'	51'	Flying Jibboom from cap 20'
" royal	24'	36'	Spanker Boom 60'	
" pole	6'	—	" Gaff 38'	

GRAMPUS, Schooner, 10 guns, 1821 (Eckford's instructions, 1821)

	Masts				Yards & Booms		
	Length	Dia.	Head		Length	Dia.	Arms
Main	78' 8"	18½"	8' 0"	Main Boom	54' 9"	12"	—
Fore	75' 8"	20"	8' 0"	" Gaff	27' 4"	8"	—
Main top	26' 2"	7½"	—	Fore Gaff	27' 4"	8"	—

	Masts				Yards & Booms		
	Length	Dia.	Head		Length	Dia.	Arms
Fore top	26' 2"	8½"	—	Fore Yard	50' 0"	11½"	2' 6"
Main topgalt	13' 1"	5"	—	" top "	33' 4"	7½"	3' 0"
Fore topgalt	13' 1"	5½"	—	" topgalt "	22' 0"	5"	1' 0"
Main pole	1' 0"	2½"	—	Squaresail			
Fore pole	1' 0"	2½"	—	Yard	13' 11"	4½"	—
Bowsprit	29' 1"	18"		" Boom	45' 0"	9"	
Jibboom	37' 0"	9"		Lower stud.			
				Yard	8' 8"	3"	
				Fore top stud			
				Yard	12' 0"	3½"	
				Gaff tops'l			
				Yard	22' 8"	4½"	
N.B. Topmast, topgalt and royal pole are in one stick.				Ringtail	8' 4"	3"	
				" Boom	25' 0"	6"	
				Lower stud.			
				boom	31' 6"	7"	
				Fore top stud.			
				boom	26' 6"	5½"	

GUERRIERE, Frigate, 44 guns, 1813, built at Phila. (Dimensions dated 1814)

	Masts		Yards		
	Length	Head	Length	Dia.	Arms
Fore	93'	16'	81' 8"	22¼"	4' 9"
" top	58'	9' 4"	61' 3"	15¼"	5'
" topgalt	28'	—	40'	10"	2'
" royal	20' 8"	—	27'	6⅛"	1' 1"
" pole	36'	—	18' 1"	4¼"	0' 8"
Main	104'	18'	94'	23½"	4' 9"
" top	62'	10'	69' 6"	17¼"	5' 10"
" topgalt	31'	—	45'	11¼"	2' 6"
" royal	23'	—	30'	7¼"	1' 7"
" pole	40'	—	20'	5"	0' 10"
Mizzen	83' 3"	14'	72'	18"	4' 6"
" top	48' 6"	7' 9"	46'	11½"	3' 2"
" topgalt	22'	—	30'	7¼"	1' 6"
" royal	17'	—	17' 5"	4¾"	0' 10"
" pole	30'	—	12' 4"	3¼"	0' 5"
Bowsprit	65'		Spritsail Yard 61'	17¼"	5' 0"
Jibboom	43'				
Flying Jibboom	53'				
Spanker Boom	62'				
" Gaff	30'				

HORNET, Brig, 16 guns, 1805

	Masts		Yards				Masts		Yards	
	Length	Head	Length	Arms			Length	Head	Length	Arms
Fore	64' 6"	9' 9"	56'	—	Main pole		14'	—	—	
" top	39'	4' 11"	43'		Bowsprit		45' 9"	Spritsail		
" topgalt	20' 4"	—	26'					Yard	43'	
" pole	14'	—	—		Jibboom		31'			
Main	74'	11'	62'	—	Spanker Boom		50'			
" top	39'	4' 11"	43'		Spanker Gaff		30'			
" topgalt	20' 4"	—	26'							

INDEPENDENCE, Razee, 54 guns, 1836 (Incomplete list, 1838)

| | Masts | | | Yards | | |
	Length	Head	Dia.	Length	Arms	Dia.
Bowsprit outboard	47.09'	—	38.34"			
Fore	105.8'	17.61'	35.27"	93.40'	3.92'	21.92"
" top	60.72'	9.71'	20.26"			
" topgalt	30.36'	—	10.12"	44.36'	2.43'	9.31"
" royal	20.64'	—	—			
" pole	10.32'	—	—			
Main	115.0'	19.14'	38.34"	101.52'	4.26'	23.86"
" top	66.0'	10.56'	20.26"			
" topgalt	33.05'	—	11.0"	48.22'	2.65'	10.12"
" royal	22.44'	—	—			
" pole	11.22'	—	—			
Mizzen	omitted	14.35	26.84"	66.36'	3.63'	13.86"
" top	49.05'	7.92'	14.35"			
" topgalt	24.75'	—	8.25"	31.34'	1.72'	6.58"
" royal	10.83'	—	—			
" pole	8.42'	—	—			
Jibboom outboard	36.72'	2.20'	19.46"			
Flying " "	29.37'	5.58'	12.62"			

JOHN ADAMS, Ship Sloop, 18 guns, 1830 (Dimensions dated 1835)

| | Masts | | | Yards | | |
	Length	Dia.	Head	Length	Dia.	Arms
Fore	not given			62'	—	2' 8"
" top	42' 6"	14¾"	6' 6"	44'		3'
" topgalt	36' 6"	8½"	—	29' 6"	6¾"	1' 6"
" pole	16'	—	—	17' 6"	4"	9"
Main	not given			72'	—	4' 6"
" top	47'	15"	7' 0"	52'	—	3' 6"
" topgalt	39' 10"	8½"	—	35'	7"	1'
" pole	18'	—	—	22' 6"	4½"	1'
Mizzen	not given			50'	—	2' 8"
" top	37'	15"	5'	36'	—	2' 9"
" topgalt	28' 9"	6½"	—	22' 6"	6¾"	1'
" pole	12'	—	—	16'	3½"	6"
Bowsprit	not given					
Jibboom	37'	11"	—			
Flying Jibboom	not given					
Spanker gaff	35'					
" boom	45'					

LEXINGTON, Storeship, 1840 (Dimensions dated May 1, 1844)

| | Masts | | | Yards | | |
	Length	Head	Dia.	Length	Arms	Dia.
Fore	71' 6"	12' 6"	26"	66'	4'	16"
" top	43'	7'	14"	50'	4' 3"	11½"
" topgalt	22'	—	8¼"	35'	2'	7½"
" royal	15'	—	6¾"	25'	1' 2"	5"
" pole	6'	—	—			
Main	76' 6"	12' 6"	26"	66'	4'	16"
" top	43'	7'	14"	50'	4' 3"	11½"

	Masts			Yards		
	Length	Head	Dia.	Length	Arms	Dia.
Main topgalt	22′	—	8¼″	35′	2′	7½″
" royal	15′ pole	6′	6¾″	25′	1′ 2″	5″
Mizzen	61′ 6″	10′ 3″	18″	51′	2′ 6″	11¼″
" top	34′	5′ 6″	11″	38′	2′ 9″	8½″
" topgalt	18′	—	6¾″	26′	1′ 2″	5¼″
" royal	12′ pole	6′	5½″	20′	0′ 10″	4″

Topgalt, royal and pole in one stick all three masts

Bowsprit outboard	26′	—	26″	
Jibboom "	24′	2′	14″	
Flying " "	15′	6′	8¼″	
Spanker boom	38′ pole	2′	8¼″	
" gaff	29′ "	6′	6½″	poles are not included in the length
Fore gaff	25′ "	1′ 6″	6½″	
Main "	19′ "	1′	5½″	
Swing booms	40′		8¼″	

Breadth of fore and main tops 14′ 4″; mizzen top 11′; Fore and main after topmast crosstrees 8′ 6″; Mizzen topmast crosstrees 6′ 6″

MACEDONIAN, Frigate, 38 guns, 1812, prize (Spars and sails as taken off, 1818)

Length of the bowsprit outboard	40′	Diameter	2′ 7″	
inboard	16′			
whole length	57′ 6″			
Length of the jibboom	44′	"	1′ 1¼″	
" head	2′ 3″			
Length of flying jibboom	44′ 8″	"	8¼″	
" " head	1′			
Spritsail yard	53′	"	11½″	
" " arms	4′			
Extreme length of foremast	87′ 8″	Diameter	2′ 4″	
head	14′ 6″			
" " " foretopmast	53′ 10″	"	1′ 5½′	
head	10′ 4″			
Length of fore topgallant mast to hounds	25′ 6″	"	9½″	in one, total length 48′ 3″
Length of fore royal mast	17′ 6″	"	7″	
skysail to truck	5′ 3″	"	4¾″	
Extreme length of mainmast	94′ 6″	Diameter	2′ 8″	
head	15′ 8″			
" " of maintopmast	59′ 0″	"	1′ 6¼″	
head	11′ 11″			
Length of main topgaltmast to hounds	27′ 8″	"	9¾″	in one, total length 54′ 2″
Length of main royal mast	19′ 0″	"	8″	
Skysail mast to truck	7′ 6″	"	5¾″	
Extreme length of mizzenmast	69′ 6″	Diameter	1′ 9″	
head	12′			
" " mizzen topmast	46′	"	1′ 2″	
head	7′			
Length of mizzen topgaltmast to hounds	28′ 9″	"	7″	in one, total length 38′ 11″
Length of mizzen royal mast	14′	"	5½″	
Skysail mast to truck	4′ 2″	"	4″	

Extreme length of main yard	84'	arms	3' 8"	diameter	1' 7½"
topsail "	63' 3"	"	6' 0"	"	1' 2"
topgalt "	43' 8"	"	2' 9"	"	0' 9"
royal "	30'	"	2'	"	0' 6"
Extreme length of fore yard	74'	"	3' 6"	"	1' 6"
topsail "	56'	"	5' 6"	"	1' 0¾"
topgalt "	39'	"	2' 9"	"	0' 8"
royal "	27'	"	2'	"	0' 5½"
Extreme length of mizzen yard	68'	"	9' 0"	"	1' 1"
topsail "	43'	"	3' 9"	"	10"
topgalt "	28' 6"	"	1'	"	5¾"
royal "	19'	"	0' 7"	"	4½"

Lower stud yards	20' long	5" diameter	
fore top ditto	19' "	5"	"
" topgalt ditto	15' "	3¾"	"
" royal ditto	10' "	3"	"
Main topmast ditto	20' "	5"	"
" topgalt ditto	15' "	3¾"	"
" royal ditto	11' "	3¼"	"
Gaff	43' "	9"	"
Boom	58' "	11¼"	"

Length of the lower studdingsail booms each	49', diameter 9½"		
" " " fore topmast " " "	39'	"	7½"
" " " " topgalt " " "	29' 6"	"	6"
" " " " royal " " "	21'	"	4"
" " " main topmast " " "	44' 8"	"	7½"
" " " " topgalt " " "	33'	"	6"
" " " " royal " " "	23'	"	4"

Fore top is 18' 6" wide and 12' fore and aft
Main   "   "   20'   "   "   13' 9" "   "   "
Mizzen "   "   15' 6" "   "   8' 10" "   "   "

Sails

Item	Head	Foot	Hoist	Inner Leach	Tack	Outer Leach
Fore course	62'	62'	37' 6"			
Fore topsail	41' 6"	62'	45' 6"			
" topgalt	33'	41' 6"	25'			
" royal	23' 6"	33'	17' 6"			
" skysail	17'	23' 6"	13'			
Mainsail	73'	80'	38' 6"			
" topsail	49'	73'	53'			
" topgalt	37' 6"	49'	27' 6"			
" royal	26'	37' 6"	19' 6"			
" skysail	18'	26'	14'			
Mizzen tops'l	32'	43' 6"	41' 6"			
" topgalt	25'	32' 6"	16'			
" royal	16'	25' 6"	14' 6"			
Jib of jib		29' 6"	69'	65'		
Flying jib		29' 6"	73'	62'		
Main jib long		42'	73'	78'		
" " short		38'	88'	72'		
Main staysail		60'	72'	45'		
Middle "		39'	37' 6"	38' 6"	19'	
" topgalt "		34' 6"	38' 6"	38' 6"	15' 6"	
Main royal "		30'	30'	22' 6"	11'	

Item	Head	Foot	Hoist	Inner Leach	Tack	Outer Leach
Fore topmast "		26'	54'	47'		
Mizzen staysail		36'	41'	37'	18'	
Spanker	38'	54'	30'	54'		
Gaff topsail		39'	63'	53'		
Upper topgalt staysail		32' 6"	35'	28' 6"	15'	
Foretopmast stud sail	19' 6"	35' 6"	—	46'	—	54'
"topgalt"	14'	26'	—	25'		31' 6"
Main topmast stud sail	22'	26'	—	54'	—	63' 6"
" topgalt "	15'	27' 6"	—	27' 6"	—	35'
Fore royal stud sail	8' 6"	15'	—	17'	—	21'
Main royal "	9'	17'	—	19' 6"	—	23'
Lower stud sail	43'	43'	38' 6"			
" " " No. 5	38'	38'	38' 6"			
Storm mizzen	24'	27'	30'	47'		
Mizzen skysail	12'	16' 6"	9'			
Fore storm staysail	} dimensions not taken					
Mizzen " "						

NEW YORK, Frigate, 36 guns, 1800 (Dimensions dated 1800)

	Masts			Yards	
	Length	Head		Length	Arms
Fore	80' 4"	12' 6"		70'	3' 10"
" top	50' 2"	7' 3"		50'	4' 3"
" topgalt	40'			35'	1' 8"
" pole	13' 4"			26'	1'
Main	87' 4"	13' 2"		76'	4'
" top	52' 9"	7' 6"		55'	4' 6"
" topgalt	42'			30'	1' 10"
" pole	14'			27'	1'
Mizzen	80' 4"	9' 9"		55'	3'
" top	39'	5' 8"		38'	3'
" topgalt	42'			27'	1' 6"
" pole	14'			omitted	
Bowsprit outboard	37'		spritsail yard	50'	4' 3"
Jibboom	53'		" topsail "	35'	1' 8"
Ensign staff	26' 5"		Spanker Boom	51'	
Jack "	13' 2"		" Gaff	37' 4"	

PENNSYLVANIA, Ship of the Line, 120 guns, 1837 (Dimensions dated 1837)

	whole length Masts	whole length Yards		whole length Masts	whole length Yards
Fore	121'	100'	Mizzen steps on orlop	99'	80'
" top	63'	75'	" top	55'	52'
" topgalt	37' 6"	48'	" topgalt	33'	33'
" royal	22'	23'	" royal	20'	23'
" skysail	17'	—	" skysail	10'	—
Main	132'	110'	Bowsprit outboard	54'	
" top	70'	82'	Jibboom from cap	43'	
" topgalt	41'	52'	Flying jibboom from cap	24'	
" royal	24'	36'	Spanker boom		61' 6"
" skysail	18'	—	" gaff		38' 10"

PHILADELPHIA, Frigate, 36 guns, 1799 (See dates given within)

Dr.—The Committee of Merchants for Masting Frigate *Philadelphia*, 1800. To

1 Main mast 92′ 6″ (Whole length, head 13)		
Cheeks and paunch	57′	each
Hounds and Bracketts	6′ 6″	each
Main Tressel trees	16¾″	
Bolsters	3″	
Cross trees	54′ 6″	
Main top	19′ 6″	
Swivel stocks	7′ 2″	
Top rail	18′	
Main cap	16¾″	
1 Fore mast	83′ 3″	
Hounds and Bracketts	6′ 6″	
Tressel trees	15½″	
Bolsters	3″	
Cross trees	51′	
Fore top	18′	
Swivel stocks	7′	
Top rail	17′	
Fore cap	15½″	
1 Mizen mast	82′ 3″	
Hounds and Bracketts	4′ 6″	each
Tressel trees	12½″	
Bolster	2″	
Cross trees	25′	
Mizen top	13′ 6″	
Toprails	12′	
Mizen cap	12½″	
1 *Main topmast*	55′ 6″	
Tressel trees	9″	
3 Cross trees	10′	long
Cap	9″	
1 *Fore topmast*	50′	
Tressel trees	8¼″	
3 Cross trees	9′	
Cap	8¼″	
1 *Mizen topmast*	41′	
Tressel trees	6¾″	
2 Cross trees	7′	
Cap	6¾″	
1 Main topgalltmast	44′	
Fidd	7″	
1 Fore topgalltmast	40′	
Fidd	7″	
1 Mizen topgalltmast	33′	
Fidd	5″	
1 Bow sprit	55′ 6″	
2 Bees ford	7′	
Chocks under	5′	
Cap	12½″	
Saddle and 6 cleats		
1 Jib boom	55′ 6″	
Martingale	14′	

1 Fore Yard		72′ 6″
Battens		36′ 3″
2 Cleats		
Cross jack yard		58′
Battens		29′
2 Cleats		
1 Sprit sail yard		52′
Battens		13′
2 Cleats		
1 Main topsail yard		58′
Battens		29′
2 Cleats		
1 Fore topsail yard		52′
Battens		26′
2 Cleats		
1 Mizen topsail yard		41′ 6″
Battens		20′ 9″
2 Cleats		
1 Spritsail topsail yard		34′ 9″
Battens		
2 Cleats		
1 Main topgalt yard		38′ 8″
Battens		
2 Cleats		
1 Fore topgalt yard		34′ 9″
Battens		8′ 6″
2 Cleats		
1 Mizen topgalt yard		27′ 8″
Batten		7′ 6″
2 Cleats		
1 Main royal yard		29′
2 Cleats		
1 Fore royal yard		26′
2 Cleats		
1 Mizen royal yard		20′ 9″
2 Cleats		
1 Spanker boom		58′
Jaws		18″
1 Hollow cleat		
1 Saddle		
1 Mizen boom		36′
1 Hollow cleat		
1 Mizen gaft		36′
1 ditto		41′
Jaws for ditto		18″
1 driver yard		34′ 9″
2 Lower Sterring sail booms		45′
2 do yards		26′
2 Main top mast do booms		43′
2 Yards		24′
2 Fore do do booms		38′
2 do do do yards		21′ 6″
2 Main topgalt do booms		29′
2 do do yards		16′ 6″

2 Fore topgalt steering sail booms	26'
2 do	16'
1 Ensign staff	28'
2 Jack staffs	14'
2 Fire booms	30'
1 David	39'
	Cost	$1993.39

Philadelphia, April 26th, 1800

Dr The Committee of Merchants for Spare Spars, &c.

1 Main topmast	55' 6"
1 Mizen topmast	41'
1 Main topgalt mast	44'
1 Fore topgalt mast	40'
1 Main topsail yard	58'
1 Fore topsail yard	52'
1 Main topgalt yard	38' 8"
1 Fore topgalt yard	34' 9"
2 Lower steering sail booms	45'
2 ditto yards	26'
2 Main topmast ditto booms	43'
2 ditto yards	24'
2 Fore top mast do booms	38'
2 ditto yards	21' 6"
2 Main topgalt ditto booms	29'
2 ditto yards	16' 6"
2 Fore topgalt ditto booms	26'
2 ditto yards	16'
1 Fore topmast	50'
18 Rough spars	
2 Buoys 10" each	
39' 6 x 8 scantling	
6 spars	

April 26, 1800   Cost of spare spars $ 551.96

For Launch

1 Main mast	32'	1 Main boom	19'
1 Main topmast	6'	1 Foremast	30'
1 Main gaft	5'	1 Fore gaft	6'
Jaws	6"	Jaws	6"

For barge

1 Main mast	29' 6"	1 Fore mast	28' 6"

Pinnace

1 Fore mast	19'	1 jigger mast	12'
1 Fore yard	12'	1 Sprit	12'

Jolly boat

1 Main mast	12' 6"	2 Sprits	12' 6"
1 Fore mast	11' 6"	8 Boat hook staffs	
		Coast of spars	$ 41.67

May 8th cash	$1000.00		
June 7th cash	1632.60		
	$2632.60		$2587.02

A Bill of Top Stuff for Frigate *City of Philadelphia*

4 Pieces Main trussle trees	14 feet	18 in. by	9 in.
4 pieces Fore trussle trees	13½ "	17	8½
4 pieces Mizen trussle trees	10	16	6½

3 pieces Cross trees	20	5	9
3 pieces Cross trees	19	5	9
3 pieces Cross trees	15	4	7
4 pieces Caps	6½	14	14
4 pieces Caps	6	13	13
4 pieces Caps	5	11	11
2 pieces Caps	6½	13	13

Three planks 10 feet long 4 inches thick to be cut through and through and to have 9 inch spring from end to end one way. 20 white oak 1½ plank 20 feet long and not less than 12 in. wide.

Bill to Jacob Lamb. June 20, 1799.

Dimensions of Masts and Yards for Frigate *City of Philadelphia*
(From Humphreys' Letter Book, Pennsylvania Historical Society)

Spar	Whole Length	Diameter	Head, or Arm
Main mast	92.6	28	13.
Foremast	83.3	25	12.
Mizen mast	82.3	19¼	9.
Main topmast	55.6	16⅜	7.
Fore topmast	50.	15½	6.3
Mizen topmast	41.	12½	5.
Main topgalt mast	44.	9	17.6
Fore topgalt mast	40.	8¼	16.
Mizen topgalt mast	33.	6¾	13.
Bowsprit. Outboard 39'.	55.6	28	
Jibboom	55.6	12½	15.
Main yard	81.6	19	4.
Fore yard	72.6	16¾	3.9
Cross jack yard	58.	12½	3.
Main topsail yard	58.	13½	4.9
Fore topsail yard	52.	12½	4.4
Mizen topsail yard	41.6	9¼	3.
Main topgalt yard	38.8	8¾	2.
Fore topgalt yard	34.9	8	2.
Mizen topgalt yard	27.8	6¼	1.6
Main royal yard	29.	6¾	1.6
Fore royal yard	26.	6¼	1.6
Mizen royal yard	20.9	5	1.
Spanker boom	58.	13	
Driver yard	34.9	8	
Lower stunsail booms	45.	9	
ditto yard	26.	5¼	
Main topmast stun sail boom	43.	8½	
ditto yard	24.	5	
Fore topmast stun sail boom	38.	8	
ditto yard	21.6	4¾	
Main topgalt ditto boom	29.	6	
ditto yard	16.6	3½	
Fore topgalt ditto boom	26.	5¼	
Mizen gaff	36.	10	
Ensign staff	28.	6	
Jack staff	14.	3	
Dolphin striker	9.6		
Fire booms	30.	9	

Main top 19.6 feet wide; Fore top 18. feet; Mizen top 13.6 feet.
Received above dimensions from Captn William Jones, one of the Committee of Merchants.

GERMANTOWN, Corvette, 1844 (Approved establishment)

	Masts & Booms			Yards		
	Length	Dia.	Head	Length	Dia.	Arms
Fore	76′ 3″	26″	13′ 6″	73′ 2″	17¼″	3′ 1″
" top	45′ 9″	16″	8′	56′ 4″	14¼″	5′ 2″
" topgalt	22′ 10″	9″	—	34′ 8″	7¼″	2′
" royal	15′ 6″	—	—	22′ 10″	4⅝″	1′
" pole	5′ 6″	—	—	—	—	—
Main	83′	28″	14′ 6″	79′ 6″	18¾″	3′ 4″
" top	49′ 9″	15¼″	8′	61′	15¼″	5′ 6″
" topgalt	24′ 10″	9″	—	37′ 8″	7⅞″	2′ 1″
" royal	16′ 10″	—	—	24′ 10″	5″	1′ 2″
" pole	6′	—	—	—	—	—
Mizzen	72′ 4″	20½″	10′ 10″	56′ 4″	11⅞″	4′ 6″
" top	37′ 4″	11″	6′	39′ 9″	10″	3′ 8″
" topgalt	18′ 8″	6¾″	—	24′ 6″	5⅛″	1′ 4″
" royal	12′ 8″	—	—	16′ 2″	3¼″	9″
" pole	4′ 6″	—	—	—	—	—
Bowsprit outboard	32′	28″				
Jibboom from cap	26′	14⅛″	9″			
Flying Jibboom whole length	46′ 9″	8½″	4′			
Spanker Gaff	33′	7″	5′ 0″			
" Boom	44′	10⅛″	2′			
Fore Gaff	none	—	—			
Main "	none	—	—			

JAMESTOWN, Corvette, 1844 (Approved establishment)

	Length	Dia.	Head	Length	Dia.	Arms
Fore	77′	26″	14′ 5″	75′	18½″	3′ 6″
" top	46′	15¼″	8′	56′	15″	4′ 6″
" topgalt	25′	9¼″	—	35′	8½″	2′
" royal	17′	—	—	26′	5½″	1′ 6″
" pole	7′ 9″	—	—	—	—	—
Main	84′	28″	14′ 5″	80′	18½″	3′ 6″
" top	50′	15¼″	8′	60′	15¾″	5′
" topgalt	25′	9¼″	—	38′	8¾″	1′ 6″
" royal	17′	—	—	28′	5¾″	1′ 6″
" pole	7′ 9″	—	—	—	—	—
Mizzen	73′	21″	10′ 9″	55′	11½″	3′ 1″
" top	37′ 4″	11¼″	6′	38′	10″	3′
" topgalt	18′ 9″	7″	—	23′	5½″	1′ 6″
" royal	18′ 8″	—	—	13′	3½″	9″
" pole	5′ 9″	—	—	—	—	—
Bowsprit outboard	32′ 5″	26″	—			
Jibboom from cap	39′	14¾″	2′ 4″			
Flying jibboom whole length	46′ 8″	8¾″	5′			
Spanker gaff	36′	8″	5′			
" boom	48′	10″	1′			
Fore gaff	36′	8″	5′			
Main gaff	23′	6½″	1′			

PLYMOUTH, Corvette, 1844 (Approved establishment)

	Length	Dia.	Head	Length	Dia.	Arms
Fore	77′ 3″	25½″	14′ 3″	76′ 3″	18″	3′ 3″
" top	47′ 6″	15¼″	7′ 6″	59′ 6″	14″	6′
" topgalt	23′ 4″	9″	—	36′ 2″	7½″	2′
" royal	16′ 3″	—	—	25′ 3″	5″	1′ 2″

Fore pole	8'	—	—	—	—	—
Main	82' 10"	27½"	14' 3"	76' 3"	18"	3' 3"
" top	47' 6"	15¼"	7' 6"	59' 6"	14"	6'
" topgalt	23' 9"	9"	—	36' 2"	7½"	2' 0"
" royal	16' 3"	—	—	25' 3"	5"	1' 2"
" pole	8'	—	—	—	—	—
Mizzen	66'	19"	10' 10"	51' 9"	10¾"	2' 10"
" top	37' 3"	10¾"	5' 11"	41'	10¼"	4' 9"
" topgalt	18' 6"	6½"	—	24' 1"	5¼"	1' 3"
" royal	12' 9"	—	—	17'	4"	9"
" pole	6'	—	—	—	—	—
Bowsprit outboard	32'	27"	—			
Jibboom from cap	25' 11"	13¾"	1' 6"			
Flying Jibboom whole length	46' 8"	8"	3' 11"			
Spanker Gaff	33'	7"	4' 3"			
" Boom	44'	10"	1'			
Fore Gaff	26'	6"	3'			
Main "	23'	6½"	1'			

PORTSMOUTH, Corvette, 1844 (Approved establishment)

Fore	76'	26"	15'	74'	18½"	3' 6"
" top	48' 6"	16"	8'	55'	13¾"	—
" topgalt	25'	9"	—	36' 2"	8½"	2' 1"
" royal	17'	—	—	26'	6"	1'
" pole	6'	—	—	—	—	—
Main	84'	27"	15'	74'	18½"	3' 6"
" top	48' 6"	16"	8'	55'	13¾"	—
" topgalt	25'	9"	—	36' 2"	8½"	2' 1"
" royal	17'	—	—	26'	6"	1'
" pole	*7'	—	—	—	—	—
Mizzen	*	19"	11'	55'	13¾"	—
" top	37' 6"	13"	6'	39'	9"	3' 6"
" topgalt	18'	6½"	—	26'	6¼"	1' 4"
" royal	12' 6"	—	pole 5'	18'	4¼"	—
Bowsprit outboard	31'	27"	—			
Jibboom from cap	25'	14"	—			
Flying jibboom whole length	40'	8¼"	—			
Spanker Boom	44'	10¼"	—			
" Gaff	33'	7½"	—			
Fore Gaff	— none	—	—			
Main Gaff	— none	—	—			

* head of mizzen mast is 2' above main top

ST. MARYS, Corvette, 1844 (Approved establishment)

Fore	77' 3"	25⅜"	12' 10½"	74'	18"	3' 6"
" top	47' 7"	15"	7' 7"	56' 3"	14½"	5'
" topgalt	25' 4"	9½"	—	36' 7"	7"	2'
" royal	16' 10"	7½"	8' 6"	24' 7"	5"	1'
" pole	5'	3¼"	—	—	—	—
Main	85'	27¾"	14' 2"	77' 6"	18⅝"	3' 6"
" top	52' 4"	15"	8' 1"	58' 4"	14½"	5' 0"
" topgalt	25' 4"	9½"	—	37' 1"	8¼"	2'
" royal	16' 10"	7½"	8' 6"	24' 3"	5"	1'
" pole	6'	4"	—	—	—	—

	Masts & Booms			Yards		
	Length	Dia.	Head	Length	Dia.	Arms
Mizzen	65′ 5″	19″	11′ 10″	57′	12¼″	4′
" top	40′ 1″	13⅛″	6′ 1″	40′ 3″	9½″	3′ 3″
" topgalt	20′	7½″	—	26′ 2″	5½″	1′
" royal	15′ 3″	5′ 6″	7′	19′ 2″	4″	9′
" pole	4′	2¾″	—	—	—	—
Bowsprit outboard	42′ 9″	27¾″	—			
Jibboom from cap	26′	—	—			
Flying Jibboom whole length	44′	—	—			
Spanker Boom	48′ 2″	9½″	3′			
" Gaff	37′ 6″	8″	4′ 5″			
Fore Gaff	25′	7½″	1′ 5″			
Main Gaff	22′ 3″	7¼″	1′			

SARATOGA, Corvette, 1844 (Approved establishment)

	Length	Dia.	Head	Length	Dia.	Arms
Fore	76′	24″	13′ 2″	68′	16¼″	3′ 6″
" top	45′	16″	7′ 9″	52′	11½″	4′ 9″
" topgalt	23′	9¼″	—	34′	7½″	1′ 9″
" royal	15′ 9″	5⅞″	—	25′	4¾″	10″
" pole	6′	5″	—	—	—	—
Main	83′	27″	14′ 2″	76′	17¼″	3′ 6″
" top	49′	16″	8′	57′	12½″	5′
" topgalt	25′	9½″	—	38′	8″	2′
" royal	17′	6″	—	28′	5¼″	1′
" pole	6′	5½″	—	—	—	—
Mizzen	66′ 6″	19¼″	11′	49′ 6″	11½″	2′ 9″
" top	39′	12¾″	6′ 4″	36′ 6″	8½″	3′ 6″
" topgalt	20′	7¼″	—	23′ 6″	5¼″	1′ 4″
" royal	13′ 8″	4½″	—	16′	3½″	6″
" pole	6′	5½″	—	—	—	—
Bowsprit outboard	32′	27″	—			
Jibboom from cap	23′	12″	—			
Flying Jibboom whole length	44′	8″	8′			
Spanker Boom	39′	9″	—			
" Gaff	30′	7″	9′			
Fore Gaff	26′ 6″	6¼″	—			
Main Gaff	19′ 6″	5¾″	—			

POTOMAC, Frigate, 44 guns, 1822 (Dimensions dated 1839)

	Masts			Yards		
	Length	Dia.	Head	Length	Dia.	Arms
Main	105′	34.6″	18′	95′	20″	4′ 9″
" top	63′	19.3″	9′ 7″	71′ 6″	16″	6′
" topgalt	32′	11″	—	45′	9.5″	2′ 6″
" royal	22′	8.8″	—	30′	6.5″	1′ 6″
" pole	10′	—	—	—	—	—
" skysail gunter mast	37′	6.3″	—	20′	4.5″	1′
Fore	95′	31.5″	16′	84′	18.5″	4′ 6″
" top	56′	19.3″	9′ 6″	62′	14.7″	5′ 3″
" topgalt	29′	11″	—	41′	9″	2′ 3″
" royal	20′	7.5″	—	27′	6″	1′ 4″
" pole	9′	—	—	—	—	—
" skysail gunter mast	34′	5.5″	—	18′	4″	9″
Mizzen	84′	24″	12′ 4″	66′	14″	7′
" top	46′ 4″	13.5″	6′ 8″	45′	10″	3′ 6″

	Masts				Yards		
	Length	Dia.	Head		Length	Dia.	Arms
Mizzen topgalt	24'	8.5"	—		30'	6"	1' 6"
" royal	17'	6"	—		19'	4"	9"
" pole	7' 6"	—	—		—	—	—
" skysail gunter mast	28'	4.6"	—		13'	3"	6"
Bowsprit	66'	—	—	Spritsail	62'	14.7"	5' 3"
Jibboom	50'	14.3" at cap	—				
Flying Jibboom	54'	9.5"	4'				
Jib of Jibboom	40'	—	—				
Spanker Boom	50'	11"	—				
" Gaff	35' 8"	8.5"	4'				
Main "	30'	8"	—				
Fore "	30'	8"	—				
Dolphin Striker	17'	7½"	2' pole				

			Length	Dia.
Fore topmast stunsail	boom		49'	10"
do.	yard		28'	5.5"
" topgalt "	boom		36' 6"	7"
do.	yard		21'	4"
" royal "	boom		24' 6"	4.5"
do.	yard		14'	3"
Main swing boom			51' 3"	10.5"
do. yard			31'	5.5"
" topmast stunsail	boom		42' 6"	9"
do.	yard		24'	5"
" topgalt "	boom		32'	6.5"
do.	yard		18'	4"
" royal "	boom		21'	4"
do.	yard		12'	3"
Mizzen topgalt "	boom		22' 5"	4"
do.	yard		12'	2.8"
" royal "	boom		15'	3"
do.	yard		8'	2.3"
Forecastle awning yard			20'	
Smoke sail yard			16'	
jack staff above cap			16'	

Main trysail mast	11" dia.
" " "	11" "
Mizzen " "	9" "

PRESIDENT, Frigate, 44 guns, 1800 (Dimensions dated 1801)

	Masts		Yards	
	Length	Head	Length	Arms
Fore	90'	14' 8"	81'	4' 3"
" top	58'	7' 9"	60'	5'
" topgalt	47'	—	41'	2'
" royal pole	17'	—	30'	1'
Main	100'	15' 5"	90' 6"	4' 6"
" top	61' 7"	7' 9"	66'	5'
" topgalt	50'	—	44'	2'
" royal pole	18'	—	32'	1'
Mizzen	87'	11' 3"	66'	3' 6"
" top	45'	5' 8"	45'	3' 6"
" topgalt	37'	—	32'	1' 6"
" royal pole	13' 3"	—	24'	1'

	Masts			Yards	
	Length	Head		Length	Arms
Bowsprit	67'	outboard 42'	Spritsail	60'	3' 6"
Jibboom	64'		" topsail	41'	
Flying jibboom	29'		Spanker Boom	67'	
Ensign staff	30'		" gaff	46'	
Jack staff	16'				

Dimensions of Spars of U.S. Frigate PRESIDENT (From Humphreys' Notebook)

Spar	Whole Length	Size	Heads Arms
Main mast	100.	2.7¾	16.11
Fore mast	91.4	2.4½	15.3
Mizen mast (this must have stepped on orlop)	86.	1.10	13.6
Main topmast (exclusive of heel block)	62.	1.7	9.6
Fore topmast ditto	58.	1.7	8.6
Mizen topmast ditto	50.	1.3	7.7½
Main topgaltmast (exclusive of pole)	33.	.11	
Fore topgaltmast ditto	30.6	.11	
Mizen topgaltmast ditto	26.	.8½	
Main royal mast	22.	.7¼	
Fore royal mast	20.4	.7¼	
Mizen royal mast	17.4	.6	
Main sky scraper mast	16.6	.5¾	
Fore sky scraper mast	15.3	.5¾	
Mizen sky scraper mast	13.	.4¾	
Main yard	92.	1.9	3.10
Fore yard	80.	1.6¾	3.4
Cross jack	72.	1.1¼	6.
Main topsail yard	69.	1.3	5.9
Fore topsail yard	60.	1.1¼	5.
Mizen topsail yard	45.	.10	3.9
Main topgalt yard	44.6	.9½	2.7
Fore topgalt yard	40.	.8½	2.4
Mizen topgalt yard	30.	.6¼	1.3
Main royal yard	30.	.6¼	1.3
Fore royal yard	26.6	.5⅛	1.1
Mizen royal yard	20.	.4¼	.10½
Main skysail yard	20.	.4¼	.9
Fore skysail yard	18.	.4	.8
Mizen skysail yard	13.4	.3½	.7
Spritsail yard	60.	1.1¼	.5
Bowsprit	65.3	2.7¾	
Jibboom	48.	1.2	
Flying jibboom	53.	.9½	
Spanker boom	69.	.13¼	
Gaff	45.	.10	
Ringtail boom	30.	.6¾	
Ring tail yard	15.	.4	
Lower steering sail swinging boom	50.2	.10	
ditto yard	26.3	.5¼	
Maintop mast steeringsail boom	47.6	.9¾	
ditto yard	26.3	.5¼	
Fore ditto boom	41.6	.8¼	
Fore ditto yard	22.10	.7	

Spar	Whole Length	Size	Heads Arms
Main topgalt steering sail booms	35.6	.7	
Ditto yards	19.8	.4	
Fore ditto booms	31.	.6¼	
Ditto yards	17.1	.3¾	
Mizen topgalt ss boom	23.	.4¾	
Ditto yards	13.	.2¾	
Main royal ss booms	23.	.4¾	
Ditto yards	13.	.2¾	
Fore royal ss booms	20.9	.4	
Ditto yards	12.	.2	
Mizen royal ss booms	15.6	.2	
Ditto yards	8.10	.2	

Dimensions of hermaphrodite schooner built by Wm. Sequin 1814, bought by Savage and Dryan and sold to the U.S. called the PROMETHEUS

Spar	Length	Head (Pole, or Arm)	Spar	Length	Head (Pole, or Arm
Fore mast	62.	9.	Fore topgallant yard	26.	1. arms
Fore topmast	34.	5.	Fore royal	18.	.9 inchs
Topgallantmast	28.	12. pole	Main yard	48.	2.
Main mast	83.	8.	Main topsail yard	36.	.18 inchs
Main topmast	36.	12. pole	Main topgallant yard	22.	.12 inchs
			Main boom	58.	
Fore yard	50.	2. arms	Jibboom	38.	10. pole
Fore topsail yard	38.	2. "	Fore and main gaff	30.	

82 feet straight rabbet. 27 foot beam. 11′ 4″ hold.

Dimensions of schooner REVENGE spars, 1807

Spar	Length	Size	Spar	Length	Size
Main mast	79.	8.	Fore topmast	40.	14. pole
Fore mast	77.	8.	Gunter mast	37.	
Fore yard	61.	2.	Main topmast	36.	14. pole
Topsail yard (fore)	36.	2.	Jibboom	49. outboard 24 feet	
Topgallant yard "	26.	1.	Flying jibboom	38. " 14	
Royal yard "	18.	.9 inchs	Fore gaft	28.	
Main yard	56.	2.	Main gaft	26.	
Topsail yard	32.	2.	Ringtail boom	26.	
Topgallant yard	24.	1.	Ringtail gaft	14.	
Royal yard	16.	.9 inchs			

RALEIGH, Frigate, 32 guns, 1776.

	Dia.	Length	Dia. Head
Mainmast	3′ 3″	86′	1′
Topmast	1′ 4″	50′	6″
Topgallant mast	8″	28′	2″
Foremast	2′ 1″	79′	11″
Foretopmast	1′ 3″	46′	5½″
Fore-topgallant mast	7″	26′	2″
Mizzen mast	1′ 6″	74′	8″
Mizzen topmast	11″	37′	4½″
Mizzen top-gallant mast	5″	18′	2″
Bowsprit	2′ 2″	51′	
Jib boom	1′	36′	
Main yard	1′ 6″	70′	
Main topsail yard	1′ 1″	54′	
Main topgallant yard	7″	36′	
Fore yard	1′ 4″	64′	

	Dia.	Length	Dia. Head
Fore topsail yard	1' 1"	50'	
Fore topgallant yard	6"	30'	
Spritsail yard	9"	45'	
Spritsail topsail yard	7"	35'	
Mizzen yard	10"	66'	
Crossjack yard	10"	50'	
Mizzen topsail yard	8"	36'	
Mizzen topgallant yard	4½"	22'	
Main studdingsail booms	9"	38'	
Fore studdingsail booms	9"	38'	
Topgallant studdingsail booms	5"	25'	
Ensign staff	6"	30'	
Jack staff	3"	15'	
Lower studdingsail booms	8"	40'	
Driver yard	5"	22'	
Driver boom	—	35'	

(Signed)—Thomas Thompson

SYREN, Brig, 16 guns, 1803 (1807)

	Masts		Yards	
	Length	Head	Length	Arms
Fore	59' 4"	10' 5"	53' 8"	2' 6"
" top	37'	6'	38' 8"	2' 9"
" topgalt	31' 6"	—	26' 10"	1' 5"
" pole	16'	—	20'	8"
Main	64'	10' 5"	53' 8"	2' 6"
" top	37'	6'	38' 8"	2' 9"
" topgalt	31' 6"	—	26' 10"	1' 5"
" pole	16'	—	20'	8"
Bowsprit	39'	Spritsail Yard	38' 8"	
Jibboom	32' 10"	Main Boom	57'	
Flying jibboom	31'	" gaff	31'	
Martingale double	9' 2"			

UNITED STATES, Frigate, 44 guns, 1797 (Dimensions by Fox, 1807)

	Masts		Yards		
	Length	Head	Length	Arms	
Fore	90'	14' 7"	81' 2"	3' 5"	
" topmast	54' 10"	8'	58'	4' 10"	
" topgalt	27' 5"	4'	41'	2' 1"	
" royal	19' 5"	—	29'	1'	
Main	100'	16' 3"	91' 4"	3' 10"	
" top	60' 11"	8' 11"	65' 3"	5' 5"	
" topgalt	30' 6"	4' 6"	43' 6"	2' 4"	
" royal	21' 7"	—	32' 7"	1' 2"	
Mizzen	86'	12' 8"	65' 3"	2' 9"	
" top	45' 8"	6' 8"	43' 6"	2' 9"	
" topgalt	22' 10"	3' 4"	29'	1' 8"	
" royal	16' 2"	—	21' 9"	9"	
Bowsprit	64'	outboard 43' 6"	58'	2' 5"	spritsail
Jibboom	46' 7"	" 30' 8"			
Flying jibboom	51' 8"	" 20' 6"			
Martingale	15' 6"				
Jack staff	17'				
Ensign staff	33' 10"		Spanker Boom	65' 3"	
			" Gaff	45' 8"	

Later set (Dimensions as of 1815)

	Masts			Yards		
	Whole Length	Dia.	Head	Whole Length	Dia.	Arms
Fore	89′ 9½″	2′ 6½″	11′ 6″	81′ 6″	1′ 4″	4′
" top	59′	1′ 6¾″	8′ 9″	65′ 6″	1′ 2″	5′ 6″
" topgalt	32′ 11″	10½″	5′ 1½″	41′ 6″	8¾″	2′
" royal	19′ 11″	7½″	—	29′ 2″	6¼″	1′
" pole	17′ 1″	6″	—	24′	4″	—
Main	101′ 6½″	3′	17′	92′ 2″	1′ 11¾″	4′
" top	63′ 2″	1′ 6¾″	9′	69′ 9″	1′ 2½″	5′ 6″
" topgalt	35′ 10″	11″	5′	48′ 6″	9″	2′
" royal	22′	7½″	—	33′	6¾″	1′ 2″
" pole	18′	6″	—	24′	4¼″	—
Mizzen	78′	1′ 10″	12′ 10″	69′ 6″	1′ ¾″	4′ 6″
" top	45′ 9″	1′ 2¼″	6′ 7″	52′	9″	3′
" topgalt	26′ 8½″	7¼″	3′ 5″	30′ 6″	8″	1′ 6″
" royal	16′ 2″	4½″	—	22′	5″	9½″
" pole	13′	4″	—	16′ 4″	3″	—
Bowsprit	65′ out 43′ 6″	2′ 8″	—	60′		4′ 6″ sprit
Jibboom	48′ 6″	1′ 1½″				
Flying jibboom	58′	9″				
Jib o' jibboom	42′ 8½″	8¼″ to 4″				
Martingale	15′					

Spanker Boom 66′ x 1′
" Gaff 46′ 9″ x 10″

VINCENNES, Ship Sloop 2nd Class, 18 guns, 1826 (Dimensions dated 1826)

	Masts		Yards	
	Whole Length	Head	Whole Length	Arms
Fore deck to cap	57′ 6″	12′ 6″	64′	3′
Main " " "	64′ 6″	13′ 6″	70′	3′ 3″
Mizzen " " "	56′	10′ 3″	49′	2′ 9″
Fore top	43′ 6″	6′ 10″	50′ 6″	4′ 9″
Main "	47′ 3″	7′ 6″	53′ 6″	5′
Mizzen "	35′ 3″	6′	39′	3′
Fore topgalt	22′ 3″	—	31′	2′
Main "	24′	—	32′	2′
Mizzen "	19′	—	23′	1′
Fore royal pole	15′	—	21′	1′
Main " "	16′	—	23′ 6″	1′
Mizzen " "	12′	—	15′	9″
Fore skysail pole	7′	—	—	—
Main " "	7′ 3″	—	—	—
Mizzen " "	6′	—	—	—
Bowsprit out, from rabbet to cap	31′			
Jibboom from cap	23′ 6″			
Flying jibboom from cap	17′ 6″	5′		
Dolphin striker	12′ 6″	1′ 9″		

Spanker Boom 37′ 6″ 2′ 3″
" Gaff 30′ 5″
Main Gaff 20′ 1′

VIXEN, Brig, 12 guns, 1804 (Dimensions dated 1806)

	Masts		Yards	
	Length	Head	Length	Arms
Fore	49' 7"	8' 5"	46'	2' 2"
" top	30' 9"	4' 11"	32'	3' 4"
" topgalt	26' 4"	—	21'	1' 4"
" pole	12' 5"	—	15'	5"
Main	55' 7"	9'	46'	2' 2"
" top	30' 9"	4' 11"	32'	3' 4"
" topgalt	26' 4"	—	21'	1' 4"
" pole	12' 5"	—	15'	5"
Bowsprit	29' 4"		Spritsail 32'	3' 4"
Jibboom	28'		Spanker Boom 47'	
Flying jibboom	29' 3"		" Gaff 30'	

WASP, Ship Sloop, 16 guns, 1806 (Dimensions dated 1807)

	Masts		Yards	
	Length	Head	Length	Arms
Fore	63'	9' 10"	56'	2' 4"
" top	37' 9"	5' 6"	41'	3' 5"
" topgalt	18'	—	27'	2' 3"
" pole	15'	—	20'	9"
Main	70'	11'	62'	2' 7"
" top	42'	6' 1"	45'	3' 9"
" topgalt	20'	—	30'	2' 6"
" pole	16'	—	22'	10"
Mizzen	60'	8' 6"	41'	1' 8"
" top	31' 6"	4' 7"	30'	1' 10"
" topgalt	15'	—	20' 8"	1' 8"
" pole	12'	—	15' 6"	7"
Bowsprit	43' 6" outboard 29' 6"		Spritsail 41'	1' 8"
Jibboom	34'		Main Boom 41'	
Flying jibboom	38' 4"		" Gaff 27'	
Martingale	11' 6"			

YORKTOWN, Ship Sloop 3rd Class, 16 guns, 1838 (Dimensions dated 1838)

	Masts Whole Length	Yards Whole Length		Masts Whole Length	Yards Whole Length
Fore	65' 6"	60' 9"	Mizzen	54' 6"	52'
" top	42'	45'	" top	32'	34'
" topgalt	21'	30' 6"	" topgalt	16'	21'
" royal	13'	20' 6"	" pole	5'	—
" pole	6'	—	Bowsprit outboard 30'		
Main	72'	67' 6"	Jibboom from cap 22' 9"		
" top	45'	50' 6"	Flying Jibboom from cap 13' 3"		
" topgalt	22'	34'	Spanker Boom 34'		
" royal	14'	22' 9"	Spanker Gaff 28'		
" pole	7'	—			

HASSAN BASHAW, Brig, 1798

	Masts Length	Head	Dia.	Yards Length
Fore	56' 8"	8' 3"	23"	48'
" top	36'	5'	20"	36'
" topgalt	29'	—	12"	25'

	Length	Masts Head	Dia.	Yards Length
Fore pole	10'	—	—	20'
Main	73'	8'	28"	42'
" top	33'	4' 9"	20"	33'
" topgalt	27'	—	12"	22'
" pole	9'	—	—	17'

Boom	52' 6"
Gaff	30'

Bowsprit 40' outboard 27'
Jibboom   29' outboard from cap
    Fore top 13' 6" width
    Main top 12' "
Martingale not given

Spritsail yard 32'
Jibboom and flying jibboom in one
Mainsail to peak well
6 shrouds aside lower
4 topmast shrouds aside
1 standing backstay and 1 breast stay

1 long boat with well &
windlass
1 yawl to nest
1 yawl on stern

PEACOCK, Ship Sloop, 18 guns, 1828 (Dimensions dated 1828)

	Length	Masts Dia.	Head		Length	Masts Dia.	Head
Main	70'	1' 11"	12' 2"	Fore pole	9' 9"	—	—
" top	42'	13.2"	7'	Mizzen	52' 7"	1' 3.3"	9' 9"
" topgalt	21'	7.9"	—	" top	33' 7"	9.2"	5' 7"
" royal	16' 2"	5.1"	—	" topgalt	16' 10"	5.1"	—
" pole	10' 10"	—	—	" royal	12' 11"	4.1"	—
Fore	63'	1' 8.7"	10' 10"	" pole	8' 8"	—	—
" top	37' 9"	11.9"	6' 3"	Rake of masts ⅜"	⅜"	⅞"	Bowsprit ¾
" topgalt	18' 10"	7.1"	—				
" royal	14' 5"	5.3"	—	Yards not given			

WASHINGTON, Revenue Brig, 1846 (Dimensions dated 1846)

	Length	Masts Head	Dia.	Length	Yards Arms	Dia.
Main cap to deck	43' 6"	8'	19"	48' 10"	2' 10"	10½"
" whole	52' 10"					
Fore cap to deck	41' 9"	8'	19"	48' 10"	2' 10"	10½"
" whole	50' 9"					
Fore & main top	29'	4' 10"	9½"	37' 6"	3' 2"	8½"
Fore & Main topgalt	16'	—	6½"	24' 2"	1' 6"	5"
Fore & Main Royal	10' 8"	3'	—	17' 3"	10"	3¾"
Bowsprit outboard	16' 4"	—	19"			
Jibbom "	16'	—	9½"			
Flying "	12' 6"	—	5½"			
Main boom	42' 10"	—	9"			
" gaff	27' 9"	4'	7"			
Fore "	21'	2' 4"	6"			
Martingale	8'	1' 4"	4½"			

1 stern boat 20'
2 quarter boats 20'

SHIPS' BOATS

BARGE: This class of boat in the American Navy, 1830–1860, was a sharp-ended whaleboat sometimes used in lieu of a gig in rough water. Some vessels also carried a surfboat in addition to their allowance. The surfboat, or lifeboat, was invariably carried in quarter davits.

SURVEY SHIPS were fitted with special boats; these were a launch 32' x 10' x 4' 4", carvel-planked and square-sterned. Two cutters were also fitted: these were clench-built with full, sharp sterns; the first cutter was 29' 6" x 7' 8" x 2' 10"; the second cutter was 26' 10" x 6' 10" x 2' 8". The cutters were fitted with bilge keels. Survey boats were first built for the *Peacock* in 1828, and their designs were used thereafter.

BEACH BOATS: Many ships on the Mexican coast during the war with Mexico were fitted with a special class of boat—square-

sterned surfboats about 40' x 11' x 5'. Beach boats were employed in landing troops on shore and were fitted with a bow gun (a boat howitzer).

NAVAL BOATS: The American Navy gave a great deal of attention to the design of ships' boats in the years between 1820 and 1840. As a result, naval boats used aboard sailing men-of-war in this period were on excellent models and far superior to craft of the same type built since the Civil War.

William Easby at the Washington Navy Yard, John Wade at Boston, and Peter Herbert at the Norfolk Yard were noted for their boats. It was rare for a design of a boat to be prepared by a constructor; such plans were usually the work of the master, or acting master, boatbuilder in the navy yards. Easby usually acted for the Board in standard boat designs 1820–30.

PRESIDENT in 1806 had

1 launch, sloop rigged
1st cutter, lug rigged, 2 masts
2nd cutter, settee rigged, 2 masts
3rd cutter, sliding gunter rigged, 2 masts
4th cutter, sprit sails, 2 masts

Jolly boat, lateen rig
1st gig, lateen rig, one mast
2nd gig,   do.
Ship sloops in War of 1812 usually carried 4 to 6 boats, Brigs, 3 to 4 boats

1821 schooners carried launch 23' x 7' x 2' 10".

1st cutter 20' 4" x 5' 3" x 2' 3"

stern boat 18' x 4' 7" x 2' 0½"

Boats for a 44-gun ship in 1820

Launch	34' x 9' 7" x 3' 9"	
1st cutter	32' x 8' x 3' 7"	
2nd cutter	28' x 7' x 3' 2"	

3rd cutter	26' x 6' 6" x 2' 11"	(stern boat)
Two quarterboats	25' x 6' 3" 2' 9"	
Gig	28' x 5' x 2'	

Boats of a 74 in 1820

Launch	38' x 10' 6" x 4'
1st cutter	36' x 8' 8" x 3' 8"
2nd cutter	27' x 6' 8" x 2' 10" quarter
3rd cutter	25' 6" x 6' 8" x 2' 7"
4th cutter	27'

5th cutter	25'
1st gig	30'
2nd gig	28'
Life boat	27' x 7' x 3' quarter
Jolly boat	20'

JOHN ADAMS, 1832, boats

Launch	29' 6"	16 oars 16'
1st cutter	27' x 6' 9" x 2' 7"	12 oars 14'
Quarterboat	25' x 5' 6" x 2' 3"	12 oars 14'
Quarterboat	24' x 5' 10" x 2' 3"	10 oars 14'

Quarterboat	24' x 5' 10" x 2' 3"	10 oars 14'
Jolly boat	20' x 5' 2" x 2' 1½"	8 oars 17'
Gig	26' x 4' 6" x 2' 1½"	5 oars 17'

GRAMPUS, Schooner, 1830, boats

1 Cutter	9 oars 13'
1 Quarterboat	5 oars 15'

1 Launch	12 oars 15'
2 Quarterboats	4 oars 14'

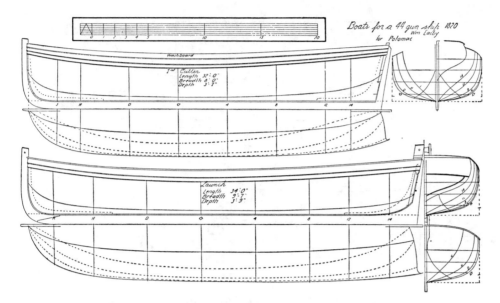

Figure 145. First cutter and launch for POTOMAC.

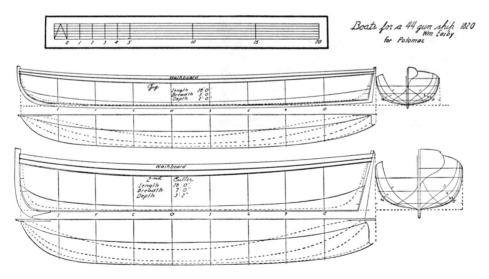

Figure 146. Gig and second cutter for POTOMAC.

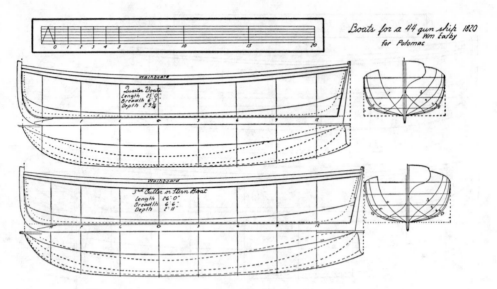

Figure 147. Quarter boat and third cutter for POTOMAC.

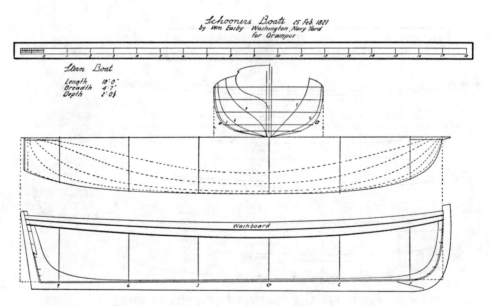

Figure 148. Stern boat for schooner GRAMPUS.

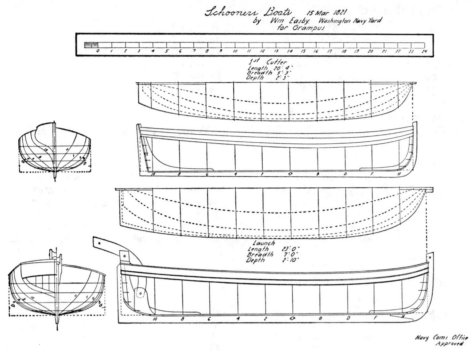

Figure 149. First cutter and launch for GRAMPUS.

BAINBRIDGE, Brig, 1843, boats

Launch	24' x 7' x 2' 10"	14 oars 15'
Cutter	21' 6" x 5' 10½" x 2' 4"	10 oars 13'
Two quarterboats	22' x 5' 2" x 23"	5 oars 15'
Sternboat	17' x 4' 8" x 20"	4 oars 14'

CUMBERLAND, class 1847, boats

Launch	34' x 9' 6"	Two quarterboats	28' x 7' x 2' 6"
Three cutters	32' x 9'	Stern boat	28'
	30'	Gig	28'
	26'		

PLYMOUTH, 1845, boats

Launch	Two quarterboats
Two cutters	Stern boat

(No dimensions exist. See establishment for Corvette 1st Class below.)

ALBANY, 1844, boats

Launch	36' x 8' 6" x 3' 6"	18 oars 15'	Quarterboat	27' x 6' 6"	12 oars 13'
Cutter	32' x 7' 6" x —	16 oars 14'	Quarterboat	26' x 6' 6"	12 oars 13'
Cutter	26' x 6'	12 oars 13'	Stern boat	25' 6" x 5' 6"	5 oars 16'

DECATUR and class, 1838

Launch	30' x 8' 6" x 3' 8"	16 oars 15'
Cutter	27' 6" x 7' 2" x 2' 10"	14 oars 14'
Quarterboat	25' x 5' 10" x 2' 6"	12 oars 13'
Quarterboat	25' x 5' 10" x 2' 4"	12 oars 13'
Stern boat	21' 6" x 4' 8" x 2' 2"	5 oars 16'
Dinghy	16' 6" x 5' x 1' 8"	4 oars 14'

Allowances of boats, U.S.N., 1835–1848
From Notebook of Master Boatbuilder John Wade of the Boston Navy Yard

RAZEE—*Independence*

	length	depth	beam		length	depth	beam
Launch	36'	x 4' 4"	x 10' 1"	Cutter	27'	x 2' 6"	x 6' 9"
"	33'	x 4'	x 9'	Whaleboat	28'	x 2' 5"	x 7' 2"
Cutter	30'	x 3'	x 7' 11"	Barge	34'	x 2' 6"	x 6' 6"
"	27'	x 2' 9"	x 7' 2"	Gig	34'	x 1' 10"	x 5' 2"

74-gun ships to be allowed one additional gig and two cutters, or one cutter and a second launch

FRIGATE—(*Potomac* and class)

	length	depth	beam		length	depth	beam
Launch	34'	x 4' 2"	x 9' 6"	Cutter	27'	x 2' 6"	x 6' 9"
"	31'	x 3' 10"	x 8' 5"	Whaleboat	28'	x 2' 5"	x 7' 2"
Cutter	28'	x 2' 10"	x 7' 5"	Barge	28'	x 2' 4"	x 6'
"	25' 6"	x 2' 7"	x 6' 8"	Gig	28'	x 1' 8"	x 5'

CORVETTE 1st Class (*Portsmouth* and class) (*Cumberland* and *Macedonian*)

	length	beam	depth		length	beam	depth
Launch	30'	x 8' 5"	x 3' 10"	Cutter	26'	x 6' 6"	x 2' 4"
Cutter	27' 6"	x 7' 5"	x 2' 10"	"	26'	x 6' 6"	x 2' 4"
"	25'	x 6' 8"	x 2' 6"	"	25'	x 6'	x 2' 3"

SLOOP 2nd Class (*Vandalia, Cyane,* and class)

	length	depth	beam		length	depth	beam
Launch	29'	x 3' 8"	x 8' 3"	Cutter	26'	x 2' 4"	x 6' 6"
Cutter	26' 6"	x 2' 9"	x 7' 2"	"	25'	x 2' 2"	x 6'
"	26' 2"	x 2' 4"	x 6' 6"				

SLOOP 3rd Class (*Decatur* and class)

	length	depth	beam		length	depth	beam
Launch	26'	x 3' 4"	x 7' 4"	Cutter	25'	x 2' 3"	x 6'
Cutter	24'	x 2' 8"	x 6' 6"	"	24'	x 2' 2"	x 5' 10"
"	25'	x 2' 3"	x 6'				

BRIG (*Bainbridge* and class)

	length	depth	beam		length	depth	beam
Launch	24'	x 3' 0"	x 6' 10"	Cutter	22'	x 2' 2"	x 5' 6"
Cutter	22'	x 2' 6"	x 6'	"	22'	x 2' 2"	x 5' 6"

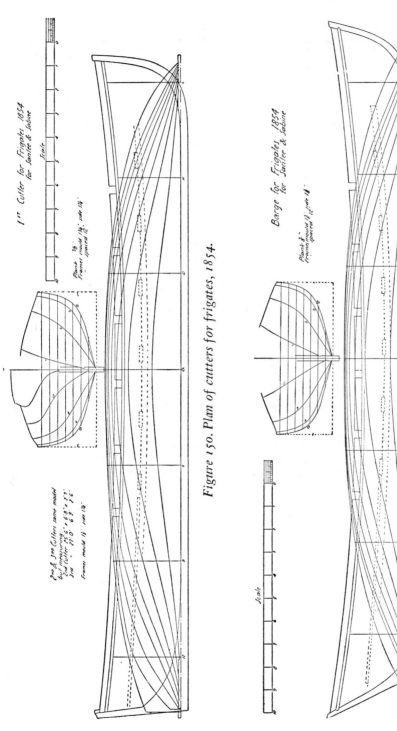

1ˢᵗ Cutter for Frigates 1854
for Santee & Sabine

Scale

Plank ⅞" mde 1¼"
Frames mould 1¾"
" spaced 12"

2ⁿᵈ & 3ʳᵈ Cutters same model
but measuring.
2ⁿᵈ Cutter 25'6" . 6'8" . 2'7".
3ʳᵈ " 27'0" . 6'9" . 2'6".

Frames mould 1¾" mde 1¼"

Figure 150. Plan of cutters for frigates, 1854.

Barge for Frigates 1854
for Santee & Sabine

Plank ⅞" mould 1¼" mde 1⅛"
Frames spaced 12"

Scale

Figure 151. Barge for frigates, 1854.

509

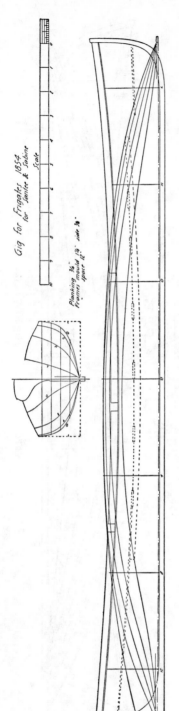

Gig for Frigates 1854
for Janite & Sabine
Scale

Planking ¾"
Frames mould ⅜" side ⅜"
Frames space 12 ⅔"

Figure 152. Gig for frigates, 1854.

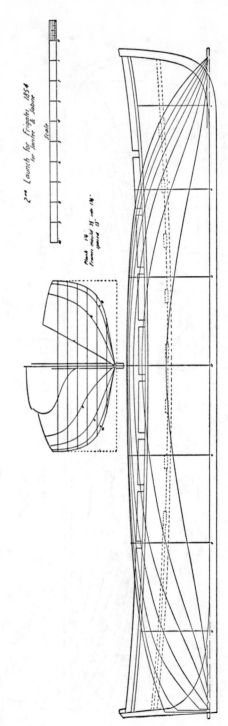

2ⁿᵈ Launch for Frigates 1854
for Janite & Sabine
Scale

Plank ⅝"
Frames mould 1½" side 1¾"
Frames spaced 13"

Figure 153. Second launch for frigates, 1854.

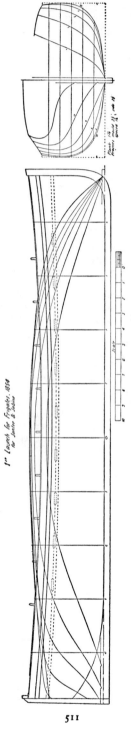

Figure 154. First launch for frigates, 1854.

BRIGANTINE (*Dolphin* and class)

	length	depth	beam			length	depth	beam
Launch	24′ x	3′	x 6′ 10″		Cutter	22′ x	2′ 1″	x 5′ 6″
Cutter	22′ x	2′ 6″	x 6′		"	22′ x	2′ 1″	x 5′ 6″

SCHOONERS (*Boxer* and class)

	length	depth	beam
Cutter	22′ x	2′ 6″	x 6′
"	22′ x	1′ 1″	x 5′ 3″
"	22′ x	1′ 1″	x 5′ 3″

N.B. Most captains exceed their allowances by carrying their own gig.

Rough Copy of Directions for Building a Revenue Cutter, 1829. (From Samuel Humphreys' Offset Book.)

Keel of white oak sided 9″
Deadwood amidships to be sided 9″
Deadwood fore & aft of live oak to be sided 9″
Sternpost knee of live oak fayed on keel and to the foreside of inner sternpost and over this knee the deadwood is to be built keeping the shortest pieces below.
4 bolts to be driven the knee viz. 2 through the knee and keel before the deadwood bolts are driven. Care must be taken that the deadwood bolts and sternpost knee bolts do not come into contact. The bolts of knee and deadwood to be rivetted on the underside of keel and aft side of sternpost. Bolts through the knee to be of diameter ¾″; bolts through the deadwood to be diameter ⅞″.
Inner sternpost live oak, main sternpost live oak sided 9″
Stem of live oak sided 9″
Apron of live oak sided 1′ 3″
The deadwood and apron bolts to one foot above the floating line of copper, dia. ¾″
Floor timbers, futtocks, toptimbers of live oak sided 6″
To be moulded at floor heads 6½″
To be moulded at port sill or planksheer 4″
To be moulded at rail 3¾″
To be completely framed, frame bolts dia. ¾″
Every other floor timber to be bolted with one copper bolt dia. ¾″
The alternate floor timbers to be bolted after the keelson is fitted with copper bolts, dia. ¾″ with a drift added.
Keelson live oak sided 9″
Main transom live oak to be bolted with 2 iron bolts dia. ⅞″
The remaining transoms of live oak sided 7″ and bolted with ⅞″ dia. copper bolts
Knightheads and hawsepieces of live oak sided 9″
Outside plank: the running plank of white oak 2¼″ thick. The outside plank abreast the deck 3″ thick; from thence the plank will gradually and fairly diminish to the thickness of the running plank of bottom. The upper edge of the plank next below the planksheer 2½″ thick.
Planksheer of white oak or yellow pine 2½″ thick. From Planksheer to Rail the space will be boarded outside only with narrow 1″ white oak or yellow pine boards fastened to stanchions 27″ asunder. To have five ports on each side and two in the stern with shutters.
No strake or plank outside from the light waterline upwards amidships to be in width more than 8″
The fastenings of outside plank from keel to one foot above load water line to be of copper; spike may be composition, bolts copper. There will be no treenails.
Each strake to be fastened to one frame, comprising two timbers, with 3 composition spikes of 6″ length where plank is 2¼″ in thickness and one copper bolt ⅝″ dia. to be drove through and rivetted inside. Butt bolts and woodends bolts of copper ⅝″ dia.
Ceiling Plank of yellow pine 2″ thick
Breast Hooks of live oak two below deck hook to be fayed and fastened before ceiling is put on and fastened with copper bolts ¾″ dia.
Clamps white oak or yellow pine 3″ thick at upper edge and 2½″ at lower edge.
A list or air strake 6″ wide to be formed next below the strake under the ceiling
Beams of yellow pine sided 9″ moulded 7½″ to be kneed at each end with one lap and one lodge knee sided 5″ excepting mast beams which are to have a dagger knee in lieu of lap knee, to be bolted with ¾″ dia. bolts.
Deck plank yellow pine 2½″ thick width not to exceed 8″. To be fastened with iron spikes and plugged. Partners of masts of live oak to be kneed.
To be fitted with a trunk cabin as per draught
To be coppered to the waterline 8′ aft and

7' forward with 24 oz. copper

To have a complete set of masts and spars. The principal ones to be of the following names and dimensions:—

Mainmast	58' 2"	whole length,	7' head	
Foremast	56' 6"	"	"	7' "
Fore Yard	36'	"	"	
Fore tops'l yard	24'	whole length		
Foretopgalt "	16'	"	"	
Fore topmast	31' and 12' pole			
Fore gaff	17'			
Main Gaff	16'			
Main Boom	32'			
Bowsprit outboard	12'			

Lowermasts and bowsprit of yellow pine, remaining spars of spruce and to be in proportion.

To have one foresail, one mainsail, one jib, one foretopsail, No. 1 canvas

One squaresail, one topgalt sail, one lower studdingsail, one gaff topsail, one flying jib of light canvas. An awning fore and aft with No. 2 canvas, with stanchions complete.

To have three shrouds to the foremast on each side and two to each side on the mainmast of 5½" rope.

The forestay 7" with remaining standing and running rigging to be in one proportion of the best russia hemp, to be patent laid and of equal fineness and strength with that used in the Navy. The blocks for the sheet, halyards, braces to be patent bushed. To have one hempen cable 9" and one prog chain cable 1" dia. 60 fathoms. Two anchors each weighing 500 lbs. clear of stock. The anchor for chain cable to have an iron stock. To have all fixtures necessary for working a chain cable. One hawser 6", 75 fathoms. One kedge anchor with anchor stock weighing 300 lbs. clear of stock. To have a capstan, camboose, hammock stanchions, waist clothes, ring and eye bolts for relieving tackles, two iron davits on each quarter for boats.

All the outside planking including the deck planking to be planed. Forecastle floor in lengths about 14'. To have 16 berths. Trunk cabin to have a skylight and two sliding lights on each side and is fitted with four berths and lockers. To have store rooms between the stern frame and after bulkhead of cabin in length about — feet; to have magazine beneath cabin floor. To have two store rooms, one on each side, before the cabin in length 6 feet. The length of the cabin floor including storerooms 19'. To have two scuttles near the storerooms leading to the hold. The scuttle leading to the magazine to have raised coamings and a cap of lead. To have the necessary bars and locks. To have two boats of suitable size. To have two coats of paint. To have casks sufficient to carry 1500 gals. of water.

Dimensions of a Revenue Cutter for the North as drawn for the Treasury Dept. May 1829

Length between perpendiculars 62'			
Beam moulded	18'		
Depth in hold	8'		
Deadwood	2½'		
Throats	9"	9' 1½"	9' 1½"
Ceiling	2"	deduct spring of beam 4"	4"
Hold	8' 0"		8' 9½"
	9' 1½"	deck plank 2½"	2½"
		port sill above deck	8"
		Height to top of planksheer	9' 8"
		Planksheer to rail	2' 1"
		rail cap	3"
		Whole Height	12' 0"

No 3 Dimensions of a Gun Boat & Materials

Length between perpendiculars 55'

Breadth moulded 17' — (6"?)

Depth from the ceiling to upper part of the deck beams 4' 6"

Nine inches dead rising to half floor

Keel sided 9 inches & moulded 12 inches deep

Floor timbers. Sided 6 inches & moulded on the keel 7 inches, at the head 5 inches

Futtocks moulded at the foot 5 inches, at the wale 3½ inches

Keelson sided 10 inches & moulded 10 inches, and bolted through every other floor timber with bolts ⅞th of an inch diameter

Stem sided 9 inches and as deep fore & aft as possible

Two wales 7 inches wide & 3½ inches thick of good oak

Running plank 2 inches thick of oak or yellow pine

Ceiling plank 2 inches thick of yellow pine

An air streak 4 inches wide under the clamp for the free admission of air

Three beams in midships to support the guns. Sided 12 inches, moulded 9 inches in the middle & 6 at the end. Two carlines let in fore & aft sided 12 inches and 9 inches thick, four cross carlines sided 8 inches & 4½ inches thick with double lodging knees & one hanging knee under each beam, to run down as far as the form of the sides will admit.

The bed for the gun carriage to traverse upon; to be 15 feet in diameter & to be raised in the middle 3 inches & at each side to be level, to be laid on the deck plank of good sound white oak. To have a groove 8 inches wide & 3 deep, to be 3(?) feet in diameter for the wheel of the gun carriages to traverse in.

Note on back of drawing:

Drawn at the Request of Edward Preble Esq and forwarded by your Humble Servant
Jacob Coffin

Stancheons—under the beams 5 inches square

Combings for the hatches fore & aft 14 inches deep, & 4½ inches thick yellow pine fitted with close hatches or gratings.

Fore & aft beams. Sided 8 inches & moulded 6 inches in the middle & 4 inches at the ends, of yellow pine.

Thowells to be iron let into a bolster nailed on the plank shear

Oars to be rowed in grummets

Schooner rigged with the masts stept into the keelson.

Rudder 3 feet 4 inches at the bottom—back to be diminished to form a handsome rudder.

To have a bilge piece on each side of the bottom to run parallel with the keel, 3 feet 6 inches therefrom 28 feet long sided 7 inches & 10 inches deep, bolted on the floor timbers

Cable bitts placed before the mast with cross pieces for the cable

Deck plank 2½ inches thick, perfectly clear from sap & defects

Comm^re Preble's Ideas
Adopted
Letter attached to C & R plan #80-7-19

Capstans, 1806

Dimensions of parts on each ship

Part	gun deck United States	spar deck United States	gun deck President	spar deck President	gun deck Essex	spar deck Essex	Syren
Dia. of drum head	4′ 7″	3′ 11″	4′ 6″	3′ 9″	3′ 11″	3′ 5″	2′ 10½″
Large hoop dia.	1′ 1″	9½″	11″	9½″	10½″	9″	8½″
Next in dia.	4′ 1¼″	3′ 6″	3′ 9¾″	3′ 2¼″	3′ 6″	3′ 0″	2′ 5½″
Length of bar holes	2′ 8¼″	2′ 1½″	2′ 6″	2′ 0¼″	1′ 11¼″	2′ 1″	—
Holes athwartships	1′ 0″	10½″	1′	10½″	1′	8″	7½″
Hole in drumhead for head of barrel, square	4½″	4¾″	4½″	4½″	5″	5¼″	3¾″
*Length of whelps	1′ 3″	1′ 2½″	1′ 3″	1′ 0½″	1′ 2″	1′ 2½″	10½″
*Whelps fore and aft at heel	3′ 5″	3′ 4″	3′ 8″	3′ 5″	3′ 8″	3′ 4″	3′ 1″
Do. just below moulding	11½″	7″	10½″	7″	7¼″	6″	5″
Do. athwartships at heel	7½″	5″	8″	4¾″	5¼″	4½″	3¼″
Barrel in dia.	9″	7½″	7¼″	6¼″	6½″	5½″	5″
Spindles in dia. between upper and lower capstans	2′	1′ 7⅛″	2′	1′ 9″	1′ 4″	1′ 8″	1′ 1¼″
Do. at head	—	7″	6″	—	5¾″	—	3½″
Do. at heel	—	5″	4½″	—	4″	—	3″

* There appear to be errors in these dimensions, probably due to the transposing of some dimensions by the clerk who prepared the original copy.

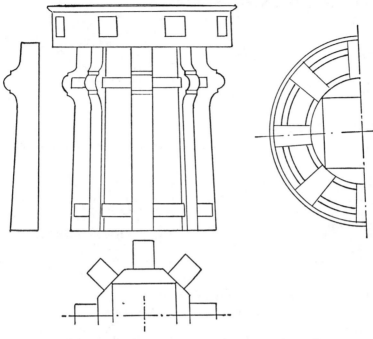

Figure 155. A United States Navy capstan of the period 1803–1820. Capstans were not standard designs.

Gun Mounts 1806

	President	United States	Essex
Length of carriage	5′ 6″	5′ 11½″	4′ 5¾″
Breadth of fore part of bracket	1′ 10½″	2′ 1″	1′ 9″
Ditto after part	11⅜″	1′ 0″	10½″
Bracket sided	5⅜″	5½″	4⅜″
Breadth of transom	1′ 0″	1′ 2¾″	11″
Transom sided	5¼″	5⅜″	4⅜″
Breadth fore part of carriage	2′ 4½″	2′ 3″	1′ 9¾″
Do. after part	3′ 2½″	3′ 0″	2′ 3¼″
Fore Axle tree fore and aft	6½″	7¼″	5″
Do. deep	8½″	7¼″	7½″
Dia. fore truck	1′ 5½″	10″	1′ 4″
Fore truck thick	5½″	6″	—
Aft Axle fore and aft	1′ 0½″	11⅜″	12″
Do. deep	6¾″	6¾″	4¾″
After Truck dia.	1′ 3½″	1′ 4″	1′ 2″
" " thick	5½″	—	—
Bed bolt dia.	1½″	1¼″	⅞″
Breeching in clear	5″	4⅞″	4″
Bolts through bracket dia.	1⅛″	1¼″	¾″
Gunbolt in aft end bracket in clear	2″	2⅜″	1⅞″
Gunbolt in aft part of aft axletree in clear	1¾″	—	—
Bolt in transom Dia.	1½″	—	¾″
Trunion hole dia.	6″	—	5″

Carronade mount of the UNITED STATES, 1796

Length of skid	7′ 0″	Aft " "	6″
Breadth	2′ 4″	Eyebolts dia	⅞″
Thick	7″	Dia of eyes in bolts	3⅝″
Length of beds	4′ 0″	Dia in clear	1⅞″
Breadth fore end	1′ 8″	Breechings in clear	5″
" aft "	1′ 10″	Bolts in skids and beds	¾″
Fore end thick	7″		

NORTH CAROLINA, 74-gun Ship

Her hammock stanchions were ordered placed 4′ 9″ apart and were to be approximately 24″ high.

Ironwork on 42-pdr. carronade mount, Nov. 11, 1818

2 nose plates 4¾″ x 1″	36 lbs.	Eyebolts 1¼″ dia.	23
Ring train and truck plates 3″ x 1″	75	Slide Plates 2″ x ½″	20
Filler plate 3½″ x ⅝″	14	7⅞″ bolts	18
Straight bolts 1⅛″ dia	30	Train, fighting and naval bolts 3″	60
Traverse plates 4″ x ⅞″	12	Tiller 1½″ x 1½″	18
" bolts 3¾″ dia.	35	Screw 2½″ dia	24

Rigging for gunboats building on the Ohio 1805

Rigging item	Circum.	Rigging item	Circum.
Bowsprit shrouds	4″	Runners tackles	3½″
" horses	3″	Deck tackles	3″
Forestay	7″	Jackstay	4″
Collar	5″	Square sail halyards	2½″
Leg to forestay	7″	Yard ropes sq. sail	2″
Shrouds	6½″	Horses " "	3″
Lanyards	2½″	Truss " "	3″
Topmast lift double	4½″	Topmast stay	3″
" tackles	1¾″	" shrouds	3½″
Jib stay	4″	" Halyards	3″
" halyards	2″	Sq. sail braces	2½″
Fore halyards	2½″	" " lifts	2½″
Main sheet	3″	Topsail lifts	2″
Main throat halyards	2½″	" horses	2¼″
Peak halyards	2¾″	" braces	1¾″
Throat downhauls	1½″	" buntline	1″
Peak "	1½″	" clewlines	1″
Boom pendants	4½″	" bowlines	1″
" tackles	2½″	" sheets	2½″
Fore sheet	3″	Foot rope for boom	2½″
" downhauler	1¼″	Gaff topsail halyards	1″
Jib sheet	2″	Tackle for do.	1″
" downhauler	1½″	Stay for gaff topsail	1½″
" pendants	7½″	Pendants halyards	¾″
Runners	5¾″	Ensign halyards	¾″

(WARREN & FALMOUTH)
General Instructions for building a Sloop of War
of 626²⁄₉₅ tons Carpenters Measurement

Keel

Of white oak, to be a number of pieces not more than 3 Scarphs to be in length not more than 10' nor less than 9'. Each scarph to be fastened with 5 copper bolts of dia. 1" taking care that they are driven in the space between the floors and rivetted with copper rings. There will be driven in the lips of each scarph 2 copper bolts each ¾" diameter. The scarphs to be plain without jogs and 2 coaks let in at 2' apart in each scarph, 2' in length, 2½" in thickness and 8" in breadth.

The keel when finished will be sided 1' 2½" and moulded clear of rabbet (which will be cut close to the upper edge of the keel and form the base line) 1' 6½".

To be finished with a shoe or false keel in lengths of 12' to be put on after the keelson and floor bolts are driven and rivetted as hereafter described; to be in thickness 7½", making the whole depth of the keel below the rabbet when finished 2' 2". To be bolted athwartships at about 6' asunder with copper bolts ¾" in diameter.

False Keel

To be fastened to keel with copper bolts ⅝" in diameter and 1' 3" in length. The false keel as well as the bottom of the keel to be coppered before they are fastened together.

Dead wood

Amidships and abaft sided same as the keel from sternpost to Frame P, (from foreside of Frame P); 1' 8" in depth amidships; and Forward and aft by the rising staff; to be scarphed together with scarphs in length [*missing*] and so divided as to come between the scarphs of the keel. Let the lower piece of after deadwood be shortest in the form of a wedge, the point forward, and let a knee be fayed on the front of the heel of inner post and along the keel with arm length of 4' 6"; body 6'.

Taking care that one bolt thro the throat goes through the post close to its heel & one thro the after end of the keel.

Let the front of the arm of this knee be square so that the ends of the pieces composing the deadwood may fay well against it, tennoning each piece into the arm.

The deadwood amidships will be fastened with copper bolts in length 2 and ⅓rd the thickness of the deadwood where it is less than 10" deep; diameter of bolts ⅝".

Let these bolts be no closer than simply to make the deadwood fay well to the keel inasmuch as the floor and keelson bolts will make it perfectly secure. To be fastened abaft with 1⅛" dia. copper bolts well driven at about 2' 2" apart in a fore and aft direction & so as to clear the rabbet on each side. The forward piece of the deadwood to be live oak trimmed to the mould-depth & length of the mould. The bolts to be rivetted under the keel, on back of post & front of stem upon copper rings.

Stern Post Knee

of live oak faying on top of deadwood, the arm running to the berth deck— this knee to be sided the same as the deadwood Body to be in length about 11' fastened with copper bolts to be driven thro the posts & rivetted upon copper rings upon the after side. Bolts 1⅛" in diameter.

The knee will be coaked into the deadwood in the same manner as the scarphs of the keel

Stern
Post

of live oak sided the same as the keel and moulded at the height of the cross-seam clear of the rabbet 1′ 0″ and moulded at the heel clear of the rabbet 2′ 6″. Bearded at the keel aft side to say 8′ 6″.

To keep its full siding on aft side of cross-seam. If the piece will not work its full moulding size all the way, let it do so as far down as light waterline; from thence to the heel the back may be of white oak, jogging it at the butt 2½″ or 3″ into the front piece. The heel of the front piece will have two tennons in the keel—the after piece one.

Inner
Post

of live oak fayed upon the sternpost from one foot above the cross-seam down to the keel sided at head 1′ 10″ the sides parallel down to the aft side of the after cant timber where it will be snaped so as to fay well with it & below it will be regulated by the bearding line as per moulds. Moulded at head 8″—at heel 1′ 2″ and to be bolted into the post below the loadline down to the head of the stern post knee with copper bolts 1⅛″ diameter nett.

The bolts thro the knee will be sufficient for it fastening below & above the loadline the bolts will be iron of the same size

Stem

of live oak sided the same as the keel; the length, shape etc. determined by the moulds. The scarph to be 4′ 6″ in length excepting the one upon the forefoot of keel which will be made as long as possible but not less than 4′ 6″.

The scarphs to be jogged about 2¼″ & a space left for a well-seasoned live oak or locust key to be driven in so as to set the lips well home.

Apron

of live oak to be sided 1′ 8″; the length to be determined by the moulded. Moulded at head 10″ at heel 2′ 6″.

Fastened to the stem with copper bolts below the loadline and iron above it—in diameter 1⅛″ nett.

To be driven at 2′ 2″ apart and rivetted upon rings on the front of the stem. Scarphs to be in length 2′ 9″.

Floors
1st Futtock
2nd do.
3rd do.
Top &
Half-top
Timbers
Moulded

of live oak sided 10½″
 do. do. 10½″
 do. do. 10½″
 do. do. 10½″

of live oak sided 10″
at throat of floors amidships 1′ 3″
at floor ribbands 10½″
at 1st futtock heads 9⅜″
at 2nd futtock heads 8¼″
at 3rd futtock heads 7¼″
at top timber heads 6″

These are the mouldings the timbers are to hold when dubbed off inside and out ready for the planking. The throat of the floors forward and aft will be regulated by the cutting-down line as marked on the rising staff. The floors had better be first fayed to their stations; then the floor ribband run keeping them in place by cleats nailed on their sides and up and down the sides of the keel & a ribband nail thro the ribband driven within an inch of the head. Then let the frame be put together keeping them 2″ apart by furrings in the wake of the bolts which will be square iron with edges chamfered—in diameter 1″. Three bolts in each scarph.

In planking let the furrings be taken out so as to admit the salt which must rest on the fillings between the frames. In raising the frames let the heels of the 1st futtocks be hoisted upon the ribband until the sirmark comes nearly to its place then the head of the frame be raised having previously lifted up the floor timber forward of the frame about to be raised so as to give room for bolting it into the sides of its appropriate floor.

The throats of the floors to be bolted as the frames are raised with a copper bolt in each 1⅛″ in diameter.

The cutting-down having previously been dubbed off.

Cant Timbers

to be fayed closely together without furrings and ¾″ taken off the side of each timber between the bolts leaving in their wake about 4″ as stops, thus a more free circulation will be given the air.

Take care that the pitching spots on the heels of cant moulds be correctly transferred to the heels of the timbers and deadwood so that when raised the timbers may be kept at their proper heights. The heels of the cants to have 2″ left on their insides so that they may be let that much into the deadwood with a jog 1 foot from their heels & when fairly dubbed off for planking let their heels be secured with one copper bolt in each; 1⅛″ diameter.

Cant timbers to be sided the same as the square timbers.

Snapings

of 2 futtocks & lower half-cants as follows

Q commences 6″ below 3rd beveling line and snapes to 8½″ at bearding line or heel.

R commences 3″ above 5th bevelling line & snapes to 8½″ at bearding line or heel.

S commences 7″ above 5th bevelling line & snapes to 2½″ at bearding line or heel.

T commences 8″ below 5th bevelling line and snapes to 2½″ at bearding line or heel.

U commences 9″ below 4th bevelling line & snapes to 5″ bearding line or heel.

38 commences at 11″ above 6th bevelling line & snapes to 0″ at bearding line or heel, or "off to nothing."

37 commences 9″ above 7th bevelling line & snapes to 0″ at bearding line or heel; this snape commences on top timber.

36 commences 11″ above 6th bevelling line & snapes off to nothing at bearding line or heel.

35 commences at 10″ below the 7th bevelling line & snapes off to nothing at bearding line or heel.

34 commences 2″ above 6th bevelling line & snapes off to nothing at bearding line or heel.

33 commences 11″ above 6th bevelling line & snapes off to nothing at bearding line or heel.

32 commences 4″ above 6th bevelling line and snapes off to nothing at bearding line or heel.

Snapings of Cants 1st Futtock

38 commences 5″ above 2nd bevelling line and snapes to 9½″ at bearding line or heel.

37 commences 6″ above 2nd bevelling line & snapes to 9½″ at bearding line or heel.

36 commences 5″ below 2nd bevelling line & snapes to 9½″ at bearding line or heel.

35 commences 32″ below 2nd bevelling line & snapes to 9½″ at bearding line or heel.

34 commences at 10″ below 2nd bevelling line & snapes to 9½″ at bearding line or heel.

33 commences 32″ below 2nd bevelling line & snapes to 9½″ at bearding line or heel.

32 commences 26″ above 3rd bevelling line & snapes to 7½″ at bearding line or heel.

Keelson

of white oak in two depths, or in three, so that the whole depth shall be the same—each depth sided 1′ 2½″; moulded 11″.

The scarphs not to come over the scarphs of the keel so as to make a good shift, 6′ in length. Fayed without hook or jog & two coaks in each—coaks 8″ wide and 2½″ thick, 1′ long.

The upper piece will be fayed fairly on the lower one & coaks let into them all fore and aft—coaks to be in length 1′ 4″ and in width & thickness as above. The after end of the keelson will be jogged over the after floor timber and will be continued to the sternpost knee against which it will be fayed & the space if any under the keelson at the jog be filled by a chock faying between the deadwood & keelson.

Stemson

of live oak sided same as the keelson & be fayed with a scarph upon the fore end of the keelson which will be jogged down like the after end of the dead-wood. Scarphs will be not less than 4′ long. Fayed with a jog of 2″ leaving room for a key with which to set it home & along the apron up to the birth deck—moulded at head 10″.

There will be driven thro the keelson & each floor timber one copper bolt 1¼″ in diameter: rivetted upon rings on the underside of the keel and to be driven on one side thro one floor and on the opposite side thro the other floor taking care that they go clear of the rabbet of the keel & on the opposite side to the floor bolts. Those driven thro the keelson and stemson to be of the same size and rivetted upon rings upon the front of the stem. After the bolts are all driven down and the corners of the keelson chamfered off let there be a capping of 3½″ oak plank 12″ wide filling the space between the chamfers fayed all fore and aft & well nailed with iron upon the top of the keelson. This cap will prevent the keelson being wounded by the mortices for the heels of the after deck stanchions—let it be finished with a 1″ chamfer on each corner.

Knightheads & Hawse Pieces

sided 1′ 2″; moulded at head and heels as per moulds. To be bolted into the apron and each other with iron at about 2′ 2″ apart. Iron 1″ in diameter. They will have their heels snaped off so as to fay well against the fore side of the fore-most cant timber. They had better be fitted & put together on the ground before being raised; then taken apart and hoisted to their places & fastened piece by piece as the easiest method. Let there be an iron bolt driven thro the foremost cant timber into each of the heels of the knightheads & hawse pieces 1″ in diameter.

Hawse Holes

when leaded to be in the clear 1′ 1″ diameter.

In running the ribbands let the frames be set in & out as may be required in consequence of their having sprung in raising—strong wrainstaves & chains will accomplish this point and prevent a great deal of unnecessary dubbing & weakening of the timber. In bevelling the timber let the stock of the bevel be kept square with the back of the timber.

Running Plank of the Bottom

to be of white oak 3½″ thick. Bilge Strakes at floor heads to be 5 in number on each side; the middle strake 5″ in thickness the strake above & below it 4½″; & above and below these two 4″.

To be dubbed flush with the running plank of the bottom. No plank to be more than 12″ wide at amidships.

Wales

to be 6 in number on each side—the two middle ones to be 6″ thick and those above & below diminishing gradually until they work fair or flush with the running plank of the bottom below & with the strake between the ports under the rail which will be 3″ thick leaving the ship's side free of any projection below the rail. The planks will all be put on with fair edges without hooks or jogs & the fastenings will be of copper from the lower edge of the wales amidships down to the keel. The running plank with 9″ spikes or small bolts are to be preferred & the thickstuff with bolts ⅝″ diameter nett: in length twice and one-third the thickness of the plank thro which it is to be driven. There will be so many of these fastenings as will draw the plank well to the timbers and the residue to be locust treenails after a 1¼″ auger. The treenails will be in number a proportion to the metal fastenings as three to one—that is to say there will be three treenails to one metal fastening. The points of the treenails will be dipped in tar previously to being driven & they will go well thro the ceiling & finally be cut off on the outer and inner sides of the ship; the heads to be caulked in a triangular manner & the points to be wedged with heart pine wedges. In addition to the above fastenings the thick stuff on the bilges will be bolted with ¾″ copper; the bolts to be about 10′ apart in each strake and so driven that those in one strake may come between those in the strake above & below & not in the same timber. *Note.* Instead of treenails from light waterline say from about 9′ below the port cills amidships let bolts be substituted to go thro and be rivetted upon rings. To be of copper as high as within 4′ of the port cills and all above of iron. Let two bolts in each strake go thro each frame & rivet on the ceiling & two short fastenings. The plank will thus be square-fastened from the keel up to the ports but in the topsides it will be cross fastened with short fastenings—that is to say there will be one spike and one short bolt in each strake and every timber.

Butt bolts will be driven into the bottom as high as the wales and copper bolts nett ⅞″ diameter for each butt. To be driven thru the frame next on each side the one on which the strake butts & to be rivetted on the ceiling on copper or composition rings. These bolts will not be driven until after the strake above and below the one where the butts are to go, are to be caulked.

In shifting butts in the planking let there be at least 6′ between each & let there be three strakes at least between every two butts on the same timber. Let all the plank be so bevelled that the seams shall be outgauged about, or rather more than, 1/16″ for every inch the plank is in thickness; so as to prevent it from caulking off etc. Let the butts be well opened so as to receive the oakum—a butt of 5/16″ is little enough for a 3″ plank.

In planking let the sap be avoided as much as possible and in all cases where a plank may have any sap on its edge let the heart side be put on the timbers. Let the hooding ends of the running plank be ¼″ less in the rabbet of post & stem than its thickness amidships.

Bilge Strakes at floor heads there will be 4 in number on each side; the two middle ones 5″ thick and the strakes on each side of these 4½″. To be chamfered off to 4″ at floor heads if not covered by the clamps—thick strake 3 in number—in thickness 5″ and 4½″. Fasten the clamps and thick stuff with bolt twice & one third the thickness of the plank thro which they are driven; to be nett ¾″ diameter. The plank to be well drawn down on the timbers and all the seams bevelled so as to make square work. The same shift of butts to be observed as on the outside of the ship. There will be no hooking or jogging except on the clamps. The forward and after ends of the strakes to be as narrow as to shew the same number of strakes below the clamps of the birth deck as there are amidships.

Berth Deck Clamps to be 3 strakes in number; in thickness 6″, 5″ & 4″, jogged down into each other 1½″ and the jogs 8′ in length; the lower edge to be chamfered to 4″.

Berth Deck Beams of heart pine free from sap sided 13″ and moulded by gundeck mould 11″. To be kneed at each end with one lodge knee sided 6½″; arms to be in length—

and more if to be had, 4'. There will be 1″ trimmed off from the upper edge of the clamps under the lodge knees to admit air leaving a jog of about 6″ next each beam for the knees to rest on. After the beams are cut off to their proper lengths let there be holes bored about 4′ 6″ in length into the ends of the beams by a pump boring bitt 2″ inside dia. to be filled with coarse salt & plugged up. Let their ends be grooved across from corner to corner with a 1″ gouge & from the plug down to the end and along the underside to about 2″ within the clamp.

The knees to be fastened through the sides of the ship with 1″ dia. copper bolts. Three bolts through the body of each knee of iron, of the same size thro the beams—three bolts through the arms. Let the point of each knee be nailed into the beam with two 5″ spikes to prevent its splitting. The bolts to be rivetted on substantial rings. Let the knees be kept in the middle of the beams between their upper and lower edges so as to divide the wood equally above and below for bolting. The knees will be jogged 1½″ into the side of the beams at about 2′ from their ends taking nothing off the beams at the end of the knee nor anything between the jog and the side of the ship—nor will any wood be taken from the beam below the knee from its point to the jog it being chined in & the knee faying down closely upon it. There will be a space left at the jog running quite to the lower edge of the beam for a seasoned key of locust to be driven in after the knees are bolted. *Note.* By letting the arms of the knees lay upon the clamps & their bodies along the beams greater length may be had if required.

Ledges	of heart pine free from sap to square 5″. One between each beam except where the rooms may be too large so that in no case must the space between beam and ledge be more than 2′.
Carlins	or fore-and-aft pieces of heart pine free from sap to square 7″ in three ranges—one in the middle of the deck & one on each side dividing the ledges into 4 lengths.
Plank	of heart pine free from sap shakes or large knots & not more than 10″ in width: 2½″ thickness. Average length to be 40′. To be fastened into the beams with 6″ spikes, into the ledges with 5″ spikes which are to be punched down so as to admit above the heads a heart pine plug to be put in dipped in white lead, ¾″ in thickness.
Partners	of fore and main masts of heart pine square 8″—to be kneed with four lap knees each, sided 6″ and bolted with ¾″ dia. iron. Those of mizzen mast same size; knees sided 5½″ and bolted with iron a full ⅝″ diameter.
	There will be a half-beam in the wake of the main hatch with a ledge on each side of it; the half-beam sided 2″ less than, and moulded the same at the side of the ship as the whole beams—to continue the same moulding size 4′ 6″ from the side and taper thence to the coamings of the hatch into which it will be let down, to 8″ secured to the coamings by two lap knees sided 5″ & kept 1″ from the top of the beam. Kneed at side of ship like the whole beams. Neither knees beams ledges or plank of the deck will be planed except the coamings, side of hatches, edges of beams etc. to be rounded.
Mast steps Fore & Main	to be of white oak formed as those of the frigates. The side base pieces to outer sides from keelson 2′; sided 10″ and 5′ in length. Secured to floors by iron bolts 1″ diameter—cross pieces sided 10″, moulded 1′ 6″, in clear apart 1′ 10″. Fore and aft pieces sided 10″ and in the clear apart 11″.
Mizzen step	of live oak to be placed on the birth deck.
Pumps	will step on the floor timber running down to within 2½″ of it & be supported on one side by a jog upon the keelson and on the other by a jog upon the step.

Stanchions — of white oak reaching from top of keelson to under side of each beam to square 6½″. Chamfered an inch on each corner to within 5″ of the head and heel which will remain square; tennoned into oak cap, under the beams.

Breasthook — of the birth deck live oak in length 14′ and sided 11″. The deck plank will be nailed into the hook which will be fayed well against the timbers and bows of the ship. Two hooks below this, same length & size as deck hook and moulded in the throat clear of the stemson 11″; all to be fayed against the timbers & fastened with 9 bolts, copper, 1⅛″ diameter. The throat bolts to be driven from the inside and rivetted upon the front of stem on a ring; the others driven from the outside & rivetted upon rings. If there should not be depth enough from the throat of the breasthooks to admit their jogging over the stemson and faying along the bow leaving the moulding size, here called for, the deficiency will be made up by chocks fayed on the back of breasthooks against the bows & sides of stemson.

Waterways — of white oak finished 11″ in depth and 12″ breadth; averaging in length 40′ as near as possible. The edge next the deck trimmed to 4″ and next to side of ship 4½″. The edge next to deck to be chined in 2″, the wood taken off thence by a straight line across as per margin.

There will be two strakes of pine 4″ thick and 10″ broad next the waterways—the waterway and the strake next to it will be let nicely down 1½″, dovetailed over the beams and ledges. The inside strake will be let down the same depth by taking the wood out of the top of the beams thus giving a jog against the edge of the plank quite across. These strakes will be bolted thro the waterways & side of the ship with two bolts between every two beams, of copper ¾″ diameter (one bolt may serve). The inner lower edge of the inner plank to be chamfered to the thickness of the deck plank.

Stanchions — in one row stepped on birth deck of white oak—one under every gun deck beam, squared 5½″ and chamfered as in the hold.

Coamings & Ledges — of hatches to be in height above the deck plank 4½″—sided 6″.

Spirketting — of white oak to be 3½″ thick and 11″ wide.
Having a list of 3″ above it—at the upper edge of the list as also of the list below there will be primings cut for salting. Let them be kept clear of the list so as to contain the salt in order to get which into the rooms under the ports it will be necessary to bore 1¼″ auger holes thro cills over each room which can be afterwards plugged up.

Gun deck Clamps — of white oak 6″ thick and of a width sufficient to fill the space down to the upper edge of the list which they will form jogged into each other as those on the deck below.

Gun deck Beams — of heart yellow pine free from sap sided 14″ or 15″.
moulded 12½″ or 13″ managed as those below & springing by 4½″ in 31′.

Knees — of live oak or white oak limbs or roots, lodge & dagger, lodge side 7½″ and dagger 8″. Arms to be 4′ 6″ long. Bodies of daggers long enough to butt on berth deck waterways. To have one lodge & one dagger at each side of the beam. Fastening 1″ dia. iron.

Ledges — of heart yellow pine free from sap—number same as below & square 6½″.

Carlins — Do.   square 8½″.

Coamings

of fore & main hatch 1′ 10″ in width, 6½″ thick, to be let down upon oak fore and afters squaring 8½″ so that the whole depth when finished will be 2′ 6½″. The height above deck plank to be 1′ 6½″. Those of the after hatch to be the same depth but ½″ less siding. The head ledges will have a bolt driven thro them and the coamings at each corner of the hatch and two bolts in each ledge between the coamings and the beam, of 1⅛″ dia. iron. The fore and aft pieces on which the coamings are to rest will be chined down 1″ on their upper sides & about ½ the thickness of the coamings, into which the coamings will be fitted by a corresponding chine upon their lower edges, for the purpose of resisting the pressure of the caulking. They will be secured at each end by a knee siding 5½″.

Plank

of this deck to be heart pine free of sap 3½″ thick and not more than 10″ wide; average length 40′. To be fastened to the beams with 8″ iron spikes, 7″ spikes in ledges. To be managed as those on the birth deck and the plank to be planed on both sides. Thick strake next the waterway jogged down as on birth deck, 5″ thick.

Waterways

of white oak, average in length as near as possible to 40′; edge next the deck to be 5″ thick, next the side 5″; whole depth finishing with port cill 1′ 10″, 12″ wide.

Spirketting

Gundeck spirketting 5″ thick.

Waist Plank

of heart pine 4″ to 3″ thick.

Rail Cap

of white oak 6″ thick, scarphs hooked into each other & in length 3′ 6″. Projecting without outside the planking 3″ and inboard inside planking 1¼″.

Ring & Eye Bolts

Omitted from instructions.

Partners

of fore and main masts of live oak 9″ depth & 1′ 3″ breadth framed so much as to admit wedges all around in thickness 4″. Knees as on the berth deck with lap knees sided 6″ bolted with same size iron as those on deck below.
of mizzen mast live oak depth 7″ and breadth 10″; knees as above sided 5″, bolted as on deck below.

Breasthook

of live oak sided 1′ and 15′ in length. Moulded at throat not less than 1′ 2″ and the deck plank to be nailed onto this hook which will fay well against the timbers as on deck below. A hook between decks same size—all fastened with 1⅛″ dia. iron.

Catheads

of tough white oak sided 1′ 2″ and moulded 1′ 1″. They will rest upon the rail mould so as to cut it half off and fay against the inside of the waist & be secured by iron bolts through the side of a diameter of 1⅛″.

Poop Clamps

of roundhouse will be heart pine 3½″ thick. *Note.* It is possible that this may be altered to a hurricane house. (stern cabin)

Poop Beams

of heart pine one half to be sided 9″ and the other 7″—moulded 6½″. The larger ones to be kneed with a lodge knee at each end to be kept close to the lower edge of the beam and the small beams let down into the knees like ledges—to be bolted with ¾″ dia. iron. The beams of this deck will spring so much by a regular curve that there shall be more height amidships than at the sides by 4″ and the height of sides between gun deck plank and round house beams will be 6′.

Forecastle Beams	will be same size as those of poop, managed in the same manner but springing by the gundeck mould.
Planking	of poop and forecastle decks will be 2″ thick of heart pine free from sap and fastened with 5″ iron spikes plugged and planed on both sides.
Waterways	of poop & forecastle, or planksheer white oak 3″ thick. Chines down about 3″ within the timbers to be the thickness of the deck plank so as to lead the water to the gun deck.
Bowsprit	must fay close upon the apron & stem head; there will be a chock over the bowsprit between the knightheads and let into them 1″ on its lower side at each end which will make the chocks 2″ longer than the space between the knightheads along the lower edge of the chock.
Breasthook	over bowsprit to be up & down 9″ and fore and aft 10′
Port Cills	of live oak 6″ thick. Take care that these cills make a fair sheer & the decks kept at their proper distance from them.
Rudder	will be of the common straight necked kind; the back of the post had better be bearded somewhat so as to take less bearding from the rudder. The back of the post will be trimmed the moulding way per draught.
Iron Tiller	to be in length clear of rudder head per draught 9′, 4½″ square at rudder head and 2½″ square at inner end, with the edges chamfered.
Deck Hooks abaft	one for each deck fayed against the timbers same size as breasthooks & one beneath the berth deck, all live oak and bolted as the breasthooks.
Outside of Ship	to be planed from about 6′ below the port cills up to the rail and the waist inside as also the poop and forecastle decks and all spike heads plugged same as decks.
Caulking	Let the oakum be made from the best junk, not more than ⅓rd wont be driven quite home to the timber—the seams payed with pitch taking care to cover the oakum well so as to leave no part bare & that the work be not caught by rain unpayed.
Watering	When the ship is caulked as high as the gun deck let her be watered by pumping or otherwise until the water reaches the fore end of the keel and then let there be several buckets full thrown down each space between the timbers through the list under the gun deck & the leaks that may appear marked by two or three careful men under the bottom. Let this be done twice all around the ship and then let the water be let out by an auger hole or two abaft in the wake of the sternpost knee or deadwood; the pitch having been scraped away from the seams previous to watering. The bottom will then be payed with pitch boiled so hard as not to fly off in driving the coppering nails.
Coppering	After the bottom is thus payed the copper will be put on, having previously been punched with a countersink punch and nailed directly on the pitch without any doubling—unless otherwise directed to use felt—so as to avoid its being quilted as much as possible. Previously to putting on the copper & while the work is progressing the seams are to be fitted flush with spun yarn. Let the sheets of copper be nailed first in their middle, then diverging towards their outer edges so as to prevent puckering.

Channels   of white oak of a width sufficient to permit the lanyards to clear the ridge rope of the hammock stanchions—thickness at ship side 4½″ and 3¼″ at outer edge—to be bolted with 1″ dia iron.

Chains   in three links—the one around the deadeye to be in length below the deadeye to its diameter—toe link in length 1′ 4″. The middle link to fill up between the two as per draught.

The deadeyes to strap so as to stand athwartships instead of fore and aft

Chains   Fore and main of iron—to be 1⅜″ full—mizzen 1⅛″ nett. Chain bolts fore and main 1½″ diameter, mizzen 1¼″. Ringbolts, size of ring only 1¼″. Preventer plates made from square iron 1¼″ x 1¼″—mizzen 1⅛″ square. To be semicircular & swaged & when finished they will be in breast

Preventer Plates   for the fore and main breadth 1¾″, thickness 1″

mizzen, breadth 1½″, thickness ⅞″; in length about 2′.

The chain bolts will be driven thro the sides above and below the deck so as to be drifted out when necessary & in order to give them additional strength let them be upset about 5″ in from the head so as for that distance they shall be ⅙th larger than where they go through the timbers; by this means the timbers will not be so much wounded as though they held their full size and the bolts will have the strength which is required.

Channel Stays

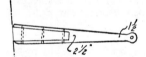

Four on the main and fore channels each, on each side, and three on each of the mizzen channels. Secured by an arm, and underneath and across the channel forming a knee; the stays to be all in breadth 2¼″; at the top the thickness is 1⅜″ and at the bottom ¾″. The arm will be of the same size. There will be an eye at the upper end 3″ in the clear and a ring bolt through the lower end of the same size as those of the preventer plates and in range with the bolts at the lower ends of the two links. There will be a ring in every other chain bolt 5″ in the clear 1¼″ dia. iron.

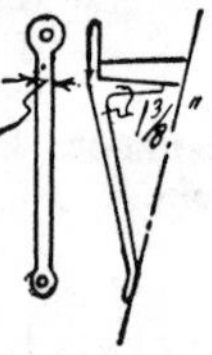

Swinging Stun'sail Boom Irons

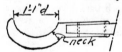

one on each end of fore channel 2½″ square at neck and 1½″ at outer ends. Arm to be 3′ in length from heel to eye at the outer end.

Channel Cranes   for supporting the spare spars & yards—to embrace the channel above and below—one on the main and one on the mizzen on each side—neck to be 2¼″ square; saddle round in dia 2¼″ and to fit yard 1′ 1″ diameter.

Cable bitts   of white oak, one pair, square 1′ 1½″ and to step into the birth deck tapering from full size at lower edge of gun deck beam to heel 9″ square.

Crosspiece is 10′ in length, 1′ 1″ up and down, 1′ 5″ fore and aft and 1′ 4″ from deck to under side. Rounded on aft side. May be made in two pieces; the piece next to bitts may be of oak ¾ of the whole breadth and the after piece of heart pine treenailed into the other. The crosspiece is held in place by a

hook and eye bolt—the eye bolt to be driven into the fore side of it near the upper edge so as to keep the arms of it close alongside the inside of the bitt and the hook is fastened into the bitt.

There will be a ringbolt about half way along the body of the bitt rider the size of the deck stopper bolt and an eye bolt thro the end of the knee 1¼″ in diameter. The eyes of all bolts whether for rings or eyes must be close with throat pieces welded in them so as to make them strong.

Bowsprit Bitts	square 1′ tapered to 9″ at berth deck. Deck stopper ring bolts—4 on each side—the aftermost bolt to be at the after part of main hatchway 1¼″ diameter, ring 5″ in the clear.
Hammock Stanchions	To be in length so that the ridge rope shall be as high as the forecastle and poop decks and in breadth, in the clear 1′ 1″. The stanchions will be let down onto, not into, the rail to avoid wounding it. The outside legs of the stanchion will mortice thro the moulding of the rail leaving a full inch of wood outside of them; the rail on the inside is scored in for the leg to ship into & then a staple will be driven across it in the rail.
Note	The rooms in the frame must be filled in with live oak or well seasoned white oak from keel to birth deck. The filling is driven from the outside except where it may be necessary to drive it from both sides to make close work. To be well caulked and payed on both sides. The ship must be secured by her wales, breast and deck hooks before filling in to prevent the frames from spreading. This will render a ceiling in the hull unnecessary with the exception of the thick strakes directed for the floor & futtock heads. These thick strakes should be bolted thro and thro at proper distances and well rivetted on rings. Let all spike heads above load line be well plugged.
Galleries	to be so placed as to embrace the after port for the entrance into the gallery. The tiller to ship under gun deck.

Circular 14 Dec. 1825

Chains	not to be secured until masts are in & then so as to give the greatest room to the ports & the best spread to the rigging so as not to obstruct the ports. Dead-eyes to stand athwartships instead of fore and aft

Circular 31 Dec. 1825

Armament	the port fixtures to be calculated for long 24 pound medium guns port cills 22″ from the deck

Circular of 9 Feb. 1826

Note. Of the points & particulars which in building must remain as directed by the building instructions prepared by Mr. Doughty for the sloops to be built to his draught or as corrected from the directions of the Board viz.

Sloops built by Mr. Doughty's draught must comport with the first building instructions issued by the Board in

The sidings of the keel and deadwood fore and aft
  " " of stem and stern posts
  " " apron
  " " " all the square frame timbers
  " " " " cants

& the snapings of all cants which by Mr. Doughty have not been furnished

March 4 1826 to Captain Crane
March 15 1826 to Comm'r's Barron & Biddle

Warren commenced building June 1826
Falmouth "   " December 1826

Reference 142–8–20

Comment:—

This is typical of the building instructions issued by the Board of Navy Commissioners and shows the attention given to detail specification as well as the method of making alterations through the transmission of circulars or form letters to all yards. Usually these circulars were made endorsements on the original building instructions if made prior to the start of actual construction of a vessel. The building instructions were often issued in a printed booklet or a broadside sheet, a practice which was followed in the United States Navy when private yards were to bid, at least as early as the War of 1812.

The copper used in naval ships in 1826 was in sheets about 14 inches wide and from 36 to 48 inches long. Following British practice, the copper was in various weights—32, 28, 18 and 16 oz. per square foot. The heaviest was used in three or four strakes around the water line and down on the bows to the fore gripe. Twenty-eight-ounce copper was used to cover the remaining portion of the bottom with the thin stuff, 18 and 16 oz., used between the main and false keels, on the shoe of the rudder and in other close places. To punch the copper, it was first marked with two straight lines from corner to corner and then lines were drawn parallel to these about 3 or 4 inches apart. Where these lines crossed, punched holes were made for nailing. The plates lapped at all edges; those forming butts lapped toward the stern and those forming seams lapped downward. The lapping seems to have been in reverse order to that employed in the British service.

Some of the terms used in the instructions are now obsolete. "Chining" meant cutting a square rabbet; "faying" fitted with a tight joint; the "rising-staff" was a marked staff made in the mould loft for establishing the height of the throat of each floor timber. "Coaks" were blocks fitted in the seam between two timbers to lock them against longitudinal movement. "Jogging" is now usually called notching.

Dimensions of Gunboats and Materials

Length between perpendiculars	71'-0"
Breadth moulded	18'-0"
Depth from ceiling to upper side of deck beams at O on middle line	5'-1"
Trunk in length	37'-0"
Floor timbers sided	7"
Moulded on keel	7"
Moulded at Floor heads	6"
Lower futtocks sided	6"

Toptimbers sided 6" moulded at topside 4"

Keel sided 10" and 9" deep and reduced at the ends to 7" siding.

Keelson to be 9" sided and 10" deep, and to be bolted to the keel through every other floor timber with one bolt ¾" diameter

Stem to be sided 8" at head and of the siding of keel below

Stern post sided 8" and of the siding of the keel below—reduced to 5" at the back of the heel and to be moulded at the rabbet the same as the stem.

Wales to be 3 strakes on each side and 3" thick.

Running plank of the bottom to be 2" thick

Ceiling to be 2" thick and a strake left out under the clamps 6" wide for the admission of air to the frames—and the frame timbers to be kept 2" apart, for the same purpose

Clamp to be 2½" or 3" thick and the beams to let down 1" into them.

Beams to be 10 in number sided as per draught and moulded 7".

Knees two to each beam and one hanging ditto to each of the 2nd beams from bow and stern, all of which to be sided 5"

Stanchions—one stanchion to be placed underneath each of the 3 foremost and 3 aftermost beams

Coamings—4 pieces sided 5" and 14" above the deck to run from the 3rd to 8th beam from forward, the two amidships ones to be in the clear 3'-3", to admit the gun to be housed between them; between the coamings on each side to have gratings fitted for admission of air below, and 15 thwarts fitted under the gratings on each side to ship at pleasure for rowers. Tholes of iron placed between each and 17 in number on each side to enable the boat to be rowed either end foremost as occasion may suggest.

Netting cranes—to have 15 double netting cranes on each side spaced clear of the tholes; the lower part to ly 9″ above the bolster on the gunwales to admit the oars to play freely under it and the breadth of the crane to project from the gunwale; the upper part of the eye for the ridge rope to be no higher than 4′ from the deck and the spread of the crane in the clear 11″, which space just admits a hammock.

Bitts—a pair of bitts situated afore the mast 5″ square with a crosspiece stretching from one to the other for pins and the ends to project 8 or 10″ to belay topsail sheets.

Deck plank to be 2″ thick free from all sap shakes and other defects and to be quartered.

Oars; the longest to be 25′ and made light as strength will permit; the shortest 23′ and made of good ash if it is to be had.

Pumps, one on each side the mast close to the foremost bulkhead of wardroom 6″ in the bore, to be placed as clear of the masts and oars as possible.

Rudder, broad at the heel 2′ 9″ fitted with two braces and to have an iron strap over the head securely bolted athwartships.

Hawse holes, to have two hawse holes forward and the like number aft; the holes to be in the clear 6″.

Ringbolts—through the sides—12 forward and 12 aft, of 1⅛″ iron for working the guns—other ring and eye bolts fitted as per draught.

Timber heads—4 on each side forward and 4 aft sided 6″ and 10″ above gunwale.

Catheads 4 in number to project 18″ beyond the bows and quarter sided 6″ and fitted so that the skid can traverse clear and the guns work freely over them.

Breasthooks—2 in the holds.

Guns—to have 2 circles of iron fitted on deck forward and aft for the gun skids to traverse on; the inner one to be 3″ broad; the outer one same breadth and ⅝″ thick. The outer part of small one to be distant from the center of the pin 6′ 2″; it is necessary that the circles be fitted exact that in case the carriages and skids may be ordered from this place that they shall fit to exactness—and it is more over proper that the upper surface of the circles should lie level with each other that the skids may traverse freely over them and all the trucks have equal bearing. The wardroom to be situated abaft the foremost mast beam and to extend 6′ 4″ aft, to be fitted with 2 berths on each side. Abaft the after bulkhead the magazine and officers storeroom is to be placed, to be fore and aft 4′; the magazine to be on the starboard side and 4′ wide with a passage adjoining; the officers storeroom to occupy the opposite side.

The cabin to commence from the magazine bulkhead and to extend aft 12′ 8″ and to be fitted with 2 berths on each side. A platform to be laid on the keelson from the foremost bulkhead of wardroom to the aftermost bulkhead of cabin and a board on each side to be left loose to deposit shot on the ceiling.

Dimensions of Masts and Spars for the Gunboats Building at Ohio Sloop Rigged

Main mast whole length	57′	
" head	7′	
" diameter at partners	1′ 4″	
Main Boom	50′	
" Gaff	25′	
Bowsprit without board	18′	

and length inboard to run to the centerpin of skids where the heel is secured by running the end into a strap fitted to a temporary pin which fits into the center pin of skid and to go with an iron clasp fitted to the stemhead. When ever the gun is run on the skids the bowsprit unships.

Topmast whole length	24′		
" head	4′		
Crossjack Yard	32′	whole length	
Topsail Yard	23′	"	"

Josiah Fox, Navy Constructor
Navy Yard, Washington, 10 Sept., 1805

Index

and List of Naval Vessels

1775–1855